A Short-Title List

THE CHAPIN LIBRARY
WILLIAMS COLLEGE

A SHORT-TITLE LIST

Compiled by

LUCY EUGENIA OSBORNE

PORTLAND, MAINE

The Southworth-Anthoensen Press

LONDON; BERNARD QUARITCH, LTD.

1939

Preface

WHEN the late Alfred Clark Chapin began in 1915 to collect rare books as a gift to Williams College, he was acting upon a settled plan, which was to form a well-rounded library, representing in an organized way by means of rare books, every field of thought capable of being so represented. This project was original with Mr. Chapin, for no other person had ever before conceived and carried out such a plan in connection with an educational institution in this country.

Beginning with a perfect copy of the Eliot Indian Bible, a first edition, 1661, 1663, Mr. Chapin continued to buy, building up as the three main divisions, Incunabula, English Literature and Americana. These were supplemented as time went on, by Continental Literature after 1500; Bibles and Liturgies; Early Manuscripts; Science; Ballads and Broadsides; and illustrated books. In the course of eight years some nine thousand volumes had been acquired, and in that year, 1923, they were presented to the President and Trustees of Williams. Subsequently, still through Mr. Chapin's generosity, more books were added, so that at the present time they number just under twelve thousand.

Since Mr. Chapin was governed always by a determination to secure only books in fine condition, his gift comprises distinguished copies from such great libraries as the Hoe, Huth, Britwell, Pembroke, Amherst and Vernon, to name but a few. A glance at the List itself will reveal many more, of equal distinction. While he acquired more than five hundred Incunabula, including the Subiaco Cicero, the first Oxford book and the Caxton Cato, he was interested also in fine books from modern presses. He gave such attention to the field of Americana that, beginning with the 1471 Mela, the titles in this section present a picture of the origins and development of this country, and of its history over a period of several hundred years.

Preface

Born at South Hadley, Massachusetts, March 8, 1848, Mr. Chapin had a long life, for he lived until October 2, 1936. The acquiring of rare books for his Alma Mater was one of his great pleasures, for he felt and hoped that the Library would fall naturally into place in the life of the College. To further the usefulness of his gift, this Short-Title List has been compiled.

If the Chapin material comprised but one subject, a simple arrangement in one alphabet would be sufficient for this List. Since, however, the range is wide, some twenty divisions are necessary. For the most part these have lent themselves to a conventional arrangement by author and title. Two in particular, however, have received different treatment, these being Americana and Bibles. The former is in strict chronological order, while the latter is in a classified arrangement.

In material so extensive in scope, certain items must necessarily present a question as to position, for they belong as properly in Americana as in Incunabula and the section of English before 1641. These divisions are all so important and it is so desirable that each should be displayed in its entirety, that at the risk of a little duplication such items as are common to all three sections are included in each. As to form of title, each in spelling and accents follows the title-page from which it is taken. An index at the end of the volume will, it is hoped, obviate any difficulties engendered by the division of material.

Wherever it is especially significant to use them, bibliographical references are given. Among the authorities thus cited are Hain's *Repertorium Bibliographicum*, the *Gesamtkatalog der Wiegendrucke*, the British Museum *Catalogue of Books printed in the XVth Century*, and the *Short-Title Catalogue*, their symbols being H, GW, BMC and STC respectively. In many instances where previous ownership is known and is of interest, this provenance is noted in parentheses to complete the entry.

LUCY EUGENIA OSBORNE

vi

Contents

Contents

A Short-Title List

Early Manuscripts

GREEK

ITALIAN

LATIN

[3]

XIII Liber visionis Esaiae prophetae, cum prologo et expositione S. Hieronymi. [North of France, beginning of 13th century]. fol. 177 leaves. vellum. (William Morris)

XIV Acta Apostolorum, cum glossis. [14th century]. fol. 105 leaves. vellum. (Dunn)

XIV Processionarium. [Italian execution, 14th century]. obl.8vo. 16 leaves. vellum. (Wallace). (fragment)

XIV Psalterium. [Lower Rhine, at or near Cologne, 14th century]. thick 12mo. 223 leaves. vellum. (Hazlitt–Huth)

XIV Psalterium . . . ad usum ord. S. Francisci. [English execution, 14th century]. 64mo. 184 leaves. vellum. (William Constable–Dunn)

XIV Voragine, Jacobus de. Legenda aurea. [Italian execution, 14th century]. 4to. 228 leaves. vellum

XV Antiphonarium Romanum. [Italy, late 15th century]. fol. 151 leaves. parchment

XV Hieronymus. Flores ex veris dictis. [Italian execution, first half 15th century]. 4to. 63 leaves. paper. (Huth)

XV Horae B. V. M. [North of France, second half 15th century]. 4to. 123 leaves. vellum. (Huth)

XV Horae B. V. M. Use of Autun. [North of France, second half 15th century]. 4to. 103 leaves. vellum. (H. W. Poor)

XV Horae B. V. M. Use of Rome. [Amiens, c.1460]. 8vo. 81 leaves. vellum. (De Levis–Sir Godfrey Webster–Cecil Brent)

XV Horae B. V. M. Use of Sens. [Rouen, second half 15th century]. 4to. 150 leaves. vellum

XV Ovidius Naso, Publius. Fastorum libri VI; De Tristibus libri V; De Ponto libri III; De Ibide; De Nuce; De Philomena; De Cuculo; Pulice; De Medicamine faciei; De Medicamine aurium. [Italian execution, 15th century]. fol. 204 leaves. vellum. (Libri sale, 1859, No. 751; Phillipps sale, 1897, No. 575)

Early Manuscripts

XV   Psalterium Benedictinum.   [German execution, 15th century]. fol.   108 leaves.   parchment

XV   Virgilius Maro, Publius.   Bucolica, Aeneis et Georgica.   [Italian execution, 15th century].   fol.   213 leaves.   vellum. (Huth)

FRENCH

XVII   Portolan Charts of Claude Arnaud.   Marseilles 1660-1661.   fol. 14 charts.   parchment

Blockbooks

Apocalypsis Sancti Johannis.   [Bavaria, c. 1450].   48 leaves.   fol. (Huth–Murray)

Incunabula

Adrianus Carthusiensis. De remediis utriusque fortunae. Cologne, A. ter Hoernen, 8 Feb. 1471. 4to. (Inglis). (H*96; BMC. I. 201; GW 228)

Ægidius de Colonna. *See* Columna, Ægidius

Ælianus, *Tacticus*. De instruendis aciebus. Rome, E. Silber, 15 Feb. 1487. 4to. (S. G. Hamilton). (GW 310; BMC. IV. 107)

Æmilius Probus. *See* Nepos, Cornelius

Æneas Sylvius, Piccolomini. *See* Pius II, *Pope*

Æsopus. Vitae et fabulae [Latin]. Antwerp, G. Leeu, 26 Sept. 1486. fol. (Murray). (H 329; GW 349)

Alban, *Saint*. Legenda S. Albani Hungarici martyris. [Cologne, Printer of Legenda S. Albani, c. 1473]. 4to. (Thomas Brooke). (GW 515)

Alberti, Leone Battista. De re aedificatoria. Florence, N. Laurentii, 29 Dec. 1485. fol. (Charles R. Fox–Britwell). (H*419; GW 579)

Albertus de Saxonia. De proportionibus. Venice, B. de Vitalibus for H. de Durantibus, 29 Jan. 1494. 4to. (H586; BMC. V. 546; GW 791)

Albertus Magnus. De animalibus. Mantua, Paul von Butzbach, 12 Jan. 1479. fol. (Sussex–Vernon). (H*546; GW 588)

—— De mysterio missae. Ulm, J. Zainer, 29 May 1473. sm. fol. (H*449; BMC. II. 520; GW 700)

Albumasar. De magnis coniunctionibus. Augsburg, E. Ratdolt, 31 March 1489. 4to. (Dunn). (H*611; BMC. II. 383; GW 836)

—— Introductorium in astronomiam. Augsburg, E. Ratdolt, 7 Feb. 1489. 4to. (Murray). (H*612; BMC. II. 382; GW 840)

Alchabitius. Libellus isagogicus. Venice, E. Ratdolt 1485. 4to. (H *617; BMC. V. 290; GW 844)

Alexander Magnus. Historia Alexandri Magni. Strassburg, M. Schott, 10 Dec. 1488. fol. (Murray). (H*791; GW 888)

Alexander de Sancto Elpidio. De ecclesiastica potestate. Turin, J. Suigus & B. de Benedictis, 10 Feb. 1494. 4to. (H6582; GW 929)

Alvarottus, Jacobus. Super feudis. Venice [Printer of the Alvarottus] 10 July 1477. fol. (H*886; GW 1589)

Ambrosius, *Saint*. De officiis. Milan, C. Valdarfer, 7 Jan. 1474. 4to. (H*910; BMC.VI. 725; GW 1611)

——— Hexameron. Augsburg, J. Schüssler, c. 5 May 1472. fol. (H*903; GW 1603)

——— Passio SS. Protasii et Gervasii. Milan, C. Valdarfer, 7 Jan. 1474. 4to. (H*910; BMC.VI. 725; GW 1611)

——— Passio SS. Vitalis et Agricolae. Milan, C. Valdarfer, 7 Jan. 1474. 4to. (H*910; BMC.VI. 725; GW 1611)

——— Vita S. Agnetis. Milan, C. Valdarfer, 7 Jan. 1474. 4to. (H*910; BMC.VI. 725; GW 1611)

Ambrosius de Spira. *See* Spiera, Ambrosius

Ammianus Marcellinus. Historiae. Rome, G. Sachsel and B. Golsch, 7 June 1474. fol. (Pembroke). (H*926; GW 1617)

Andreae, Johannes. Additiones ad Durantis speculum iudiciale. [Strassburg, G. Husner, before 25 March 1475]. fol. (H. V. Jones). (H*1083; GW 1675)

——— Super arboribus consanguinitatis. Nuremberg, F. Creussner 1478. fol. (Huth). (H*1032; GW 1690)

Anianus. Compotus cum commento. Lyon, J. DuPré, 12 Oct. 1489. 4to. (Dunn–Murray). (H 5595; GW 1953)

Anthologia Graeca Planudea. Florence, L. de Alopa, 11 Aug. 1494. 4to. (Spencer–Wodhull). (H*1145; BMC.VI. 666; GW 2048)

Antichristus. Antichristus [Latin & French]. [Paris] M. LeNoir [?1500]. 4to. (Techener–Andrews). (Pellechet 807)

Antoninus Florentinus. Confessionale. [Esslingen] C. Fyner [n. a. 1474]. 4to. (Paul Schmidt). (H*1171; BMC.II. 513; GW 2092)

——— ——— [Louvain, J. de Paderborn, c. 1485]. 4to. (GW 2100)

Apollinaris Sidonius. *See* Sidonius, Apollinaris

Apollonius Rhodius. Argonautica. Florence [L. de Alopa] 1496. 4to. (W. J. Ibbett–Syston Park–Sykes). (H*1292; BMC.VI. 667; GW 2271)

Appianus, *of Alexandria*. Historia Romana. Venice, E. Ratdolt, B. Maler and P. Löslein 1477. 2 v. 4to. (H*1307; GW 2290)

Incunabula

Appianus, *of Alexandria.* Historia Romana. [Venice] Wendelin of Speyer 1472. fol. (Prince Eugène de Savoie–Vernon). (H *1306; GW 2293)

Apuleius Madaurensis, Lucius. Opera. Rome, C. Sweynheym and A. Pannartz, 28 Feb. 1469. fol. (Sir Robert Peel–J. A. Brooke). (H *1314; GW 2301)

Aquino, Thomas de. *See* Thomas de Aquino

Aretinus, Leonardus. *See* Bruni, Leonardo *Aretino*

Aretio, Angelus de. *See* Gambilionibus, Angelus de

Aristophanes. Comoediae novem [Greek]. Venetiis, apud Aldum, 15 July 1498. fol. (H*1656; GW 2333)

Aristoteles. Opera [Greek]. Venetiis, Aldus Manutius 1495-8. 5 v. in 6. fol. (Hoe–Robert Lenox Kennedy). (H*1657; GW 2334)

—— Ethica ad Nicomachum. Politica. Oeconomica. [Strassburg, J. Mentelin, before 10 April 1469]. fol. (H*1762; GW 2367)

—— Ethica ad Nicomachum. Oxford [Printer of Expositio S. Hieronymi] 1479. 4to. (Pembroke). (H 1749; GW 2373; STC 752)

—— Oeconomica. [Venice, C. Valdarfer, c. 1470]. 8vo. (H 1774; GW 2435)

—— Problemata. [Leipzig, C. Kachelofen, c. 1489/90]. 4to. (Dunn). (H*1725; BMC. III. 625; GW 2457)

Arsocchi, Francesco de. Bucolica. Florence, A. Miscomini, 19 April 1494. 4to.

Astesanus. Summa de casibus conscientiae. Cologne, H. Quentell, 31 Aug. 1479. fol. (H*1894; GW 2755)

Astrolabii canones. [Venice, Paganinus de Paganinis, c. 1497/8]. 4to. (H*1898; BMC. V. 458; GW 2759)

Athanasius, *Saint.* Enarrationes in Epistolas S. Pauli. *See* Theophylactus

Auctores vetustissimi. [Venice] B. de Vitalibus [not before August] 1498. 4to. (H*12527; BMC. V. 548)

Auctoritates utriusque testamenti. *See* Nicolaus de Hanapis

[8]

Incunabula

Augustine, *Saint*. Confessiones. Milan, J. Bonus, 21 July 1475. 4to. (Dunn). (H 2031; BMC. VI. 728; GW 2894)

———— De arte praedicandi. [Strassburg, J. Mentelin, c. 1466]. fol. (H*1956; GW 2871)

———— De civitate dei. Rome, C. Sweynheym & A. Pannartz 1468. fol. (H 2047; GW 2875)

———— ———— Venice, Johann and Wendelin of Speyer 1470. fol. (H*2048; GW 2877)

———— ———— Venice, N. Jenson, 2 Oct. 1475. fol. (G. Turri). (H*2051; GW 2879)

———— ———— [Italian]. [Florence, A. Miscomini, n.a.1483]. fol. (H 2072; GW 2892)

———— Commentarium Thomae Waleys & Nicolaus Trivet super . . . De civitate dei. [Strassburg, J. Mentelin, n. a. 1468]. fol. (H *2056; GW 2883)

———— De disciplina christiana. [Cologne, U. Zell, c. 1470]. 4to. (H 1963a; BMC. I. 183; GW 2900)

———— De spiritu et littera. [Cologne, Printer of Dictys, c. 1470]. 4to. (Thomas Brooke). (H 2043; GW 2924)

———— De vita beata. [Cologne, U. Zell, c. 1470]. 4to. (Thomas Brooke). (H*1960; GW 2932)

———— Sermo de verbis evangelicis. [Cologne, Printer of Dictys, c. 1470]. 4to. (Thomas Brooke). (H 1993a; GW 2918)

Pseudo Augustine. Meditationes. [Milan, J. A. and B. de Honate, c. 1480/82]. 8vo. (BMC. VI. 740; GW 2970)

———— Regula S. Augustini. *See* Hugo de S. Victore

———— Sermo de festo praesentationis Mariae. [Cologne, U. Zell, c. 1470]. 4to. (Thomas Brooke). (H 1992; GW 2993)

Balbus, Johannes. Catholicon. Mainz [J. Gutenberg?] 1460. fol. (Amherst–T. N. Vail). (H*2254; GW 3182)

———— ———— Augsburg, G. Zainer, 30 April 1469. fol. (Britwell). (H*2255; GW 3183)

Bartolus de Saxoferrato. Tractatus procuratoris. Rome, S. Plannck, 16 Jan. 1486. 4to. (Sykes–Syston Park–Murray–Dunn). (H 2648; BMC. IV. 86)

Incunabula

Becket, Thomas à. *See* Thomas (Becket), *Archbishop of Canterbury*

Beda. Historia ecclesiastica gentis Anglorum. [Strassburg, H. Egge-stein, c. 1475/8]. fol. (Marquess of Bute–Aldenham Abbey–W. H. Crawford–Britwell). (H 2732; GW 3756)

Benivieni, Girolamo. Bucolica. Florence, A. Miscomini, 19 April 1494. 4to.

Bergomensis, Jacobus Philippus. *See* Jacobus Philippus de Bergamo

Pseudo Bernardus. Speculum de honestate vitae. [Cologne, U. Zell, c. 1473]. 4to. (Thomas Brooke). (H 2901; GW 4072)

Bertholdus. Horologium deuotionis. [Basel, J. Amerbach, n. a. 1490]. 8vo. (H*2993=*2990=*8928; BMC. III. 753; GW 4175)

Bertrand, Pierre. De iurisdictione ecclesiastica. Paris, J. Philippi, 2 April 1495/6. 4to. (H 3002; GW 4179)

Bible. *German* [1475/6]. Augsburg [G. Zainer 1475/6]. fol. (H *3133; GW 4298)

———— *Italian*. 1471. [Venice, A. de Ambergau] 1 Oct. 1471. 2 v. fol. (H 3148; GW 4321)

———— *Latin* [c. 1454/5]. [Mainz, J. Gutenberg, c. 1454/5, n. a. Aug. 1456]. fol. (H 3031; GW 4201). (One leaf)

———— [n. a. 1470]. [Strassburg, A. Rusch, n. a. 1470]. fol. (Sussex). (H*3034; GW 4209)

———— [n. a. 1474]. [Basel, B. Richel, n. a. 1474]. fol. (William Morris). (H*3041; GW 4212)

———— [n. a. 1475]. [Basel, B. Ruppel and B. Richel, n. a. 1475]. 2 v. fol. (G. C. Thomas). (H*3038; *3044; GW 4213)

———— 1475. Venice, F. Renner and N. de Frankfordia 1475. fol. (H*3054; GW 4216)

———— 1476. Venice, N. Jenson 1476. fol. (H*3061; GW 4222)

———— 1477. Nuremberg, A. Koberger, 30 July 1477. fol. (H *3065; GW 4227)

———— 1478. Venice, R. von Nimwegen and T. von Reynsburg 1478. fol. (H*3070; GW 4231)

———— 1480. Venice, F. Renner 1480. 4to. (H. W. Poor). (H *3078; GW 4241)

Incunabula

Bible. *Latin.* 1480. Ulm, J. Zainer, 29 Jan. 1480. fol. (H*3079; GW 4242)

——— 1480. Nuremberg, A. Koberger, 14 April 1480. fol. (H 3076; GW4243)

——— 1481. Venice, L. Wild 1481. fol. (H*3082; GW4247)

——— [1481]. [Strassburg, A. Rusch, shortly after 23 Sept. 1481]. 4v. fol. (H*3173; GW4282)

——— 1481. Venice [J. Herbort for] J. de Colonia, N. Jenson and Company, 31 July 1481. 4v. fol. (H*3164; GW4286)

——— 1483. Venice, F. Renner 1483. 4to. (Sunderland). (H *3089; GW4253)

——— 1498. Venice, S. Bevilaqua, 8 May 1498. 4to. (H*3124; GW4280)

——— *N. T. Latin.* 1462. Mainz, J. Fust and P. Schoeffer, 14 Aug. 1462. fol. (G. Livermore). (H*3050; GW4204)

——— [1481]. [Strassburg, A. Rusch, shortly after 23 Sept. 1481]. fol. (H*3173; GW4282)

——— *Apocalypse. Italian* [c. 1467/8]. Apocalypsis cum glosis N. de Lyra [Italian]. [?Rome, U. Han, c. 1467/8]. 4to. (?H 9383; BMC. IV. 143)

Bidpai. Directorium humane vite. [Strassburg, J. Prüss, c. 1488/93]. fol. (W. H. Crawford–H. Wellesley–Murray). (H*4411; BMC. I. 125)

Boccaccio, Giovanni. Ameto. Treviso, M. Manzolo, 22 Nov. 1479. 4to. (Pinelli–Wodhull). (H*3287; BMC.VI.888; GW4429)

——— De casibus virorum illustrium. [Strassburg, G. Husner, c. 1474/5]. fol. (H*3338; GW4430)

——— Genealogiae deorum. Venice, Wendelin of Speyer 1472. fol. (Hoe–Groves). (H*3315; GW4475)

Boethius. De consolatione philosophiae. Nuremberg, A. Koberger, 24 July 1473. fol. (Britwell). (H*3398; GW4573)

Bonacursius, Dominicus. *See* Montemagno, Bonaccursius de

Bonaventura, *Saint.* De triplici via. [Cologne, U. Zell, c. 1475, before 18 Sept. 1477]. 4to. (Dunn). (H*3498; BMC.I. 193; GW 4706)

Incunabula

Bonaventura, *Saint*. Opuscula. Brescia, B. Misinta for A. Britannicus, 17 Dec. 1495. 4to. (HC*3467; GW 4649)

Pseudo Bonaventura. Auctoritates utriusque testamenti. *See* Nicolaus de Hanapis

———— Meditationes vitae Christi [Italian]. Venice, P. Maufer and N. de Contugo, 10 March 1483. 4to. (Dunn). (GW 4789)

———— Sermones de morte. [Paris, A. Chappiel for] R. Gourmont [after 1500?]. 8vo. (GW 4803)

———— Sermones de tempore et de sanctis. Zwolle [P. van Os] 1479. fol. (Hewlett–Groves). (GW 4810)

Boniface VIII, *Pope*. Liber sextus Decretalium. Mainz, P. Schoeffer, 5 April 1473. fol. (J. E. Millard). (H*3590; GW 4853)

Boninsegni, Jacopo Fiorino de. Bucolica. Florence, A. Miscomini, 19 April 1494. 4to.

Bonstetten, Albertus de? Passio sancti Meinradi. Basel, M. Furter, 20 Sept. 1496. 4to. (Huth). (H*12453; BMC. III. 784)

Bonum universale de proprietatibus apum. *See* Thomas Cantipratensis

Borghi, Pietro. Aritmetica mercantile. Venice, E. Ratdolt, 2 Aug. 1484. 4to. (H 3660; BMC. V. 289; GW 4936)

———— ———— Venice, J. Leoviller 1488. 4to. (Dunn). (H 3661; BMC. V. 406; GW 4937)

Brandt, Sebastian. Das narrenschiff. [Nuremberg, G. Stuchs, after 1 March 1497]. 8vo. (H*3747; BMC. II. 471; GW 5055)

———— ———— Basel, J. Bergmann, 1 March 1498. 4to. (H*3751; GW 5062)

Breviarium Camaldulense. 1484. Florence, A. Miscomini, 13 April 1484. 8vo. (Psalterium only). (GW 5191). vellum

Breydenbach, Bernhard von. Peregrinatio in terram sanctam. Mainz, E. Reuwich, 11 Feb. 1486. fol. (H*3956; GW 5075)

———— ———— [German]. Mainz, E. Reuwich, 21 June 1486. fol. (Murray). (H*3959; GW 5077)

Bruni, Leonardo *Aretino*. De bello Italico adversos Gothos gesto. [Venice] N. Jenson 1471. fol. (Sir Richard Colt Hoare). (H *1559; GW 5601)

Incunabula

Bruni, Leonardo *Aretino*. De duobus amantibus. [Paris, P. de Keysere & J. Stoll, c. 1473]. 4to. (Pellechet 4850)

——— De nobilitate. *See* Montemagno, Bonaccursius de

——— Epistolae familiares. [Milan? Printer of Bruni Aretino, Epistolae familiares] 1472. fol. (Dunn). (H*1565; GW 5606)

——— Historiae Florentini populi [Italian]. Venice, J. LeRouge, 12 Feb. 1476. fol. (Syston Park). (H*1562; GW 5612)

——— ——— Florence, B. di Libri, 5 June 1492. fol. (Sir Robert Throckmorton). (H 1563, *13173; GW 5613)

Brutus, Marcus. *See Pseudo* Brutus

Pseudo Brutus. Epistolae. [Paris] U. [Gering], M. [Crantz] & M. [Friburger 1472]. 4to. (La Vallière–Crevenna). (H 12885)

Burgo, Dionysius de. *See* Dionysius de Burgo S. Sepulchri

Burgo, Lucas de. *See* Lucas de Burgo S. Sepulchri

Burley, Walter. De vita et moribus philosophorum. [Nuremberg, A. Koberger, c. 1472]. fol. (H*4112; GW 5785)

Bury, Richard de. Philobiblon. Cologne [Printer of Augustinus de fide] 1473. 4to. (Thomas Brooke). (H*4151; BMC. I. 232)

Caesar, Caius Julius. Commentarii. Rome, C. Sweynheym & A. Pannartz, 12 May 1469. fol. (Milini–Pembroke–Murray). (H *4212; GW 5863)

——— ——— Treviso, M. Manzolo, 30 June 1480. fol. (Britwell). (H*4217; GW 5868)

——— ——— Venice [P. Pincius for] B. Fontana, 13 April 1499. fol. (H*4221; GW 5872)

Calandri, Filippo. Aritmetica. Florence, L. Morgiani and J. Petri, 1 Jan. 1491/2. 8vo. (H4234; BMC.VI.681; GW 5884)

Calpurnius Siculus, Titus. Bucolica. Rome, C. Sweynheym and A. Pannartz [not before 5 April 1471]. fol. (Pembroke). (H *14733; BMC.IV. 13)

Cantipratensis, Thomas. *See* Thomas Cantipratensis

Capella, Marcianus. *See* Marcianus Capella

Caracciolus, Robertus. Sermones de timore divinorum iudiciorum. Venice, J. de Colonia and J. Manthen 1475. 4to. (H 4467; BMC. V. 226; GW 6110)

Incunabula

Caracciolus, Robertus.   Sermones quadragesimales de poenitentia. [Venice] B. da Cremona 1472.   fol.&4to.   (Pinelli).   (H 4426; BMC.V. 207; GW 6064)

Carvajal, Bernardinus.   Oratio in die circumcisionis a. 1484 habita. [Rome, S. Plannck, c. 1488/90].   4to.   (H*4546; BMC. IV. 93; GW 6147)

———— Oratio super praestanda solenni obedientia. [Rome, S. Plannck 1493, after 19 June].   4to.   (GW 6145)

Cassiodorus.   Historia ecclesiastica tripartita.   Augsburg, J. Schüssler, c. 5 Feb. 1472.   fol.   (H*4573; GW 6164)

Cato, Dionysius.   Disticha Catonis.   Augsburg [A. Sorg] 2 Nov. 1475. fol.   (H*4711; GW 6277)

———— ———— Tr. by W. Caxton.   [Westminster, W. Caxton, after 23 Dec. 1483].   fol.   (G. Watson Taylor–Charles Barclay).   (H 4754; GW 6361; STC 4853)

Cato, Marcus Porcius.   De re rustica.   *See* Scriptores rei rusticae

Cavalca, Domenico.   Pungi lingua.   Florence, N. Laurentii [c. 1476/ 7].   fol.   (Pembroke).   (GW 6409)

———— Specchio di croce.   Milan [A. Zarotus] 1 Sept. 1484.   4to. (GW 6419)

Celsus, Aulus Cornelius.   De medicina.   Florence, N. Laurentii 1478. fol.   (W. H. Crawford–Dunn).   (H*4835; GW 6456)

———— ———— Venice, P. Pincius for B. Fontana, 6 May 1497.   fol. (Sunderland).   (H*4838; GW 6459)

Cepio, Coriolanus.   Gesta Petri Mocenici.   Venice, B. Maler, E. Ratdolt and P. Löslein 1477.   4to.   (Sunderland–Andrews).   (H *4849; BMC.V. 244; GW 6473)

Chaucer, Geoffrey.   The Canterbury tales.   [Westminster, W. Caxton, c. 1478].   fol.   (H 4921; GW 6585).   (One leaf)

Chiarini, Giorgio.   *See* Mercanzie ed usanze dei paesi

Chronicles of England.   [London, William de Machlinia, c. 1486]. fol.   (Bryan Fairfax–Francis Child–Earl of Jersey).   (GW 6673; STC 9993)

Chrysostom.   *See* John, Chrysostom, *Saint*

Incunabula

Cicero, Marcus Tullius. De oratore. [Subiaco, C. Sweynheym & A. Pannartz, before 30 Sept. 1465]. 4to. (Pembroke–Murray). (H*5098; GW 6742)

—— —— [Venice, P. Pincius] 15 July 1495. fol. (C. H. Weir–W. C. H. Vere). (H 5110; GW 6752)

—— Epistolae familiares. [Venice] N. Jenson 1471. 4to. (Meerman–Syston Park). (H 5168; GW 6806)

—— —— [Venice, Wendelin of Speyer] 1471. fol. (Sunderland). (H*5167; GW 6807)

—— —— [Venice, Adam of Ambergau] 1471. fol. (Didot–Dunn). (H 5169; GW 6808)

—— Orationes Philippicae. Rome, U. Han [c. 1470]. 4to. (Pembroke–J. A. Brooke). (H 5134; BMC. IV. 21; GW 6794)

—— —— Venice, J. Tacuinus, 22 March 1494. fol. (H*5139; GW 6797)

—— Rhetorica ad C. Herennium. [Venice, T. de Blavis] 1476. fol. (C. H. Weir–W. C. H. Vere). (H*5060; GW 6719)

Claudianus, Claudius. Opera. Vicenza, J. Dusensis, 27 May 1482. fol. (Cracherode–Sykes–Syston Park). (H*5370; BMC. VII. 1048; GW 7059)

Cologne Chronicle. Cologne, J. Koelhoff the Younger, 23 Aug. 1499. fol. (Bement). (H*4989; GW 6688)

Colombo, Christophoro. Epistola de insulis nuper inventis [Latin]. [Rome, S. Plannck, after 29 April 1493]. 4to. (H 5489; GW 7177)

—— —— (Basel, J. Bergmann 1494). 4to. (Marquis d'Adda–Murray). (H*15942; BMC. III. 794)

Colonna, Francesco. Hypnerotomachia Poliphili. Venetiis, in aedibus Aldi Manutii, Dec. 1499. fol. (Vernon). (GW 7223)

Colonne, Guido delle. Historia destructionis Troiae [Italian]. Venice, A. della Paglia, B. da Fossombrone & Marchesino di Sauioni 1481. fol. (Britwell). (H 5523; GW 7242)

Columella, Lucius Junius Moderatus. Rei rusticae. *See* Scriptores rei rusticae

Incunabula

Columna, Ægidius. In Aristotelis de anima commentum. Pavia, C. de Canibus for H. de Durantibus, 26 July 1491. fol. (H 129; GW 7202)

Conradus de Mure. Repertorium vocabulorum. Basel, B. Ruppel, c. 1470/2. fol. (H*11642; GW 7424)

Corpus iuris civilis. *See* Justinianus, Flavius Anicius

Pseudo Crates. Epistolae. [Paris] U. [Gering], M. [Crantz] & M. [Friburger 1472]. 4to. (La Vallière–Crevenna). (H 12885)

Crescenzi, Pietro. Liber ruralium commodorum. Louvain, J. de Paderborn, 9 Dec. 1474. fol. (John Towneley–Heber–D. S. Ker–Britwell). (H*5829; GW 7821)

Curtius Rufus, Quintus. De rebus gestis Alexandri Magni. [Rome] G. Lauer [c. 1471?]. 4to. (Syston Park). (H 5879; GW 7872)

Dante Alighieri. La commedia. [Venice] Wendelin of Speyer 1477. fol. (Richard Grenville–Vernon). (H 5942; GW 7964)

——— ——— Florence, N. Laurentii, 30 Aug. 1481. fol. (H *5946; GW 7966)

——— ——— Venice, O. Scotus, 23 March 1484. fol. (Vernon). (H 5947; GW 7967)

——— ——— Brescia, B. de Boninis, 31 May 1487. fol. (Vernon). (H 5948; GW 7968)

——— ——— Venice, P. de Quarengiis, Bergomensis, 11 Oct. 1497. fol. (Vernon). (H*5953; GW 7972)

——— Convivio. Florence, F. Bonaccorsi, 20 Sept. 1490. 8vo. (H 5954; GW 7973)

Decisiones Rotae Romanae. [Rome] S. Riessinger (Part II dated 11 Dec. 1483). fol. (H*604[9]; GW 8205)

Dialogus creaturarum. Gouda, G. Leeu, 6 June 1481. fol. (Aug. Stewarde–Lionel Dalbye–Thomas Payne–Wodhull–Andrews). (H 6125)

Dialogus linguae et ventris. [Cologne, L. von Renchen, c. 1495]. 4to. (GW 8278)

Diodorus Siculus. Bibliotheca historica [Latin]. Bologna [B. Azoguidus] 1472. fol. & 4to. (H 6188; BMC. VI. 799)

Diogenes Laertius. Vitae et sententiae philosophorum. Venice, N. Jenson, 14 Aug. 1475. fol. (Hopetoun). (H*6199; BMC.V. 175; GW 8379)

―――― ―――― Venice [B. Locatellus] 18 Jan. 1490. 4to. (H *6202; BMC.V. 438)

Dionysius de Burgo S. Sepulchri. Commentarius super Valerium Maximum. [Strassburg, A. Rusch, c. 1470]. fol. (McCarthy). (H *4103; BMC.I. 63; GW 8411)

Dionysius Periegetes. Cosmographia siue de situ orbis. Venice, B. Maler, E. Ratdolt, P. Löslein 1477. 4to. (Pinelli–Wodhull–Dunn). (H*6226; BMC.V. 244; GW 8426)

―――― ―――― Paris, G. Wolff & T. Kerver (for J. Petit) 22 June 1499. 4to. (Learmont). (H*6230; GW 8429)

Directorium humanae vitae. *See* Bidpai

Donatus, Aelius. Commentarius in Terentium. [Venice] Wendelin of Speyer [c. 1472]. fol. (Pembroke). (H 6383; BMC.V. 163; GW 9035)

Duns Scotus, Johannes. Quaestiones super Sententias. [Venice] V. de Spira [c. 1476?]. 4to. (Egerton–Wodhull–Dunn). (H *6454; BMC.V. 248; GW 9092)

Durandus, Gulielmus. Rationale divinorum officiorum. Rome, U. Han, 23 June 1473. fol. (Dunn). (H 6473; BMC.IV. 23; GW 9104)

―――― ―――― Ulm, J. Zainer, 3 Dec. 1473. fol. (William Morris). (H*6474; BMC.II. 521; GW 9105)

―――― ―――― Vicenza, H. Liechtenstein 1478. fol. (H*6480; BMC.VII. 1037; GW 9115)

Epistolae graecae. Venice, Aldus Manutius [29] March; [not before 17 April] 1499. 2 parts in 1. 4to. (H*6659; BMC.V. 560)

Epistolae illustrium virorum. (Lyon) N. Wolff, 13 Feb. 1499. fol. (H*6662)

Eschenbach, Wolfram von. Parsival. [Strassburg, J. Mentelin] 1477. fol. (H*6684; BMC.I. 59)

―――― Titurel. [Strassburg, J. Mentelin] 1477. fol. (H*6683; BMC.I. 59)

Estwood, John.   Summa astrologiae judicialis.   Venice, J. L. Santritter, 7 July 1489.   fol.   (Biblioteca Bologna Comunitativa–Magnani).   (H*6685; BMC.V.462)

Etymologicum.   Ἐτυμολογικὸν μέγα.   Venice, Z. Callierges, 8 July 1499.   fol.   (Pembroke–Earl of Cromer).   (H*6691; BMC.V.580)

Euclides.   Elementa.   Venice, E. Ratdolt, 25 May 1482.   fol.   (H *6693; BMC.V.285; Thomas–Stanford 1a)

Eusebius *Caesariensis*.   *See* Eusebius *Pamphili, Bp*.

Eusebius *Cremonensis*.   Epistola de morte Hieronymi.   [Blaubeuren, C. Mancz, c.1475].   fol.   (H*6718; BMC.II.564)

Eusebius *Pamphili, Bp*.   Chronicon.   Venice, E. Ratdolt, 13 Sept. 1483.   4to.   (Dunn).   (H*6717; BMC.V.287)

——— ———— [Milan] P. de Lavagna [c.1475].   4to.   (H*6716; BMC.VI.703)

——— Historia ecclesiastica.   [Strassburg, H. Eggestein, c.1475].   4to. & fol.   (Copy 1, Huth; 2, Dunn).   (H*6708; BMC.I.73)

——— ——— Rome [J. de Lignamine] 15 May 1476.   fol.   (Dunn).   (H*6710; BMC.IV.34)

——— ——— Mantua, J. Schall, 15 July 1479.   fol.   (H*6711; BMC.VII.933)

Eutropius.   Breuiarium historiae Romanae.   Rome [G. Lauer] 20 May 1471.   4to.   (W. H. Crawford–Dunn).   (H*6726; BMC.IV.36)

Exhortatio de celebratione missae.   [Esslingen, C. Fyner 14]73.   4to.   (Copy 1, Dunn; 2, Paul Schmidt).   (H*6775; BMC.II.512)

Fasciculus temporum.   *See* Rolewinck, Werner

Florius, Franciscus.   De duobus amantibus.   [Paris, P. de Keysere & J. Stoll, c.1473].   4to.   (Pellechet 4850)

Fortunatianus, Chirius.   Rhetorica.   [Venice, C. de Pensis, c.1494].   4to. (Martini–Hoskier).   (H 7306)

Froissart, Jean.   Chroniques.   Paris, A. Vérard [1495-7].   4 v. in 3.   fol.   (Utterson).   (Pellechet 4932)

Incunabula

Frontinus, Sextus Julius. De aquaeductibus. [Rome, ?E. Silber, c. 1486]. fol. (H 7389; BMC. IV. 123)

—— Strategematicon liber. Rome, E. Silber, 1 June 1487. 4to. (S. G. Hamilton). (BMC. IV. 107)

Gafurius, Franchinus. Practica musicae. Milan, G. Le Signerre, 30 Sept. 1496. fol. (Bement). (H 7407; BMC. VI. 789)

—— Theorica musicae. Milan, P. de Mantegatiis, 15 Dec. 1492. fol. (H 7406; BMC. VI. 785)

Gaguin, Robert. Compendium de origine et gestis Francorum. Paris, A. Bocard for D. Gerlier, 31 March 1497. fol. (H 7411)

—— —— Paris, T. Kerver, ad idus ianurias 1500. fol. (H *7413)

Gambilionibus, Angelus de. De criminibus seu de maleficiis. Paris, M. Crantz, U. Gering, M. Friburger, 7 Sept. 1476. 4to. (Syston Park–Dunn). (H 1624)

Gaza, Theodorus. Γραμματικὴ εἰσαγωγή [With other tracts]. Venetiis, in aedibus Aldi Romani, 1495. fol. (Montaigne–Pembroke). (H *7500; BMC. V. 553)

Gellius, Aulus. Noctes Atticae. Venice, A. de Paltasichis 1477. fol. (Grimaldi). (H *7520; BMC. V. 251)

Gerson, Jean Charlier de. Conclusiones de diversis materiis moralibus. [Cologne, U. Zell 1466?]. 4to. (J. Enschedé). (H 7640; BMC. I. 180)

—— —— [Paris, U. Gering, M. Crantz & M. Friburger, c. 1473]. 4to. (Huth). (Pellechet 5144)

—— De auferibilitate pape. [Paris, U. Gering, M. Crantz & M. Friburger, c. 1473]. 4to. (Huth). (Pellechet 5133)

—— De pollutionibus nocturnis. [Esslingen, C. Fyner] [?1473]. 4to. (Paul Schmidt). (H *7699; BMC. II. 512)

Gesta Romanorum. Louvain, J. de Paderborn [c. 1483]. 4to. (Britwell). (Pellechet 5244; Campbell 825; Polain 1643)

—— [Nuremberg, A. Koberger] 4 Mar. 1494. 4to. (H 7748; Pellechet 5256)

Gobii, Joannes. Scala coeli. Ulm, J. Zainer 1480. fol. (H *9406; BMC. II. 526)

Incunabula

Grapaldus, Franciscus Marius. De partibus aedium. Parma, A. Ugo-
letus [c. 1494]. 4to. (Copy 1, S. G. Hamilton; 2, Sunderland–
Dunn). (H7868; BMC.VII.945)

Gratianus. Decretum. Basel, M. Wenssler, 19 Aug. 1481. fol. (H
*7895)

Gregory IX, *Pope*. Decretales. Venice, N. Jenson, 8 May 1479. fol.
(Dunn–Alfred Heales). (H*8007; BMC.V.180)

Guido de Colonna. *See* Columna, Guido de

Guido de Monte Rocherii. Manipulus curatorum. [Germany, Printer
of the Lotharius with the date Mccccxlviii]. fol. (Dunn–J. A.
Brooke). (H*8157; BMC.III.707)

—— —— Strassburg [M. Flach] 10 May 1487. 4to. (Dunn).
(H8194; BMC.I.147)

Henricus de Firmaria. Passio Domini. Oppenheim [? J. Köbel, c. 1500].
4to. (Yemeniz–Huth). (H*7123)

Henry of Hesse. Regulae ad cognoscendum peccatum. [Esslingen,
C. Fyner] [? 1473]. 4to. (Paul Schmidt). (Part of H*7699;
BMC.II.512)

Herbarius. [Mainz, P. Schoeffer, c. 1484]. 4to. (Amherst). (H
8444 var. 2; Schreiber V: 4204)

Hermes Trismegistus. De potestate et sapientia Dei. Paris [J. Higman &] W. Hopyl, 31 July 1494. 4to. (Inglis–Dunn–J. A.
Brooke). (H8462)

Herodianus. Historia de imperio post Marcum. Bologna, P. de Benedictis, 31 Aug. 1493. fol. (H*8467; BMC.VI.827)

Herodotus. Historiae. Venice, J. LeRouge [before December] 1474.
fol. (H*8[4]69; BMC.V.213)

Hesiod. Opera et dies. Rome, C. Sweynheym and A. Pannartz [not
before 5 April 1471]. fol. (Pembroke). (H*14733; BMC.IV.
13)

Hierocles. In aureos versus Pythagorae opusculum. Padua, B. de Val-
dezoccho, 17 April 1474. 4to. (H*8545; BMC.VII.906)

Hieronymus. Epistolae. [Strassburg, J. Mentelin, n. a. 1469]. fol.
(Marquess of Bute–Aldenham Abbey–William Morris–Dunn). (H
*8549; BMC.I.53)

[20]

Hieronymus. Epistolae. Mainz, P. Schoeffer, 7 Sept. 1470. 2 v. fol. (Wodhull–Dunn). (H*8553; BMC. I. 26)

────── Expositio in simbolum apostolorum. Oxford, 17 Dec. 1468 [sic] [1478]. 4to. (Pembroke). (STC 21443)

────── Liber cōtra Heluidiū de virginitate sancte dei genitricis Marie. [Cologne, Printer of Dictys, c. 1471]. 4to. (Thomas Brooke). (H 8575)

────── Vitas patrum. Ulm, J. Zainer [c. 1479]. fol. (H*8594; BMC. II. 528)

────── ────── [German]. [Strassburg, ? J. Prüss, c. 1482]. fol. (H*8603; BMC. I. 168)

────── ────── Augsburg, J. Schobsser, 19 Dec. 1492. fol. (Murray). (H 8607; BMC. II. 378)

Hippocrates. De insomniis. [Rome, O. Servius, c. 1481]. 4to. (H *3779=8671; BMC. IV. 130)

Historia septem sapientum Romae. [Lyon, G. Balsarin, c. 1488]. 4to. (Copinger II: 3001)

Homerus. Ποίησις ἅπασα. Florence [B. Nerlius, not before 13 Jan. 1488/9]. 2 v. fol. (John Pearson). (H 8772; BMC. VI. 678)

Honorius Augustodunensis. De imagine mundi. [Nuremberg, A. Koberger ? 1472]. fol. (Heber). (H*8800; BMC. II. 411)

Horae B. V. M. *Paris use*. Ces presentes heures a lusaige de Paris. Paris (P. Pigouchet] for S. Vostre, 25 April 1500. 8vo. (Pittar)

────── *Roman use*. Ces p̄sentes heures a lusage de Rōme. Paris (P. Pigouchet) for S. Vostre, 20 Aug. 1496. 8vo. (Didot). (H 8851). vellum

────── ────── *Greek*. Horae . . . secūdum consuetudinem romanae curiae. [Venice] Aldus Manutius, 5 Dec. 1497. 16mo. (W. H. Crawford). (H 8830; BMC. V. 558)

Horatius Flaccus, Quintus. Carmina. Carmen seculare. Epodon. Ars poetica. [With the commentaries of Acro and Porphyrio]. [Rome, W. de Wila or B. Guldinbeck, c. 1474/5]. fol. (H 8899)

────── Opera. Milan, P. de Lavagna, 29 April 1477. fol. (Sunderland–Gaskell). (H 8871; BMC. VI. 704)

Horatius Flaccus, Quintus.   Opera.   Florence, A. Miscomini, 5 Aug.
1482.   fol.   (H 8881; BMC. VI. 637)

Hortus sanitatis.   Ortus sanitatis.   Mainz, J. Meydenbach, 23 June
1491.   fol.   (H*8944; BMC. I. 44)

Hours.   *See* Horae B. V. M.

Hugo de Sancto Victore.   De sacramentis Christianae fidei.   [Augs-
burg, G. Zainer, c. 1476].   fol.   (H*9023; BMC. II. 325)

———— ———— Strassburg [Printer of the 1483 Jordanus de Quedlin-
burg] 30 July 1485.   fol.   (Frederick William I; Bibl. Regia Bero-
linensi).   (H*9025; BMC. I. 133)

———— Didascalon.   [Strassburg, Printer of Henricus Ariminensis, c.
1474].   fol.   (H*9022; BMC. I. 78)

———— Regula S. Augustini [Latin and Italian].   [Rome, in domo F.
de Cinquinis 1479].   4to.   (Dunn).   (Part of H 10328, 16086)

Hyginus.   Poetica astronomica.   Venice, E. Ratdolt, 14 Oct. 1482.
4to.   (Huth).   (H*9062; BMC. V. 286)

———— ———— Venice, T. de Blavis, 7 June 1488.   4to.   (H*9065;
BMC. V. 318)

Imitatio Christi.   [Augsburg] G. Zainer [before 5 June 1473].   fol.
(H*8589; BMC. II. 318)

———— [Ulm, J. Zainer] 1487.   8vo.   (H*9091; BMC. II. 530)

———— [Venice, A. de Zanchis, after 1500(?)].   8vo.   (Marcel
Schwob–Amherst).   (De Backer 9)

———— [*Italian*].   [Florence, A. Miscomini, c. 1485].   4to.   (Appar-
ently agrees with BMC. VI. 645 with exception of first word on fol.
[2 recto] which in Chapin copy is "Incomicia")

Institoris, Henricus.   *See* Sprenger, Jacob *and* Henricus Institoris

Isidorus.   De responsione mundi.   Augsburg, G. Zainer, 7 Dec. 1472.
fol.   (Wodhull–Heber–Dunn).   (H*9302; BMC. II. 317)

———— Etymologiae.   [Strassburg, J. Mentelin, c. 1473].   fol.
(Hoskier–Dunn).   (H*9270; BMC. I. 57)

Itinerarium seu peregrinatio beatae Mariae virginis.   [Ulm, J. Reger
1490].   4to.   (Yemeniz–Huth).   (H*9322, but with 36 leaves;
BMC. II. 540)

Incunabula

Jacobus Philippus de Bergamo. De claris selectisque mulieribus. Ferrara, L. de Rubeis, 29 April 1497. fol. (Groves). (H*2813; BMC. VI. 613)

Jacobus de Theramo. Belial. Augsburg, J. Schüssler, 2 July 1472. fol. (J. E. Hodgkin). (BMC. II. 329)

Johannes Damascenus. Gesta Barlaam et Josaphat. [Strassburg, H. Eggestein, c. 1475]. 4to. (Kloss). (H*5913; BMC. I. 73)

Johannes de Capua. *See* Bidpai

John, Chrysostom, *Saint*. Dialogi de dignitate sacerdoti. [Cologne, U. Zell, n. a. 1472]. 4to. (Thomas Brooke). (H*5048; BMC. I. 187)

—— Homiliae super Joannem. Rome [G. Lauer] 29 Oct. 1470. fol. (Hoe). (H*5036; BMC. IV. 36)

—— Homiliae super Matthaeum. [Strassburg, c. 1466]. fol. (H *5034; BMC. I. 51)

—— Sermo de penitentia. [Esslingen] C. Fyner [? 1473]. 4to. (Part of H*1171; BMC. II. 513; GW 2092)

—— —— [Louvain, J. de Paderborn, c. 1485]. 4to. (Part of GW 2100)

Jordanus *Nemorarius*. Elementa arithmetica. Paris, J. Higman & W. Hopyl, 22 July 1496. fol. (H 9436)

Jordanus de Quedlinburg. Postillae de tempore. Strassburg [Printer of 1483 Jordanus] 1483. fol. (Monastery of S. Peter, Salzburg). (H*9438; BMC. I. 131)

Josephus, Flavius. De antiquitate Judaica. De bello Judaico. Augsburg, J. Schüssler, 28 June; 23 Aug. 1470. fol. (Britwell). (H *9451; BMC. II. 327)

Justinianus, Bernardus. Oratio habita apud Sixtum IV. [Rome, S. Plannck, c. 1485]. 4to. (Sykes–Syston Park–Murray–Dunn). (H*9644; BMC. IV. 90)

Justinianus, Flavius Anicius. Digestum vetus. Venice, J. Rubeus, 21 Nov. 1477. fol. (Britwell). (H*9546; GW 7657)

—— Institutiones. Mainz, P. Schoeffer, 23 May 1476. fol. (H *9498; GW 7590)

Justinus. Epitome in Trogi Pompeii Historias. [Venice, J. Rubeus Vercellensis. A. Vercellensis, c. 1494]. fol. (H*9653; BMC. V. 421)

Juvenalis, Decimus Junius. Saturae. [Venice, Wendelin of Speyer, c. 1472/3]. fol. (H 9672; BMC. V. 164)

———— ———— Venice, J. Tacuinus, de Tridino, 28 Jan. 1494/5. fol. (Dunn). (H*9710; BMC. V. 529)

Lactantius, Lucius Coelius Firmianus. Opera. Rome, C. Sweynheym and A. Pannartz 1468. fol. (Amherst–Richter–Hoskier). (H *9807; BMC. IV. 4)

———— ———— [Venice] Wendelin of Speyer 1472. fol. (H *9810; BMC. V. 160)

———— ———— Venice, J. de Colonia and J. Manthen, 27 Aug. 1478. fol. (H*9814; BMC. V. 233)

———— ———— Venice, B. Locatellus for O. Scotus, 11 Oct. 1494. fol. (Édouard–Léon Roger, Comte du Nord). (H*9817; BMC. V. 443)

Laet, Jaspar. Prognosticaten [Dutch]. Antwerp, G. Leeu 1491. 4to.

Lamsheim, Johann. Speculū officii misse expositorium. (Heidelberg) H. Knoblochtzer, 29 June 1495. 4to. (Dunn–J. A. Brooke). (BMC. III. 672)

LeFèvre d'Étaples, Jacques. Elementa musicalia. Paris, J. Higman & W. Hopyl, 22 July 1496. fol. (H 9436)

———— Epitome in duos libros arithmeticos … Boecij. Paris, J. Higman & W. Hopyl, 22 July 1496. fol. (H 9436)

LeForestier, Jourdain. *See* Jordanus *Nemorarius*

LeGrand, Jacques. Sophologium. [Strassburg, Printer of Henricus Ariminensis, n.d.]. fol. (Dunn). (H*10469; BMC. I. 81)

Lichtenberger, Johann. Prognosticatio [Latin]. Modena, D. Rocociola [not after 1500]. 4to. (Sykes–Syston Park–Murray–Dunn). (H 10081; BMC. VII. 1064)

Livius, Titus. Historiae Romanae decades. [Rome] U. Han [c. 1470]. 2 v. fol. (Britwell). (H 10129; BMC. IV. 20)

———— ———— [Venice] Wendelin of Speyer 1470. 2 v. fol. (De Vinne). (H 10130; BMC. V. 154)

Incunabula

Livius, Titus. Historiae Romanae decades. Treviso, J. Rubeus Vercellensis 1485. fol. (Dunn). (H*10136; BMC.VI. 897)

———— ———— Venice, P. Pincius, 3 Nov. 1495. fol. (Henry Ellis Allen). (H*10141; BMC.V. 496)

Lombardus, Petrus. Liber Sententiarum. Venice, Wendelin of Speyer, 10 March 1477. fol. (Charles Butler). (H 10186; BMC.V. 248)

———— ———— Basel, N. Kesler, 22 Sept. 1488. fol. (H*10195; BMC. III. 766)

Lucanus, Marcus Annaeus. Pharsalia. Venice, Guerinus, 14 May 1477. fol. (Sykes–Britwell). (H*10233; BMC.V. 252)

Lucas de Burgo S. Sepulchri. Somma di aritmetica geometria proporzioni e proporzionalità. Venice, P. de Paganinis, 10-20 Nov. 14[9]4. fol. (H 4105; BMC.V. 457)

Lucianus. Vera historia [With other tracts]. Venice, S. Bevilaqua, 25 Aug. 1494. 4to. (Syston Park). (H*10261; BMC.V. 519)

Lucidarius. Le lucidaire. [Lyon, Jean de La Fontaine, c. 1500]. sm. 4to. (Audenet–Yemeniz–Huth–Murray)

Lucretius Carus, Titus. De rerum natura. Verona, P. Fridenperger, 28 Sept. 1486. fol. (Devonshire–Britwell). (H 10282; BMC. VII. 953)

Ludolphus de Suchen. Iter ad Terram Sanctam. [Strassburg, H. Eggestein, n.d.]. fol. (S. G. Hamilton). (H*10307; BMC. I. 74)

Lyra, Nicolaus de. Postilla super psalterium cum additionibus Pauli Burgensis et M. Doringii replicis. [Mantua, P. de Butzbach, c. 1477]. fol. (H 10376; Reichling I: 164)

Macer Floridus. De viribus herbarum. [?Genf, n.d.]. 4to. (Wodhull). (Veröffentlichungen der Gesellschaft für Typenkunde. Tafel 1634)

Macrobius. In Somnium Scipionis expositio. Saturnalia. Venice, N. Jenson 1472. fol. (Huth). (H 10426; BMC.V. 172)

———— ———— Brescia, B. de Boninis, 6 June 1483. fol. (Huth). (H*10427; BMC. VII. 968)

Magnus, Jacobus. *See* LeGrand, Jacques

Mahomet II. Epistolae magni Turci. [Treviso, G. de Lisa, de Flandria 1474?]. 4to. (Ch. Schefer). (H*10502; BMC. VI. 885)

Incunabula

Mancinus, Dominicus.　De passione domini.　(Paris, J. Higman, c. 1484).　4to.　(Walter Sneyd)

────── De quattuor virtutibus.　Paris, J. Higman, 22 Dec. 1484.　4to. (Walter Sneyd).　(HC 10630)

────── ────── Paris, G. Mittelhus 1488.　4to.　(Britwell).　(H *10632)

Mandeville, *Sir* John.　Itinerarius [German].　Strassburg, J. Prüss 1484. fol.　(Arthur Dalrymple).　(H 10649; BMC. I. 119)

Manilius, Marcus.　Astronomica.　Nuremberg, J. Müller of Königsberg [c. 1472].　4to.　(Pembroke).　(H*10703; BMC. II. 456)

Marchesinus, Joannes.　Mammotrectus super Bibliam.　Venice, N. Jenson, 23 Sept. 1479.　4to.　(H*10559; BMC. V. 180)

Marcianus, Capella.　De nuptiis Philologiae et Mercurii.　Modena, D. Bertocus, 15 May 1500.　fol.　(Dunn).　(H*4371; BMC. VII. 1068)

Martialis, Marcus Valerius.　Epigrammata.　[Venice] Wendelin of Speyer [c.1470/71].　4to.　(Morin d'Herouville–Wodhull–Amherst–Richter).　(H*10809; BMC. V. 164)

────── ────── Venice, T. de Blavis, 12 June 1482.　fol.　(F. Hopkinson).　(H*10815; BMC. V. 317)

────── ────── Venice, B. de Tortis, 17 July 1485.　fol.　(Dunn). (H*10819; BMC. V. 324)

Mela, Pomponius.　Cosmographia siue De situ orbis.　Milan [P. Castaldi] 25 Sept. 1471.　8vo.　(H 11014; BMC. VI. 699)

────── ────── Venice, B. Maler, E. Ratdolt, P. Löslein 1478.　4to. (La Vallière–Wodhull–Andrews).　(H*11016; BMC. V. 245)

────── ────── Venice, E. Ratdolt, 18 July 1482.　4to.　(H 11019; BMC. V. 286)

────── ────── Salamanca 1498.　4to.　(Huth).　(H 11021)

La mer des hystoires.　Paris, P. Le Rouge 1488.　2 v.　fol.　(Murray). (Proctor 8092)

Mercanzie ed usanze dei paesi.　[Often attributed to G. Chiarino]. Florence [B. di Libri] for P. Pacini [c. 1490].　8vo.　(Biblioteca Bologna Comunitativa–Magnani).　(H 4955; BMC. VI. 660)

[26]

Merlin. Le premier [second] volume de Merlin. [Paris, A. Vérard 1498]. 2 v. fol. (Britwell). (H 11086; Macfarlane 54)

——— Les prophecies de Merlin. Paris, A. Vérard 1498. fol. (Britwell). (H 11086; Macfarlane 54)

Missale Dominicanum s. Ord. Praedicatorum. Venice, O. Scotus, 24 Dec. 1482. 4to. (H*11289; BMC. V. 277)

Missale Hildeshemense. Nuremberg, G. Stuchs, 17 Sept. 1499. fol. (BMC. II. 472)

Modestus. De vocabulis rei militaris. Rome, E. Silber, 7 June 1487. 4to. (S. G. Hamilton). (H 11444; BMC. IV. 108)

Molitoris, Ulricus. De lamiis et pythonicis mulieribus. [Strassburg, J. Prüss, c. 1488-93]. 4to. (W. L. Andrews). (H*11535; BMC. I. 126)

Mombritius, Boninus. De dominica passione. Milan, A. Zarotus [1474]. 4to. (H 11542; BMC. VI. 712)

Monstrelet, Enguerrand de. Chroniques de France. Paris, for A. Vérard, c. 1497. 3 v. in 2. fol. (Huth)

Montemagno, Bonaccursius de. De nobilitate. [Florence, apud S. Jacobum de Ripoli, c. 1480]. 4to. (Dunn–Heber)

Müller, Johann. Calendarium. Venice, B. Maler, E. Ratdolt, P. Löslein 1476. 4to. (Vernon). (H*13776; BMC. V. 243)

——— Epitoma in Almagestum Ptolemaei. Venice, J. Hamman, 31 Aug. 1496. fol. (H*13806; BMC. V. 427)

Nepos, Cornelius. Vitae imperatorum. Venice, N. Jenson, 8 March 1471. 4to. (H*5733; BMC. V. 167)

Nicolaus de Hanapis. Auctoritates utriusque testamenti. [Strassburg, H. Eggestein, c. 1470/2]. fol. (Vernon). (H*3535; BMC. I. 70)

Nider, Johannes. De morali lepra. [Nuremberg, A. Koberger, n. a. 1471]. fol. (Millard–Dunn). (H*11813; BMC. II. 411)

Niger, Franciscus. Grāmatica. Basel, J. Wolff de Pforzheim, 21 March 1500. 4to. (Carthusian Monastery, Buxheim–W. H. Cummings). (H*11860; BMC. III. 778)

Niger, Petrus. *See* Schwartz, Peter

Nuremberg chronicle. *See* Schedel, Hartmann

Incunabula

Origenes.   Contra Celsum et in fidei Christianae defensionem libri. Rome, G. Herolt, Jan. 1481.   fol.   (H*12078; BMC. IV. 126)

Orosius, Paulus.   Historiae.   Augsburg, J. Schüssler, c. 7 June 1471. fol.   (Copy 1, Harley–Cassano–Spencer–Barclay; 2, Dunn).   (H *12101; BMC. II. 328)

Orpheus.   'Αργοναυτικά. 'Υμνοι.   Florence [B. Ricardinus] for F. Giunta, 19 Sept. 1500.   4to.   (Boutourlin–Huth).   (H*12106; BMC. VI. 690)

Ortiz, Alfonso.   Los tratados.   Seville, J. Pegnitzer, M. Herbst and T. Glockner 1493.   fol.   (Huth).   (H 12109)

Ovidius Naso, Publius.   Opera.   Bologna, B. Azoguidus 1471.   fol. (Pembroke–Murray).   (H 12136; BMC. VI. 798)

——— ——— [Venice] J. Rubeus [before Dec.] 1474.   fol.   (H 12138; BMC. V. 214)

——— ——— Vicenza, H. Liechtenstein, 12 Aug.; 10 May 1480.   fol. (Hibbert–Wodhull).   (H*12141; BMC. VII. 1037)

——— ——— Venice, B. Rizus, 27 Nov. 1486; 13 Jan. 1486/7.   fol. (Count Melzi of Milan–Hoe).   (H*12143; BMC. V. 400)

——— Fasti.   Venice, B. de Tortis, 24 Dec. 1482.   fol.   (H 12238; BMC. V. 322)

——— Metamorphoses.   [Venice, F. de Comitibus, n. d.].   4to. (Spencer–Heber–Britwell).   (H 12153; BMC. VII. 1134)

Palladius, Rutilius Taurus Aemilianus.   De re rustica.   *See* Scriptores rei rusticae

Panormitanus, Nicolaus.   Consilia seu allegationes.   [Strassburg, H. Eggestein, after 10 Oct. 1474].   fol.   (Dunn).   (H*12343; BMC. I. 69)

Parker, Henry.   Dives and Pauper.   London, R. Pynson, 5 July 1493. fol.   (Charles Longuet Higgins–Halsey).   (H 6109; STC 19212)

Paulinus *Nolanus*.   Vita Ambrosii.   Milan, C. Valdarfer, 7 Jan. 1474. 4to.   (H*910; BMC. VI. 725; GW 1611)

Paulus de Bergamo.   Apologia religionis Fratrum Eremitarum ordinis S. Augustini.   Rome, in domo F. de Cinquinis, 18 July 1479.   4to. (Dunn).   (Part of H 10328, 16086; BMC. IV. 76)

Incunabula

Paulus de Bergamo. Historia Sanctae Monicae ex libris S. Augustini. [Rome, in domo F. de Cinquinis, after 9 April 1479]. 4to. (Dunn). (Part of H 10328, 16086; BMC. IV. 76)

Paulus de Sancta Maria. *See* Sancta Maria, Paulus de

Paulus Florentinus. Breviarium totius juris canonici. Memmingen, A. Kunne 1486. fol. (Proctor–Murray). (H*7161; BMC. II. 604)

Peckham, John. Prospectiua communis. [Milan] P. de Corneno [1482/3?]. fol. (H*9425; BMC. VI. 759)

Persius, Aulus Flaccus. Saturae. [Venice, Wendelin of Speyer, c. 1472/3]. 4to. (H 9672; BMC. V. 164)

Petrarca, Francesco. Canzoniere. Venice [G. di Pietro, not before 13 Aug.] 1473. fol. (Huth). (H 12757; BMC. V. 199)

——— De remediis utriusque fortunae. Cremona, B. de Misintis & C. Parmensis, 17 Nov. 1492. fol. (Pinelli–Wodhull). (H*12793; BMC. VII. 956)

——— De vita solitaria. Milan, U. Scinzenzeler, 13 Aug. 1498. fol. (Henry Ellis Allen). (H 12797; BMC. VI. 774)

——— Historia Griseldis. [Cologne, U. Zell, c. 1472]. 4to. (H *12813; BMC. I. 186)

——— Sonetti e canzoni. Venice, P. de Pasqualibus & Dominicus Bertochus, 7 June 1486. fol. (H 12764)

——— Trionfi. Venice, P. de Pasqualibus & Dominicus Bertochus, 8 April 1488. fol. (H 12788)

Petrus de Tarentasia. *See* Thomas de Aquino *and* Petrus de Tarentasia

Petrus Lombardus. *See* Lombardus, Petrus

Petrus Ravennas. Artificiosa memoria. Venice, B. de Choris, de Cremona, 10 Jan. 1491/2. 4to. (H*13697; BMC. V. 466)

Phalaris. Epistolae. [Paris] U. [Gering], M. [Crantz] & M. [Friburger 1472]. 4to. (La Vallière–Crevenna). (H 12885)

Philelphus, Franciscus. Saturae. Milan, C. Valdarfer, 13 Nov. 1476. 4to. (Kloss–Britwell). (H*12917; BMC. VI. 726)

Philippus, Jacobus. Reformatorium vitae clericorum. Basel, M. Furter, 22 Feb. 14[9]4. 8vo. (HC 13720; BMC. III. 782)

Incunabula

Piccolomini, Æneas Sylvius. *See* Pius II, *Pope*

Pico della Mirandola, Giovanni Francesco. Heptaplus de septiformi sex dierum geneseos enarratione. [Florence, B. di Libri, c. 1489]. fol. (Joseph Knight). (H*13001; BMC.VI.662)

Pisis, Reynerus de. Pantheologia. [Basel, B. Ruppel, c. 1477]. 2 v. fol. (H*13014; BMC.III.716)

Pius II, *Pope*. Epistola ad Mahumetem. Treviso, G. de Lisa, de Flandria, 12 Aug. 1475. 4to. (H*177; BMC.VI.884)

—— Historia Bohemica. Rome, J. Schurener with J. N. Hanheymer, 10 Jan. 1475. 4to. (Dunn). (H*255; BMC.IV.56)

—— Historia de duobus amantibus. [Sant' Orso, G. da Reno, c. 1475]. 4to. (Britwell). (H*218; BMC.VII.1027)

—— Historia rerum ubique gestarum. Venice, J. de Colonia and J. Manthen 1477. fol. (H*257; BMC.V.233)

Platina, Bartholomaeus de. De honesta voluptate. Cividale, G. de Lisa, de Flandria, 24 Oct. 1480. 4to. (Yemeniz). (H*13052; BMC.VII.1094)

—— Vitae pontificum. [Treviso] J. Rubeus Vercellensis, 10 Feb. 1485. fol. (Hodgkin). (H*13048; BMC.VI.897)

Plato. Opera. Venice, B. de Choris & S. de Luere, 13 Aug. 1491. fol. (H*13063; BMC.V.465)

Plautus, Titus Maccius. Comoediae. Venice, Wendelin of Speyer 1472. fol. (Cracherode–Wodhull). (H 13074; BMC.V.160)

Plinius Secundus, Caius (*Pliny the elder*). Historia naturalis. Rome, C. Sweynheym and A. Pannartz [n.a. 30 Aug.] 1470. fol. (Huth). (H*13088; BMC.IV.9)

—— —— Venice, N. Jenson 1472. fol. (Syston Park). (H *13089; BMC.V.172)

—— —— [Italian]. Venice, N. Jenson 1476. fol. (W.H. Crawford). (H*13105; BMC.V.176)

Plinius Secundus, Caius (*Pliny the younger*). Epistolae. [?Rome, J. Schurener, c. 1474]. 4to. (Pembroke). (H 13108; Proctor 3523)

Plotinus. Opera. Florence, A. Miscomini, 7 May 1492. fol. (H *13121; BMC.VI.640)

Incunabula

Plutarchus. Apophthegmata. [Venice] Wendelin of Speyer 1471. 4to. (Huth). (H*13140; BMC.V.157)

—— Problemata. [Ferrara, A. Belfortis, c.1477?]. 4to. (Pembroke–W.H.Dutton). (BMC.VI.603)

—— Vitae parallelae. [Strassburg, A. Rusch, c.1470]. fol. (Kloss). (H*13124; BMC.I.62)

—— —— [Rome] U. Han [c.1470]. 2v. fol. (Charles Butler). (H*13125; BMC.IV.21)

—— —— Venice, N. Jenson, 2 Jan. 1478. 2v. fol. (Pier Crinito–W.H.Crawford). (H*13127; BMC.V.178)

—— —— Venice, G. Ragazzo, 7 Dec. 1491. fol. (H13129; BMC.V.501)

Poggius Florentinus. Historia Florentina. Venice, J. Rubeus, 8 March 1476. fol. (Hopetoun). (H*13172; BMC.V.215)

—— —— [Italian]. Florence, B. di Libri, 3 Sept. 1492. fol. (Sir Robert Throckmorton). (H1563, *13173; GW5613)

Politianus, Angelus. Miscellaneorum centuria prima. Florence, A. Miscomini, 19 Sept. 1489. fol. (Pembroke–Murray). (H*13221; BMC.VI.638)

—— Opera. Venetiis, in aedibus Aldi Romani, July 1498. fol. (Franciscus Avantius). (H*13218; BMC.V.559)

Polybius. Historiae. Rome, C. Sweynheym and A. Pannartz, 31 Dec. 147[2]. fol. (Spencer–Heber–Britwell). (H*13246; BMC. IV.16)

Pontificale Romanum. Rome, S. Plannck, 20 Dec. 1485. fol. (Ashburnham–Dunn). (H13285; BMC.IV.86)

Portolano. Venice, B. Rizus, 6 Nov. 1490. 4to. (Albani–Huth). (H 13302; BMC.V.402)

Priscianus. Opera. Venice, Wendelin of Speyer 1480. fol. (Pembroke–Murray). (H13355; BMC.V.156)

Processionarium ord. Praedicatorum. Seville, M. Ungut & S. Polonus, 3 April 1494. 8vo. (H13380)

Provocatio. Prouocacio inuitatoria. [Venice, H. Liechtenstein, c. 1493]. 4to.

Psalterium graecum. Venice, Laonicus & Alexander, 15 Nov. 1486. 4to. (Huth). (H*13453; BMC.V.409)

———— Venice, Aldus Manutius [?1497]. 4to. (Sunderland–Dunn). (H13452; BMC.V.563)

Ptolemaeus, Claudius. Almagest. *See* Müller, Johann

———— Cosmographia. Vicenza, H. Liechtenstein, 13 Sept. 1475. fol. (Huth). (H*13536; BMC.VII.1035)

———— ———— Ulm, L. Holle, 16 July 1482. fol. (H*13539; BMC. II.538)

———— ———— Rome, P. de Turre, 4 Nov. 1490. fol. (C.L.F. Robinson). (H*13541; BMC.IV.133)

Pulci, Bernardo, *tr.* *See* Virgilius Maro, Publius. Bucolica

Pulci, Luca. Il driadeo. [Florence, apud Sanctum Jacobum de Ripoli 1483?]. 4to. (H13575; BMC.VI.624)

———— La giostra di Lorenzo de Medici. Florence [?A. Miscomini] 18 March 1481. 4to. (Reichling IV: 69)

Quintilianus, Marcus Fabius. Declamationes. Venice, Lucas Dominici F., 2 Aug. 1481. fol. (H13657; BMC.V.280)

———— Institutiones oratoriae. Rome, C. Sweynheym and A. Pannartz [after 30 Aug. 1470]. fol. (Milini–Richter–Hoskier). (H13645; BMC.IV.11)

———— ———— [Venice] N. Jenson, 21 May 1471. fol. (Dunn). (H*13647; BMC.V.168)

Rampegollis, Antonius de. Biblia aurea. [Strassburg] J. (Reinhard) Grüninger, 6 Dec. 14[9]6. 4to. (H*13687; BMC.I.110)

Regiomontanus. *See* Müller, Johann

Repertorium haereticae pravitatis. Valencia [for] M. Albert, 16 Sept. 1494. fol. (Dunn). (H13875)

Repkow, Eyke von. Remissorium mitsamt dem wichbild und lehenrecht. Augsburg, A. Sorg, 16 Dec. 1482. fol. (H13866)

Retza, Franciscus de. Comestorium vitiorum. Nuremberg [J. Sensenschmidt and H. Kefer] 1470. fol. (H*13884; BMC.II.403)

Rivanellus, Julianus. Suprascriptiones litterarum. Venice [B. Locatellus for G.] B. Sessa [c. 1498]. 4to.

Incunabula

Rodericus Zamorensis. Speculum vitae humanae. Rome, C. Sweynheym and A. Pannartz 1468. 4to. (Huth). (H*13939; BMC. IV.4)

———— ———— [Cologne, U. Zell 1472]. 4to. (Fratres Minorum Recollectorum, Bruges–Syston Park). (H*13933; BMC. I.187)

———— ———— [Paris, U. Gering, M. Crantz & M. Friburger, 22 April 1472]. fol. (McCarthy–Reagh–Huth). (HC 13935; Copinger 5138; Claudin: Histoire I: 45-49)

———— ———— Paris, U. Gering, M. Crantz & M. Friburger, 1 Aug. 1475. fol. (Dunn). (H 13945)

Rolewinck, Werner. De sacramento et valore missarum. [Paris, L. Symonel, R. Blandin, J. Simon & G. de Russangis, c. 1475]. 4to. (John Symmons–Dunn)

———— Fasciculus temporum. Louvain, J. Veldener, 29 Dec. 1476. fol. (H*6920)

———— ———— Venice, G. Walch 1479. fol. (Dunn). (H*6924; BMC.V.274)

———— ———— Venice, E. Ratdolt, 24 Nov. 1480. fol. (Murray). (H*6926; BMC.V.283)

———— ———— [Venice] E. Ratdolt, 21 Dec. 1481. fol. (H*6928; BMC.V.285)

———— ———— [Lyon, M. Hus, c. 1495]. fol. (Dunn). (Copinger II: 2437)

Roma. [Historia et descriptio urbis Romae]. Rome [A. Freitag] 11 July 1492. 12mo.

———— ———— Rome, S. Plannck 14(93). 8vo.

Rosarium beate Marie v̄gīs [Carthusian]. [? Antwerp, G. Leeu, after 1487?]. 16mo.

Rufinus, Tyrannius. Expositio symboli Hieronymi. [Cologne, U. Zell, c. 1472]. 4to. (Dunn). (H*8578; BMC. I.191)

Sabellicus, Marcus Antonius Coccius. De vetustate Aquileiensis patriae cum aliis. [? Venice] Antony of Avignon [with type 105R of R. de Novimagio, c. 1482/3]. 4to. (Copy 1, Heber–Britwell; 2, Fazackerley–Heber–Britwell). (H*14058)

Incunabula

Sabellicus, Marcus Antonius Coccius.   Rerum Venetarum decades. Venice, A. Torresanus, 21 May 1487. fol. (H.V. Jones). (H *14053; BMC. V. 308)

Sacro Busto, Johannes de.   Sphaera mundi. [Venice] E. Ratdolt [before 4 Nov.] 1485. 4to. (Britwell). (H*14111; BMC. V. 290)

———— ———— Venice [Jacobus Pentius] 28 Jan. 1500. 4to. (H 14126)

Sallustius Crispus, Caius.   Opera.   [Fivizzano, J. de Fivizzano 1474]. 4to. (Pembroke–Murray). (Proctor 6879)

———— ———— Florence, apud Sanctum Jacobum de Ripoli 1478. fol. & 4to. (Boutourlin–Dunn). (H 14206; BMC. VI. 622)

———— Bellum Catilinariū . . . bellum Jugurthinū.   Paris, A. Bocard, 13 Jan. 1497/8. 4to. (H 14232)

Sancta Maria, Paulus de.   Additiones ad postillas Nicolai de Lyra cum replicis Matthiae Doering. Venice, F. Renner 1483. fol. (Part of GW 4287)

———— Scrutinium scripturarum.   [Strassburg, J. Mentelin, n.a. 1471]. fol. (Wodhull–Dunn). (H*10763; BMC. I. 54)

Savonarola, Girolamo.   Apologia dei Frati di san Marco.   [Florence, B. di Libri 1497?]. 4to. (Huth). (BMC. VI. 652)

———— Compendium reuelationum [Italian].   Florence, F. Bonaccorsi, 18 Aug. 1495. 4to. (Huth). (H 14334; BMC. VI. 674)

———— De simplicitate christianae vitae [Italian].   Florence, L. Morgiani, 31 Oct. 1496. 4to. (Huth). (H 14358; BMC. VI. 685)

———— Dell' amore di Gesù.   [Florence, B. di Libri 1495?]. 4to. (Huth). (BMC. VI. 658)

———— Dell' orazione mentale.   [Florence, c. 1496]. 4to. (Huth)

———— Dichiarazione del misterio della croce. [Florence, B. di Libri, c. 1495]. 4to. (Huth). (BMC. VI. 661)

———— Epistola a suoi diletti fratelli in Cristo Gesù. [Florence, B. di Libri, after 15 July 1497]. 4to. (Huth). (BMC. VI. 651)

———— Epistola a tutti gli eletti di Dio. [Florence, B. di Libri, after 8 May 1497]. 4to. (Huth). (BMC. VI. 651)

———— Epistola alla Contessa della Mirandola. [Florence, B. di Libri, c. 1495]. 4to. (Huth). (H 14465; BMC. VI. 664)

Incunabula

Savonarola, Girolamo.   Epistola alle suore del terzo ordine di san Domenico.   [Florence, B. di Libri, after 17 Oct. 1497].   4to. (H 14468; BMC.VI. 652)

―――― Epistola contra sententiam excommunicationis contra se nuper iniuste latam [With Italian translation of Filippo Cioni].   [Florence, J. Petri, after June 1497].   4to.   (Huth).   (BMC.VI. 618)

―――― Esposizione del salmo lxxix Qui regis Israel.   Florence, L. Morgiani and J. Petri, 8 June 1496.   4to.   (Huth).   (H 14436, 14439; BMC.VI. 684)

―――― Esposizione sopra l'Ave Maria.   [Florence, B. di Libri, c. 1495].   4to.   (H 14449; BMC.VI. 663)

―――― Expositio in septem gradus Bonauenturae [With Italian translation by Filippo Cioni].   [Florence, B. di Libri, not before Feb. 1497/8].   4to.   (Huth).   (H 14450; BMC.VI. 653)

―――― Expositio orationis dominicae (With Epistola della comunione [Italian]).   [Florence, B. di Libri, c. 1496].   4to.   (Huth).   (H 14445; BMC.VI. 659)

―――― Expositio super psalmo Miserere.   [Ferrara, L. de Rubeis, de Valentia, after May 1498].   4to.   (Britwell).   (H 14418; BMC. VI. 614)

―――― Libro della vita viduale.   [Florence, c. 1495].   4to.   (Huth). (H 14368)

―――― Predica dell' arte del bene morire.   [Florence, B. di Libri, after 2 Nov. 1496].   4to.   (Huth).   (H 14390; BMC.VI. 662)

―――― Sermone dell' orazione.   [Florence, B. di Libri 1495].   4to. (Huth).   (BMC.VI. 659)

―――― Sopra i dieci comandamenti di Dio.   Florence [B. di Libri] 24 Oct. 1495.   4to.   (Huth).   (H 14443; BMC.VI. 650)

―――― Trattato contro gli astrologi.   [Florence, B. di Libri, c. 1490]. 4to.   (Huth).   (H 14378; BMC.VI. 661)

―――― Trattato del sacramento.   [Florence, B. di Libri, c. 1495]. 4to.   (Huth).   (H 14353; BMC.VI. 659)

―――― Trattato dell' umiltà.   [Florence, B. di Libri 1495].   4to. (Huth).   (H 14374; BMC.VI. 659)

―――― Triumphus crucis.   [Florence, B. di Libri 1497?].   fol.   (H *14342; BMC.VI. 652)

Incunabula

Schatzbehalter. Nuremberg, A. Koberger, 8 Nov. 1491. fol. (John Pearson). (H*14507; BMC. II. 434)

Schedel, Hartmann. Liber chronicarum. Nuremberg, A. Koberger, 12 July 1493. fol. (H*14508; BMC. II. 437)

—— —— Augsburg, J. Schönsperger, 1 Feb. 1497. fol. (W. M. Tilghman). (H 14509; BMC. II. 370)

Schwartz, Peter. Tractatus contra perfidos Judaeos. Esslingen, C. Fyner, 6 June 1475. fol. & 4to. (Huth). (H*11885; BMC. II. 514)

Scott, Michael. Liber physiognomiae. [Venice, J. de Fivizzano, Lunensis] 1477. 4to. (Pinelli–Wodhull). (H*14550; BMC. V. 242)

Scriptores rei rusticae. Cato. Varro. Columella. Palladius Rutilius Taurus Aemilianus. Venice, N. Jenson 1472. fol. (Pembroke). (H*14564; BMC. V. 173)

Seneca, Lucius Annaeus. Epistolae. [Strassburg, A. Rusch, c. 1469/70]. fol. (Pittar–Sunderland). (H*14597; BMC. I. 62)

—— Opera philosophica. Epistolae. Naples, M. Moravus 1[4]75. fol. (Wodhull). (H 14590; BMC. VI. 861)

—— —— Treviso, B. de Colonia 1478. fol. (H*14591; BMC. VI. 892)

—— Proverbia. [Rome, J. Gensberg, c. 1475]. 4to. (H 14644)
—— Tragoediae. Venice, J. Tacuinus, de Tridino, 7 April 1498. fol. (H*14670; BMC. V. 533)

Sermones thesauri novi. Strassburg [Printer of the 1483 Vitas patrum] 1483. fol. (Proctor 419)

Sidonius, Apollinaris. Epistolae et carmina. [Utrecht, N. Ketelaer & G. de Leempt 1473]. fol. (Huth). (H*1286)

Silius Italicus. Punica. Rome, C. Sweynheym and A. Pannartz [not before 5 April 1471]. fol. (Pembroke). (H*14733; BMC. IV. 13)

Simon Januensis. Clauis sanationis. Venice, G. Anima Mia, Tridinensis, 13 Nov. 1486. fol. (H*14749; BMC. V. 410)

Sixtus IV, *Pope*. Bulla indulgentiarum de aedificatione ecclesiae Nordlingensis. [Augsburg, H. Kästlin, after 9 Feb. 1479]. fol. (Copinger II: 5529). (Broadside)

Incunabula

Le songe du vergier. [Lyon] J. Maillet, 20 March 1491. fol. (Payne–Wodhull–Andrews). (H 16006)

Spiera, Ambrosius. Quadragesimale de floribus sapientiae. Venice, Wendelin of Speyer, 18 Dec. 1476. fol. (H*919)

Spirito, Lorenzo. Altro Marte. Vicenza, S. de Gabis, 9 April 1489. fol. (Gaisford–Dunn). (H*14960; BMC.VII. 1051)

Sprenger, Jacob *and* Henricus Institoris. Malleus maleficarum. [?Speyer, P. Drach, c. 1490]. fol. (H*9238)

Statham, Nicholas. Abridgment of cases to the end of Henry VI. [Rouen, G. Le Talleur for] R. Pynson [1490]. fol. (H 15092; STC 23238)

Statuta Angliae. Noua statuta (1328-1497). [London] R. Pynson [?1500]. fol. (STC 9265)

Statuta Mediolani. Milan, P. de Suardis, 20 Dec. 1480. fol. (Britwell). (H 15009, first part; BMC.VI. 758)

———— Tabula. Milan [J. A. de Honate] 30 Nov. 1482. fol. (Britwell). (H 15009(2); 15010; BMC.VI. 741)

Suardus, Andreas. Additiones ad salutationem angelicam. [?Reggio d'Emilia, A. Portilia, c. 1484]. 8vo. (Copinger II: 5669)

Suetonius Tranquillus, Caius. Vitae Caesarum. [Venice] N. Jenson 1471. 4to. (Spencer–Barclay). (H*15117; BMC.V. 170)

Suidas. Λεξικόν. Milan, J. Bissolus & B. Mangius, 15 Nov. 1499. fol. (Duke of Grafton–Heber–Britwell). (H*15135; BMC.VI. 792)

Tacitus, Publius Cornelius. Germania. (Bologna, B. Azoguidus 1472). fol. (H 6188; BMC.VI. 799)

———— ———— [Nuremberg, F. Creussner, c. 1473/4]. fol. (H *15224; BMC.II. 447)

Tambaco, Johannes de. Consolatio theologiae. [Mainz, P. Schoeffer, c. 1470-75]. 4to. (Kloss). (H*15235; BMC.I. 38)

Tartagnus, Alexander, *de Imola*. Consilia. Venice, J. Rubeus, 23 Dec. 1477. fol. (William Morris–Dunn). (H*15265; BMC.V. 217)

Terentius Afer, Publius. Comoediae. [Schussenried, Printer of Gracchus et Poliscena of 1478]. fol. (Pembroke–J. A. Brooke). (H *15370; BMC.II. 568)

Incunabula

Terentius Afer, Publius.   Comoediae.   Strassburg, J. Grüninger, 1 Nov. 1496.   fol.   (Christopher Wordsworth–Lossing).   (H *15431; BMC. I. 110)

———— ———— Venice, S. de Luere for L. de Soardis, 5 July 1497. fol.   (Sunderland–J. A. Brooke).   (H*15429; BMC. V. 573)

———— ———— Strassburg, J. Grüninger, 11 Feb. 1499.   fol.   (H *15432; BMC. I. 113)

———— Comedien [German].   Strassburg, J. Grüninger, 5 March 1499.   fol.   (H 15434; BMC. I. 113)

Theocritus.   Εἰδύλλια.   Venetiis, characteribus ac studio Aldi Manucii Romani, Feb. 1495.   fol.   First Issue.   (Earl of Peterborough). (H*15477; BMC. V. 554)

———— ———— ———— Second Issue.   (Ashburnham–Edward Davenport)

Theophrastus.   De historia et causis plantarum.   Treviso, B. Confalonerius, 20 Feb. 1483.   fol.   (H*15491; BMC. VI. 894)

Theophylactus.   Enarrationes in Epistolas S. Pauli.   Rome, U. Han, 25 Jan. 1477.   fol.   (H*1902; BMC. IV. 25)

Theramo, Jacobus de.   *See* Jacobus de Theramo

Thomas de Aquino.   Catena aurea.   [Augsburg, G. Zainer, c. 1476]. fol.   (Goldschmidt).   (H*1328; BMC. II. 323)

———— De veritate catholicae fidei.   [Strassburg, Printer of Henricus Ariminensis, c. 1469].   fol.   (H*1385; BMC. I. 77)

———— ———— Rome, A. Pannartz, 20 Sept. 1475.   fol.   (J. E. Hodgkin).   (H 1387)

———— Expositio super libros Posteriorum et De interpretatione Aristotelis. Fallaciae [With the Quaestiones of Dominicus de Flandria]. [Venice] O. de Luna, 28 Sept. 1496.   fol.   (Dunn).   (H 1495; BMC. V. 567)

———— Postilla in Job.   [Esslingen] C. Fyner 1474.   fol.   (W. H. Crawford–Dunn).   (H*1397; BMC. II. 513)

———— Quaestiones de potentia Dei.   [Cologne, J. Koelhoff the Elder, c. 1475].   fol.   (Dunn).   (H*1414; BMC. I. 219)

———— Summa, pars prima.   [Padua] A. de Stendal, 5 Oct. 1473.   fol. (Boutourlin–Dunn).   (H*1440; BMC. VII. 911)

Incunabula

Thomas de Aquino. Summa, prima secundae. Venice, A. Torresanus, B. de Blavis, M. de Paterbonis, T. de Blavis 1483. fol. (H*1449; BMC.V. 306)

—— Summa, secunda secundae. [Strassburg, J. Mentelin, n. a. 1466]. fol. (H*1454; BMC. I. 51)

—— Summa, secunda secundae. [Esslingen, C. Fyner] 1472. fol. (H*1460; BMC. II. 511)

—— Super primo libro Sententiarum. Venice, A. de Strata, 21 June 1486. fol. (H*1474; BMC.V. 294)

—— Super quarto libro Sententiarum. Cologne, H. Quentell, 2 Feb. 1480. fol. (Dunn–Goldschmidt). (H*1483; BMC. I. 262)

—— Tractatus de corpore Christi. [Cologne, Printer of Augustinus de Fide] 8 April 1473. 4to. (W. L. Andrews). (H 1374; BMC. I. 232)

—— *and* Petrus de Tarentasia. De septem sacramentis. [Louvain, J. de Paderborn, c. 1485]. 4to. (Part of GW 2100)

Thomas (Becket), *Archbishop of Canterbury*. Vita et processus. Paris, J. Philippi, 27 March 1495/6. 4to. (H 15510)

Thomas Cantipratensis. Der bien boeck. Zwolle, P. van Os, 15 Jan. 1488. fol. (Kloss–Vernon). (H 4186)

Thucydides. De bello Peloponnesiaco. [Treviso, J. Rubeus Vercellensis 1483?]. fol. (Dunn). (H*15511; BMC.VI. 896)

Thwrocz, Johannes de. Chronica Hungarorum. Augsburg, E. Ratdolt, 3 June 1488. 4to. (Huth). (H*15518; BMC. II. 381)

Todsünden. Hienach volget ein schöne materi vō den siben todsünden vñ von den syben tugendē. Augsburg, J. Bämler, 15 Nov. 1474. fol. (Carl Becher–Murray). (H*15535)

Tundalus. De raptu animae Tundali. [Speyer, J. and C. Hist 1483]. 4to. (H*15540; BMC. II. 502)

Turrecremata, Johannes de. Expositio Psalterii. Rome, U. Han, 4 Oct. 1470. 4to. (H*15695; BMC. IV. 21)

—— —— Mainz, P. Schoeffer, 11 Sept. 1474. fol. (Heber–Britwell). (H*15698; BMC. I. 31)

—— —— Rome, W. Han, 21 Feb. 1476. 4to. (Dunn). (H *15700; BMC. IV. 74)

Incunabula

Turrecremata, Johannes de.   Expositio Psalterii.   Mainz, P. Schoeffer, 7 Jan. 1478.   fol.   (Dunn).   (H*15701; BMC. I. 34)

Urbanus Bellunensis.   Institutiones graecae grammatices.   Venetiis, in aedibus Aldi Manutii Romani, Jan. 1497.   4to.   (Britwell).   (H*16098; BMC. V. 558)

Ursula, *Saint.*   Navicula Sanctae Ursulae.   [Strassburg, J. Grüninger? for B. Kistler, c. 1497].   4to.   (Carmelite Convent, Ratisbon).   (Copinger II: 5909)

Utino, Leonardus de.   Quadragesimale aureum.   [Venice, F. Renner de Heilbronn, n. a. 23 Oct.] 1471.   4to.   (Augustinian Monastery, Munich–J. Gomez de La Cortina).   (H*16124; BMC. V. 191)

—— Sermones de Sanctis.   [Augsburg, Monastery of SS. Ulrich and Afra] 1474.   fol.   (H*16130; BMC. II. 339)

—— —— [Paris, U. Gering, M. Crantz and M. Friburger] 31 March 1475.   fol.   (Sir Joseph Yates–Henry Yates Thompson).   (H*16131)

Valerius Flaccus, Caius.   Argonautica.   Bologna, U. Rugerius and D. Bertochus, 7 May 1474.   fol.   (Albani–Heber–Britwell).   (BMC. VI. 805)

Valerius Maximus, Caius.   Facta et dicta memorabilia.   Mainz, P. Schoeffer, 14 June 1471.   fol.   (Huth).   (H*15774; BMC. I. 27)

Valla, Laurentius.   Antidotum in Poggium.   Siena, Henricus de Harlem, 8 May 1490.   fol.   (Dunn).   (H 15825; BMC. VII. 1101)

—— Elegantiae. De ego mei tui sui.   Venice, N. Jenson 1471.   4to.   (Syston Park–Thomas–Stanford–Groves).   (H 15802; BMC. V. 171)

Valturius, Robertus.   De re militari.   Verona, J. de Verona 1472.   fol.   (Huth).   (H*15847; BMC. VII. 948)

—— —— Verona, B. de Boninis, 17 Feb. 1483.   fol.   (Pembroke).   (H 15849; BMC. VII. 952)

Varro, Marcus Terentius.   De lingua latina.   [Venice, Printer of Basilius, De vita solitaria, 1471].   4to.   (Payne–Henry Drury–Dunn).   (BMC. V. 187)

—— —— [Venice, J. de Colonia and J. Manthen, c. 1474].   4to.   (Pembroke).   (H 15858; BMC. V. 230)

Incunabula

Varro, Marcus Terentius. Rerum rusticarum. *See* Scriptores rei rusticae

Vegetius Renatus, Flavius. De re militari. Rome, E. Silber, 29 Jan. 1487. 4to. (S. G. Hamilton). (H*15913; BMC. IV. 107)

Verardus, Carolus. Historia Baetica. [Basel] I. B[ergmann] 1494. 4to. (Marquis d'Adda–Murray). (H*15942; BMC. III. 794)

Vergerius, Petrus Paulus. De ingenuis moribus. [Louvain] J. de Paderborn [c.1474-5?]. 4to. (Dunn). (H15984; Campbell 1724)

Vincentius Bellovacensis. Speculum historiale. [Strassburg, A. Rusch, c. 1473]. 2 v. fol. (Proctor 254)

Virgilius Maro, Publius. Opera. Venice, Wendelin of Speyer 1470. fol. (Pembroke–Murray). (BMC. V. 154)

———— ———— Vicenza, L. Achates 1479. fol. (BMC. VII. 1031)

———— ———— Venice, B. de Tortis, 1 Oct. 1483. fol. (BMC. V. 323)

———— ———— Venice, A. de Paltasichis, 1 Sept. 1488. fol. (BMC. V. 355)

———— ———— Nuremberg, A. Koberger 1492. fol. (BMC. II. 436)

———— Bucolica. Tr. into Italian by B. Pulci. Florence, A. Miscomini, 19 April 1494. 4to. (BMC. VI. 643)

Vita et processus Sancte Thome. *See* Thomas (Becket), *Archbishop of Canterbury*

Vitruvius Pollio, Marcus. De architectura. [Rome, ? E. Silber, c. 1486]. fol. (BMC. IV. 124)

Vocabularius cum teutonico. [Augsburg, G. Zainer 1473-4]. fol. (Huth). (BMC. II. 321)

———— [Strassburg, Printer of Henricus Ariminensis, n. d.]. fol. (Huth). (BMC. I. 80)

Voragine, Jacobus de. Legenda aurea. Nuremberg, J. Sensenschmidt & A. Frisner, 26 March 1476. fol. (Shipperdson–Dunn). (Copinger II^{II}: 6411)

———— ———— Nuremberg, A. Koberger, 11 April 1481. fol. (Syston Park). (BMC. II. 419)

———— ———— Cologne [U. Zell] 19 May 1482. fol. (William Morris–Dunn). (BMC. I. 196)

Incunabula

Voragine, Jacobus de. Legenda aurea. [Italian]. [Venice] N. Jenson [c. 1475]. fol. (Pembroke). (Copinger II^{II}: 6497)

Xenophon. De vita tyrannica. [Venice, ?A. de Ambergau, c. 1471]. 4to. (Sykes–Syston Park–Dunn). (H 16228?; BMC. V. 189)

Aldines

Æschylus. Tragoediae sex. Venice, in aedibus Aldi et Andreae soceri, Feb. 1518. 8vo. (Hoe)

Æsopus. Vita, & fabellae. Venetiis, apud Aldum, Oct. 1505. fol. (Boutourlin–J. W. Bruce)

Antoninus Augustus. Itinerarium provinciarum. (Venetiis, in aedibus Aldi 1518). 8vo. (Dunn–L. W. Hodson)

Apollonius Rhodius. Argonautica. (Venice, in aedibus Aldi et Andreae soceri, April 1521). 8vo. (Sykes)

Apuleius Madaurensis, Lucius. Metamorphoseos. Venice, in aedibus Aldi, et Andreae soceri, May 1521. 12mo.

Arator. Historiae Apostolicae libri duo. (Venetiis, apud Aldum, June 1502). 4to. (Hoblyn–Wodhull)

Ariosto, Ludovico. Orlando Furioso. Venice, in casa de' figliuoli di Aldo 1545. 4to. (Labouchere)

Aristophanes. Comoediae novem [Greek]. Venetiis, apud Aldum, 15 July 1498. fol. (H*1656; GW 2333)

Aristoteles. Opera [Greek]. Venetiis, Aldus Manutius 1495-8. 5 v. in 6. fol. (Hoe–Robert Lenox Kennedy). (H*1657; GW 2334)

Athenaeus. Opera [Greek]. Venetiis, apud Aldum et Andream socerum, Aug. 1514. fol. (Peterborough)

Bembo, Pietro. Gli Asolani. Venice, case d'Aldo Romano, March 1505. 8vo.

Bible. *Greek*. Venetiis, in aedib. Aldi et Andreae soceri, Feb. 1518. fol. (Roxburghe–Sir James Lewis Knight–Bruce)

Bible. *Latin*. Romae, ex typographia Apostolica Vaticana 1592. fol.

Bobali Sordo, Savino de. Rime amorose. In Venetia, presso Aldo 1589. 4to. (Britwell)

Boccaccio, Giovanni. Il Decamerone. In Vinegia, nelle case d'Aldo Romano & d'Andrea Asolano, Nov. 1522. 8vo. (Vernon)

Bolzanus. *See* Urbanus Bellunensis

Bordone, Benedetto. Isolario. In Vinegia, ad instantia ... del ... M. Federico Toresano 1547. fol.

Aldines

Callimachus. Hymni. (Venetijs, in aedib. Aldi, Jan. 1513). 8vo.

Castiglione, Baldassare. Il libro del cortegiano. In Venetia, nelle case d'Aldo Romano & d'Andrea d'Asola, April 1528. fol. (W.H. Corfield)

Caterina da Siena, *Saint*. Epistole. In Vinetia, appresso Federico Toresano 1548. 4to. (Sunderland)

Catullus, Caius Valerius. Carmina. Venetiis, in aedibus Aldi, Jan. 1502. 8vo.

Cicero, Marcus Tullius. De philosophia. Venetiis, in aedibus Aldi et Andreae Asulani soceri, May, Aug. 1523. 2 v. 8vo. (Sykes–Syston Park)

———— Epistolarum ad Atticum. Venetiis, in aedibus Aldi, et Andreae soceri, June 1513. 12mo. (Beaufoy)

———— Opera. Venetiis, apud Aldum 1578-83. 10v. in 11. fol. (Coret y Perez–Hudnut)

———— Orationum. Venetiis, in aedibus Aldi, et Andreae soceri, Jan., May, Aug. 1519. 3 v. 8vo. (Huth)

Colonna, Francesco. Hypnerotomachia Poliphili. Venetiis, in aedibus Aldi Manutii, Dec. 1499. fol. (Vernon). (GW 7223)

Dante Alighieri. Le terze rime. Venetiis, in aedib. Aldi, Aug. 1502. 8vo. First Aldine Edition, First and Second Issues

Dionysius Periegetes. Poema de orbis situ. Venetijs, in aedib. Aldi, Jan. 1513. 8vo.

———— ———— ———— 1518. 8vo.

Dolce, Lodovico. Giocasta. Aldi filii in Vinegia 1549. 24mo.

Epistolae graecae. Venice, Aldus Manutius [29] March; [not before 17 April] 1499. 2 parts in 1. 4to. (H*6659; BMC. V. 560)

Euripides. Hecuba, & Iphigenia in Aulide. Venetiis, in aedibus Aldi, Dec. 1507. 8vo. (Kloss)

———— Tragoediae. Venetiis, apud Aldum, Feb. 1503. 2 v. 8vo. (Dunn)

Fortunio, Francesco. Regole grammaticali. In Vinegia, in casa de' figliuoli di Aldo 1541. 12mo.

Aldines

Gaza, Theodorus. Γραμματικὴ εἰσαγωγή [With other tracts]. Venetiis, in aedibus Aldi Romani 1495. fol. (Montaigne–Pembroke). (H*7800; BMC. V. 553)

Gellius, Aulus. Noctium Atticarum. Venetiis, in aedibus Aldi, et Andreae soceri, Sept. 1515. 12mo. (Alexander Boswell–Charles Eliot Norton)

Gregory Nazianzen. Carmina. Venetiis, ex Aldi Academia, June 1504. 4to.

Herodotus. Libri novem. Venetiis, in domo Aldi, Sept. 1502. fol. (Heredia–Didot–Hoe)

Homerocentra. (Venetiis, apud Aldum, June 1502). 4to. (Gaignat–Wodhull)

Homerus. Opera [Greek]. [Venetiis, in aedibus Aldi et Andreae Asulani soceri, June 1517]. 2 v. 8vo. (Renouard–Thomas Baring)

Horae B. V. M. *Roman use. Greek.* Horae ... secūdum consuetudinem romanae curiae. [Venice] Aldus Manutius, 5 Dec. 1497. 16mo. (W. H. Crawford). (H 8830; BMC. V. 558)

Johannes Damascenus. Hymni. (Venetiis, apud Aldum, Jan. 1501). 4to. (Gaignat–Wodhull)

Justinus. Trogi Pompei Externae historiae. Venetiis, in aedibus Aldi et Andreae Asulani soceri, Jan. 1522. 8vo.

Juvenalis, Decimus Junius. Iuvenalis. Persius. Venetiis, in aedibus Aldi, Aug. 1501. 8vo. First Issue. (Hopetoun)

Juvencus. De evangelia historia. (Venetiis, apud Aldum, June 1502). 4to. (Hoblyn–Wodhull)

Lactantius, Lucius Coelius Firmianus. Divinarum institutionum. Venetiis, in aedibus Aldi, et Andreae soceri, April 1515. 8vo.

Lippomano, Luigi. De vitis sanctorum. Venetiis 1581. 6v. fol. (Syston Park)

Livius, Titus. Historiae Romanae decades. Venetiis 1518-33. 5 v. 8vo. (Chorier–Knox–Slade)

Lucianus. Dialogi. Venetiis, in aedibus Aldi, & Andreae Asulani soceri, Oct. 1522. fol. (Peterborough)

——— Opera. Venetiis, in aedib. Aldi, June 1503. fol. (Renouard–Hoe)

Aldines

Lycophron. [Alexandra, sive Cassandra: poema]. (Venetijs, in aedib. Aldi, Jan. 1513). 8vo.

Martialis, Marcus Valerius. Epigrammata. Venetiis, in aedibus Aldi, Dec. 1501. 8vo.

Medici, Lorenzo de'. Poesie volgari. In Vinegia, in casa de' figliuoli di Aldo 1554. 8vo.

Mela, Pomponius. De situ orbis. Venetiis, in aedibus Aldi, et Andreae soceri, Oct. 1518. 8vo. (Dunn–Hodson)

Natta, Marcus Antonius. De Deo libri XV. Venetiis, apud Paulum Manutium 1560. fol. (Syston Park–Hoe)

—— De libris suis. Venetiis [Paulus Manutius] 1562. fol. (Syston Park–Hoe–C. L. F. Robinson)

Ovidius Naso, Publius. Opera. Venetiis, Oct., Dec. 1502; Feb. 1503. 3 v. 8vo. (Hawtrey–Huth)

—— —— Venetiis, in aedibus haeredum Aldi, et Andreae soceri 1533. 3 v. 8vo. (V. Clement)

Paetus, Lucas. De mensuris. Venetiis [Paulus Manutius] 1573. fol. (Syston Park–Hoe)

Pausanias. (Descriptio Greciae). Venetiis, in aedibus Aldi, et Andreae soceri, July 1516. fol. (Syston Park)

Petrarca, Francesco. Le cose volgari. In Vinegia, nelle case d'Aldo Romano, July 1501. 8vo. (Copy 1, Huth; 2, Dauphin–Earl of Jersey–S. P. Avery)

Philostratus. De vita Apollonii. Venetiis, in aedibus Aldi, Feb. 1502 (Colophon of the Greek text dated March 1501; Preface to Latin text dated May 1504). fol. (Huth)

Pindarus. Opera. Venetijs, in aedib. Aldi, et Andreae Asulani soceri, Jan. 1513. 8vo.

Plato. Opera [Greek]. Venetiis, in aedib. Aldi, et Andreae soceri, Sept. 1513. fol.

Plinius Secundus, Caius (*Pliny the younger*). Epistolae. Venetiis, in aedib. Aldi, et Andreae Asulani soceri, Nov. 1508. 8vo. (Huth)

Plutarchus. Opuscula. Venetiis, in aedibus Aldi & Andreae Asulani soceri, March 1509. fol. (F. Paley)

Aldines

Plutarchus. Parallela. Venetiis, in aedibus Aldi, et Andreae soceri, Aug. 1519. fol. (J. H. Voss)

Poetae christiani veteres. Venetiis, Jan. 1501; June 1502. 2 v. 4to. (Gaignat–Wodhull; Hoblyn–Wodhull)

Politianus, Angelus. Omnia opera. Venetiis, in aedibus Aldi Romani, July 1498. fol. (Franciscus Avantius). (H*13218; BMC.V. 559)

Proba Falconia. Vergili centones. (Venetiis, apud Aldum, June 1502). 4to. (Gaignat–Wodhull).

Propertius, Sextus Aurelius. Elegiae. Venetiis, in aedibus Aldi, Jan. 1502. 8vo.

Prosper d'Aquitaine. Epigrammata. (Venetiis, apud Aldum, Jan. 1501). 4to. (Gaignat–Wodhull)

Prudentius, Aurelius Clemens. Opera. (Venetiis, apud Aldum, Jan. 1501). 4to. (Gaignat–Wodhull)

Psalterium graecum. Venetiis, Aldus Manutius [?1497]. 4to. (Sunderland–Dunn). (H 13452; BMC.V.563)

Quintilianus, Marcus Fabius. Institutiones oratoriae. Venetiis, in aedibus Aldi, et Andreae soceri, Aug.1514. 4to. (Wodhull)

Sallustius Crispus, Caius. Opera. Venetiis, in aedibus Aldi, et Andreae Asulani soceri, April 1509. 8vo.

Sedulius, Coelius. Mirabilium divinorum libri. (Venetiis, apud Aldum, June 1502). 4to. (Hoblyn–Wodhull)

Seneca, Lucius Annaeus. Tragoediae. Venetiis, in aedibus Aldi et Andreae soceri, Oct. 1517. 8vo. (Carvalho)

Solinus, Julius. Polyhistor. (Venetiis, in aedibus Aldi 1518). 8vo. (Dunn–Hodson)

Sophocles. Tragoediae. Venetiis, in Aldi Romani academia, Aug. 1502. 8vo. (Alexander Boswell–W. F. Prideaux)

Statius, Publius Papinius. Sylvarum libri. Venetiis, in academia Aldi ...Nov. 1502. 8vo. (Syston Park)

Stephanus Byzantius. De urbibus [Greek]. Venetiis, apud Aldum Romanum, Jan. 1502. fol.

Tertullian, Quintus Septimus. Apologeticus. Venetiis, in aedibus Aldi, et Andreae soceri, April 1515. 8vo.

Aldines

Theocritus. Εἰδύλλια. Venetiis, characteribus ac studio Aldi Manucii Romani, Feb. 1495. fol. First Issue. (Earl of Peterborough). (H*15477; BMC.V.554)

———— ———— ———— Second Issue. (Ashburton–Edward Davenport)

Thucydides. De bello peloponnesiaco [Greek]. Venetiis, in domo Aldi, May 1502. fol. (Samuel Butler)

Tibullus, Albius. Elegiae. Venetiis, in aedibus Aldi, Jan. 1502. 8vo.

Trent, Council of. Canones, et decreta. Romae, apud Paulum Manutium, Aldi F., 1564. fol. (Samuel Butler)

Turco, Carlo. Calestri tragedia nuova. In Vinetia 1585. 8vo.

Urbanus Bellunensis. Institutiones graecae grammatices. Venetiis, in aedibus Aldi Manutii Romani, Jan. 1497. 4to. (Britwell). (H *16098; BMC.V.558)

Vibius Sequester. De fluminibus. (Venetiis, in aedibus Aldi 1518). 8vo. (Dunn–Hodson)

Vico, Aenea. Omnium Caesarum verissimae imagines. [Venice, Paulus Manutius] 1554. 4to. (Syston Park–Hoe)

Victor, P. De regionibus urbis Romae. (Venetiis, in aedibus Aldi 1518). 8vo. (Dunn–Hodson)

Virgilius Maro, Publius. Bucolica. Georgica. Aeneida. Venetiis, ex aedibus Aldi Romani, April 1501. 8vo. (Sunderland)

———— ———— Venetiis, in aedibus Aldi et Andreae soceri, Oct. 1514. 8vo. (Joannes Auratus–Huth)

Xenophon. Omnia, quae extant. Venetiis, in aedibus Aldi, et Andreae Asulani soceri, April 1525. fol. (H.Capilupus)

Books Printed in England, Scotland & Ireland, and English Books and Books by English Authors Printed Abroad 1475-1640

This list includes not only titles in Literature, but such titles in Americana, Bibles, Liturgical books, Incunabula and Science as fall within the limits indicated above.

[Abbot], George.   A briefe description of the whole world.   London, for W. Sheares 1634.   12mo.   (STC 31)

Acosta, José de.   The naturall and morall historie of the East and West Indies.   Tr. by E. Grimston.   London, V. Simmes 1604.   sm. 4to.   (G. Robinson–J. Lancaster).   (STC 94)

Acton [or Athon], John.   Constitutiones legitime seu legatine regionis Anglicanae.   Paris, W. Hopyl for (London) W. Bretton (after 13 Sept. 1506).   fol.   (STC 17109)

[Adamson, John].   Tὰ τῶν μουσῶν εἰσόδια. The muses welcome.   Edinburgh, T. Finlason 1618.   fol.   First Edition.   (STC 140)

[———]   Tὰ τῶν μουσῶν ἐξόδια; planctus & vota musarum.   Edinburgh, A. Hart 1618.   fol.   First Edition.   (STC 142)

Adlington, William, *tr.*   *See* Apuleius Madaurensis, Lucius

Ælianus, *Tacticus*.   The tactiks of Aelian. Englished ... by I. Bingham.   London [M. Bradwood 1616].   fol.   First Edition, First Issue.   (Dunn).   (STC 161)

Alabaster, William.   Roxana.   London, W. Jones 1632.   8vo.   (Copy 1, Lefferts; 2, Bridgewater).   (STC 250)

Aleman, Mateo.   The rogue [Tr. by J. Mabbe].   London, Part I [G. Purslowe]; Part II, G. Elde 1623.   fol.   First Edition, Second Issue.   (STC 289)

——— ——— Oxford, W. Turner 1630.   fol.   Second Edition.   (STC 290)

Alexander, William, *Earl of Stirling*.   Aurora.   London, R. Field 1604.   sm. 4to.   First Edition.   (STC 337)

——— The mapp and description of New-England.   London, for N. Butter 1630.   sm. 4to.   (W. O. Massingberd).   (STC 342)

——— The monarchick tragedies.   London, Part I, V. S[immes]; Part II, G. Elde 1604.   sm. 4to.   First Edition under this title.   (STC 343)

English to 1640

Alexander, William, *Earl of Stirling*.   The monarchicke tragedies.
London, V. Simmes 1607.   sm. 4to.   Second Edition.   (John G.
Bourinot–H.V. Jones).   (STC 344)

———— A paraenesis to the prince.   London, R. Field 1604.   sm. 4to.
First Edition.   (STC 346)

———— Recreations with the muses.   London, T. Harper 1637.   fol.
First Edition.   (Purdy).   (STC 347)

Aleyn, Charles.   The historie of ... Henrie ... the seventh.   London,
T. Cotes 1638.   8vo.   First Edition.   (STC 353)

[Allott, Robert].   Englands Parnassus.   London, for N. L[ing], C.
B[urby] and T. H[ayes] 1600.   8vo.   First Edition.   (STC 378)

[————] Wits theater of the little world.   [London] I. R [oberts] 1599.
8vo.   First Edition. [Dedication unsigned].   (STC 382)

An almond for a parrat.   [Attrib. to T. Nash].   Imprinted at a place,
not farre from a place [? 1590].   sm. 4to.   First Edition.   (STC 534)

Amadis, de Gaule.   The ancient ... history of Amadis de Gaule.   Booke
I, tr. by A. Munday; II, tr. by L. Pyott.   London, N. Okes 1619.
fol. in sixes.   Second Edition.   (STC 544)

———— The third [and fourth] booke of Amadis de Gaule.   Tr. by A.
M[unday].   London, N. Okes 1618.   fol. in sixes.   First Edition.
(STC 543)

———— The moste excellent and pleasaunt booke.   Tr. by T. Paynell.
London, H. Bynneman [c. 1572].   sm. 4to.   First Edition.
(Maurice Hewlett).   (STC 545)

Ammianus Marcellinus.   The Roman historie. Tr. by P. Holland.   London, A. Islip 1609.   fol.   First Edition.   (STC 17311)

An answer to a certain godly mañes lettres.   [n.p. 1557].   8vo.   (W.
Maskell–Huth).   (STC 658)

Appianus, *of Alexandria*.   An auncient historie and exquisite chronicle
of the Romanes warres. Tr. by W. B.   London, R. Newbery and
H. Bynneman 1578.   sm. 4to.   First Edition.   (Ralph Sheldon).
(STC 713)

Apuleius Madaurensis, Lucius.   The XI. bookes of the Golden Asse.
Tr. by W. Adlington.   London, T. Harper 1639.   sm. 4to.   Fifth
Edition.   (Levy).   (STC 721)

Ariosto, Ludovico.   Ariosto's Satyres. Tr. by G. Markham [or rather R. Tofte].   London, N. Okes 1608.   sm.4to.   First Edition. (STC 744)

[———] Orlando Furioso. Tr. by Sir J. Harington.   London, G. Miller 1634.   fol.   Third Edition.   (E. N. Crane).   (STC 748)

Aristoteles.   *Ethica.* Textus ethicorum. Tr. by L. Bruni.   Oxford [?T. Rood] 1479.   4to.   (Pembroke).   (GW 2373; STC 752)

Arnalte.   *See* San Pedro, Diego

[Arnold, Richard].   [Chronicle of London].   [Antwerp, A. van Berghen 1503?].   fol.   First Edition.   (STC 782)

——— ——— [London, P. Treveris 1521?].   fol.   Second Edition. (Ashburnham).   (STC 783)

The arte of English poesie.   *See* [Lumley, John, *Lord*?]

Arthur, *King.*   [Le morte Darthur]. Tr. by Sir T. Malory.   London, W. Stansby 1634.   4to.   Seventh Edition.   (Huth).   (STC 806)

Ascham, Roger.   Disertissimi viri Rogeri Aschami . . . familiarium epistolarum libri tres.   London, H. Bynneman 1581.   8vo.   Third Edition.   (STC 828)

——— A report and discourse . . . of the affaires of Germany.   London, J. Daye [1570?].   sm.4to.   First Edition.   (STC 830)

——— The scholemaster.   London, J. Daye 1570.   sm.4to.   First Edition.   (STC 832)

——— ——— London, J. Daye 1579.   sm.4to.   Fourth Edition. (STC 835a)

—— The schoolmaster.   London, A. Jeffes 1589.   sm.4to.   Fifth Edition.   (STC 836)

Ashton, Peter, *tr.*   *See* Giovio, Paolo

[Asser, Joannes, *Menevensis*].   Aelfredi regis res gestae.   [London, J. Day 1574].   fol.   First Edition.   (T. Brooke).   (STC 863)

Aston, Edward, *tr.*   *See* Boehme, Johann

Augustine, *Saint.*   [De civitate Dei]. St. Augustine of the citie of God. Tr. by J. Healey.   [London] G. Eld 1610.   fol.   First Edition. (T. Cholmondeley).   (STC 916)

Pseudo Augustine, *Saint.* The glasse of vaine glorie. Tr. by W. Prid. London, J. Windet 1593. 12mo. Third Edition. (W. Bonar). (STC 930a)

———— A right Christian treatise, entituled S. Augustines praiers. Tr. by T. Rogers. London, H. Denham 1581. 12mo. First Edition. (STC 950)

Avila y Zuñiga, Luis de. The comentaries of Don Lewes de Auela . . . which treateth of the great wars in Germany. London, R. Tottell 1555. 8vo. First Edition. (Inglis). (STC 987)

[Aylmer, John, *Bp.*]. An harborowe for faithfull and trewe subiectes. Strasborowe [London, J. Daye] 1559. sm. 4to. First Edition. (Jolley–Laing). (STC 1006)

[Ayscu, Edward]. A historie contayning the warres . . . betweene England and Scotland. London, G. Eld 1607. sm. 4to. First Edition. (STC 1014)

B., J., *merchant. See* Browne, J.

B., W., *tr. See* Appian, *of Alexandria*

Babington, John. Pyrotechnia. London, T. Harper 1635. sm. fol. First Edition. (Sir Jenison Gordon). (STC 1099)

———— A short treatise of geometrie. London, T. Harper 1635. sm. fol. First Edition. (Sir Jenison Gordon). (STC 1100)

Bacon, Francis, *Viscount Saint Albans.* Certaine miscellany works. London, J. Haviland 1629. sm. 4to. First Edition. (STC 1124)

———— The charge of Sir Francis Bacon . . . touching duells. [London, G. Eld] 1614. sm. 4to. First Edition. (STC 1125)

[————] A declaration of the practices & treasons . . . committed by Robert late Earle of Essex. London, R. Barker 1601. sm. 4to. First Edition. (STC 1133)

———— The elements of the common lawes of England. London, Assigns of J. More 1630. sm. 4to. First Edition in this form. (STC 1134)

———— The essayes. London, J. Haviland 1625. sm. 4to. Eleventh Edition. (STC 1147)

———— The historie of the raigne of King Henry the seventh. London, W. Stansby 1622. fol. First Edition. (STC 1160)

Bacon, Francis, *Viscount Saint Albans*.   History naturall and experimentall, of life and death.   London, J. Haviland 1638.   12mo. Second Edition in English.   (STC 1158)

———— Instauratio magna.   London, J. Bill 1620.   fol.   First Edition. (Joseph Knight).   (STC 1163)

———— Of the advancement . . . of learning.   Oxford, L. Lichfield 1640.   sm. fol.   First Edition.   (STC 1167)

———— Sir Francis Bacon his apologie.   London [R. Field] 1604.   8vo. First Edition.   (STC 1111)

———— Sylva sylvarum.   London, J. H[aviland] 1627.   fol.   First Edition, Second Issue.   (STC 1169)

———— The twoo bookes of Francis Bacon.   London [T. Purfoot] 1605.   sm. 4to.   First Edition.   (STC 1164)

Bacon, Roger.   The mirror of alchimy.   London [T. Creed] 1597. sm. 4to.   First Edition.   (STC 1182)

Bailey, Walter.   Two treatises.   London, I. Beale 1626.   sm. 4to. (Huth).   (STC 1197)

Baker, George, *tr*.   *See* Gesner, Conrad

Baldwin, William.   *See* Mirror for magistrates

Bale, John.   Illustrium maioris Britanniae scriptorium . . . summariū. [Wesel, D. van den Straten] Gippiswici per J. Overton 1548.   4to. First Edition, First Issue.   (STC 1295)

———— The image of both churches.   London, J. Daye and W. Seres [1550?].   8vo.   Second Edition.   (STC 1298)

———— *tr*.   *See* Gardiner, Stephen

Barckley, *Sir* Richard.   A discourse of the felicitie of man.   London [R. Field] 1598.   4to.   First Edition.   (STC 1381)

Barclay, Alexander, *tr*.   *See* Brandt, Sebastian; Sallustius Crispus, Caius

Barclay, John.   Barclay his Argenis. Tr. by K. Long.   London [E. Purslow] 1636.   4to. in eights.   Second Edition.   (Britwell). (STC 1395)

Barksted, William.   *See* Marston, John, *and* William Barksted

[Barlow, William].   Magneticall advertisements.   London, E. Griffin 1616.   sm. 4to.   First Edition, First Issue.   (STC 1442)

Barnes, Robert.   *See* Tyndale, William

Barret, Robert.   The theorike and practike of moderne warres.   London [R. Field] 1598.   fol.   First Edition.   (STC 1500)

Bartholomaeus, *Anglicus*.   Bartholomeus de proprietatibus rerum. London, in aed. T. Bertheleti 1535.   fol.   Second Edition, First Issue.   (STC 1537)

———— Batman vppon Bartholome, his booke. [Tr. by J. de Trevisa]. London, T. East 1582.   fol.   (Charles Lilburn).   (STC 1538)

Bate, John.   The mysteries of nature and art.   London, T. Harper 1635. sm. 4to.   Second Edition.   (Castle Craig–Thomas Stevenson). (STC 1578)

[Bateman, Stephen].   The doome warning all men to the iudgemente. [London] R. Newbery 1581.   4to. in eights.   First Edition.   (W. Bayntun).   (STC 1582)

B[axter], N[athaniel].   Sir Philip Sydneys Ourania.   London, E. Allde 1606.   4to.   First Edition.   (Hoe–Hagen).   (STC 1598)

Beaumont, Francis.   Poems.   London, R. Hodgkinson 1640.   sm. 4to. First Edition.   (G. W. Steeves).   (STC 1665)

———— *and* John Fletcher.   A king and no king.   London, for T. Walkley 1625.   sm. 4to.   Second Edition.   (Hailstone–Poor). (STC 1671)

Beaumont, *Sir* John.   Bosworth-field.   London, F. Kingston 1629.   8vo. First Edition.   (STC 1694)

Becon, Thomas.   The reliques of Rome.   London, J. Day 1563.   8vo. Second Edition.   (STC 1755)

Beda.   Historia ecclesiastica gentis Anglorum.   [Strassburg, H. Eggestein, c. 1475/8].   fol.   First Edition.   (2 copies: 1, Marquess of Bute–Aldenham Abbey–W. H. Crawford–Britwell).   (GW 3756)

———— The history of the church of Englande. Tr. by T. Stapleton. Antwerp, H. Laet 1565.   sm. 4to.   First Edition.   (Bement). (STC 1778)

———— Opera.   Basle, J. Herwagen 1563.   8 v.   fol.   Third Collected Edition

Bellenden, John, *tr.*   *See* Boece, Hector

Bible. *English*. The byble in Englyshe. [Paris, F. Regnault and London] R. Grafton & E. Whitchurch, Apryll 1539. fol. First Edition. (Lea Wilson–Dunn–Gardner–Huth). (STC 2068)

———— The byble in Englyshe. London, R. Grafton, November 1541. fol. in eights. Sixth Edition. (J. W. Knightley). (STC 2075)

———— The byble. London, J. Daye and W. Seres, 17 August 1549. fol. in sixes. (C. D. Ginsberg). (STC 2077)

———— The bible. Geneva, R. Hall 1560. 4to. First Edition. (STC 2093)

———— The byble in Englyshe. London, J. Cawood 1560-1. 4to. in eights. (STC 2094)

———— The. holie. bible. London, R. Jugge [1568]. fol. in eights. First Edition. (STC 2099)

———— The. holie. bible. London, R. Jugge 1572. fol. in eights. (STC 2107)

———— The bible. London, Deputies of C. Barker 1597. fol. in sixes. (STC 2168)

———— The holy bible. London, R. Barker 1611. fol. First Edition. (C. D. Ginsberg). (STC 2216)

———— The holy bible. London, R. Barker 1616. sm. fol. (Huth). (STC 2245)

Bible. *O. T. English*. The holie bible. Douay, L. Kellam 1609-10. 2 v. 4to. First Edition. (Huth). (STC 2207)

Bible. *O. T. Genesis. English*. A commentarie. London, H. Middleton 1578. sm. 4to. (STC 4393)

Bible. *O. T. Psalms. English*. The psalter. London, R. Barker 1604. sm. fol. (Sir John Savill). (STC 2404)

———— ———— Edinburgh [E. Tyler for] R. Young 1636. fol. (Huth). (STC 16606)

———— ———— ———— fol. Second Edition. (STC 16607)

Bible. *O. T. Psalms. English. Metrical*. The whole booke of psalms. London 1604. sm. fol. (Sir John Savill). (STC 2512a)

———— The whole booke of psalmes. London 1614. sm. 4to. (Julian Marshall). (STC 2549)

Bible. *O.T. Psalms. English. Metrical.* The whole booke of psalmes. London 1618. fol. (Huth). (STC 2560)

———— The whole booke of psalms. London 1621. 12mo. First Edition, Second Issue. (STC 2575)

———— The whole booke of psalms. London 1627. sm. fol. (Ashburton–G.C. Thomas). (STC 2599)

———— The psalmes. Tr. by King James I. Oxford, W. Turner 1631. 8vo. First Edition. (STC 2732)

———— ———— London, T. Harper 1636. fol. (STC 2736)

———— A paraphrase upon the psalmes. By G. S[andys]. London [A. Hebb] 1636. 8vo. First Edition. (STC 21724)

———— A paraphrase upon the divine poems. By G. Sandys. London 1638. sm. fol. First Edition. (Sussex–Sutherland). (STC 21725)

———— The psalmes ... paraphras'd ... by R. B[rathwaite]. London, R. Young 1638. 8vo. First Edition. (John Pearson). (STC 3581)

Bible. *O.T. Psalms. Latin. Metrical.* Psalmorum ... paraphrasis poetica. (By G. Buchanan). [Paris] apud H. & R. Stephanum [c. 1565]. 8vo. First Complete Edition

Bible. *O.T. The books of Solomon.* The bokes of Salomon. London, W. Copland 1551. 24mo. (Ashburnham). (STC 2758)

———— The song of songs. Middelburgh, R. Schilders 1587. 8vo. First Edition. (Huth). (STC 2769)

Bible. *N.T. English.* The newe testament. Tr. by M. Coverdale. London, R. Wolfe 1549. 8vo. (Ashburnham). (STC 2858)

———— The new testament. Londini, in officina T. Gaultier 1550. 8vo. (G.C. Thomas). (STC 2821)

———— The newe testament. London, R. Jugge [1552]. 4to. (Mexborough). (STC 2867)

———— The new testament. Rhemes, J. Fogny 1582. 4to. First Edition. (STC 2884)

———— The new testament. Dort, I. Canin 1603. 8vo. (Ashburnham). (STC 2903)

———— The ... new testament. London 1617. fol. (Huth). (STC 2918)

Bible. *N. T. English.* A confutation of the Rhemists translation. By
T. Cartwright. [Leyden, W. Brewster] 1618. fol. (J. Hammond Trumbull). (STC 4709)

———— The . . . new testament. London, A. Mathewes 1633. fol.
(P. Hamilton). (STC 2947)

Bible. *N. T. Irish.* Tiomna nuadhr ar d Tighearna agus ar slanaightheora Iosa Criosd. Dublin, J. Franke 1602. fol. First Edition,
Second Issue. (Baron Foley). (STC 2958)

Bible. *N. T. Spanish.* El testamento nvevo. (London) en casa de R.
del Campo (R. Field) 1596. 8vo. (STC 2959)

Bible. *N. T. Gospels.* The gospels of the fower euangelistes. London, I. Daye 1571. sm. 4to. First Edition. (STC 2961)

Bible. *Miscellaneous.* The images of the old testament. Lyons, I.
Frellon 1549. sm. 4to. (STC 3045)

———— *See also* Paradin, C.

[Biddulph, William]. The travels of foure English men and a preacher.
Edited by T. Lavender. London, F. Kyngston 1612. sm. 4to.
Second Edition. (White Kennett). (STC 3052)

[Bidpai]. The morall philosophie of Doni. Tr. by Sir T. North. London, S. Stafford 1601. sm. 4to. Second Edition. (Wrest Park).
(STC 3054)

[Bieston, Roger]. The bayte & snare of fortune. London, J. Wayland [1550?]. sm. fol. First Edition. (Huth). (STC 3055)

[Bignon, Jerome]. A briefe, but an effectuall treatise of the election of
popes. London, V. S[ims] 1605. 4to. First Edition. (STC
3058)

Billingsley, *Sir* Henry, *tr. See* Euclides

Bingham, John, *tr. See* Ælianus, *Tacticus*

Bishop, John. Beautifull blossomes. London, for H. Cockyn 1577.
sm. 4to. First Edition. (STC 3091)

[Blackwood, Adam]. Martyre de la royne d'Escosse. Edimbourg
[Paris] J. Nafeild 1587. 8vo. First Edition. (H. de Lucinge).
(STC 3107)

Blaxton, John. The English usurer. London, J. Norton 1634. sm.
4to. First Edition. (C. H. Blackburn–A. G. Tibbitts). (STC
3129)

Blenerhasset, Thomas. *See* Mirror for magistrates

Blundeville, Thomas. The fower chiefest offices. London, W. Seres [1570?]. sm. 4to. Second Edition. (STC 3153)

────── The foure chiefest offices. London, H. Lownes 1609. sm. 4to. Sixth Edition. (Thomas, Earl of Kinnoull). (STC 3157)

────── M. Blundevile his exercises. London, J. Windet 1597. sm. 4to. Second Edition. (STC 3147)

────── ────── London, W. Stansby 1622. sm. 4to. Fifth Edition. (F. H. C. Day). (STC 3150)

Bluom, Joannes. The booke of five collumnes of architecture. Tr. by I. T. [London, J. Okes] for W. and R. Peake 1635. fol. (STC 3163)

Boanerges. Boanerges. Or the humble supplication of the ministers of Scotland. Edinburgh 1624. 4to. Second Edition. (STC 3171)

[Boccaccio, Giovanni]. The Decameron. London, I. Jaggard 1620. sm. fol. First Edition. (H. Cunliffe). (STC 3172)

────── [De casibus illustrium virorum]. The tragedies . . . of all such princes as fell from theyr estates. London, J. Wayland [1555?]. fol. Fourth Edition. (Chew). (STC 3178)

Boece, Hector. Heir beginnis the hystory and chroniklis of Scotland. Tr. by J. Bellenden. Edinburgh, T. Davidson [1540?]. fol. First Edition. (STC 3203)

[Boehme, Johann]. The fardle of facions. Tr. by W. Watreman. London, J. Kingston and H. Sutton 1555. sm. 8vo. First Edition. (White Kennett). (STC 3197)

────── The manners, lawes, and customes of all nations. Tr. by E. Aston. London, G. Eld 1611. sm. 4to. (White Kennett). (STC 3198)

Borde, Andrew. The breuiary of healthe. London, W. Powell 1557. sm. 4to. in eights. Third Edition. (Frederick Perkins–George Chalmers–Charles Butler). (STC 3375)

Bossewell, John. Workes of armorie. London, in aed. R. Tottelli 1572. 4to. in eights. First Edition. (Hugh Grantham–Lord Berwick–Ashburnham–Sir Henry Hope Edwardes–Dunn). (STC 3393)

Bourchier, John, *second Lord Berners, tr.* *See* Froissart, Jean; Guevara, Antonio de

Bourne, William. A regiment for the sea. London, T. East, n. d. sm. 4to. Sixth Edition. (C. L. F. Robinson). (STC 3427)

[Bradford, John]. All the examinacions of . . . Iohn Bradforde. London, W. Griffith 1561. 8vo. First Edition. (Aldenham Abbey–Tempsford Hall). (STC 3477)

[Bradshaw, William]. A treatise of divine worship. [Middelburgh, R. Schilders] 1604. 8vo. First Edition. (STC 3528)

—— Twelve generall arguments. [Amsterdam?] 1605. 8vo. First Edition. (STC 3531)

[Brandt, Sebastian]. Stultifera navis. Tr. by A. Barclay. London, J. Cawood 1570. fol. Second Edition. (STC 3546)

[Brathwaite, Richard]. Ar't asleepe husband? London, R. Bishop 1640. sm. 8vo. First Edition. (Sir Robert Johnson Eden). (STC 3555)

—— The English gentleman. London, J. Haviland 1630. sm. 4to. First Edition. (STC 3563)

—— The English gentlewoman. London, B. Alsop and T. Fawcet 1631. sm. 4to. First Edition. (STC 3565)

—— Essaies upon the five senses. London, A. Griffin 1635. 12mo. Second Edition. (STC 3567)

[——] Natures embassie. London [R. Field] for R. Whitaker 1621. 8vo. First Edition, First Issue. (William Brice–M. C. D. Borden–C. L. F. Robinson). (STC 3571)

—— The schollers medley. London, N. O[kes] 1614. sm. 4to. First Edition. (Griswold–Chew). (STC 3583)

[——] A strange metamorphosis of man. London, T. Harper 1634. 12mo. First Edition. (Huth). (STC 3587)

—— A survey of history. London, J. O[kes] 1638. sm. 4to. Second Edition. (White Wallingwells). (STC 3583a)

—— Times curtaine drawne. London, J. Dawson 1621. 8vo. First Edition. (Thomas Gaisford–Andrews). (STC 3589)

[——] The two Lancashire lovers. London, E. Griffin 1640. 8vo. First Edition. (Hoe–C. L. F. Robinson). (STC 3590)

[Brathwaite, Richard]. Whimzies. London, F. K[ingston] 1631. 12mo. First Edition. (Lefferts–Chew). (STC 3591)

———— tr.   See Silesio, Mariano

Brende, John, tr.   See Curtius Rufus, Quintus

[Breton, Nicholas]. Pasquils mad-cappe. London, A. M[athewes] 1626. sm. 4to. First Edition. (Hoe–Hagen). (STC 3676)

[Bridges, John?]. A ryght pithy, pleasaunt anp[sic] merie comedie: intytuled Gammer gurtons nedle. London, T. Colwell 1575. sm. 4to. First Edition. (STC 23263)

A briefe relation of the discovery . . . of New England. London, J. Haviland 1622. sm. 4to. (Huth). (STC 18483)

Briggs, Henry. Logarithmicall arithmetike. London, G. Miller 1631. fol. First Edition in English. (Henry, Duke of Kent–Thomas Philip, Earl de Grey). (STC 3740)

[Brinsley, John]. A consolation for oure grammar schooles. London, R. Field 1622. sm. 4to. (White Kennett). (STC 3767)

Brisset, Georges. The apologie. [London] for W. Barley and J. Baily 1610. sm. 4to. First Edition. (Huth). (STC 3791)

Brome, Richard. The northern lasse. London, A. Mathewes 1632. sm. 4to. First Edition. (McKee). (STC 3819)

———— The sparagus garden. London, J. Okes 1640. sm. 4to. First Edition, Second Issue. (STC 3820)

———— See also Heywood, Thomas, and Richard Brome

[Brooke, Christopher, and William Browne]. Two elegies. London, T. S[nodham] 1613. sm. 4to. First Edition. (Britwell). (STC 3831)

B[rowne], J. The merchants avizo. London, J. Norton 1607. sm. 4to. (Huth). (STC 1049)

[Browne, William]. Britannia's pastorals [Book I]. London, T. Snodham [1616]. fol. Second Edition. (STC 3915)

———— ———— Book II. London, T. Snodham 1616. fol. First Edition. (STC 3915)

———— See also Brooke, Christopher, and William Browne

Bruni, Leonardo Aretino, tr.   See Aristoteles

Brunschwig, Hieronymus.   The noble experyence of the vertuous handywarke of surgeri.   Southwarke, P. Treveris 1525.   fol.   First Edition.   (STC 13434)

B[uchanan], G[eorge].   Ane detectioun.   [London, J. Day 1571?].   8vo.   First Edition, "actioun" Issue.   (STC 3981)

—————— Rerum Scoticarum historia.   Edimburgi, A. Arbuthnet 1582.   fol.   First Edition.   (STC 3991)

[Bullinger, Heinrich].   The christen state of matrimony.   Tr. by M. Coverdale.   London, J. Mayler 1543.   8vo.   Seventh Edition? (Huth).   (STC 4047)

[Burton, Robert].   The anatomy of melancholy.   Oxford, J. Lich-field and J. Short 1621.   sm. 4to. in eights.   First Edition.   (J. Cresswell).   (STC 4159)

[——————] —————— —————— 1624.   fol.   Second Edition.   (STC 4160)

[——————] —————— Oxford [J. Lichfield] 1628.   fol.   Third Edition.   (G. H. Wailes).   (STC 4161)

[——————] —————— —————— 1632.   fol.   Fourth Edition.   (G. E. Cox).   (STC 4162)

[——————] —————— Oxford, for H. Cripps [Printed by R. Young, Edin-burgh; L. Lichfield, Oxford; W. Turner, Oxford; with cancels by M. Flesher, London] 1638.   fol.   Fifth Edition.   (STC 4163)

Bury, Richard de.   Philobiblon.   Cologne [Printer of Augustinus de Fide] 1473.   sm. 4to.   First Edition

[Busche, Alexander van den].   The orator.   Tr. by L. P[yott].   Lon-don, A. Islip 1596.   sm. 4to.   First Edition.   (E. H. Barker).   (STC 4182)

Butler, Charles.   The feminine monarchie.   London, J. Haviland 1623.   sm. 4to.   Second Edition.   (STC 4193)

—————— The feminin' monarchi'.   Oxford, W. Turner 1634.   sm. 4to.   Third Edition.   (STC 4194)

Byrd, William.   Liber primus sacrarum cantionum quinque vocum.   London, T. East 1589.   4to.   First Edition.   (Huth).   (STC 4247)

C., Ro.   A true historicall discourse of Muley Hamets.   London, T. Purfoot 1609.   sm. 4to.   First Edition.   (STC 4300)

Calvin, Jean.　Certaine homilies. Tr. by R. Horne.　Rome [London, H. Singleton] 1553.　8vo.　First Edition.　(STC 4392)

———— A commentarie … vpon … Genesis. Tr. by T. Tymme.　London, H. Middleton 1578.　4to. in eights.　First Edition.　(STC 4393)

———— The institution of christian religion. Tr. by T. Norton.　London, R. Wolfe and R. Harrison 1561.　fol. in eights.　First Edition.　(Learmont).　(STC 4415)

———— ———— London, H. Middleton 1587.　sm. 4to. in eights.　Seventh Edition.　(STC 4422)

———— A very profitable treatise. Tr. by S. Wythers.　London, R. Hall 1561.　8vo.　First Edition.　(Britwell).　(STC 4467)

Camden, William.　Britannia.　London, for R. Newbery 1586.　8vo.　First Edition.　(Walter Skirrow–William Twopenny–Steeves).　(STC 4503)

[————] The historie of the … princesse Elizabeth. Tr. by R. N[orton].　London [N. Okes?] 1630.　fol.　First Edition.　(Thomas Millington–Purdy).　(STC 4500)

[————] Remaines.　London, G. E[ld] 1605.　sm. 4to.　First Edition.　(STC 4521)

[————] ———— London, J. Legatt 1614.　sm. 4to.　Second Edition.　(Shadwell Court–Bement).　(STC 4522)

Camus, Jean Pierre.　Admirable events. Tr. by S. DuVerger.　London, T. Harper 1639.　8vo.　First Edition, Second Issue.　(STC 4550)

[Capgrave, John].　[Nova legenda Anglie].　London, W. de Worde 1516.　fol.　First Edition.　(Huth).　(STC 4601)

[————] Here begynneth the kalendre of the newe Legende of Englande. Part III. Hylton, Walter. [Scala perfectionis Book IV]. Hereaftre foloweth a deuote boke.　London, R. Pynson 1516.　sm. 4to.　First Edition of the "kalendre". Third Edition of Hylton.　(Huth).　(STC 4602)

[Caradoc of Llancarvan].　The historie of Cambria.　London, R. Newbery and H. Denham 1584.　sm. 4to. in eights.　First Edition.　(STC 4606)

Carew, Richard. The survey of Cornwall. London, S. S[tafford] 1602. 4to. First Edition. (Pembroke). (STC 4615)

———— tr. *See* Estienne, Henri; Tasso, Torquato

Carew, Thomas. Poems. London, J. D[awson] 1640. 8vo. First Edition, Second Issue. (STC 4620)

Carion, Johann. The three bokes of cronicles. Tr. by W. Lynne. London [J. Day] 1550. sm. 4to. in eights. First Edition. (H. V. Jones). (STC 4626)

Carleton, George. A thankfull remembrance. London, M. Flesher 1627. sm. 4to. Third Edition. (John Brand–Lefferts–Poor). (STC 4642)

C[artwright], J[ohn]. The preachers travels. London [W. Stansby] 1611. sm. 4to. First Edition. (STC 4705)

Cartwright, Thomas. A confutation of the Rhemists translation. [Leyden, W. Brewster] 1618. fol. in fours. First Edition. (J. Hammond Trumbull). (STC 4709)

[Cartwright, William]. The royall slave. Oxford, W. Turner 1639. sm. 4to. First Edition. (Percy FitzGerald). (STC 4717)

Casas, Bartolomé de las. The Spanish colonie. Tr. by M. M. S. London [T. Dawson] 1583. sm. 4to. (Britwell). (STC 4739)

Castiglione, Baldassare. The courtyer. Tr. by T. Hoby. London, W. Seres 1561. sm. 4to. First Edition. (STC 4778)

Cato, Dionysius. Booke callyd Caton. Tr. by W. Caxton. Westminster, W. Caxton 1483. fol. First Edition. (G. Watson Taylor–Charles Barclay). (GW 6361; STC 4853)

———— Cato variegatus. Tr. by Sir R. Baker. London, A. Griffin and A. Bowler 1636. sm. 4to. First Edition. (STC 4863)

———— Catonis disticha moralia. [London, W. Seres] 1561. Two 8vo. sheets. (STC 4845a)

Cawdrey, Robert. A treasurie or store-house of similes. London, T. Creede 1600. sm. 4to. First Edition. (Newdigate). (STC 4887)

Caxton, William, tr. *See* Cato, Dionysius

Celestina. The Spanish bawd. Tr. by J. Mabbe. London, J. B[eale] 1631. fol. First Edition. (STC 4911)

[63]

[Cervantes Saavedra, Miguel de]. The history of Don-Quichote [Part I]. Tr. by T. Shelton. [London, W. Stansby 1620?]. sm. 4to. Second Edition. (Huth). (STC 4916)

[———] ——— [Part II]. London [G. Purslow] 1620. sm. 4to. First Edition. (Huth). (STC 4917)

[———] Travels of Persiles and Sigismunda. London, H. L[ownes] 1619. sm. 4to. First Edition. (Bridgewater–Hanrott–Gardner– Corser–Huth). (STC 4918)

Cespedes [y Maneses], Gonzalo de. Gerardo the unfortunate Span- iard. Tr. by L. D[igges]. London [G. Purslow] for E. Blount 1622. sm. 4to. First Edition. (Isaac Reed–Samuel Egerton Brydges–Britwell). (STC 4919)

Chaloner, Sir Thomas, tr. See Erasmus, Desiderius

Chamberlain, Robert. Nocturnall lucubrations. London, M. F[lesher] 1638. 8vo. First Edition. (S. Van de Weyer). (STC 4945)

Chapman, George. The conspiracie, and tragedie of Charles Duke of Biron. [London] G. Eld 1608. sm. 4to. First Edition, Second Issue. (STC 4968)

——— The gentleman usher. London, V. S[immes] 1606. sm. 4to. First Edition. (John Pearson). (STC 4978)

——— May-Day. London, for J. Browne 1611. sm. 4to. First Edition. (Mitford–H.V. Jones). (STC 4980)

——— The warres of Pompey and Caesar. London, T. Harper 1631. sm. 4to. First Edition, First Issue. (Hoe). (STC 4992)

——— The widdowes teares. London, for J. Browne 1612. sm. 4to. First Edition (corrected state). (STC 4994)

——— See also Homerus; Marlowe, Christopher, and George Chap- man

——— and James Shirley. The ball. London, T. Cotes 1639. sm. 4to. First Edition. (STC 4995)

——— The tragedie of Chabot. London, T. Cotes 1639. sm. 4to. First Edition. (Copy 1, McKee; 2, A. C. Swinburne). (STC 4996)

Charles I, King of England. A true relation and journall of the . . . ar- rivall . . . at Madrid. London, J. Haviland 1623. sm. 4to. First Edition, Second Issue. (STC 5032)

Chaucer, Geoffrey. The workes. London, T. Godfray 1532. fol.
First Edition. (Chew–H.V. Jones). (STC 5068)

———— ———— London [J. Kingston?] for T. Petit [c. 1550]. fol.
Third Edition, with Petit colophon. (William Frere). (STC
5072)

———— The woorkes. London, J. Kingston 1561. fol. Fourth Edition, Third Issue. (James Phelps). (STC 5076)

———— The workes. London [A. Islip] for G. Bishop 1598. fol.
Fifth Edition, with Bishop imprint. (James, Marquis of Carnavon–
William H. Morley). (STC 5077)

———— The workes. London, A. Islip 1602. fol. Sixth Edition.
(STC 5080)

———— The Canterbury tales. [Westminster, W. Caxton 1478]. One
leaf. (STC 5082)

Chauliac, Guy de. *See* [Guido, *de Cauliaco*]

Chertsey, Andrew, *tr*. *See* Ten Commandments

Chettle, Henry. *See* Munday, Anthony, *and* Henry Chettle

Chillingworth, William. The religion of protestants. Oxford, L. Lichfield 1638. fol. First Edition. (STC 5138)

Chronicles of England. [London, W. de Machlinia 1486]. fol. Third
Edition of "Caxton's Chronicle." (Bryan Fairfax–Francis Child–
Earl of Jersey). (STC 9993)

———— Cronycle of Englonde. London, W. de Worde 1520. fol.
Eighth Edition of "St. Alban's Chronicle." (STC 10001)

Chrysostom. *See* John, Chrysostom, *Saint*

Churchey, George, *tr*. *See* Dubravius, Johannes

Churchyard, Thomas. The firste part of Churchyardes chippes. London, T. Marshe 1578. sm. 4to. Second Edition. (Henry Irving). (STC 5233)

———— A generall rehearsall of warres. London, E. White 1579. sm.
4to. First Edition, Second Issue. (STC 5235)

———— A lamentable, and pitifull description, of the wofull warres in
Flaunders. London, R. Newbery 1578. sm. 4to. First Edition.
(STC 5239)

Churchyard, Thomas, *and* Richard Robinson, *tr.*   *See* Meteren, Emanuel van

Cicero, Marcus Tullius.   The thre bookes of Tullyes offices. Tr. by R. Whittinton.   London, W. de Worde 1534.   8vo.   First Edition. (Frederick Perkins).   (STC 5278)

[Cleland, James].   The Scottish academie.   London [Oxford, J. Barnes] for E. White 1611.   sm. 4to.   First Edition, Second Issue.   (STC 5393a)

Cocles, Bartholomaeus.   A pleasant history: declaring the whole art of phisiognomy. Tr. by T. Hill.   [London] W. Jaggard 1613.   8vo. Third Edition.   (Huth).   (STC 13483)

Coke, *Sir* Edward.   *See* Littleton, *Sir* Thomas

Colonne, Guido delle.   The auncient historie and onely trewe and syncere cronicle of the warres betwixte the Grecians and the Troyans. Tr. by J. Lydgate.   London [J. Wayland for] T. Marshe 1555. fol.   Second Edition (with undated colophon).   (2 copies: 1, E. M. Cox).   (STC 5580)

[———] The life and death of Hector. Tr. by J. Lydgate.   London, T. Purfoot 1614.   fol.   First Edition.   (STC 13346a)

Comines, Philippe de.   The historie of Philip de Commines.   London, A. Hatfield 1596.   fol.   First Edition.   (Sir Henry Grey).   (STC 5602)

[Conestaggio, Girolamo Franchi de].   The historie of the uniting of ... Portugall to the crowne of Castill.   London, A. Hatfield 1600. fol. in sixes.   First Edition.   (Robert Byerley–Edward Delanoy Little).   (STC 5624)

Cooke, John.   Greenes Tu quoque.   London, for T. Dewe 1622.   sm. 4to.   Second Edition.   (Kershaw).   (STC 5674)

Cooper, Thomas.   Coopers chronicle.   *See* Lanquet

——— Thesaurus linguae Romanae & Britannicae.   London [J. Charlewood?] 1573.   fol.   Second Edition.   (STC 5687)

Copland, Robert, *tr.*   *See* [Guido, *de Cauliaco*]

[Corneille, Pierre].   The second part of the Cid. Tr. by J. Rutter.   London, I. Okes 1640.   12mo.   (STC 5771)

[Cornwallis, *Sir* William]. Essayes of certaine paradoxes. London [G. Eld?] for T. Thorp 1616. sm.4to. First Edition. (STC 5779)

Coryate, Thomas. Coryats crambe. London, W. Stansby 1611. 4to. First Edition. (STC 5807)

—— Coryats crudities. London, W. S[tansby] 1611. 4to. First Edition. (Huth). (STC 5808)

—— The Odcumbian banquet. [London, G. Eld] 1611. sm.4to. First Edition. (STC 5810)

The costlie whore. London, A. Mathewes 1633. sm.4to. First Edition, Third Issue. (Hoe). (STC 25582a)

Cotgrave, Randle. A dictionarie of the French and English tongues. London, A. Islip 1611. fol. First Edition. (STC 5830)

[Cotton, *Sir* Robert Bruce]. A short view of the long life and raigne of Henry the Third. [London] 1627. sm.4to. First Edition. (STC 5864)

[——] —— [London] 1627. 4to. Third Edition. (STC 5864)

Coverdale, Miles, *tr. See* Bible. *N. T. English.* 1549; Holy Roman Empire; Luther, Martin

Cranmer, Thomas. A defence of the true and catholike doctrine of the sacrament. London, R. Wolfe 1550. sm.4to. First Edition. (STC 6000)

—— Gravissimae . . . Italiae, et Galliae academiarū censurae. Londini, in officina T. Berthleti 1530. sm.4to. First Edition. (STC 14286)

Croce, Giovanni. Musica sacra. Tr. by R. Hole. London, T. East 1608. 4to. First Edition. (Huth). (STC 6040)

Crofts, Robert. The terrestriall paradise. London, T. Harper 1639. 12mo. First Edition. (Heber). (STC 6044)

Crudelitatis Calvinianae. [Cologne?] 1585. 8vo. First Edition. (W. W. Robinson)

Curtius Rufus, Quintus. The historie of Quintus Curtius. Tr. by J. Brende. London, R. Tottell 1553. sm.4to. First Edition. (STC 6142)

[Cushman, Robert].   A sermon preached at Plimoth . . . December 9.
1621.   London, I. D[awson] 1622.   sm. 4to.   First Edition.   (Britwell).   (STC 6149)

D., J., *Gent.*   The knave in graine.   London, J. O[kes] 1640.   sm. 4to.
First Edition.   (Henry Bradshaw–Kemble–Devonshire).   (STC
6174)

Daborn, Robert.   A christian turn'd Turke.   London, for W. Barren-
ger 1612.   sm. 4to.   First Edition.   (Roxburghe–Chew).   (STC
6184)

Dacres, Edward, *tr.*   *See* Machiavelli, Niccolò

D[anett], T[homas].   A survey of Fraunce.   London, for L. Becket
1618.   sm. 4to.   First Edition, Second Issue.   [The sheets of "A
continuation of the historie of France" London, T. East for T.
Charde, 1600 (STC 6234), with a new title, dated 1618].   (STC
6234a)

Daniel, Samuel.   The works.   London [V. Simmes] for S. Waterson
1602.   sm. fol.   Second Edition, Second Issue.   (STC 6237)

———— The whole workes.   London, N. Okes 1623.   sm. 4to.   First
Complete Edition.   (STC 6238)

———— Certaine small poems.   London, G. Eld 1605.   8vo.   Third
Collected Edition.   (Purdy).   (STC 6239)

———— The first fowre bookes of the civile wars.   London, P. Short
1595.   sm. 4to.   First Edition, Second Issue.   (STC 6244)

———— The civile wares.   London [H. Lownes] 1609.   sm. 4to.   First
Complete Edition.   (STC 6245)

———— The first part of the historie of England.   London, N. Okes
1612.   sm. 4to.   First Edition.   (Hagen).   (STC 6246)

———— A panegyrike congratulatory.   London, V. S[immes] [1603].
fol.   First Edition, Second Issue.   (STC 6259)

———— A panegyrike congratulatorie.   London [R. Read?] for E.
Blount 1603.   8vo.   Second Edition.   (Copy 1, Heber–Corser;
2, Purdy).   (STC 6260)

———— *tr.*   *See* Giovio, Paolo

Daus, John, *tr.*   *See* Philippson, Joannes, *Sleidanus*

[Davenant, *Sir* William]. The cruell brother. London, A. M[ath-ewes] 1630. sm. 4to. First Edition. (William Holgate–Kershaw). (STC 6302)

[———] The just Italian. London, T. Harper 1630. sm. 4to. First Edition. (STC 6303)

——— Madagascar. London, J. Haviland 1638. 12mo. First Edition. (STC 6304)

——— The platonick lovers. London [M. Parsons?] 1636. sm. 4to. First Edition. (J. P. Collier). (STC 6305)

[———] Salmacida spolia. London, T. H[arper] 1639. 4to. First Edition. (Newdigate–Kern). (STC 6306)

——— The tragedy of Albovine. London [N. Okes?] for R. M[oore] 1629. sm. 4to. First Edition. (STC 6307)

——— *See also* Jones, Inigo, *and Sir* William Davenant

D[avenport], R[obert]. A pleasant and witty comedy called, a new tricke to cheat the Divell. London, J. Okes 1639. sm. 4to. First Edition. (E. F. Leo). (STC 6315)

Davies, John, *of Hereford*. Microcosmos. Oxford, J. Barnes 1603. sm. 4to. First Edition. (STC 6333)

[———] Mirum in modum. London [V. Simmes] 1602. sm. 4to. First Edition. (G. W. Steeves). (STC 6336)

——— The muses-teares. London, G. Eld 1613. sm. 4to. First Edition. (STC 6339)

——— The scourge of folly. London, E. A[llde] [1611]. 8vo. First Edition. (Chew). (STC 6341)

——— Summa totalis . . . an addition to Mirum in modum. London, W. Jaggard 1607. sm. 4to. First Edition. (H. W. Poor). (STC 6337)

——— Wittes pilgrimage. London [R. Bradock 1605?]. sm. 4to. First Edition. (Corser). (STC 6344)

Davies, *Sir* John. Nosce teipsum. London, R. Field 1599. sm. 4to. First Edition, Second Issue. (E. M. Cox). (STC 6355)

——— ——— London, H. Ballard 1608. sm. 4to. Fourth Edition. (STC 6357)

Day, James. A new spring of divine poetrie. London, T. C[otes] 1637. sm. 4to. First Edition, Second Issue. (STC 6410)

Day, John. Humour out of breath. London, for J. Helmes 1608. sm. 4to. First Edition. (McKee–Huth–Hagen). (STC 6411)

[———] The ile of gulls. London [A. Mathewes] 1633. sm. 4to. Second Edition. (W. J. Ibbett–Buxton Forman). (STC 6414)

Day, Richard. A booke of christian prayers. London, J. Daye 1578. 4to. First Edition. (John Pearson). (STC 6429)

——— A booke of christian praiers. London [H. Lownes] 1608. 4to. Fifth Edition. (Towneley–Bement). (STC 6432)

A declaration of the demeanor and cariage of Sir Walter Raleigh. London, B. Norton and J. Bill 1618. sm. 4to. First Edition. (STC 20654)

A declaration of the state of the colonie and affaires in Virginia. London, T. S[nodham] 1620. sm. 4to. First Edition, Second Issue. (Ives). (STC 24835)

[Dee, John]. A letter, containing a most briefe discourse apologeticall. London, P. Short 1599. 4to. First Edition. (William Prest– Corser–Huth). (STC 6460)

Dekker, Thomas. The magnificent entertainment: given to King James. London, T. C[reede] 1604. sm. 4to. First Edition. (Huth). (STC 6510)

——— Satiro-mastix. London, for E. White 1602. sm. 4to. First Edition. (Hoe). (STC 6521)

——— The second part of the honest whore. London, E. Allde 1630. sm. 4to. First Edition. (Bridgewater). (STC 6506)

——— A strange horse-race. London, for J. Hunt 1613. sm. 4to. First Edition. (STC 6528)

——— A tragi-comedy: called, Match mee in London. London, B. Alsop and T. Fawcett 1631. sm. 4to. First Edition. (Bridge-water). (STC 6529)

——— Troia-nova triumphans. London, N. Okes 1612. sm. 4to. First Edition. (STC 6530)

——— The wonder of a kingdome. London, R. Raworth 1636. sm. 4to. First Edition. (STC 6533)

English to 1640

Dekker, Thomas, *and* John Webster. The famous history of Sir Thomas Wyat. London, E. A[llde] 1607. sm. 4to. First Edition. (Halliwell–Huth). (STC 6537)

——— West-ward hoe. London, sold by J. Hodgets 1607. sm. 4to. First Edition. (STC 6540)

De La Warre, *Baron.* *See* West, Thomas

Demosthenes. The three orations of Demosthenes. Tr. by T. Wilson. London, H. Denham 1570. sm. 4to. First Edition. (STC 6578)

Derendel, Peter, *tr.* *See* Paradin, Claude

[Digges, *Sir* Dudley]. The defence of trade. London, W. Stansby 1615. sm. 4to. First Edition. (STC 6845)

Digges, Leonard. A geometrical practise, named Pantometria. London, H. Bynneman 1571. sm. 4to. First Edition. (STC 6858)

Digges, Leonard, *tr.* *See* Cespedes y Meneses, Gonzalo de

Dodoens, Rembert. A niewe herball. Tr. by H. Lyte. Antwerp, H. Loë, and sold at London by G. Dewes 1578. fol. First Edition. (STC 6984)

Doni, Antonio Francesco. *See* Bidpai

Donne, John. Deaths duell. London, T. Harper 1632. sm. 4to. First Edition. (E. F. Leo). (STC 7031)

——— Devotions upon emergent occasions. London, A. M[athewes] 1624. 12mo. First Edition. (Hagen). (STC 7033)

——— Poems. London, M. F[lesher] 1633. sm. 4to. First Edition. (2 copies: 1, Patrick Hume, Earl of Marchmont). (STC 7045)

[———] Pseudo-martyr. London, W. Stansby 1610. sm. 4to. First Edition. (STC 7048)

——— A sermon vpon the eighth verse of the first chapter of the Acts of the Apostles. London, for T. Iones 1624. sm. 4to. (STC 7052)

Douglas, Gavin, *tr.* *See* Virgilius Maro, Publius

Dowland, John, *tr.* *See* Ornithoparcus, Andreas

Drant, Thomas, *tr.* *See* Horatius Flaccus, Quintus

Drayton, Michael. The battaile of Agincourt. London [A. Mathewes] 1627. fol. First Edition. (STC 7190)

Drayton, Michael.   The muses elizium.   London, T. Harper 1630. sm. 4to.   First Edition.   (Purdy).   (STC 7210)

―――― The owle.   London, E. A[llde] 1604.   sm. 4to.   (John Pearson).   (STC 7211)

―――― Poems.   London [V. Simmes?] 1605.   8vo.   First Collected Edition.   (Purdy).   (STC 7216)

―――― ―――― London, W. Stansby [1619].   fol.   Sixth Edition. (STC 7222)

―――― [Poly-Olbion]. A chorographicall description.   London, for J. Marriott, J. Grismand and T. Dewe 1622.   fol.   First Edition, Third Issue.   (William Penicott).   (STC 7228)

―――― The second part, or A continuance of Poly-Olbion.   London, A. Mathewes 1622.   fol.   First Edition, Second Issue.   (William Penicott).   (STC 7229)

[Drue, Thomas].   The life of the Dutches of Suffolke.   [London] A. M[athewes] 1631.   4to.   First Edition.   (Halliwell–Huth).   (STC 7242)

Drum, Jacke.   Jacke Drums entertainment.   London [W. Stansby] 1618.   sm. 4to.   Second Edition, Second Issue.   (Ernest E. Baker). (STC 7245)

DuBec[-Crespin], Jean.   The historie of . . . Tamerlan. Tr. by H. M[ildmay?].   London [R. Field] 1597.   sm. 4to.   First Edition. (STC 7263)

Dubravius, Johannes.   A newe booke of good husbandry. Tr. by G. Churchey?   London, W. White 1599.   sm. 4to.   First Edition. (White Knights–Hoe).   (STC 7268)

[Dudley], Robert, *Earl of Leicester*.   Lawes and ordinances.   London, C. Barker [1586].   4to.   First Edition.   (STC 7288)

Dugdale, Gilbert.   The time triumphant.   London, R. B[lore] 1604. 4to.   First Edition.   (STC 7292)

Du Verger, Susan, *tr*.   *See* Camus, Jean Pierre

Eden, Richard, *tr*.   *See* Martyr, Peter, *Anglerius*; Prudent le Choyselat

Edinburgh University.   Νοστῳδία. In . . . Jacobi Magnae Britanniae . . . regis . . . felicem in Scotiam reditum, Academiae Edinburgensis congratulatio.   Edinburgh, A. Hart 1617.   sm. 4to.   First Edition.   (STC 7487)

Edmondes, *Sir* Clement.   Observations upon Caesars Commentaries. London, for W. Ponsonby 1604.   fol.   First Edition, Third Issue. (Inscribed "Ex dono Francisci Vere militis. 1604").   (STC 7490)

Elyot, *Sir* Thomas.   The boke, named The governour.   London, T. East 1580.   8vo.   Eighth Edition.   (STC 7642)

———— The castell of helth.   London, T. Berthelet 1541.   8vo.   Fifth Edition.   (STC 7647)

———— The dictionary.   Londini, in aed. T. Bertheleti 1538.   fol. First Edition.   (Amherst).   (STC 7659)

———— The image of governance.   Londini, in officina T. Bertheleti 1541.   sm. 4to.   First Edition.   (STC 7664)

England. *Privy Council. Star Chamber.*   A decree of Starre-Chamber, concerning printing.   London, R. Barker and Assignes of J. Bill 1637.   sm. 4to.   First Edition.   (STC 7757)

England. *Proclamations.*   A proclamation concerninge punyshment of transgressours. [London, T. Berthelet, after 1533].   fol. (William Herbert–Francis Grant)

———— Orders . . . for the reliefe . . . of the dearth of graine, 2 January 1586-7.   London, C. Barker 1586.   sm. 4to.   First Edition in 4to. (Charles Butler).   (STC 8161[a])

———— A publication of his Maties edict . . . against private combats. London, R. Barker 1613 [o.s.].   sm. 4to.   Second Edition.   (STC 8498)

———— The Kings Maiesties declaration . . . concerning lawfull sports. London, B. Norton and J. Bill 1618.   4to.   First Edition.   (STC 8566)

———— ———— London, R. Barker and Assignes of John Bill 1633. sm. 4to.   First Edition.   (STC 9257)

England. *Public Documents. Statutes.*   (Nova statuta, ab anno primo Edward III ad annum XII Henrici VII, 1328-1497).   [London] R. Pynson [? 1500].   fol.   (STC 9265)

———— [35 Henry VIII]. Henry the eyght.   Londini, in aed. T. Bertheleti 1544.   fol.   Fourth Edition.   (STC 9410)

———— Anno secundo, & tertio, Edouardi Sexti.   [London] R. Grafton 1552.   fol.   (STC 9426)

England. *Public Documents. Statutes.* Magna Charta cum statutis quae antiqua vocantur. Londini, in aed. R. Tottelli 1556. 8vo. (S. Robert Gordon–T. Holt White). (STC 9278)

Erasmus, Desiderius. [Adagia]. Proverbes or adagies ... gathered out of ... Erasmus by R. Taverner. London [R. Bances] 1539. 8vo. First Edition. (Thomas Brooke). (STC 10437)

———— Apophthegmes. Tr. by N. Udall. London, J. Kyngston 1564. 8vo. Second Edition. (STC 10444)

———— Flores. Tr. by R. Taverner. Londini, ex aed. R. Taverner 1540. 8vo. First Edition. (Thomas Brooke). (STC 10445)

———— The praise of folie. Tr. by Sir Thomas Chaloner. London, T. Berthelet 1549. sm. 4to. First Edition. (STC 10500)

———— ———— London, T. P[owell?] 1549. sm. 4to. Second Edition. (STC 10501)

[Estienne, Henri]. A world of wonders. Tr. by R. Carew. London [R. Field] 1607. fol. First Edition, First Issue. (H. V. Jones). (STC 10553)

Euclides. The elements of geometrie. Tr. by Sir H. Billingsley. London, J. Daye 1570. fol. First Edition. (STC 10560)

(F., N.). The fruiterers secrets. London, R. B[radock] 1604. sm. 4to. First Edition. (STC 10650)

F., T. Newes from the north. London, E. Allde 1585. sm. 4to. Second Edition. (Bridgewater). (STC 24062a)

Fabyan, Robert. Fabyans cronycle. London, W. Rastell 1533. 2 v. fol. Second Edition. (Huth). (STC 10660)

———— The chronicle of ffabyan. [London, R. Grafton for] W. Bonham 1542. 2 v. fol. Third Edition. (Huth). (STC 10661)

———— The chronicle of Fabian. London, J. Kingston 1559. 2 v. fol. Fourth Edition, Second Issue. (Huth). (STC 10664)

Fairfax, Edward, *tr.* *See* Tasso, Torquato

Favyn, André. The theater of honour and knight-hood. London, W. Jaggard 1623. fol. First Edition. (STC 10717)

The fayre maide of the exchange. London, A. G[riffin] 1637. 4to. Third Edition. (H. S. Fuller–Hagen–Clawson). (STC 13319)

Fenn, John, *tr.* *See* Osorio da Fonseca, Jeronimo, *Bp.*

Fenner, Dudley. A short and profitable treatise, of lawfull and unlaw-
full recreations. Middleburgh, R. Schilders 1590. 8vo. Second
Edition. (STC 10777)

Fenton, *Sir* Geoffrey. Golden epistles. London, R. Newbery 1582.
4to. in eights. Third Edition. (STC 10796)

———— *tr. See* Guicciardini, Francesco

Fenton, Roger. A treatise of usurie. London, F. Kingston 1612. 4to.
Second Edition. (STC 10807)

Ferne, *Sir* John. The blazon of gentrie. London, J. Windet 1586.
4to. in eights. First Edition. (Edmund Philips–Huth). (STC
10825)

Field, Nathaniel. *See* Massinger, Philip *and* Nathaniel Field

[Fisher, Jasper]. Fuimus Troes. London, J. L[egatt] 1633. 4to.
First Edition. (H. V. Jones–Clawson). (STC 10886)

[Fisher, John, *Cardinal*]. A godlie treatisse declaryng the benefites . . .
of prayer. London, J. Cawood 1560. 8vo. First Edition. (STC
10888)

[————] Here after foloweth a mornynge remembraūce . . . of . . .
Margarete countesse of Rychemonde. London, W. de Worde
[1509]. 4to. in sixes. First Edition. (Sir William Tite–Dunn).
(STC 10891)

Fitz-Geffrey, Charles. The blessed birth-day. Oxford, J. Lichfield
1634. sm. 4to. First Edition. (STC 10935)

[Fitzherbert, *Sir* Anthony]. Diuersite de courts. Londini, in ed. R.
Pynsonis 1526. 8vo. First Edition? (Sir William Tite–Charles
Butler). (STC 10946)

———— La graunde abridgement. [London] in aed. R. Tottell 1565.
fol. Third Edition. (STC 10956)

[Fitzherbert, John]. The boke of husbandry. London, T. Berthelet
[not before 1534]. 8vo. Third Edition. (STC 10996)

[————] Surveyinge. Londini, in aed. T. Bertheleti 1546. 8vo. Sixth
Edition. (STC 11011)

Fleming, Abraham. The diamond of devotion. London, H. Denham
1586. 12mo. Second Edition. (STC 11042)

———— *tr. See* Virgilius Maro, Publius

[Fletcher, Giles, *the younger*]. Christs victorie. Cambridge, C. Legge 1610. sm. 4to. First Edition. (STC 11058)

Fletcher, John. The elder brother. London, F. K[ingston] 1637. 4to. First Edition. (Stoneleigh Abbey–Huth). (STC 11066)

—— The faithfull shepherdesse. London, A. M[athewes] 1634. sm. 4to. Third Edition. (Bridgewater–Clawson). (STC 11070)

—— Monsieur Thomas. London, T. Harper 1639. 4to. First Edition. (McKee). (STC 11071)

—— The night-walker. London, T. Cotes 1640. 4to. First Edition. (STC 11072)

—— Rule a wife and have a wife. Oxford, L. Lichfield 1640. 4to. First Edition. (David Laing–Buxton Forman). (STC 11073)

—— The tragedy of Thierry King of France. London, for T. Walkley 1621. 4to. First Edition. (STC 11074)

—— The tragoedy of Rollo Duke of Normandy. Oxford, L. Lichfield 1640. 4to. Second Edition. (McKee). (STC 11065)

—— Wit with-out money. London, T. Cotes 1639. First Edition. sm. 4to. (STC 1691)

—— *See also* Beaumont, Francis, *and* John Fletcher

—— *and* William Shakespeare. The two noble kinsmen. London, T. Cotes 1634. sm. 4to. First Edition. (Huth). (STC 11075)

[Fletcher, Phineas]. Brittain's Ida. London, for T. Walkley 1628. 8vo. First Edition. (Huth). (STC 11057)

—— Locustae. [Cambridge] T. and J. Buck 1627. 4to. First Edition. (Hugh Perkins). (STC 11081)

[——] The purple island. Cambridge, Printers to the University 1633. 4to. First Edition. (STC 11082)

[——] Sicelides. London, J. N[orton] 1631. 4to. First Edition. (Purdy). (STC 11083)

[Flores, Juan de]. Histoire de Aurelio et Isabelle. Antwerp, en casa de J. Steels 1556. 8vo. First Edition. (Heber). (STC 11092)

Florio, Giovanni. A worlde of wordes. London, A. Hatfield 1598. fol. in sixes. First Edition. (Kern). (STC 11098)

[Ford, John]. The chronicle historie of Perkin Warbeck. London, T.P[urfoot?] for H. Beeston 1634. 4to. First Edition. (Bridgewater). (STC 11157)

[——] The fancies, chast and noble. London, E. P[urslowe] 1638. 4to. First Edition. (Bridgewater). (STC 11159)

[——] Loves sacrifice. London, J. B[eale] 1633. 4to. First Edition. (Percy FitzGerald). (STC 11164)

Fortescue, *Sir* John. A learned commendation of the politique lawes of Englande. Tr. by R. Mulcaster. London, R. Tottill 1567. 8vo. First Edition. (STC 11194)

Fougasses, Thomas de. The generall historie of the magnificent State of Venice. Tr. by W. Shute. London, G. Eld and W. Stansby 1612. fol. First Edition. (Shadwell Court). (STC 11207)

Foxe, John. An abridgement of the ... Actes and monumentes ... by T. Bright. London, J. Windet 1589. 8vo. First Edition. (STC 11229)

—— Commentarii rerum in ecclesia gestarum. Argentorati, V. Rihel 1554. 8vo.

—— De Christo crucifixo concio. Londini, apud J. Dayum 1571. 4to. (STC 11247)

—— Rerum in ecclesia gestarum ... commentarij. Basileae, N. Brylinger & J. Oporinus 1559. fol.

Foxe, Luke. North-vvest Fox. London, B. Alsop and T. Fawcet 1635. sm. 4to. First Edition. (Lenox–W. T. Emmet). (STC 11221)

Frampton, John, *tr.* *See* Monardes, Nicolas

Fraunce, Abraham. The Countesse of Pembrokes Emanuel. London [T. Orwin] 1591. 4to. First Edition. (Park–Midgely–Nassau–Jolly–Corser–Locker–Collier–Steeves–Groves). (STC 11339)

—— The Countesse of Pembrokes Yuychurch. London, T. Orwin 1591. 4to. First Edition. (Park–Midgely–Nassau–Jolly–Corser–Locker–Collier–Steeves–Groves). (STC 11340)

—— The third part of the Countesse of Pembrokes Yuychurch. London [T. Orwin] 1592. 4to. First Edition. (Park–Midgely–Nassau–Jolly–Corser–Locker–Collier–Steeves–Groves). (STC 11341)

Fraunce, Abraham.   The lawiers logike.   London, W. Howe 1588. 4to.   First Edition.   (STC 11344)

Frith, John.   A boke made by Iohn Frith . . . answeringe vnto M. Mores letter.   Monster, C. Willems 1533.   8vo.   First Edition.   (STC 11381)

——— A disputacion of purgatorye.   [London, T. Godfrey?].   8vo. (STC 11387)

——— *See also* Tyndale, William

Frobisher, *Sir* Martin.   De Martini Forbisseri Angli navigatione.   Noribergae, in officina C. Gerlachin & haeredum I. Montani 1580.   8vo.

Froissart, Jean.   Here begynneth the first volume of sir Iohan Froyssart.   Tr. by J. Bourchier.   London, R. Pynson 1523.   fol.   First Edition.   (Martin, Ham Court).   (STC 11396)

——— Here begynneth the thirde and fourthe boke of sir Iohñ Froissart.   Tr. by J. Bourchier.   London, R. Pynson 1525.   fol.   First Edition.   (Martin, Ham Court).   (STC 11397a)

Fulke, William.   A defense of the sincere and true translation of the holy scriptures.   London [E. Griffin] for J. Bill 1617.   fol. in sixes. Second Edition.   (Huth).   (STC 11431a)

——— ——— London, A. Mathewes 1633.   fol. in sixes.   Third Edition.   (STC 11432)

Fuller, Thomas.   The historie of the holy warre.   Cambridge, T. Buck 1639.   fol.   First Edition.   (Sir Henry Hope Edwardes).   (STC 11464)

G., T.   The friers chronicle.   London, for R. Milbourne 1623.   4to. First Edition.   (STC 11510)

Gale, Thomas.   Certaine workes of chirurgerie.   London, R. Hall 1563.   8vo.   First Edition, First Issue.   (STC 11529)

Galvam, Antony.   The discoveries of the world.   Londini, G. Bishop 1601.   sm. 4to.   (STC 11543)

Gammer gurtons nedle.   *See* [Bridges, John?]

Gardiner, Stephen.   De vera obedientia. Tr. by J. Bale.   Rome, before ye castle of S. Angel [London, H. Singleton] 1553.   8vo.   Third Edition.   (Robert Drane).   (STC 11587)

Garnett, Henry.   A true and perfect relation of the whole proceedings against . . . Garnet . . . and his confederats.   London, R. Barker 1606.   sm. 4to.   First Edition, Third Issue.   (STC 11619)

[Garnier, Robert].   The tragedie of Antonie. Tr. by Mary Herbert, Countess of Pembroke.   London [P. Short] 1595.   8vo.   Second Edition.   (McKee–Halsey).   (STC 11623)

Gascoigne, George.   The droomme of doomes day.   London [T. East] 1576.   4to. in eights.   First Edition.   (Purdy).   (STC 11641)

———— The whole woorkes.   London, A. Jeffes 1587.   4to. in eights. Third Edition.   (Earl of Jersey–Hugh Perkins).   (STC 11638)

Gerard, John.   The herball.   London, E. Bollifant 1597.   fol.   First Edition.   (STC 11750)

Gesner, Conrad.   The newe iewell of health. Tr. by G. Baker.   London, H. Denham 1576.   4to. in eights.   First Edition.   (STC 11798)

———— See also Topsell, Edward

Gilbert, William.   Guilielmi Gilberti . . . de magnete.   London, P. Short 1600.   fol. in sixes.   First Edition.   (STC 11883)

G[ilby], A[nthony].   An answer to the deuillish detection of Stephane Gardiner.   [London, J. Day] 1547.   8vo.   First Edition.   (STC 11884)

Gildas.   The epistle of Gildas. Tr. by T. Habington.   London, T. Cotes 1638.   12mo.   First Edition.   (Lefferts).   (STC 11895)

———— Opus nouum.   n.p. (1525).   8vo.   First Edition.   (Heber– Aspland–Dunn).   (STC 11892)

Giovio, Paolo.   A shorte treatise vpon the Turkes chronicles. Tr. by P. Ashton.   London, E. Whitchurche 1546.   8vo.   First Edition. (Britwell–H. V. Jones).   (STC 11899)

———— The worthy tract of Paulus Iouius. Tr. by W. Daniel.   London, for S. Waterson 1585.   8vo.   First Edition.   (Ross Winans– H. V. Jones).   (STC 11900)

Glapthorne, Henry.   Argalus and Parthenia.   London, R. Bishop 1639. sm. 4to.   First Edition.   (STC 11908)

———— The Hollander.   London, J. Okes 1640.   sm. 4to.   First Edition.   (Bridgewater).   (STC 11909)

Glapthorne, Henry. The ladies priviledge. London, J. Okes 1640. sm. 4to. First Edition. (Bridgewater–H.V. Jones). (STC 11910)

———— Wit in a constable. London, J. Okes 1640. sm. 4to. First Edition. (STC 11914)

[Glover, Robert]. The catalogue of honor. London, W. Jaggard 1610. fol. First Edition in English. (STC 17926)

Golding, Percival, *tr*. *See* Philippson, Joannes, *Sleidanus*

Gomara. *See* Lopez de Gomara, Francesco

Gombauld, Jean Ogier de. Endimion. Tr. by R. Hurst. London, J. Okes 1639. 8vo. First Edition. (Britwell). (STC 11991)

Gomersall, Robert. The Levites revenge. London, for J. Marriott 1628. 8vo. First Edition. (STC 11992)

———— Poems. London, M. F[lesher] 1633. 8vo. First Collected Edition. (Edward Dowden). (STC 11993)

Gonsalvius Montanus, Reginaldus. A discovery and playne declaration of sundry subtill practises. Tr. by V. Skinner. London, J. Day 1569. 4to. Second Edition. (STC 11997)

[Gonzalez de Mendoza, Juan]. The historie of the great and mightie kingdome of China. Tr. by R. Parke. London, I. Wolfe 1588. sm. 4to. (F. Ouvry–Ives). (STC 12003)

Goodman, Christopher. How superior powers oght to be obeyd. Geneva, J. Crespin 1558. 8vo. First Edition. (William Makellar). (STC 12020)

Googe, Barnabe, *tr*. *See* Manzolli, Pierre Angelo

Goosecappe. *Sir* Gyles Goose-cappe knight. London, for H. Perry 1636. sm. 4to. Second Edition, Second Issue. (Duke of Buckingham & Chandos–Heber). (STC 12051)

Gorges, *Sir* Arthur, *tr*. *See* Lucanus

G[ough], J[ohn]. The strange discovery. London, E. Griffin 1640. 4to. First Edition. (STC 12133)

Gower, John. Jo. Gower de confessione amantis. London, T. Berthelette 1532. fol. Second Edition. (Huth). (STC 12143)

———— ———— London, T. Berthelette 1554. fol. Third Edition. (Buxton Forman–Clawson). (STC 12144)

Gower, John, *M.A.* *See* Ovidius Naso, Publius

[Grafton, Richard]. A chronicle at large. London, H. Denham
1568-9. fol. First Edition. (Huth). (STC 12147)

The greate herball. London, J. Kynge 1561. fol. Fourth Edition.
(Thomas Brooke). (STC 13179)

[Greene, John]. A refutation of the apology for actors. London, W.
White 1615. sm. 4to. First Edition (Langley imprint). (Mc-
Kee–Poor–Wallace). (STC 12214)

Greene, Robert. Greenes farewell to follie. London, W. White 1617.
sm. 4to. Second Edition. (Heber–Huth–H.V. Jones). (STC
12242)

――― Greenes groatsworth of witte. London, B. Alsop 1617. sm.
4to. Third Edition. (Halliwell–Huth). (STC 12247)

[―――] The historie of Orlando Furioso. London, S. Stafford 1599.
4to. Second Edition. (Bridgewater). (STC 12266)

[―――] A quip for an upstart courtier. London, G. P[urslowe]
1622. 4to. Sixth Edition. (Huth). (STC 12304)

――― The Spanish masquerado. London, R. Ward 1589. 4to. First
Edition. (STC 12309)

Greneway, Richard, *tr.* *See* Tacitus, Publius Cornelius

[Greville], Fulke, [*Baron*] *Brooke.* Certaine learned and elegant
workes. London, E. P[urslowe] 1633. fol. First Edition. (Chew).
(STC 12361)

Grimston, Edward, *tr.* *See* Acosta, José de

[Groot, Hugo de]. Christs passion. Tr. by G. Sandys. London, J.
Legatt 1640. 8vo. First Edition, First Issue. (Buxton Forman).
(STC 12397)

Guevara, Antonio de. The dial of princes. Tr. by Sir Thomas North.
[London] R. Tottill 1582. 4to. in eights. Third Edition. (STC
12429)

――― The familiar epistles. Tr. by E. Hellowes. London, for R.
Newbery 1577. 4to. in eights. Second Edition. (STC 12434)

[―――] The golden boke, of Marcus Aurelius. Tr. by J. Bourchier.
London, T. Marshe 1557. 8vo. Eighth Edition. (STC 12443)

Guicciardini, Francesco. The historie of Guicciardin. Tr. by G. Fenton. London, T. Vautroullier 1579. fol. in sixes. First Edition. (STC 12458a)

[Guido, *de Cauliaco*]. The questyonary of cyrurgens. Tr. by R. Copland. London, R. Wyer [1542]. sm. 4to. First Edition. (Huth). (STC 12468)

Gunter, Edmund. Canon triangulorum. London, W. Jones 1623. 4to. Second Edition. (STC 12519)

[————] De sectore & radio. London, W. Jones 1623. 4to. First Edition. (STC 12520)

———— [De sectore & radio]. The description and use of the sector. London, W. Jones 1624. 4to. (STC 12522)

Gwinne, Matthew. Nero. London, imp. E. Blount 1603. 4to. First Edition. (STC 12551)

Habington, Thomas, *tr*. *See* Gildas

[Habington, William]. Castara. London, A. Griffin 1634. 4to. First Edition, First Issue. (Kershaw). (STC 12583)

[————] ———— London, T. Cotes 1640, 39. 12mo. Third Edition. (C. B. Foote–E. B. Holden). (STC 12585)

———— The historie of Edward the fourth. London, T. Cotes 1640. fol. First Edition. (STC 12586)

[————] The queene of Arragon. London, T. Cotes 1640. fol. First Edition, Second Issue. (STC 12587)

H[akewill], G[eorge]. An apologie of the power and providence of God. Oxford, J. Lichfield and W. Turner 1627. fol. First Edition. (W. C. Hazlitt). (STC 12611)

Hakluyt, Richard. The principall navigations, voiages and discoveries of the English nation. London, G. Bishop and R. Newberie 1589. fol. First Edition. (STC 12625)

———— The principal navigationes, voiages . . . and discoveries of the English nation. London, G. Bishop, R. Newberie and R. Barker 1598-1600. 3 v. in 2. fol. (STC 12626)

Hall, Joseph. Characters of vertues and vices. London, M. Bradwood 1608. 8vo. First Edition. (STC 12648)

[Hall, Joseph].   Virgidemiarum [I-III].   London, J. Harrison 1602.
8vo.   Third Edition.   (Gaisford).   (STC 12718)

[———] Virgidemiarum [IV-VI].   London [R. Bradock] 1599.
8vo.   Second Edition.   (Gaisford).   (STC 12719)

[Halle, Edward].   The union of the two noble and illustre famelies.
London, R. Grafton 1550.   fol.   (STC 12723)

H[arding], S[amuel].   Sicily and Naples.   Oxford, W. Turner 1640.
4to.   First Edition.   (STC 12757)

Hardyng, John.   The chronicle of Ihon Hardyng.   Londini, ex officina
R. Graftoni 1543.   4to. in eights.   First Edition.   (Baron Bolland–
Corser–Huth).   (STC 12767)

[Harington, *Sir* John].   An anatomie of the metamorpho-sed Aiax.
London, R. Field 1596.   (STC 12772)

[———] An apologie.   [London 1596].   8vo.   (STC 12773)

[———] A new discourse of a stale subject.   London, R. Field 1596.
8vo.   First Edition.   (STC 12779)

[———] Ulisses vpon Aiax.   London, for T. Gubbins 1596.   8vo.
Second Edition.   (STC 12783)

——— *tr.   See* Ariosto, Ludovico

Harvey, William.   Exercitatio anatomica de motu cordis.   Francofurti,
Sumptibus G. Fitzeri 1628.   4to.   First Edition.   (John Pearson)

[Haughton, William].   English-men for my money.   London, J. N[or-
ton] 1626.   4to.   Second Edition.   (Bridgewater–H. V. Jones–
Clawson).   (STC 12932)

Hausted, Peter.   Senile odium.   Cantabrigiae, ex Academiae typographeo 1633.   8vo.   First Edition.   (STC 12936)

Hawes, Stephen.   The historie of graunde Amoure and la bell Pucel.
London, J. Wayland 1554.   sm. 4to.   Third Edition.   (Bridgewater).   (STC 12950)

[Hawkins, Henry].   Partheneia sacra.   [Rouen] J. Cousturier 1633.
8vo.   First Edition.   (Huth).   (STC 12958)

Hawkins, *Sir* Richard.   The observations of Sir Richard Havvkins.
London, I. D[awson] 1622.   fol.   (STC 12962)

Hayward, *Sir* John. The first part of the life and raigne of King Henrie the IIII. London, J. Wolfe 1599. 4to. (Huth). (STC 12996)

—————— The life, and raigne of King Edward the Sixt. London, for J. Partridge 1630. 4to. First Edition, First Issue. (G. W. Steeves). (STC 12998)

—————— The lives of the III. Normans, kings of England. London, R. Barker 1613. 4to. First Edition. (STC 13000)

Healey, John, *tr. See* Augustine, *Saint*

Heliodorus. An Aethiopian historie. Tr. by T. Underdowne. London, for W. Cotton 1605. 4to. in eights. Fourth Edition. (James Maidment). (STC 13044)

—————— Heliodorus his Aethiopian history. Tr. by T. Underdowne? London, F. Kyngston 1622. 4to. in eights. Fifth Edition. (John Brinton). (STC 13046)

—————— The famous historie. London, J. Dawson 1638. 4to. First Edition, Second Issue. (STC 13048)

Hellowes, Edward, *tr. See* Guevara, Antonio de

Henry VIII, *King of England*. Assertio septem sacramentorum. Londinum, in aed. Pynsonianis 1521. 4to. First Edition, First Issue. (Thomas Bramston–Huth). (STC 13078)

Henry Frederick, *Prince of Wales*. The order and solemnitie of the creation of … Prince Henrie. London, for J. Budge 1610. sm. 4to. First Edition. (Hugh Perkins–John Fuller Russell–Clawson). (STC 13161)

Herbert, George. The temple. Cambridge, T. Buck and R. Daniel 1633. 12mo. First Edition, First Issue. (STC 13183)

—————— —————— [Cambridge] T. Buck and R. Daniel 1633. 12mo. Second Edition. (Hoe). (STC 13185)

—————— —————— [Cambridge] T. Buck and R. Daniel 1634. 12mo. Third Edition. (STC 13186)

Herbert, Mary, *Countess of Pembroke, tr. See* Garnier, Robert

[Herolt, Joannes]. Sermones discipuli. London, J. Notary 1510. 4to. in eights. (Inglis–Pittar). (STC 13226)

Hervet, Gentian, *tr. See* Xenophon

Hester, John, *tr.* *See* Paracelsus, Theophrastus

[Hexham, Henry]. An experimentall discoverie of Spanish practises. n.p. 1623. 4to. (STC 22077)

[————] A second part of Spanish practises. [London, N. Okes] 1624. 4to. First Edition. (STC 22077)

(————) A tongue-combat. London 1623. 4to. First Edition

Heydon, *Sir* Christopher. A defence of iudiciall astrologie. [Cambridge] J. Legat 1603. 4to. First Edition. (STC 13266)

Heylyn, Peter. The historie of . . . St. George of Cappadocia. London, B. A[lsop] and T. F[awcet] 1631. 4to. in eights. First Edition. (STC 13272)

Heywood, Jasper, *tr.* *See* Seneca, Lucius Annaeus

Heywood, John. Iohn Heywoodes woorkes. London, H. Wykes 1566. 4to. Second Collected Edition. (STC 13286)

———— ———— London, T. Marsh 1576-7. 4to. Third Edition. (Huth). (STC 13287)

———— The spider and the flie. London, T. Powell 1556. 4to. First Edition. (Freeling–Corser–Henry Newnham Davis). (STC 13308)

Heywood, Thomas. An apology for actors. London, N. Okes 1612. 4to. First Edition. (STC 13309)

———— Englands Elizabeth. London, J. Beale 1631. 12mo. First Edition. (Sir Thomas Littleton–H.V. Jones). (STC 13313)

———— The English traveller. London, R. Raworth 1633. 4to. First Edition. (Frederick Perkins–McKee–Chew). (STC 13315)

———— The golden age. London [N. Okes] 1611. 4to. First Edition, Second Issue. (STC 13325)

———— Γυναικεῖον. London, A. Islip 1624. fol. First Edition. (Huth). (STC 13326) ·

———— The hierarchie of the blessed angells. London, A. Islip 1635. fol. First Edition. (STC 13327)

———— Londini speculum. London, J. Okes 1637. 4to. First Edition. (Devonshire). (STC 13349)

[————] The phoenix of these late times. London, N. Okes 1637. 4to. First Edition. (Corser). (STC 25228)

Heywood, Thomas.   A pleasant comedy, called A mayden-head well lost.   London, N. Okes 1634.   4to.   First Edition.   (Roxburghe–Kershaw–Huth–H.V. Jones–Levy).   (STC 13357)

———— Pleasant dialogues and dramma's.   London, R. O[ulton] 1637. 8vo.   First Edition.   (STC 13358)

———— The rape of Lucrece.   London, for N. Butter 1630.   sm. 4to. Fourth Edition.   (STC 13362)

———— The royall king, and the loyall subiect.   London, N. and J. Okes 1637.   4to.   First Edition.   (Mostyn).   (STC 13364)

[————] A true description of his Majesties royall ship.   London, J. Okes 1637.   sm. 4to.   First Edition, First Issue.   (STC 13367)

———— *and* Richard Brome.   The late Lancashire witches.   London, T. Harper 1634.   4to.   First Edition.   (James Crossley).   (STC 13373)

Hieronymus, *von Braunschweig*.   *See* Brunschwig, Hieronymus

Higden, Ranulphus.   Polycronycon. Tr. by John of Trevisa.   London, Southwerke, P. Treveris 1527.   fol.   Third Edition.   (Huth). (STC 13440)

Higgins, John.   *See* Mirror for magistrates

———— *tr.   See* Junius, Adrian

[Higginson, Francis].   New Englands plantation.   London, T. C[otes] and R. C[otes] 1630.   sm. 4to.   (Church).   (STC 13449)

[Hill, Thomas].   The gardeners labyrinth.   London, I. Wolfe 1586. sm. 4to.   First Edition.   (Charles Butler).   (STC 13487)

———— *tr.   See* Cocles, Bartholomaeus

Hilton, Walter.   *See* Hylton, Walter

Histrio-mastix.   [London] for T. Thorp 1610.   sm. 4to.   First Edition.   (Attrib. in part to J. Marston).   (Bridgewater).   (STC 13529)

Hitchcock, Robert.   A pollitique platt for the honour of the prince. London, J. Kyngston 1580.   4to.   First Edition.   (Bridgewater). (STC 13531)

Hoby, *Sir* Edward, *tr.   See* Mendoza, Bernardino de

Hoby, *Sir* Thomas, *tr.   See* Castiglione, Baldassare

Hole, Robert, *tr.* *See* Croce, Giovanni

Holinshed, Raphael. The first volume of the Chronicles of England, Scotlande, and Irelande. London [H. Bynneman] I, for L. Harrison; II, for J. Hunne 1577. 2 v. fol. First Edition. (Sir Robert Naunton–L. W. Hodson). (STC 13568[c])

H[olland], H[enry]. Herωologia Anglica. [Arnhem] imp. Crispini Passaei . . . et Jansonij . . . [1620]. fol. in sixes. First Edition. (W. H. Crawford–Bement). (STC 13582)

Holland, Philemon, *tr.* *See* Ammianus Marcellinus; Livius, Titus; Plinius Secundus, Caius; Plutarchus; Suetonius Tranquillus, Caius

Holy Roman Empire. The actes of the disputaciō. Tr. by M. Coverdale. [?Antwerp] 1542. 8vo. First Edition. (Adrianus van Hoolwick–Charles, Viscount Bruce of Ampthill). (STC 13612)

Homerus. The whole works. Tr. by G. Chapman. London [R. Field] for N. Butter [c. 1640?]. fol. First Complete Edition, Second Issue. (STC 13624a)

——The crowne of all Homers workes: Batrachomyomachia. Tr. by G. Chapman. London, J. Bill [c. 1624?]. fol. First Edition. (STC 13628)

—— Homer prince of poets. Tr. by G. Chapman. London, for S. Macham [1610?]. fol. First Edition, First Issue. (W. C. Hazlitt–A. C. Swinburne). (STC 13633)

—— 'Ομηρου 'Ιλιας. Londini, G. Bishop 1591. 8vo. First Edition printed in England. (John Lord Sommers, Baron of Evesham). (STC 13629)

—— Homers Odysses. Tr. by G. Chapman. London, R. Field [1615?]. fol. First Edition. (STC 13637)

—— The Iliads. Tr. by G. Chapman. London [R. Field 1611]. fol. First Complete Edition. (Henry Bradshaw). (STC 13634)

Hood, Robin. A merry iest of Robin Hood. London, for E. White [1594?]. 4to. Second Edition with the play. (Luttrell–Wynne–Farmer–Heber–Daniel–Huth). (STC 13692)

Hooker, Richard. Of the lawes of ecclesiasticall politie. London, J. Windet [1594-]1597. fol. First Edition. (STC 13712)

Horatius Flaccus, Quintus. A medicinable morall. Tr. by T. Drant. London, T. Marshe 1566. 4to. in eights. First Edition, First Issue. (Farmer–Frederick Perkins–Purdy). (STC 13805)

Horatius Flaccus, Quintus.   Q. Horatius Flaccus: his Art of poetry. Tr. by B. Jonson.   London, J. Okes 1640.   12mo.   First Edition. (G. W. Steeves).   (STC 13798)

Horman, William.   Vulgaria.   Londini, R. Pynson 1519.   4to.   First Edition.   (Huth).   (STC 13811)

Horne, Robert, *tr.*   *See* Calvin, Jean: Certaine homilies

[Howard, Henry, *Earl of Northampton*].   A defensatiue against the poyson of supposed prophesies.   London, J. Charlewood 1583. 4to.   First Edition.   (W. H. Phelps).   (STC 13858)

H[owell], J[ames].   Δενδρολογια. Dodona's grove.   [London] T. B[adger] 1640.   fol.   First Edition.   (STC 13872)

Hubert, *Sir* Francis.   Egypts favorite.   London, A. M[athewes] 1631. 8vo.   First Edition.   (Huth–Steeves).   (STC 13903)

——— The historie of Edward the Second.   London, B. A[lsop] and T. F[awcet] 1629.   8vo.   Second Edition.   (STC 13901)

Hudson, Henry, *and others*.   Descriptio ac delineatio geographica detectionis freti.   Amsterodami, ex officina H. Gerardi 1612.   sm. 4to.   (C. L. F. Robinson)

Hudson, Thomas, *tr.*   *See* Saluste du Bartas

Hurst, Richard, *tr.*   *See* Gombauld, Jean Ogier de

[Hutten, Ulrich von].   Of the wood called guaiacum. Tr. by T. Paynell.   Londini, in aed. T. Bertheleti 1539.   8vo.   Third Edition. (Fontaine–C. L. F. Robinson).   (STC 14026)

Hyde, Thomas.   A consolatorie epistle.   Louvain, J. Lyon 1580.   8vo. Second Edition.   (Jolley–S. Van de Weyer).   (STC 13377)

Hylton, Walter.   *See* Capgrave, John: Here begynneth the kalendre of the newe Legende of Englande

Intrationū excellentissimus liber.   London, R. Pynson 1510.   fol.   First Edition.   (Sussex–Littleton).   (STC 14116)

Jacob, Henry.   An attestation of many . . . divines.   [Middelburg, R. Schilders] 1613.   8vo.   First Edition.   (STC 14328)

——— A declaration and plainer opening of certain points.   [Middelburg, R. Schilders] 1612.   8vo.   Second Edition.   (STC 14332)

——— The divine beginning and institution of Christs true . . . church. Leyden, H. Hastings 1610.   8vo.   First Edition.   (STC 14336)

Jacob, Henry. A plaine and cleere exposition of the second commande-
ment. [Leyden, J. Marcus] 1610. 8vo. First Edition. (STC
14337)

James I, *King of England*. The workes. London, R. Barker and J.
Bill 1616(-20). fol. First Edition, Second Issue. (John Fuller
Russell). (STC 14345)

———— Βασιλικὸν Δῶρον. Edinburgh, R. Waldegrave 1603. 8vo.
Second Edition. (STC 14349)

[————] Daemonologie. Edinburgh, R. Waldegrave 1597. 4to.
First Edition. (STC 14364)

[————] A meditation upon the Lords prayer. London, B. Norton
and J. Bill 1619. 8vo. First Edition. (STC 14384)

James, Thomas, *Captain*. The strange and dangerous voyage of Captaine Thomas Iames. London, I. Legatt 1633. sm. 4to. (STC
14444)

James, Thomas, *D.D.* An apologie for Iohn Wickliffe. Oxford, J.
Barnes 1608. sm. 4to. First Edition. (George Rose). (STC
14445)

Jesus Christ. A proclamacyon of the hygh emperour. London, R.
Redman, n.d. 8vo. (Huth). (STC 14561b)

[Jewel, John, *Bp.*]. An apologie or answere in defence of the Churche
of Englande. Tr. by Lady Ann Bacon. London, R. Wolfe 1564.
8vo. First Edition. (Heber–Dundas–Sutherland–Steeves–Groves).
(STC 14591)

Jobson, Richard. The golden trade. London, N. Okes 1623. 4to.
First Edition. (Huth). (STC 14623)

John, Chrysostom, *Saint*. Τοῦ ἐν ἁγιοις Πατρὸς ἡμων Ἰωαννοῦ τοῦ
Χρυσοστόμου τὰ εὑρισκόμενα. Etonae, J. Norton 1610-13. 8 v.
fol. in sixes. (STC 14629a)

John, of Trevisa, *tr*. *See* Bate, John; Higden, Ranulphus

Jones, Inigo, *and Sir* William Davenant. The temple of love. London, for T. Walkley 1634. sm. 4to. First Edition. (Newdigate).
(STC 14719)

Jones, Zachary, *tr*. *See* LeLoyer, Pierre

Jonson, Benjamin. The workes [I]. London, W. Stansby 1616. fol.
in sixes. First Edition. (Sir Bryan Boughton). (STC 14751)

Jonson, Benjamin. The workes. The second volume. London, for R. Meighen 1631, 40, 41. fol. in fours. First Edition. (Sir Bryan Boughton). (STC 14754)

——— Ben: Ionson his Volpone. [London] for T. Thorpe 1607. 4to. First Edition. (STC 14783)

——— Ben: Ionson's Execration against Vulcan. London, J. O[kes] 1640. 4to. First Edition, Second Issue. (Cox–Levy). (STC 14771)

——— Seianus his fall. London, G. Elde 1605. sm. 4to. First Edition. (Hoe). (STC 14782)

——— tr. *See* Horatius Flaccus, Quintus

Joseph, *ben Gorion*. A compendious ... historie of the ... Iewes commune weale. Tr. by P. Morwyng. London, J. Daye 1558. 8vo. First Edition. (Inglis–Charles Butler). (STC 14795)

Josephus, Flavius. The famous ... workes. Tr. by T. Lodge. London, P. Short 1602. fol. First Edition. (STC 14809)

Junius, Adrian. The nomenclator. Tr. by J. Higgins. London, for R. Newbery and H. Denham 1585. 8vo. First Edition. (STC 14860)

Justice of Peace. [The Boke for a Iustice of peace]. The contentes of this boke. Londini, in aed. T. Bertheleti 1544. 8vo. (STC 14877)

Killigrew, Henry. The conspiracy. London, J. Norton 1638. 4to. First Edition. (STC 14958)

Killigrew, Thomas. The prisoners and Claracilla. London, T. Cotes 1641-40. 12mo. First Edition. (STC 14959)

[Kirchmeyer, Thomas]. The popish kingdome. London, H. Denham 1570. 4to. First Edition. (Huth). (STC 15011)

K[irke], J[ohn]. The seven champions of christendome. London, J. Okes 1638. 4to. First Edition. (STC 15014)

Knolles, Richard. The generall historie of the Turkes. [London] A. Islip 1621. fol. Third Edition. (William Ussher). (STC 15053)

Knox, John. An answer to a great number of blasphemous cauillations. [Geneva] J. Crespin 1560. 8vo. First Edition. (W. E. Lord). (STC 15060)

Knox, John. The appellation of Iohn Knoxe from the cruell . . . sentence. Geneva [J. Poullain and A. Rebul?] 1558. 8vo. First Edition. (Copy 1, W. Makellar; 2, Isaac Reed–Heber–Makellar). (STC 15063)

———— A confession & declaratiō of praiers. Rome [London, H. Singleton] 1554. 8vo. First Edition. (STC 15073 pt. 2)

———— The copie of a lettre delivered to the ladie Marie. Geneva, J. Poullain and A. Rebul 1558. 8vo. Second Edition. (W. Makellar). (STC 15067)

———— A faythfull admonition. Kalykow [London, H. Singleton?] 1554. 8vo. First Edition. (David Laing). (STC 15069)

———— The first blast of the trumpet. [Geneva, J. Poullain and A. Rebul?] 1558. 8vo. First Edition. (Isaac Reed–Heber–Makellar). (STC 15070)

———— A godly letter sent too the fayethfull. Rome [London, H. Singleton] 1554. 8vo. Second Edition. (STC 15073)

———— A sermon preached . . . in the publique audience of the church of Edenbrough. [London? H. Denham?] 1566. 8vo. First Edition. (W. Makellar). (STC 15075)

[Kyd, Thomas]. The Spanish tragedy. London, A. Mathewes and sold by T. Langley 1623. sm. 4to. Eleventh Edition. (Lacy–Kershaw–Huth). (STC 15093a)

Lambard, William. Ἀρχαιονομία. London, ex officina J. Daij 1568. 4to. First Edition. (Greville). (STC 15142)

———— Eirenarcha. London, R. Newbery and H. Bynneman by the Assigns of R. Tottell and C. Barker 1582. 8vo. Second Edition. (Ernest E. Baker). (STC 15164a)

———— A perambulation of Kent. London, H. Middleton 1576. 4to. First Edition. (STC 15175)

———— ———— London, E. Bollifant 1596. 4to. in eights. Second Edition. (W. Twopeny). (STC 15176)

[Laneham, Robert]. A letter: whearin, part of the entertainment vntoo the Queenz maiesty, at Killingwoorth Castl . . . iz signified. [London 1575]. 8vo. First Edition. (Bridgewater–H. V. Jones). (STC 15191)

Langham, William.   The garden of health.   London [Deputies of C.
Barker] 1579 [i.e. 1597].   4to. in eights.   First Edition.   (H.W.
Poor).   (STC 15195)

Lanquet, Thomas.   Coopers chronicle [pts. 1 and 2 by Lanquet].   London, in the house late T. Berthelettes 1560.   sm. 4to.   Third Edition.   (C. L. F. Robinson).   (STC 15218)

Lanyer, Aemilia.   Salve deus rex Iudaeorum.   London, V. Simmes 1611.
sm. 4to.   First Edition, Second Issue.   (Brand–Reed–Heber–Corser–W. H. Crawford–J. A. Brooke).   (STC 15227)

[La Perrière, Guillaume de].   The mirrour of policie.   London, A. Islip 1598.   sm. 4to.   First Edition, First Issue.   (Huth–Groves).
(STC 15228)

Latham, Simon.   Lathams falconry.   London, T. Harper 1633.   sm.
4to.   First Complete Edition.   (STC 15269)

Latimer, Hugh.   Fruitfull sermons.   London, I. Daye 1584.   4to. in
eights.   Fourth Edition.   (Huth–H.V. Jones).   (STC 15280)

—— The fyrste sermon.   London, J. Daye and W. Seres [1549].
8vo.   (STC 15273)

—— The seconde [to the seventh] sermon.   London, I. Daye and
W. Seres [1549].   8vo.   First Edition.   (STC 15274)

—— 27 sermons.   London, I. Day 1562.   4to. in eights.   First Collected Edition.   (STC 15276)

[Laud], William, *Abp*.   A speech delivered in the Starr Chamber.   London, R. Badger 1637.   4to.

Laune, Pierre de, *tr*.   *See* Liturgies. Book of common prayer. *French*

Lavender, Theophilus, *editor*.   *See* Biddulph, William

Lawrence, Leonard, *tr*.   *See* San Pedro, Diego

[Legh, Gerard].   The accedens of armory.   London, R. Tottel 1576.
4to. in eights.   Third Edition.   (Hugh Grantham–Lord Berwick–
Sir Henry Hope Edwardes–George Dunn).   (STC 15390)

[Leighton, Alexander].   An appeal to the Parliament.   [?Holland
?1628].   sm. 4to.   Second Edition.   (Tite).   (STC 15430)

Leighton, *Sir* William. The teares or lamentations of a sorrowfull soule.
London, R. Blower 1613.   sm. 4to.   First Edition.   (Groves).
(STC 15433)

[Leighton, *Sir* William]. Vertue triumphant. London, M. Brad-wood 1603. sm. 4to. First Edition. (Newdigate). (STC 15435)

Leland, John. The laboryouse iourney. London [R. Jugge for] J. Bale 1549. 8vo. First Edition. (C. Fox). (STC 15445)

[LeLoyer, Pierre, *Sieur de la Brosse*]. A treatise of specters. Tr. by Z. Jones. London, V. S[immes] 1605. sm. 4to. First Edition. (STC 15448)

[LeRoy, Pierre]. A pleasant satyre. London, Widdow Orwin 1595. sm. 4to. First Edition. (STC 15489)

Lever, Christopher. A crucifixe. London, V. S[immes] 1607. sm. 4to. First Edition. (STC 15535)

——— Queene Elizabeths teares. London, V. S[immes] 1607. sm. 4to. First Edition. (Bindley–Rice–Freeling–Corser–Gaisford). (STC 15540)

Lever, Ralph. The arte of reason. London, H. Bynneman 1573. 8vo. First Edition. (STC 15541)

Lindsay, *Sir* David. A dialogue betweene Experience and a Courtier. London, T. Purfoote 1581. 4to. in eights. (Fountaine–Walker). (STC 15678)

Linschoten, Jan Huygen van. Iohn Hvighen van Linschoten. His dis-cours of voyages. Tr. by W. Phillip. London, I. Wolfe [1598]. fol. (STC 15691)

Lisle, William. Divers ancient monuments. London, E. G[riffin] 1638. 4to. First Edition, Second Issue. (Sir Frederic Madden). (STC 15705)

Lithgow, William. The totall discourse. London, J. Okes 1640. 4to. in eights. Second Complete Edition. (STC 15713)

Littleton, *Sir* Thomas. The first part of the institutes of the lawes of England: or a commentarie upon Littleton authore E. Coke. Lon-don, for the Societie of Stationers 1628. fol. First Edition. (An-thony, Earl of Kent–Thomas Philip, Earl de Grey). (STC 15784)

Liturgies. *Breviaries. Salisbury.* Portiforiū. Paris, F. Regnault 1535. 4to. in eights. (Dunn). (STC 15833 Pars aestivalis)

Liturgies. *Hours and primers. Salisbury and General.* Hore . . . ad verū Sarisburiēsis ecclesie ritū. Parisiis, in officina N. Prevost, 18 July 1527. 4to. in eights. (STC 15953)

Liturgies. *Hours and primers. Salisbury and General.* This prymer of Salysbury vse.   Rouen [and Paris] for F. Regnault 1537.   8vo. (John Fuller Russell).   (STC 15995)

——— Thys prymer in Englyshe and in Laten.   [Rouen] N. le Roux 1538.   8vo.   (John Fuller Russell).   (STC 16007)

——— This prymer... (The Pystles and Gospels).   London, R. Redman [1538].   4to.   (D.F.Appleton–G.C.Thomas).   (STC 16008 pt. II only)

——— The primer, in Englishe and Latyn.   London, R. Grafton, 6 September 1545.   4to. in eights.   Seventh Edition.   (D.F. Appleton–G.C.Thomas).   (STC 16040)

——— The prymer in Englishe and Latine.   London, Assigns of J. Wayland 1557.   8vo.   (Dogmersfield).   (STC 16080)

Liturgies. *Manuals. Salisbury.*   Manuale ad vsum... ecclesie Sarisburiensis.   Londini [R. Caly] 1555.   4to. in eights.   (Samuel Goodenough–Ashburnham–Dunn).   (STC 16156)

Liturgies. *Missals. Salisbury.*   Missale ad vsum... ecclesie Sarum.   Parisius, N. Higman 1519.   4to. in eights.   (STC 16200)

——— Missale ad vsum ecclesie Sarisburiensis.   Lōdini, J. Kyngstō et H. Sutton 1555.   4to. in eights.   (STC 16218)

Liturgies. *Book of common prayer.*   The booke of the common prayer. Londini, in officina E. Whitchurche, 16 June 1549.   fol.   (John Gott).   (STC 16272)

——— The boke of common prayer.   Londini, in officina E. Whitchurche 1552.   fol.   (John Gott).   (STC 16279)

——— The booke of common prayer.   London, R. Barker 1604.   fol. (Sir John Savill).   (STC 16327)

——— The booke of common prayer.   London, R. Barker 1616.   fol. (Huth).   (STC 16347a)

——— ——— London, B. Norton and J. Bill 1627.   fol.   (Ashburton–G.C.Thomas).   (STC 16368)

——— *Latin.*   Ordinatio ecclesiae.   Lipsiae, in officina W. Gunteri 1551.   4to.   First Edition.   (Huth).   (STC 16423)

——— Liber precum publicarum.   Londini, T. Vautrollerius per assignationem F. Florae 1574.   8vo.   (Huth).   (STC 16427)

Liturgies. *Book of common prayer. French.* La liturgie angloise. Tr. by P. de Laune. Londres, J. Bill 1616. 4to. First Edition. (STC 16431)

—— *Irish.* Leabhar na nurnaightheadh. Tr. by W. Daniel. Dublin, J. Franckton 1608. fol. First Edition. (Thomas Baker–Godfrey Daniel – James Nugent – William Butler – Fritz Ponsonby). (STC 16433)

Liturgies. *The Scottish book of common order.* The forme of prayers. n.p. 1584. 16mo. (Britwell). (STC 16581)

Liturgies. *Church of Scotland.* The booke of common prayer. Edinburgh [E. Tyler for] R. Young 1637. fol. First Edition, First Issue. (Huth). (STC 16606)

Livius, Titus. The Romane historie. Tr. by P. Holland. London, A. Islip 1600. fol. First Edition. (Richard Caulfield). (STC 16613)

Lodge, Thomas, *tr. See* Seneca, Lucius Annaeus

London. *Orders and regulations.* The lawes of the market. London, W. Jaggard 1620. 8vo. (Huth). (STC 16718)

Long, Kingsmill, *tr. See* Barclay, John

[Lopez de Gomara, Francesco]. The pleasant historie of the conquest of the West India. Tr. by T. Nicholson. London, T. Creede 1596. sm. 4to. (STC 16808)

Lord, Henry. A display of two forraigne sects. London, T. and R. Cotes for R. Constable 1630. 4to. First Edition. (Richard Gregory–C. I. and E. Knight–W. F. Prideaux). (STC 16825)

Lower, *Sir* William. The phaenix in her flames. London, T. Harper 1639. 4to. First Edition. (STC 16873)

Lucanus, Marcus Annaeus. Lucans Pharsalia. Tr. by Sir Arthur Gorges. London, for W. Burre 1614. fol. First Edition. (STC 16885)

—— —— Tr. by T. May. London, A. M[athewes] 1635. 8vo. Third Complete Edition. (Henry Cranfurd). (STC 16889)

[Lumley, John, *Lord?*]. The arte of English poesie. London, R. Field 1589. sm. 4to. First Edition, First Issue. (L. I. Haber). (STC 20519)

[Lupton, Thomas]. A thousand notable things of sundry sortes. London, for E. White [before 1601]. 4to. (STC 16958a)

Luther, Martin. Special and chosen sermons. Tr. by W. Gace. London, T. Vautroullier 1578. 4to. in eights. First Edition. (STC 16993)

[———] A very excellent and swete exposition vpon the two & twentye psalme. Tr. by M. Coverdale. London, Southwark, J. Nicolson 1537. 8vo. First Edition. (STC 16999)

Lydgate, John, *tr. See* Colonna, Guido delle

Lyly, John. Euphues. The anatomy of wit. London, T. East 1585. 4to. Sixth Edition. (STC 17056)

——— Euphues, the anatomy of wit. [Euphues and his England]. London, I. Beale 1623. 4to. in eights. Second Edition. (C. S. Bement). (STC 17065)

——— ——— London, I. H[aviland] 1631. 4to. in eights. Third Edition. (G. W. Steeves). (STC 17066)

——— Euphues and his England. London, T. East 1586. 4to. (STC 17073)

——— Six court comedies. London, W. Stansby 1632. 12mo. First Edition, Second Issue. (W. C. Hazlitt). (STC 17089)

Lyndewode, William, *Bp.* Prouinciale. Paris, W. Hopyl for (London) W. Bretton, 23 March 1505. fol. Second Edition. (STC 17109)

Lynne, Walter, *tr. See* Carion, Johann

Lyte, Henry, *tr. See* Dodoens, Rembert

M., F., *tr. See* Pimentel, Diego

Mabbe, James, *tr. See* Aleman, Mateo; Celestina

Machiavelli, Niccolò. The arte of warre. Tr. by P. Whitehorne. London, I. Kingston 1560-62. 2 pts. sm. 4to. First Edition. (Groves). (STC 17164)

——— Nicholas Machiavel's Prince. Tr. by E. Dacres. London, R. Bishop 1640. 12mo. First Edition. (STC 17168)

Machin, Lewis. *See* Markham, Gervase, *and* Lewis Machin

Malory, *Sir* Thomas, *tr. See* Arthur, *King*

Manwood, John.   A treatise and discourse of the lawes of the forrest. London, T. Wight and B. Norton 1598.   4to. in eights.   First Edition.   (STC 17291)

———— A treatise of the lawes of the forest.   London, for the Society of Stationers 1615.   4to. in eights.   Second Edition.   (STC 17292)

[Manzolli, Pierre Angelo].   The zodiake of life. Tr. by B. Googe. London, H. Denham, 18 April 1565.   8vo.   First Complete Edition.   (STC 19150)

[————] ———— London, R. Robinson 1588.   4to.   Third Complete Edition.   (Royal Society–Huth).   (STC 19152)

Marbecke, John.   A concordāce.   [London] R. Grafton, July 1550. fol.   First Edition.   (STC 17300)

Marcellinus, Ammianus.   *See* Ammianus Marcellinus

[Markham, Gervase].   The pleasures of princes.   London, I. Norton for H. Taunton 1635.   4to.   Second Edition.   (STC 17358)

———— The second and last part of the first booke of the English Arcadia.   London, N. Okes 1613.   4to.   First Edition.   (STC 17352)

———— *tr.   See* Ariosto, Ludovico

[———— *and* Lewis Machin].   The dumbe knight.   London, A. M[athewes] 1633.   4to.   Second Edition.   (STC 17400)

———— *and* William Sampson.   The true tragedy of Herod and Antipater.   London, G. Eld 1622.   4to.   First Edition.   (A. C. Swinburne).   (STC 17401)

Marlowe, Christopher.   The famous tragedy of the rich Jew of Malta. London, I. B[eale] 1633.   sm. 4to.   First Edition.   (STC 17412)

———— The massacre at Paris.   London, E. A[llde] [?1600].   8vo. First Edition.   (Kemble–Devonshire).   (STC 17423)

———— *and* George Chapman.   Hero and Leander.   London, A. M[athewes] 1629.   sm. 4to.   Eleventh Edition.   (STC 17421)

———— ———— London, N. Okes 1637.   sm. 4to.   Twelfth Edition. (Huth).   (STC 17422)

Marmion, Shakerley.   A fine companion.   London, A. Mathewes 1633. sm. 4to.   First Edition.   (STC 17442)

Marmion, Shakerley. Hollands leaguer. London, I. B[eale] 1632. 4to. First Edition. (STC 17443)

———— [A morall poem, intituled the legend of Cupid and Psyche]. London, I. Okes 1637. 4to. First Edition. (J. G. Bourinot). (STC 17444a, but with date 1637)

Marprelate, Martin, *pseud*. [Epistle] Oh read ouer D. Iohn Bridges for it is a worthy worke. [East Molesey? R. Waldegrave, October 1588]. sm. 4to. First Edition. (STC 17453)

———— [Epitome] Oh read ouer D. Iohn Bridges for it is worthy worke. [Fawsley, R. Waldegrave, November 1588]. sm. 4to. First Edition. (S. G. Hamilton–J. A. Brooke). (STC 17454)

———— Hay any worke for Cooper. [Coventry, R. Waldegrave, March 1589]. sm. 4to. First Edition. (STC 17456)

Marston, John. The workes. London [A. Mathewes] for W. Sheares 1633. 8vo. First Edition, First Issue. (STC 17471)

[————] Tragedies and comedies. London, A. M[athewes] 1633. 8vo. First Collected Edition, Second Issue. (STC 17472)

———— The Dutch courtezan. London, T. P[urfoote] 1605. sm. 4to. First Edition. (STC 17475)

———— Parasitaster. London, T. P[urfoote] 1606. sm. 4to. Second Edition. (STC 17484)

———— The wonder of women. London, I. Windet 1606. sm. 4to. First Edition. (Locker-Lampson–Wallace). (STC 17488)

———— *attrib. author*. *See* Histrio-mastix

———— *and* William Barksted. The insatiate countesse. London, I. N[orton] 1631. sm. 4to. Third Edition, First Issue. (Bridgewater). (STC 17478)

Marten, Anthony. An exhortation, to stirre up the mindes of all her maiesties faithfull subiects. London, J. Windet 1588. 4to. First Edition. (James Maidment–Charles Lilburn). (STC 17489)

Martin, Gregory. A discoverie of the manifold corruptions of the holy Scriptures. Rhemes, J. Fogny 1582. 8vo. First Edition. (STC 17503)

Martyr, Peter. Opera. Legatio babilonica. Occeana decas. Poemata. Hispali, J. corumberger, 11 April 1511. fol. First Edition

Martyr, Peter.   De orbe novo decades.   Alcala, in contubernio A. Guillelmi, 5 November 1516.   fol.   First Edition.   (Church)

———— De orbe novo ... decades.   Paris, G. Auvray 1587.   8vo.   (Sir Arthur Helps)

———— De rebvs oceanicis et novo orbe.   Coloniae, apud G. Calenium & haeredes Quentelios 1574.   8vo.   (Robert Southey–Montino– H. V. Jones)

———— The decades of the new worlde. Tr. by R. Eden.   Londini, in aed. G. Powell (by E. Sutton) 1555.   sm. 4to.   (Huth).   (STC 647)

———— Extraict ou recveil des isles.   Paris, S. de Colines 1532.   sm. 4to.   (E. N. Crane)

———— The historie of the VVest-Indies.   London, for A. Hebb [?1625].   sm. 4to.   (STC 651)

———— The history of trauayle. Tr. by R. Eden.   London, R. Iugge 1577.   sm. 4to.   (STC 649)

———— *and others.*   Libro primo della Historia de l'Inde Occidentali; Libro secondo delle Indie Occidentali; Libro vltimo del Svmmario delle Indie Occidentali.   Vinegia, October 1534.   sm. 4to.

Martyr, Petrus, *Vermilius.*   *See* Vermigli, Pietro Martire

Mascall, Leonard.   A booke of the arte and maner how to plant and graffe all sortes of trees.   London, for I. Wight 1575.   4to.   Second Edition.   (STC 17575)

Massinger, Philip.   The Duke of Millaine.   London, B. A[lsop] 1623.   4to.   First Edition.   (STC 17634)

———— The Emperour of the east.   London, T. Harper 1632.   4to. First Edition.   (STC 17636)

———— The great Duke of Florence.   London, for J. Marriot 1636. 4to.   First Edition.   (STC 17637)

———— The maid of honour.   London, I. B[eale] 1632.   4to.   First Edition.   (Newdigate).   (STC 17638)

———— A new way to pay old debts.   London, E. P[urslow] 1633. 4to.   First Edition.   (STC 17639)

———— The picture.   London, I. N[orton] 1630.   4to.   First Edition, First Issue.   (STC 17640)

Massinger, Philip. The renegado. London, A. M[athewes] 1630. 4to. First Edition. (STC 17641)

────── The Roman actor. London, B. A[lsop] and T. F[awcet] 1629. 4to. First Edition. (STC 17642)

────── The unnaturall combat. London, E. G[riffin] 1639. 4to. First Edition. (STC 17643)

────── and Nathaniel Field. The fatall dovvry. London, J. Norton 1632. 4to. First Edition. (STC 17646)

[Maxwell, James]. Carolanna. London, E. Allde [? 1619]. 4to. First Edition. (Groves). (STC 17699)

[May, Thomas]. The reigne of King Henry the second. London, A. M[athewes] 1633. 8vo. First Edition. (Huth). (STC 17715)

[──────] The victorious reigne of King Edward the third. London, for T. Walkley and B. Fisher 1635. 8vo. First Edition. (STC 17719)

────── tr. See Lucanus

[Mayne, Jasper]. The cityе match. Oxford, L. Lichfield 1639. sm. fol. First Edition. (STC 17750)

Mendoza, Bernardino de. Theorique and practise of warre. Tr. by Sir E. Hoby. [Middelburg, R. Schilders] 1597. 4to. First Edition. (Huth). (STC 17819)

Menewe, Gracious. A confutacion of that popishe and antichristian doctryne. [Zurich? 1555?]. 32mo. First Edition. (Huth). (STC 17821)

────── A plaine subuersyon of all the argumentes. [Zurich? 1555?]. 32mo. First Edition. (Huth). (STC 17822)

M[eteren], E[manuel van]. A true discourse historicall. Tr. by T. Churchyard and R. Robinson. London, for M. Lownes 1602. sm. 4to. First Edition. (S. Van de Weyer). (STC 17846)

[──────] ────── (STC 17846 with var. title)

Middleton, Thomas. A chast mayd in Cheape-side. London, for F. Constable 1630. sm. 4to. First Edition. (Huth–Standish). (STC 17877)

────── A mad world my masters. London [J. Okes] 1640. sm. 4to. Second Edition. (Bridgewater). (STC 17889)

[Middleton, Thomas]. Michaelmas terme. London, for A. I[ohnson] 1607. sm. 4to. First Edition. (Kershaw–Huth). (STC 17890)

[——] The phoenix. London, T. H[arper] 1630. sm. 4to. Second Edition. (STC 17893)

Mildmay, Humphrey, *tr.* *See* DuBec[-Crespin], Jean

M[ill], H[umphrey]. Poems occasioned by a melancholy vision. London, I. D[awson] 1639. 8vo. First Edition. (Alexander Young). (STC 17922)

Mirror for magistrates. The first parte (by J. Higgins). London, for T. Marshe 1575. 4to. in eights. Second Edition. (William Cole–Hagen). (STC 13444)

—— The mirour for magistrates (First and last parts). (Edited by J. Higgins). London, H. Marsh 1587. 4to. in eights. First Collected Edition. (Wallace). (STC 13445)

—— A mirour for magistrates (Edited by R. Niccols). London, F. Kyngston 1609-10. 4to. in eights. Second Collected Edition. (Griswold). (STC 13446)

—— A myrrour for magistrates (Edited by W. Baldwin). London, T. Marshe 1571. 4to. in eights. Third Extant Edition. (Huth). (STC 1249)

—— The last parte (Edited by W. Baldwin). London, T. Marshe 1575. 4to. in eights. Fifth Extant Edition. (William Cole–Hagen). (STC 1251)

—— The seconde part (by T. Blenerhasset). [London] R. Webster 1578. 4to. First Edition. (Corser–Hoe–Hagen). (STC 3131)

M[offett], T[homas]. The silkewormes, and their flies. London, V. S[immes] 1599. 4to. First Edition. (Huth). (STC 17994)

[Monardes, Nicolas]. Ioyfvll newes out of the newfound world. Tr. by J. Frampton. London, T. Dawson for W. Norton 1580. 4to. (STC 18006)

Montaigne, Michel Eyquem de. The essayes. Tr. by J. Florio. London, V. Simmes 1603. fol. First Edition. (STC 18041)

—— —— London, M. Flesher 1632. fol. Third Edition. (STC 18043)

Montemayor, Jorge de. Diana. Tr. by B. Yong. London, E. Bollifant 1598. fol. First Edition. (McKee). (STC 18044)

[Montreux, Nicolas de]. Honours academie. Tr. by R. Tofte. London, T. Creede 1610. fol. First Edition. (Farmer–Park–Hill–Corser?–Longman). (STC 18053)

[Moraes, Francisco de]. The first [second] part of the ... history of ... Palmerin of England. Tr. by A. Munday. London, B. Alsop and T. Fawcet 1639. 2 pts. 4to. in eights. Fourth Extant Edition. (STC 19164)

[More, Cresacre]. The life and death of Sir Thomas More. [?Antwerp 1631]. 4to. First Edition. (STC 18066)

More, *Sir* Thomas. The workes. London, at the costes and charges of I. Cawood, I. Waly, and R. Tottell 1557. fol. First Edition. (Charles Ford). (STC 18076)

[———] Eruditissimi viri Guilielmi Rossei opus. Londini [R. Pynson] 1523. 4to. First Edition. (STC 18089)

——— [Utopia]. Libellus vere aureus. Louvain, T. Martin [1516]. 4to. First Edition. (Huth)

——— [Utopia]. A fruteful and pleasaunt worke. Tr. by R. Robinson. London, A. Vele 1551. 8vo. First Edition. (Huth). (STC 18094)

——— [Utopia]. A frutefull pleasaunt & wittie worke. Tr. by R. Robinson. London, A. Vele 1556. 8vo. Second Edition, Second Issue. (STC 18095)

——— *tr.* *See* Pico della Mirandola

Morison, *Sir* Richard, *tr.* *See* Vives, Juan Luis

Morley, Thomas. A plaine and easie introduction to practicall musicke. London, P. Short 1597. fol. First Edition. (STC 18133)

Morton, Thomas. New English Canaan. Amsterdam, J. F. Stam 1637. sm. 4to. (STC 18202)

Morwyng, Peter, *tr.* *See* Joseph, *ben Gorion*

Moryson, Fynes. An itinerary. London, I. Beale 1617. fol. in sixes. First Edition. (STC 18205)

[Mourt, G., *editor*]. A relation or iournall. London, for I. Bellamie 1622. sm. 4to. First Edition, First Issue. (Britwell). (STC 20074)

Mulcaster, Robert, *tr.* *See* Fortescue, Sir John

[Munday, Anthony]. A briefe chronicle, of the successe of times. [London] W. Iaggard 1611. 8vo. First Edition. (Inglis). (STC 18263)

────── *tr.* *See* Amadis, de Gaule; Moraes, Francisco de

[────── *and* Henry Chettle]. The death of Robert, Earle of Hunting-ton. London, for W. Leake 1601. sm. 4to. First Edition. (Daniel–Huth). (STC 18269)

[──────] The downfall of Robert, Earle of Huntington. London, for W. Leake 1601. sm. 4to. First Edition. (Daniel–Huth). (STC 18271)

Nabbes, Thomas. The bride. London, R. H[odgkinson] 1640. sm. 4to. First Edition. (Chew). (STC 18338)

────── Covent Garden. London, R. Oulton 1638. sm. 4to. First Edition. (Genest–John Duerdin–Percy FitzGerald). (STC 18339)

────── Hannibal and Scipio. London, R. Oulton 1637. sm. 4to. First Edition. (Halsey). (STC 18341)

────── Microcosmus. London, R. Oulton 1637. sm. 4to. First Edition. (STC 18342)

────── The springs glorie. London, I. D[awson] 1638. sm. 4to. First Edition, First Issue. (STC 18343)

────── Totenham Court. London, R. Oulton 1638. sm. 4to. First Edition, First Issue. (Huth). (STC 18344)

────── The unfortunate mother. London, J. O[kes] 1640. sm. 4to. First Edition. (John Scott). (STC 18346)

Napier, John. A description of the admirable table of logarithmes. Tr. by E. Wright. London, N. Okes 1616. 12mo. First Edition. (STC 18351)

────── Mirifici logarithmorum canonis descriptio. Edinburgi, ex officina A. Hart 1614. 4to. First Edition. (Lord Napier). (STC 18349a)

────── A plaine discouery of the whole Reuelation of Saint John. Edinburgh, R. Waldegrave 1593[4]. 4to. in eights. First Edition. (Ashburnham). (STC 18354)

Napier, John. A plaine discovery, of the whole Revelation of S. Iohn. [Edinburgh, A. Hart] London, for J. Norton 1611. 4to. in eights. Third Edition, Norton imprint. (STC 18356a)

—— Rabdologiae. Edinburgi, A. Hart 1617. 12mo. First Edition, Second Issue. (Huth). (STC 18357)

[Nash, Thomas]. Nashes Lenten stuffe. London [T. Judson and V. Simmes] 1599. sm. 4to. First Edition. (Utterson–Gardner–Huth). (STC 18370)

—— Pierce Penilesse his supplication to the diuell. London, A. Jeffes 1592. sm. 4to. Second Edition. (T. D. C. Graham–Mitford–Huth). (STC 18372)

—— Strange newes, of the intercepting certaine letters. London, I. Danter 1593. 4to. First Edition. (Farmer–Bindley–Chalmers–Corser–Huth). (STC 18377b)

—— *attrib. author*. *See* An almond for a parrat; Pasquill, *of England*

A necessary doctrine . . . for any christen man. London, T. Berthelet, 29 May 1543. 4to. (Huth). (STC 5170)

—— London, I. Mayler 1543. 8vo. (Heneage Legge–Huth). (STC 5175)

Nemesius, *Bp.* The nature of man. Tr. by G. Wither. London, M. F[lesher] 1636. 12mo. First Edition. (STC 18427)

Nero, *Emperor of Rome*. The tragedy of Nero. London, A. Mathewes 1633. sm. 4to. Second Edition. (STC 18431)

Neville, Alexander, *tr. See* Seneca, Lucius Annaeus

[Newnham, John]. Newnams nightcrowe. London, I. Wolfe 1590. sm. 4to. First Edition. (W. E. Bools–Bement). (STC 18498)

Newton, Thomas, *tr. See* Seneca, Lucius Annaeus

Niccols, Richard. The cuckow. London, F. K[ingston] 1607. 4to. First Edition. (Park–Corser–Huth). (STC 18517)

[——] Expicedium. London [E. Allde] 1603. 4to. First Edition, Second Issue. (Huth). (STC 18520)

—— Londons artillery. London, T. Creede and B. Alsop 1616. 4to. First Edition. (STC 18522)

—— Sir Thomas Overburies vision. [London] for R. Meighen and T. Iones 1616. 4to. First Edition. (Corser–Huth). (STC 18524)

Niccols, Richard. *See also* Mirror for magistrates

Nicholl, John.   An houre glasse of Indian newes.   London, for N. Butter 1607. sm.4to. First Edition. (Huth). (STC 18532)

Nicholson, Thomas, *tr.*   *See* Lopez de Gomara, Francesco

N[iclas], H[endrik]. Comoedia. [Antwerp? Plantin? 1574?]. 8vo. First Edition. (Rhodes–Corser–Jolley–Huth). (STC 18550)

Nicolay, Nicolas de. The nauigations . . . into Turkie. Tr. by T. Washington Jr.   London, T. Dawson 1585. sm.4to.   First Edition. (Gaddesden Park). (STC 18574)

Nicolls, Thomas, *tr.*   *See* Thucydides

Norris, *Sir* John.   Ephemeris expeditionis Norreysij & Draki in Lusitaniam. Londini, imp. T. Woodcocke 1589. sm.4to. First Edition. (Mexborough). (STC 18653)

North, *Sir* Thomas, *tr.*   *See* Bidpai; Guevara, Antonio de; Plutarchus

Northbrooke, John. Spiritus est vicarius Christi in terra. London, T. Dawson 1579. 4to. Second Edition. (Huth). (STC 18671)

Norton, Robert, *tr.*   *See* Camden, William

Norton, Thomas, *tr.*   *See* Calvin, Jean: The institution of christian religion

[——— *and* Thomas Sackville].   The tragidie of Ferrex and Porrex. London, I. Daye [c. 1570]. 8vo. Second Edition. (Thomas Pearson–Charlemont–Huth). (STC 18685)

[Nowell, Alexander]. Catechismus. Londini, in officina R. Wolfij, XVI cal. Ivl. 1570. 4to. First Edition. (STC 18701)

Nuce, Thomas, *tr.*   *See* Seneca, Lucius Annaeus

The ordenarye for all faythfull Christiās. Tr. by A. Scoloker. Londō, A. Scoloker [1548]. 8vo. (Huth). (STC 5200)

Ornithoparcus, Andreas.   Andreas Ornithoparcus his micrologus. Tr. by J. Dowland. London [T. Snodham] 1609. fol. First Edition. (Huth). (STC 18853)

Osorio da Fonseca, Jeronimo, *Bp.*   A learned and very eloquent treatie. Tr. by J. Fenn. Lovanii, apud I. Foulerum 1568. 8vo. First Edition. (Huth). (STC 18889)

Ovidius Naso, Publius.   [Fasti]. Ovids festivalls. Tr. by J. Gower. Cambridge, R. Daniel, and sold, London, by M. S[parke] Jr. 1640. 8vo.   First Edition.   (STC 18948 var.)

———— [Metamorphoses]. Ovids metamorphosis. Tr. by G. Sandys. London, W. Stansby 1626. fol.   First Complete Edition.   (STC 18964)

Owen, Lewis.   The running register.   London [F. Kingston] 1626. 4to.   First Edition.   (STC 18996)

———— Speculum Jesuiticum.   London, T. C[otes] 1629.   4to.   First Edition.   (Huth).   (STC 18997)

Oxford University.   Oxoniensis academiae funebre officium in memoriam Elisabethae Reginae.   Oxoniae, I. Barnesius 1603.   sm. 4to. First Edition.   (Philip Bliss–G. C. Thomas–McKee).   (STC 19018)

Painter, William.   The palace of pleasure [Tome I].   London, T. Marshe 1575.   4to. in eights.   Third Edition.   (Hans Stanley– David Garrick–Jolley–Huth).   (STC 19123)

———— The second tome of The palace of pleasure.   London, H. Bynneman, 8 November 1567.   4to.   First Edition.   (Hans Stanley– David Garrick–Jolley–Huth).   (STC 19124)

Palingenius, Marcellus, tr.   *See* Manzolli, Pierre Angelo

Paracelsus, Theophrastus.   A hundred and foureteene experiments and cures. Tr. by J. Hester. London, V. Simmes 1596. sm. 4to. (STC 19180)

Paradin, Claude.   The true . . . purtreatures of the woll Bible. Tr. by P. Derendel. Lyons, Iean of Tournes 1553. sm. 8vo. First Edition. (H. S. Richardson–J. Pearson).   (STC 3043)

Parke, Robert, tr.   *See* Gonzalez de Mendoza, Juan

[Parker, Henry].   Dives and Pauper.   London, R. Pynson, 5 July 1493. fol.   First Edition.   (C. L. Higgins–Halsey).   (STC 19212)

Parkes, William.   The curtaine-drawer of the world.   London, for L. Becket 1612. 4to.   First Edition.   (Simon, Lord Fraser of Lovat– Huth).   (STC 19298)

Parkinson, John.   Paradisi in sole.   London, H. Lownes and R. Young 1629.   fol. in sixes.   First Edition.   (John Vivian).   (STC 19300)

[Parsons, Robert]. A conference about the next succession to the crowne of Ingland. Imprinted at N. [Antwerp?] 1594. 8vo. First Edition. (Aldenham Abbey). (STC 19398)

[———] Elizabethae Reginae Angliae edictum. [Rome?] 1593. 8vo.

A parte of a register. [Middelburg, R. Schilders 1593]. 4to. First Edition. (Huth). (STC 10400)

Pasquill [*of England*]. A countercuffe giuen to Martin Iunior. [London, J. Charlewood] 1589. sm. 4to. First Edition. (Ames–Herbert–Maskell–Huth). (STC 19456)

[———] The first parte of Pasquils apologie. [London, J. Charlewood] 1590. sm. 4to. First Edition. (William Herbert–Mark P. Robinson). (STC 19450)

[———] The returne of the renowned Caualiero Pasquill of England. [London, J. Charlewood] 1589. sm. 4to. First Edition. (Farmer–Huth). (STC 19457)

[Paulet], William, *Marquis of Winchester*. The Lord Marques idlenes. London, E. Bollifant 1587. 4to. Second Edition. (Winchester–Clawson). (STC 19486)

Paynell, Thomas, *tr. See* Amadis, de Gaule; Hutten, Ulrich von

Peacham, Henry. The compleat gentleman. London [W. Stansby?] 1622. 4to. First Edition. (STC 19502)

——— Minerva Britanna. London, W. Dight 1612. 4to. First Edition. (F. M. R. Currer–Huth). (STC 19511)

——— The valley of varietie. London, M. P[arsons] 1638. 12mo. First Edition. (STC 19518)

Percy, Henry, *Earl of Northumberland*. A true and summarie reporte of the ... Earle of Northumberlands treasons. [London] in aed. C. Barker [1585]. sm. 4to. First Edition. (STC 19617)

Person, David. Varieties. London, R. Badger 1635. 4to. in eights. First Edition. (J. B. Barrett). (STC 19781)

Petrarca, Francesco. Phisicke against fortune. Tr. by T. Twyne. London, R. Watkins 1579. 4to. in eights. First Edition. (STC 19809)

Phaer, Thomas, *tr. See* Virgilius Maro, Publius

[Philippson], Joannes, *Sleidanus*. A briefe chronicle of the foure principall empyres. Tr. by S. Wythers. London, R. Hall 1563. sm. 4to. First Edition, First Issue. (STC 19849)

[Philippson], Joannes, *Sleidanus*. A briefe chronicle of the foure principall empyres. Tr. by S. Wythers. London, R. Hall 1563. sm. 4to. First Edition, Second Issue. (STC 19849 var.)

—— An epitome of Frossard. Tr. by P. Golding. London, T. Purfoot 1608. sm. 4to. First Edition. (G. Chalmers). (STC 11399)

—— A famouse cronicle of oure time. Tr. by J. Daus. London, I. Daie, 26 September 1560. fol. First Edition, Second Issue. (William Prest–T. F. Baily–J. Backhouse–J. Creswell). (STC 19848a)

Phillip, William, *tr. See* Linschoten, Jan Huygen van; Veer, Gerrit de

Pico della Mirandola, Giovanni Francesco. Here is cōteyned the lyfe of Iohan Picus Erle of Myrandula. Tr. by Sir T. More. London, W. de Worde [1510?]. sm. 4to. in sixes. Second Edition. (STC 19898)

Piers, *ploughman*. The vision of Pierce Plowman. London, R. Crowley 1550. 4to. (2 copies: 1, Purdy). (STC 19907a)

—— The vision of Pierce Plowman . . . Wherevnto is also annexed the Crede. London, O. Rogers, 21 February 1561. sm. 4to. Fourth Edition. (William Morris). (STC 19908)

[Pilkington, James, *Bp.*]. The burnynge of Paules church in London. London, W. Seres, 10 March 1563. 8vo. First Edition. (Joseph Gwilt–Huth). (STC 19931)

Pimentel, Diego. The deposition of Don Diego Piementellj. Tr. by F. M. London, I. Woolfe 1588. 4to. First Edition. (STC 19935)

A pleasant conceited comedy, wherein is shewed, how a man may choose a good wife from a bad. London, I. Norton 1634. sm. 4to. Seventh Edition. (STC 5600)

Plinius Secundus, Caius (*Pliny the elder*). The historie of the world. Tr. by P. Holland. London, A. Islip 1634. 2 v. fol. Second Edition. (Clanricarde). (STC 20030)

Plowden, Edmund. Les commentaries, ou reportes. London, in aed. R. Tottelli 1578, 1579. 4 pts. fol. in fours. Second Edition. (STC 20041)

Plutarchus. [Moralia]. The philosophie. Tr. by P. Holland. London, A. Hatfield 1603. fol. in sixes. First Edition. (STC 20063)

Plutarchus.   [Vitae parallelae]. The lives of the noble Grecians and
Romanes. Tr. by T. North.   London, T. Vautroullier and I. Wight
1579.   fol. in sixes.   First Edition.   (STC 20066)

————— ————— London, G. Miller 1631.   2 pts.   fol. in sixes.   Fifth
Edition.   (STC 20070)

Pole, Reginald.   Reginaldi Poli . . . ad Henricū Octauum . . . pro ecclesiasticae unitatis defensione.   Rome, apud A. Bladum [c. 1538].
fol. in sixes.   First Edition

The Popes complaint to his minion Cardinals.   [London? 1623?].   sm.
4to.   First Edition.   (Huth).   (STC 19483)

Porta, Giovanni Battista della.   De furtiuis literarum notis.   London,
apud J. Wolphium 1591.   4to.   (STC 20118)

Porter, Henry.   The pleasant history of the two angry women of Abington.   London, for W. Ferbrand 1599.   sm. 4to.   Second Edition.   (Kemble–Devonshire).   (STC 20122)

Potts, Thomas.   The wonderfull discoverie of witches.   London, W.
Stansby 1613.   sm. 4to.   First Edition.   (H. LeRoy Edgar–W. F.
Gable).   (STC 20138)

The praise of musicke.   Oxenford, I. Barnes 1586.   8vo.   First Edition.   (STC 20184)

Prayers of the byble.   London, R. Redman [c. 1532].   4 of 6 pts.
32mo.   First Edition.   (J. Dix–Samuel Addington–Thomas
Brooke)

Prid, W., *tr.*   *See Pseudo* Augustine, *Saint*

Prudent le Choyselat.   A discourse of housebandrie. Tr. by R. Eden.
London, J. Kyngston 1577.   sm. 4to.   First Edition.   (John,
Baron Crew).   (STC 20452)

Prynne, William.   Histrio-mastix.   London, E. A [llde] and W. I [ones]
1633.   4to.   First Edition, Second Issue.   (STC 20464a)

————— The unlovelinesse of love-lockes.   London 1628.   4to.   First
Edition.   (Bishop Elliet–Learmont).   (STC 20477)

Purchas, Samuel.   Purchas his pilgrim. Microcosmus.   London, W.
S[tansby] 1619.   8vo.   First Edition.   (STC 20503)

————— Purchas his pilgrimage.   London, W. Stansby 1626.   fol.
Fourth Edition, First Issue.   (Hoe).   (STC 20508)

Purchas, Samuel. Purchas his pilgrims. London, W. Stansby 1625.
4 pts. fol. First Edition. (Hoe). (STC 20509)

[Puttenham, George]. The arte of English poesie. *See* [Lumley, John, *Lord?*]

Pyott, Lazarus, *tr.* *See* Amadis, de Gaule; Busche, Alexander van den

Quarles, Francis. Divine poems. London [M. Flesher] for I. Marriott 1630. 8vo. First Collected Edition. (STC 20533)

———— Emblemes. London, G. M[iller] 1635. 8vo. First Edition, Second Issue. (STC 20540)

———— A feast for wormes. London, F. Kyngston 1620. sm. 4to. First Edition. (Huth). (STC 20544)

———— Hadassa. London [F. Kingston] 1621. sm. 4to. First Edition. (G. W. Steeves). (STC 20546)

———— Sions elegies. London, W. Stansby 1624. sm. 4to. First Edition, First Issue. (Huth). (STC 20553)

———— Sions sonets. London, W. Stansby 1625. 4to. First Edition. (Halliwell–Huth). (STC 20554)

Rainolde, Richard. A booke called the foundacion of rhetoricke. London, I. Kingston, 6 March 1563. sm. 4to. First Edition. (STC 20604)

Rainolds, John. Th'overthrow of stage-playes. [Middelburg, R. Schilders] 1599. 4to. First Edition. (STC 20616)

Ralegh, *Sir* Walter. The discoverie of the large, rich and bevvtifvl empire of Gviana. London, R. Robinson 1596. sm. 4to. First Edition. (STC 20635)

———— The history of the world. London, W. Stansby 1614. fol. in sixes. First Edition, Second Issue. (STC 20637)

———— *See also* A declaration of the demeanor and cariage

[Randolph, Thomas]. Aristippus. London, T. Harper 1630. 4to. First Edition. (R. Cholmondeley). (STC 20686)

———— ———— London [E. Purslowe] 1635. sm. 4to. Fourth Edition. (STC 20689)

———— The jealous lovers. Cambridge, Printers to the University 1632. sm. 4to. First Edition, Second Issue. (STC 20692a)

Randolph, Thomas.   The jealous lovers.   Cambridge, Printers to the University 1634.   sm. 4to.   Second Edition.   (STC 20693)

——— Poems; with the Muses looking-glasse; and Amyntas.   Oxford, L. Lichfield 1638.   2 pts.   sm. 4to.   First Edition.   (STC 20694)

Rawlins, Thomas.   The rebellion.   London, I. Okes 1640.   sm. 4to. First Edition.   (Clawson).   (STC 20770)

The returne from Pernassus [Part II].   London, G. Eld 1606.   sm. 4to. First Edition.   (Hagen).   (STC 19309)

Reynolds, John.   The triumphs of Gods revenege. 3 books.   I-II, London, F. Kyngston 1621, 1622; III, A. Mathewes 1624.   4to.   First Edition.   (W. F. Prideaux).   (STC 20942)

——— Votivae Angliae.   Utrecht 1624.   4to.   First Edition.   (STC 22092)

——— Vox coeli.   Printed in Elesium [?Utrecht] 1624.   4to.   (STC 22096a)

Ridley, Nicholas, *Bp.*   Certē godly, learned and comfortable conferences.   [Zurich, C. Froschauer?] 1556.   8vo.   First Edition.   (STC 21048)

Robinson, John.   A iust and necessarie apologie of certain Christians . . . called Brownists.   [?Leyden] 1625.   sm. 4to.   (STC 21108)

Robinson, Ralph, *tr.*   *See* More, *Sir* Thomas

Robinson, Richard, *joint tr.*   *See* Churchyard, Thomas, *and* Richard Robinson, *tr.*

Rogers, Thomas, *tr.*   *See Pseudo* Augustine, *Saint*; Thomas, *à Kempis*

[Rowlands, Richard].   Amorvm emblemata, figuris aeneis incisa studio O. Vaeni.   Antverpiae, Venalia apud auctorem 1608.   obl. 4to.

[———] Theatre des cruautez des hereticques de nostre temps.   Antwerp, A. Hubert 1607.   4to.   (T. Williams–Tite–Lord Orford– Bement)

[———] Theatrum crudelitatum haereticorum.   Antwerp, A. Hubert 1587.   4to.   First Edition

[Rowlands, Samuel].   Martin Mark-all.   London, for I. Budge and R. Bonian 1610.   sm. 4to.   First Edition.   (Bridgewater–Farmer– Park–Heber–Corser–Huth).   (STC 21400)

R[owley], S[amuel]. The noble souldier. London [J. Beale] 1634. sm. 4to. First Edition. (STC 21416)

R[owley], W[illiam]. A match at mid night. London, A. Mathewes 1633. sm. 4to. First Edition. (STC 21421)

[Rufinus, Tyrannius]. Incipit exposicio sancti Ieronimi in simbolum apostoloruz. Oxonie [T. Rood] 17 December 1468 [1478]. sm. 4to. (Pembroke). (STC 21443)

[Ruggle, George]. Ignoramus. London, T. P[urfoot] 1630. 12mo. First Edition. (STC 21445)

Rutter, Joseph, *tr.* *See* Corneille, Pierre

S., I. or J. Certaine worthye manuscript poems. London, R. Robinson for R. D[exter] 1597. 8vo. First Edition. (Gaisford). (STC 21499)

S., S. The honest lawyer. London, G. Purslowe 1616. sm. 4to. First Edition, Second Issue. (Inglis–Mitford–Lacy–Huth–H.V. Jones). (STC 21519)

Sackville, Thomas. *See* Norton, Thomas, *and* Thomas Sackville

[Saint German, Christopher]. Dialogus de fundamentis legum Anglie et de conscientia. Londini, I. Rastell 1528. 8vo. Second Edition. (STC 21559)

[———] The fyrste dyaloge in Englysshe. [London] R. Wyer [1531]. 8vo. in fours. Second Edition. (Richard Clark–Huth). (STC 21562)

[———] Here after foloweth a lyttell treatise called the newe addicions. [London] T. Bertheletus 1531. 8vo. Second Edition. (Richard Clark–Huth). (STC 21564)

[———] The secunde dyalogue. London, P. Treueris 1531. 8vo. Second Edition. (Richard Clark–Huth). (STC 21566)

[———] The dyaloges in Englishe. Londini, in aed. R. Totteli 1554. 8vo. Fourth Collected Edition. (I. F. M. Dovaston). (STC 21571)

Salkeld, John. A treatise of angels. London, T. S[nodham] 1613. 8vo. First Edition. (H.V. Jones). (STC 21621)

Sallustius Crispus, Caius. Here begynneth the famous cronycle of the warre. Tr. by A. Barclay. London, R. Pynson [c. 1520]. fol. in sixes. First Edition. (Britwell). (STC 21626)

Saltmarsh, John. Holy discoveries and flames. London, R. Y[oung] 1640. 12mo. First Edition. (Sir George Cooke). (STC 21637)

[———] Poemata sacra. Cantabrigiae, ex academiae typographeo 1636. 8vo. First Edition. (STC 21638)

Saluste du Bartas, Guillaume de. Bartas his deuine weekes & workes. Tr. by J. Sylvester. [London] H. Lownes 1605. sm. 4to. First Collected Edition. (Sir John Savile–Henry Collins). (STC 21649)

——— ——— (With The historie of Judith. Tr. by T. Hudson). London, H. Lownes 1608. sm. 4to. in eights. Second Collected Edition. (G. W. Steeves). (STC 21650)

——— ——— London, H. Lownes 1613. sm. 4to. in eights. Fourth Collected Edition. (G. C. Cuningham). (STC 21652)

——— ——— London, H. Lownes 1620, 1621. sm. fol. in sixes. Fifth Collected Edition. (STC 21653)

Sampson, William. The vow breaker. London, I. Norton 1636. sm. 4to. First Edition. (STC 21688)

——— *See also* Markham, Gervase, *and* William Sampson

[Sandys, *Sir* Edwin]. Europae speculum. Hagae Comitis 1629. sm. 4to. Fourth Edition. (White Kennett). (STC 21718)

Sandys, George, *tr.* *See* Groot, Hugo de; Ovidius Naso, Publius

[San Pedro, Diego de]. A small treatise betwixt Arnalte and Lucenda. Tr. by L. Lawrence. London, J. Okes 1639. 4to. First Edition. (Bridgewater). (STC 778)

Saville, *Sir* Henry, *tr.* *See* Tacitus, Publius Cornelius

Scoloker, Anthony, *tr.* *See* The ordenarye for all faythfull Christiãs; Viret, Pierre

Scot, Reginald. The discouerie of witchcraft. London, for W. Brome 1584. 4to. in eights. First Edition. (W. F. Prideaux). (STC 21864)

Scotland. *Acts of Parliament*. The actis of the parliament of James the sext. Edinburgh, I. Ros 1575. fol. Second Edition. (John Pearson). (STC 21881)

——— In the parliament ... begune at Striuiling. Edinburgh, I. Ros 1575. fol. (John Pearson). (STC 21883)

Scotland. *Acts of Parliament.* In the parliament haldin at Striviling. Edinburgh, I. Ros 1579. fol. First Edition. (John Pearson). (STC 21884)

——— In the parliament haldin and begun at Edinburgh. Edinburgh, H. Charteris 1582. fol. First Edition. (John Pearson). (STC 21885)

[Scott, Thomas]. Sir Walter Rawleighs ghost. Utrecht, J. Schellem 1626. sm. 4to. First Edition. (E. Solly–C. L. F. Robinson). (STC 22085)

[———] Vox populi. [Gorcum?] 1620. 4to. Third Edition. (STC 22100)

[Segar, *Sir* William]. Honor military, and ciuill. London, R. Barker 1602. fol. First Edition. (Henry Hyatt). (STC 22164)

Selden, John. Analecton Anglobritannicon. Francofurti, prodeunt ex officina Paltheniana 1615. 4to. First Edition

[———] The duello. London, G. E[ld] 1610. sm. 4to. First Edition. (STC 22171)

——— The history of tythes. [London] 1618. sm. 4to. Fourth Edition. (STC 22173)

——— Ioannis Seldeni Mare clausum. London, W. Stansby 1635. fol. in fours. First Edition. (White Kennett). (STC 22175)

——— Titles of honor. London, W. Stansby 1614. 4to. First Edition. (STC 22177)

Seneca, Lucius Annaeus. The workes. Tr. by T. Lodge. London, W. Stansby 1613-14. fol. in sixes. First Edition. (Charles Thomas–Stanford). (STC 22213)

——— The seconde tragedie of Seneca entituled Thyestes. Tr. by J. Heywood. London, in the hous late T. Berthelettes, 26 March 1560. 8vo. First Edition. (Corser–Huth). (STC 22226)

——— Seneca his tenne tragedies. Tr. by J. Heywood, A. Nevile, J. Studley, T. Nuce, T. Newton. London, T. Marshe 1581. 8vo. First Collected Edition. (STC 22221)

Serlio, Sebastiano. The first [-the fift] booke of architecture. London, S. Stafford 1611. fol. First Edition. (STC 22235)

Seymour, Anne, *Countess of Warwick*. Le tombeau de Marguerite de Valois . . . Faict premierement en d'isticques latins par les trois soeurs princesses en Angleterre [Anne, Margaret and Jane Seymour]. Depuis traduictz en . . . françois. Paris, M. Fezandat & R. Granjon 1551. 8vo. First Edition. (Pichon–Bouchart)

Shakespeare, William. Mr. William Shakespeares comedies, histories, & tragedies. London, I. Iaggard, and E. Blount. Printed at the charges of W. Iaggard, E. Blount, I. Smithweeke, and W. Aspley 1623. fol. in sixes. First Edition. (C. C. Harrison–G. L. Harrison–Kennel S. Chaffers–Mary McMillan Norton). (STC 22273)

―――― Mr. William Shakespeares comedies, histories, and tragedies. London, T. Cotes for I. Smethwick 1632. fol. in sixes. Second Edition. (C. C. Harrison–G. L. Harrison–Kennel S. Chaffers–Mary McMillan Norton). (STC 22274e)

―――― Poems. London, T. Cotes 1640. 8vo. First Collected Edition. (E. A. Crowninshield–Hugh Perkins). (STC 22344)

―――― A Yorkshire tragedie. [London, W. Jaggard] for T. Pavier 1619. sm. 4to. Second Edition. (STC 22341)

―――― *See also* Fletcher, John, *and* William Shakespeare

S[harpe], L[ewis]. The noble stranger. London, J. O[kes] 1640. sm. 4to. First Edition. (STC 22377)

Sharpham, Edward. The Fleire. London, B. A[lsop] and T. F[awcet] 1631. sm. 4to. Fourth Edition. (Narcissus Luttrell). (STC 22387)

Shelton, Thomas, *tr. See* Cervantes Saavedra, Miguel de

Sherley, *Sir* Anthony. Sir Anthony Sherley his relation of his travels into Persia. London [N. Okes] 1613. sm. 4to. First Edition. (STC 22424)

Shirley, Henry. The martyr'd souldier. London, I. Okes 1638. sm. 4to. First Edition. (STC 22435)

Shirley, James. The bird in a cage. London, B. Alsop and T. Fawcet 1633. sm. 4to. First Edition. (McKee). (STC 22436)

―――― Changes. London, G. P[urslow] 1632. sm. 4to. First Edition. (STC 22437)

―――― The constant maid. London, J. Raworth 1640. sm. 4to. First Edition. (Griswold–Ives). (STC 22438)

Shirley, James.   A contention for honour and riches.   London, E.
A[llde] 1633. sm.4to. First Edition. (McKee). (STC 22439)

———— The coronation. London, T. Cotes 1640. First Edition. (STC
22440)

———— The dukes mistris. London, J. Norton for W. Cooke 1638.
sm.4to. First Edition (with Cooke imprint). (STC 22441a)

———— The example. London, J. Norton 1637. sm.4to. First Edition. (Griswold–Ives). (STC 22442)

———— The gamester. London, I. Norton 1637. sm.4to. First Edition. (Roxburghe). (STC 22443)

———— The gratefull servant. London, B. A[lsop] and T. F[awcet]
1630. sm.4to. First Edition. (Huth). (STC 22444)

———— Hide Parke. London, T. Cotes 1637. sm.4to. First Edition. (2 copies: 1, Roxburghe). (STC 22446)

———— The humorous courtier. London, T. C[otes] 1640. sm.4to.
First Edition. (J. P. Collier–Lefferts). (STC 22447)

———— The lady of pleasure. London, T. Cotes 1637. sm.4to. First
Edition. (Bridgewater–Heber–Huth). (STC 22448)

———— Loves crueltie. London, T. Cotes 1640. sm.4to. First Edition. (Lefferts). (STC 22449)

———— The maides revenge. London, T. C[otes] 1639. sm.4to.
First Edition. (Griswold–Ives). (STC 22450)

———— The opportunitie. London, T. Cotes for A. Crooke [1640].
sm.4to. First Edition (with Crooke imprint). (STC 22451)

———— A pastorall called the Arcadia. London, I. D[awson] 1640.
sm.4to. First Edition. (H.V. Jones). (STC 22453)

———— The royall master. London, T. Cotes, and sold by I. Crooke
and R. Serger 1638. sm.4to. First Edition (London imprint).
(STC 22454)

———— St. Patrick for Ireland. London, J. Raworth 1640. sm.4to.
First Edition. (STC 22455)

———— The schoole of complement. London, E. A[llde] 1631. sm.
4to. First Edition. (STC 22456)

———— The traytor. London, for W. Cooke 1635. sm.4to. First
Edition. (STC 22458)

Shirley, James. The triumph of peace. London, I. Norton 1633. sm. 4to. (Huth). (STC 22459)

—————— The wittie faire one. London, B. A[lsop] and T. F[awcet] 1633. sm. 4to. First Edition. (STC 22462)

—————— The young admirall. London, T. Cotes 1637. sm. 4to. First Edition. (Lefferts). (STC 22463)

—————— *See also* Chapman, George, *and* James Shirley

Sidney, *Sir* Philip. The Countesse of Pembrokes Arcadia. London, for W. Ponsonbie 1590. 4to. First Edition. (STC 22539a)

—————— —————— London [R. Field] 1598. fol. in sixes. Third Edition. (STC 22541)

—————— —————— Edinburgh, R. Waldegrave 1599. fol. in sixes. Fourth Edition. (STC 22542)

—————— —————— London [H. Lownes] for M. Lownes 1605. fol. in sixes. Fifth Edition. (Viscount Curzon). (STC 22543)

—————— —————— Dublin, Society of Stationers 1621. fol. in sixes. Seventh Edition. (STC 22545)

—————— —————— London, W. S[tansby] for S. Waterson 1627. (Bk. 6, H. L[ownes] and R. Y[oung] 1628). fol. in sixes. Eighth Edition. First to have Bk. 6. (Douglas of Cavers). (STC 22547)

—————— —————— London [R. Young?] for S. Waterson and R. Young 1633. fol. in sixes. Ninth Edition. (John Spencer Smith). (STC 22549)

—————— Exequiae illustrissimi equitis. Oxonii, ex officina ... I. Barnesii 1587. sm. 4to. First Edition. (Mexborough). (STC 22551)

—————— Peplus. illustrissimi viri D. Philippi Sidnaei. Oxonii, I. Barnesius 1587. 4to. First Edition. (Mexborough). (STC 22552)

[Silesio, Mariano]. The Arcadian princesse. Tr. by R. Brathwaite. London, T. Harper 1635. 8vo. First Edition. (H. V. Jones). (STC 22553)

Silvain, Alexander. *See* Busche, Alexander van den

Skelton, John. Here after foloweth a lytell boke, whiche hath to name. Why come ye nat to courte. London, R. Kele [c. 1545]. 8vo. First Edition. (Bindley–Hibbert–Daniel–Huth). (STC 22615)

Skelton, John.   Here after foloweth the boke of Phyllyp Sparowe. London, R. Kele [c. 1545]. 8vo. First Edition. (Bindley–Hibbert–Daniel–Huth). (STC 22594)

———— Pithy pleasaunt and profitable workes.   London, T. Marshe 1568. 8vo. First Collected Edition. (Purdy). (STC 22608)

Skinner, V., tr.   See Gonsalvius Montanus, Reginaldus

Sleidanus, Joannes.   See Philippson, Joannes, Sleidanus

Smeton, Thomas.   Ad virulentum Archibaldi Hamiltonii apostatae dialogum.   Edinburgh, apud I. Rosseum 1579.   sm. 4to.   First Edition.   (D. Laing).   (STC 22651)

Smith, John.   Advertisements for the unexperienced planters.   London, I. Haviland 1631.   sm. 4to.   (Hoe–Vail).   (STC 22787).   (6th state of map)

———— A description of New England.   London, H. Lownes 1616. sm. 4to.   (Huth).   (STC 22788).   (6th state of map)

———— The generall historie of Virginia.   London, I. D[awson] and I. H[aviland] 1624. fol. (Calthorpe). (Sabin-Eames 82824:7; STC 22790)

———— The generall historie of Virginia.   London, I. D[awson] and I. H[aviland] 1632.   fol.   (Sabin-Eames 82829; STC 22790d). (4th state of maps of Ould Virginia, Virginia and Summer Ils.; 8th state of map of New England)

———— A map of Virginia.   Oxford, J. Barnes 1612.   sm. 4to.   (Huth). (STC 22791).   (4th state of map)

———— New Englands trials.   London, W. Iones 1622.   sm. 4to. Second Edition.   (STC 22793)

[Smith, Richard].   The assertion and defence of the sacramente of the aulter.   London, I. Herforde 1546. 8vo. First Edition.   (STC 22815)

———— A defence of the sacrifice of the masse.   London, W. Myddylton, 1 February 1546, 47.   8vo.   First Edition.   (STC 22821)

Smith, Sir Thomas.   De republica Anglorum.   London, H. Middleton 1583.   sm. 4to.   First Edition.   (STC 22857)

Solimon.   The tragedie of Solimon and Perseda.   London, E. Allde 1599.   8vo. in fours.   Second Edition, First Issue.   (Kemble–Devonshire).   (STC 22895)

Soto, Ferdinando de.   Virginia richly valued.   London, F. Kyngston
    1609.   sm. 4to.   (STC 22938)

[Southwell, Robert].   Marie Magdalens funerall teares.   London, for
    W. Leake 1609.   sm. 4to.   Fourth Edition.   (STC 22953)

——— Moeoniae.   London, V. Simmes 1595.   sm. 4to.   (Utterson–
    Locker-Lampson–Chew).   (STC 22955)

[———] Saint Peters complaint.   London, H. L[ownes, c. 1609].
    sm. 4to.   (Newdigate).   (STC 22961)

——— The triumphs ouer death.   London, V. Simmes 1596.   sm. 4to.
    Third Edition?   (STC 22972)

The Spanish bawd.   *See* Celestina

Speed, John.   The genealogies of holy scriptures (With map of Ca-
    naan).   [London, R. Barker? c. 1611].   fol.   Fry Edition No. 4;
    No. 14 of the map.   (C. D. Ginsberg).   (STC 23039)

——— The genealogies . . . (With map of Canaan).   [London, R.
    Barker, c. 1616].   fol. in sixes.   (Huth).   (STC 23039)

Spenser, Edmund.   Colin Clouts come home againe.   London, T.
    C[reede] 1595.   sm. 4to.   First Edition.   (Windus–Hoe).
    (Johnson 16; STC 23077)

——— Complaints.   London [T. Orwin] 1591, 90.   sm. 4to.   First
    Edition.   (Sir Henry Hope Edwardes).   (Johnson 14; STC 23078)

——— The Faerie Queene (Books I-III).   London [J. Wolfe] 1590.
    4to. in eights.   First Edition, First Issue.   (Johnson 9; STC 23080)

——— The . . . Faerie Queene (Books IV-VI).   London [R. Field]
    1596.   4to. in eights.   First Edition.   (Johnson 11; STC 23082)

——— The Faerie Queene: The shepheards calendar: together with
    the other works.   [London] H. L[ownes] (1609), 1611.   fol. in
    sixes.   (S. White).   (Johnson 19 Group I; STC 23084)

——— Fowre hymnes (With the second edition of Daphnaida).   Lon-
    don [R. Field] 1596.   sm. 4to.   First Edition.   (Chew).   (John-
    son 17; STC 23086)

[———] The shepheardes calender.   London, T. East 1581.   sm. 4to.
    Second Edition.   (Heber–Britwell).   (Johnson 3; STC 23090)

——— The shepheards calender.   London, I. Windet 1591.   sm. 4to.
    Fourth Edition.   (Purdy).   (Johnson 5; STC 23092)

Stafford, Anthony. The day of salvation. London, N. and I. Okes 1635. 12mo. First Edition. (Philip Bliss). (STC 23122)

———— Honour and vertue. London, J. Okes and sold by R. Lownds 1640. sm. 4to. First Edition, Second Issue. (STC 23126)

[Stanbridge, John]. Gradus comparationum. Londonij, apud W. de Worde, 6 November 1527. sm. 4to. (Heber–Huth). (STC 23160)

[————] Paruulorum institutio. London, W. de Worde [c. 1511]. sm. 4to.

Stapleton, Thomas, tr. See Beda

Statham, Nicholas. Abridgment of cases to the end of Henry VI. [Rouen, G. Le Talleur for] R. Pynson [1490]. fol. First Edition. (STC 23238)

Stephens, John. Satyrical essayes. London, N. Okes 1615. 8vo. First Edition. (STC 23249)

Storer, Thomas. The life and death of Thomas Wolsey Cardinall. London, T. Dawson 1599. sm. 4to. First Edition. (STC 23294)

Stow, John. The survey of London. London, E. Purslow 1633. fol. Fourth Edition. (Ralph Sheldon). (STC 23345)

Studley, John, tr. See Seneca, Lucius Annaeus

Stukeley, Thomas. The famous historye of the life and death of Captaine Thomas Stukeley. [London] for T. Pavier 1605. sm. 4to. First Edition. (Bridgewater). (STC 23405)

Suetonius Tranquillus, Caius. The historie of twelve Caesars. Tr. by P. Holland. London [H. Lownes] 1606. fol. in sixes. First Edition, Second Issue. (Charles Lilburn). (STC 23423)

Swetnam, the woman-hater. London, for R. Meighen 1620. sm. 4to. First Edition. (STC 23544)

Swinburne, Henry. A briefe treatise of testaments. London, I. Windet 1590. 4to. First Edition. (STC 23547)

Sylvester, Joshua. Panthea. London, for F. Coules 1630. sm. 4to. First Edition. (Presentation copy from the editor, James Martin, to the daughters of T. Walmisley). (Walmisley–Joseph Haslewood–Groves–Steeves). (STC 23580)

Sylvester, Joshua. The parliament of vertues royal. [London, H. Lownes 1614]. 8vo. First Edition. (W. H. Crawford). (STC 23581)

——— The second session of the parliament of vertues reall. [London, H. Lownes 1616]. 8vo. First Edition. (W. H. Crawford). (STC 23582, lacking the so-called fourth part, "Tobacco battered.")

——— *tr.* *See* Saluste du Bartas

Symonds, William. Virginia. London, I. Windet 1609. sm. 4to. First Edition. (Marshall). (STC 23594)

T., I., *tr.* *See* Bluom, Joannes

T., T. A booke, containing the true portraiture of the countenances and attires of the kings of England. London, J. de Beauchesne 1597. sm. 4to. First Edition. (Purdy). (STC 23626; 24415)

Tacitus, Publius Cornelius. The annales. Tr. by R. Greneway. London, A. Hatfield 1598. fol. in sixes. First Edition. (STC 23644)

——— The ende of Nero and beginning of Galba. Tr. by Sir H. Savile. London, E. Bollifant 1598. fol. in sixes. Second Edition. (STC 23643)

Tasso, Torquato. Godfrey of Bulloigne. Tr. by R. Carew. London, I. Windet 1594. sm. 4to. First Edition. (STC 23697)

[———] ——— Tr. by E. Fairfax. London, A. Hatfield 1600. fol. in sixes. First Edition. (STC 23698)

Taverner, John. Certaine experiments concerning fish and fruite. London [R. Field] 1600. sm. 4to. First Edition. (STC 23708)

Taverner, Richard. The garden of wysedome. Bk. I. London, E. Whytchurche [1540]. 8vo. Second Edition. (Thomas Brooke). (STC 23712)

——— The secōd booke of the garden of wysedome. London, R. Bankes 1539. 8vo. First Edition. (Thomas Brooke). (STC 23713)

——— *tr.* *See* Erasmus, Desiderius

Taylor, Jeremy, *Bp.* A sermon preached ... upon the anniversary of the Gunpowder treason. Oxford, L. Lichfield 1638. sm. 4to. First Edition. (STC 23724)

Taylor, John. All the workes. London, J. B[eale] 1630. fol. in sixes. First Edition. (Hibbert). (STC 23725)

—— Differing worships. London, for W. Ley 1640. sm. 4to. First Edition. (STC 23746)

[——] A famous fight at sea. London, I. Haviland 1627. sm. 4to. First Edition. (STC 23753)

Ten Commandments. Ihesus. The floure of the commaundementes of god. Tr. by A. Chertsey. London, W. de Worde, 8 October 1521. fol. Second Edition. (John Fuller Russell). (STC 23877)

Thame School. Schola Thamensis. [London, H. Bynneman?] 1575. fol. First Edition. (J. P. R. Lyell). (STC 23928)

Thevet, André. The new founde vvorlde. Tr. by T. Hacket. London, H. Bynneman 1568. sm. 4to. (STC 23950)

Thomas, à Kempis. [De imitatione Christi]. Of the imitation of Christ. Tr. by T. Rogers. London [H. Lownes and R. Young] 1629. 12mo. (Sir Thomas Preston). (STC 23984)

—— Soliloquium animae. London, H. Lownes and R. Young 1628. 12mo. Sixth Edition. (Sir Thomas Preston). (STC 23999)

Thomas (Becket), *Archbishop of Canterbury*. Vita et processus. Paris, J. Philippi, 27 March 1495/6. 4to. (H 15510)

[Thomas, William]. The historie of Italie. London, in the house of T. Berthelet 1549. sm. 4to. First Edition. (STC 24018)

[Thornborough, John]. A discourse plainely proving the ... necessitie of the ... union of ... England and Scotland. London, R. Field 1604. sm. 4to. First Edition. (Huth). (STC 24035)

Thucydides. The hystory. Tr. by T. Nicolls. London [S. Mierdman?] 25 July 1550. fol. in sixes. First Edition. (STC 24056)

Tisdale, Roger. Pax vobis. London, G. Eld and M. Flesher 1623. sm. 4to. First Edition. (STC 24091)

Tofte, Robert, *tr. See* Ariosto, Ludovico; Montreux, Nicolas de

[Tomkis, Thomas]. Lingua. London, A. Mathewes 1632. sm. 4to. Fifth Edition. (STC 24108)

Topsell, Edward.   The historie of fovre-footed beastes . . . Collected out of all the volumes of Conradus Gesner.   London, W. Jaggard 1607.   fol.   First Edition.   (STC 24123)

────── The historie of serpents.   London, W. Jaggard 1608.   fol. First Edition.   (STC 24124)

[Tourneur, Cyril].   The revengers.   London, G. Eld 1607.   sm. 4to. First Edition, First Issue.   (Sir John Cope).   (STC 24149)

Trevisa, John of.   *See* John of Trevisa

[Trogus, Pompeius].   The historie of Iustine. Tr. by G. W[ilkins]. London, W. Iaggard 1606.   fol.   First Edition.   (STC 24293)

A true coppie of a discourse written by a gentleman, employed in the late voyage of Spaine and Portingale.   London [T. Orwin] for T. Woodcock 1589.   sm. 4to.   First Edition.   (STC 6790)

Tunstall, Cuthbert, *Bp*.   De arte supputandi.   Londini, in aed. R. Pynsoni, 14 Oct. 1522.   4to.   First Edition.   (STC 24319)

[Turberville, George].   The booke of falconrie.   London, T. Purfoot 1611.   sm. 4to. in eights.   Second Edition.   (Scrope Berdmore– Henry C. Compton).   (STC 24325)

[──────] The noble art of venerie.   London, T. Purfoot 1611.   sm. 4to. in eights.   Second Edition.   (Scrope Berdmore–Henry C. Compton).   (STC 24329)

Turner, William.   The first and seconde partes of the herbal.   Collen [heirs of] A. Birckman 1568.   fol. in sixes.   (STC 24367)

────── A booke of the natures and properties . . . of the bathes in England.   Collen [heirs of] A. Birckman 1568.   fol.   (A. M. Broadley).   (Copy 2 of STC 24367 pt. IV)

Twyne, Thomas, *tr*.   *See* Petrarca, Francesco

Tymme, Thomas, *tr*.   *See* Calvin, Jean: A commentarie

Tyndale, William.   The whole workes of W. Tyndall, Iohn Frith, and Doct. Barnes.   London, I. Daye 1573-2.   fol.   First Edition.   (2 copies: 1, John, Duke of Bedford–Woburn Abbey).   (STC 24436)

[──────] The obediēce of a christen man.   Marlborow, H. luft [Antwerp?] 2 October 1528.   8vo.   First Edition.   (Tite–Amherst).   (STC 24446)

[Tyndale, William].   The parable of the wicked mammon.   London, W. Coplande [1560?].   8vo.   Eighth Edition.   (Charles Lilburn). (STC 24461)

Udall, Nicholas, *tr*.   *See* Erasmus, Desiderius

Underdowne, Thomas, *tr*.   *See* Heliodorus

Underhill, John.   Nevves from America.   London, J. D[awson] 1638. sm. 4to.   (Pembroke).   (STC 24518)

Vaenius, or Van Veen, Otto.   *See* Rowlands, Richard: Amorvm emblemata

[Vaughan, William].   Directions for health.   London, I. Beale 1626. sm. 4to.   Sixth Edition.   (Huth).   (STC 24617)

[———] The golden fleece.   London, for F. Williams 1626.   sm. 4to. First Edition.   (Barlow–Church).   (STC 24609)

[Veer, Gerrit de].   The true ... description of three voyages. Tr. by W. Phillip.   London, T. Pavier 1609.   sm. 4to.   (Dogmersfield–John Jay Paul).   (STC 24628)

Vermigli, Pietro Martire.   Loci communes.   Londini, ex typographia I. Kyngstoni 1576.   fol.   First Edition.   (STC 24667)

Verstegen, R., *pseud*.   *See* Rowlands, Richard

Vincent, Augustine.   A discoverie of errours.   London, W. Iaggard 1622.   fol. in fours.   First Edition.   (Mexborough).   (STC 24756)

[Vincent, Philip].   A trve relation of the late battell.   London, T. Harper 1638.   sm. 4to.   Second Edition.   (STC 24760)

Viret, Pierre.   A notable collection of . . . places of the sacred scriptures. Tr. by A. Scoloker.   London, A. Scoloker and W. Seres [?1548].   8vo.   (Huth).   (STC 24781)

Virgilius Maro, Publius.   The .xiii. bukes of Eneados. Tr. by G. Douglas.   Londō [W. Copland] 1553.   sm. 4to. in eights.   First Edition. (STC 24797)

——— The nyne fyrst bookes of the Eneidos. Tr. by T. Phaer.   London, R. Hall 1562.   4to.   First Edition.   (Britwell–H. V. Jones). (STC 24800)

——— [Bucolics and Georgics] The bucoliks. (The Georgiks). Tr. by A. Fleming.   London, T. Orwin 1589.   sm. 4to.   First Edition.   (Freeling).   (STC 24817)

Vita et processus Sancte Thome.   *See* Thomas (Becket), *Archbishop of Canterbury*

Vives, Juan Luis.   An introduction to vvysedome. Tr. by Sir R. Morison.   Londini, in aed. T. Bertheleti 1540.   8vo.   First Edition. (STC 24847)

W., J., *Gent.*   The valiant Scot.   London, T. Harper 1637.   sm. 4to. First Edition.   (Hoe–Wallace).   (STC 24910)

Wake, *Sir* Isaac.   Rex Platonicus.   Oxoniae, I. Barnesius 1615.   12mo. Third Edition.   (STC 24940)

Walsingham, Thomas.   Historia breuis.   Londini, apud H. Binneman 1574.   fol.   First Edition.   (STC 25004)

———— Ypodigma Neustriae.   Londini, in aed. J. Day 1574.   fol. First Edition.   (STC 25005)

Warner, William.   Albions England.   London, E. Bollifant 1602.   4to. in eights.   (STC 25083)

A warning for faire women.   London, V. Simmes 1599.   sm. 4to.   First Edition.   (Hoe).   (STC 25089)

Washington, Thomas, *junior, tr.*   *See* Nicolay, Nicolas de

Wastell, Simon.   Microbiblion.   London, for R. Mylbourne 1629. 12mo.   Second Edition.   (Freeling–Corser–Gaisford).   (STC 25102)

Watreman, William, *tr.*   *See* Boehme, Johann

Watson, Thomas.   Twoo notable sermons.   London, I. Cawood, 10 May 1554.   8vo.   (Huth).   (STC 25115)

Webster, John.   The deuils law-case.   London, A. M[athewes] 1623. sm. 4to.   First Edition.   (STC 25173)

———— The tragedy of the Dutchesse of Malfy.   London, N. Okes 1623.   sm. 4to.   First Edition.   (STC 25176)

———— *See also* Dekker, Thomas, *and* John Webster

Weever, John.   Ancient funerall monuments.   London, T. Harper 1631.   fol.   First Edition.   (H. B. Humphrey–Groves).   (STC 25223)

West, Thomas, *Baron De La Warre.*   The relation of the Right Honourable the Lord De-La-Warre.   London, W. Hall 1611.   sm. 4to. First Edition.   (Halsey).   (STC 25266)

Whetstone, George. A mirour for magestrates. London, R. Iones 1584. 4to. First Edition, First Issue. (STC 25341)

Whitbourne, Richard. A discourse and discovery of Nevv-Found-Land. London, F. Kyngston 1620. sm. 4to. First Edition. (STC 25372)

——— A discourse containing a loving invitation to adventurers. London, F. Kyngston 1622. sm. 4to. First Edition. (STC 25375a)

White, John, *Bp*. Diacosiomartyrion. Londini, in aed. R. Cali December 1553. 4to. in eights. First Edition. (Mark P. Robinson). (STC 25388)

[White, John, *of Dorchester*]. The planters plea. London, W. Iones 1630. sm. 4to. First Edition. (Church). (STC 25399)

Whitehorne, Peter, *tr*. *See* Machiavelli, Niccolò

[Whitforde, Richard]. Here begynneth the boke called the Pype, or Tonne, of the lyfe of perfection. London, R. Redman, 23 March 1532. 4to. in eights and fours. First Edition. (Huth). (STC 25421)

Whitney, Geoffrey. A choice of emblemes. Leyden, in the house of C. Plantyn, by R. Raphelengius 1586. 4to. First Edition. (Narcissus Luttrell–Skegg–Purdy). (STC 25438)

[Whittingham, William]. A brieff discours off the troubles begonne at Franckford. [Zurich? C. Froschauer?] 1575. sm. 4to. First Edition, Second Issue. (James Bengough). (STC 25443)

Whittinton, Robert. [Declinationes nominum]. Grammaticae Whitintonianae. Londini, in aed. W. de Worde, December 1523. sm. 4to. Eighth Edition. (Dunn). (STC 25449[a])

——— [De heteroclitis nominibus]. De heteroclitis nominibus. Londini, in aed. W. de Worde, 1 February 1524. sm. 4to. Eleventh Edition? (Dunn). (STC 25467[a])

——— [De nominum generibus]. Grammatices primae partis liber primus. [London] ex typis W. de Wordensis, 5 September 1522. sm. 4to. Seventh Edition? (Dunn). (STC 25484[a])

——— [De syllabarum quantitatibus]. Roberti Whitintoni L. secunda grammatice pars. Pt. I. [London] in aed. W. de Worden 1521. sm. 4to. Seventh Edition? (Dunn). (STC 25515)

Whittinton, Robert. [De synonymis]. Roberti Whitintoni Lichfeldiensis lucubrationes. Londini, in ed. W. de Worde, August 1523. sm. 4to. Eighth Edition? (Dunn). (STC 25533)

—— —— February 1525. sm. 4to. Ninth Edition. (Philip Bliss–Arthur Dalrymple–Amherst). (STC 25534)

—— —— March 1529. sm. 4to. Eleventh Edition. (STC 25536)

—— [Verborum praeterita]. Praeterita verborum. Londini, in aed. W. de Worde 1522. sm. 4to. Third Edition. (Dunn). (STC 25560)

—— [Vulgaria]. Vulgaria. Londini, in ed. W. de Worde 1525. sm. 4to. (Dunn). (STC 25576)

—— tr. *See* Cicero, Marcus Tullius

Wiclif, John. Two short treatises, against the orders of the Begging Friars. Oxford, I. Barnes 1608. sm. 4to. First Edition. (George Rose). (STC 25589)

Wilkins, George. The miseries of inforst mariage. London, for G. Vincent 1607. sm. 4to. First Edition. (STC 25635)

—— tr. *See* Trogus, Pompeius

[Wilkins, John, *Bp.*]. A discourse concerning a new world. London [Bk. I] I. Norton; [Bk. II] R. H[odgkinson] 1640. 8vo. (STC 25641)

Wilson, Thomas. The arte of rhetorike. London, I. Kingston 1563. sm. 4to. in eights. Fourth Edition. (STC 25802)

—— The rule of reason. London, I. Kingston 1567. sm. 4to. Fifth Edition. (F. Hopkinson). (STC 25814)

—— tr. *See* Demosthenes

Wither, George. The workes. London, I. Beale 1620. 8vo. First Edition. (STC 25890)

—— Abuses stript and whipt. London, G. Eld 1613. 8vo. Second Edition. (Joseph Turner–Charles Butler). (STC 25892)

—— —— London, H. Lownes 1615. 8vo. Sixth Edition. (STC 25896)

—— —— London, H. Lownes 1617. 8vo. Seventh Edition. (STC 25897)

Wither, George. Britain's remembrancer. [London] sold by I. Grismond 1628. 12mo. First Edition. (STC 25899)

—— A collection of emblemes. London, A. M[athewes] for R. Milbourne 1635, 34. fol. in fours. First Edition. (STC 25900b)

[——] Faire-virtue. London, for I. Grismand 1622. 8vo. First Edition, First Issue. (STC 25903)

—— Fidelia. London, N. Okes 1617. 12mo. Second Edition. (STC 25906)

—— A preparation to the psalter. London, N. Okes 1619. fol. First Edition. (Lefferts–Bement). (STC 25914)

—— A satyre: dedicated to his most excellent Maiestie. London, T. Snodham 1616. 8vo. Fourth Edition. (STC 25918)

—— The shepheards hunting. London, W. White 1615. 8vo. Second Edition. (STC 25922)

—— Wither's motto. London, for I. Marriott 1621. 8vo. Fifth Edition. (STC 25928)

—— *tr.* *See* Nemesius, *Bp.*

Wood, William. Nevv Englands prospect. London, T. Cotes 1634. sm. 4to. First Edition. (STC 25957). (2 copies)

—— —— 1635. sm. 4to. Second Edition. (Church). (STC 25958)

Woodes, Nathaniel. An excellent new comedie, intituled: The conflict of conscience. London, R. Bradocke 1581. sm. 4to. First Edition, "Philologus" issue. (Locker-Lampson). (STC 25966)

Wright, Edward, *tr.* *See* Napier, John

Wyclif, John. *See* Wiclif, John

Wythers, Stephen, *tr.* *See* Calvin, Jean: A very profitable treatise; Philippson, Joannes, *Sleidanus*

Xenophon. [Economicus] Xenophons treatise of householde. Tr. by G. Hervet. Londini, in aed. T. Bertheleti 1544. 8vo. Third Edition. (STC 26072)

Young, Bartholomew, *tr.* *See* Montemayor, Jorge de

[Zouch, Richard]. The sophister. London, J. O[kes] 1639. sm. 4to. First Edition. (Lefferts–Hoe–Huntington)

Books Printed in England, Scotland & Ireland, and English Books and Books by English Authors Printed Abroad 1641-1800

This list does *not* include Americana, Bibles and liturgical books and Science, which appear in the lists *Americana*; *Bibles*; and *Science*

A[bercromby], D[avid?]. The whole art of converse. London, for J. Hindmarsh 1683. 16mo. (Dr. Thomas Jenner–Philip Bliss)

[Adamson, Thomas]. England's defence. London, for F. Haley 1680. fol. First Edition

Addison, Joseph. Cato. London, for J. Tonson 1713. 4to. First Edition, stitched

——— A discourse on ancient and modern learning. London, for T. Osborne 1739. 4to. First Edition, uncut

——— The evidences of the christian religion. London, for J. Tonson 1730. 12mo.

——— Poems on several occasions. London, for E. Curll 1719. 8vo. First Edition

[———] Remarks on several parts of Italy. London, for J. Tonson 1705. 8vo. First Edition. (Earl of Berkshire)

[———] Rosamond. London, for J. Tonson 1707. 4to. First Edition

——— *See also* The Tatler

Æsopus. Æsop's fables. Tr. by T. Philipot & by R. Codrington. London, W. Godbid for F. Barlow 1666. fol. (Gulston–Wodhull–George Steevens–Lefferts)

——— ——— Tr. by Aphra Behn. London, H. Hills jun. for F. Barlow 1687. fol. (Ives–Clawson)

——— The fables. London, for J. Stockdale 1793. 2v. roy.8vo.

Akenside, Mark. An ode to the country gentlemen of England. London, for R. and J. Dodsley 1758. 4to. First Edition

——— An ode to the . . . Earl of Huntingdon. London, R. Dodsley 1748. 4to. First Edition

[129]

[Akenside, Mark]. The pleasures of imagination. London [S. Richardson] for R. Dodsley 1744. 4to. First Edition, First Issue

[Allestree, Richard]. The whole duty of man. London, W. Norton 1711. 8vo.

[Amory, Thomas]. The life of John Buncle. London 1756-66. 2 v. 8vo. First Edition

Anacreon. Anacreon done into English . . . [by F. Willis, T. Wood, A. Cowley, J. Oldham]. Oxford, L. Lichfield 1683. 8vo. First Edition

The ancient and present state of Poland. London, for E. Whitlock 1697. 4to.

Anderson, Robert. The life of Samuel Johnson. London, for J. & A. Arch 1795. 8vo. First Separate Edition, uncut

Andrews, Miles Peter. The Baron Kinkvervankotsdorsprakingatchdern. London, for T. Cadell 1781. 8vo. First Edition

———— The reparation. London, for T. and W. Lowndes 1784. 8vo. First Edition

A[ntrobus], B[enjamin]. Buds and blossoms of piety. London, Assigns of J. Sowle 1716. 8vo. Third Edition. (Huth)

[Arblay, Frances Burney, Madame d']. Camilla. London, for T. Payne . . . T. Cadell jun. . . . W. Davies 1796. 5 v. 12mo. First Edition

[————] Cecilia. London, for T. Payne and Son . . . and T. Cadell 1782. 5 v. 12mo. First Edition. (Henry Home of Kames)

[Arbuthnot, John?]. An appendix to John Bull. London, for J. Morphew 1712. sm. 8vo. Second Edition. (Presentation copy from Bashford Dean to W. L. Andrews)

[————] John Bull in his senses. London, for J. Morphew 1712. sm. 8vo. Third Edition. (Presentation copy from Bashford Dean to W. L. Andrews)

[————] John Bull still in his senses. London, for J. Morphew 1712. sm. 8vo. Third Edition. (Presentation copy from Bashford Dean to W. L. Andrews)

[————] Law is a bottomless pit. London, for J. Morphew 1712. sm. 8vo. Fourth Edition. (Presentation copy from Bashford Dean to W. L. Andrews)

Arnauld, Antoine. The faith of the Catholick Church. [Edinburgh] Holy Rood House 1687. 16mo. First Edition. (W. Moir Bryce)

[Arrowsmith, W.]. The reformation. London, for W. Cademan 1673. sm. 4to. First Edition, stitched

Ayres, Philip. Cupids addresse to the ladies. London, Sold by R. Bently and S. Tidmarch 1683. 8vo. First Edition. (W. F. Morgan)

—————— Emblems of love. London, for J. Wren [c. 1700]. 8vo. Second Edition. (Thomas Gaisford)

—————— Lyric poems. London, J. M. 1687. 8vo. First Edition

B., C. An address to the honourable city of London. London, for A. Banks 1681. fol. First Edition

B., J. A faire in Spittle Fields. n.p., Printed by J. C. 1652. sm. 4to. First Edition. (Huth)

B., J., *Philalelos*. Good and joyful news for England: or, the prophecy of the renowned Michael Nostradamus . . . taken out of the translations of Dr. Theo. Garencieres . . . By J. B. Philalelos. London, for A. Banks 1681. 4to. First Edition

Bacon, Francis, *Viscount St. Albans*. Cases of treason. London, Assignes of J. More 1641. sm. 4to. First Edition. (The Shakespeare library)

—————— The naturall and experimentall history of winds. Tr. into English by R[obert] G[entili]. London, for H. Moseley 1653. 12mo. First Edition in English. (Purdy)

[——————] New Atlantis. London, for J. Crooke 1660. sm. 8vo. First Edition

—————— Ordinances . . . for the better . . . administration of iustice. London, for M. Walbanke and L. Chapman 1642. sm. 4to. First Edition

—————— Baconiana [Edited by Thomas Tenison]. London, J. D. for R. Chiswell 1679. 8vo. First Edition

Baker, Daniel. Poems upon several occasions. London, for J. Jones 1697. 8vo. First Edition. (Purdy)

[Baker, Thomas]. The fine lady's airs. London, for B. Lintott [1709]. 4to. First Edition. (H. V. Jones)

[Baker, Thomas]. Hampstead Heath. London, for B. Lintott 1706. 4to. First Edition. Large paper

Bancroft, John. The tragedy of Sertorius. London, for R. Bentley and M. Magnes 1679. 4to. First Edition

Banks, John. The destruction of Troy. London, A. G. and J. P. 1679. 4to. First Edition

———— The unhappy favourite. London, for R. Bentley and M. Magnes 1682. 4to. First Edition. (Huth)

———— Vertue betray'd. London, for R. Bentley and M. Magnes 1682. 4to. First Edition

Barbon, Nicholas. A discourse concerning coining the new money lighter. London, for R. Chiswell 1696. sm. 8vo. First Edition

Barclay, Robert. An apology for the true christian divinity. [London] 1678. sm. 4to. (Thomas Milles–Henry Christy)

Baron, Robert. ΈΡΟΤΟΠΑΙΓΝΙΟΝ. London, W. W. 1648. sm. 8vo. First Edition, Second Issue. (Hugh Perkins)

———— Mirza. London, for H. Moseley [?1648]. 8vo. First Edition

———— Pocula Castalia. London, W. H. 1650. 8vo. First Edition. (White Knights–J. F. Russell–Andrews)

Bartholomew Faire. London, for R. Harper 1641. sm. 4to. First Edition

Baxter, Richard. Confesssion [sic] of his faith. London, R. W [hite] for T. Underhil and F. Tyton 1655. sm. 4to. First Edition

———— The life of faith. London, R. W [hite] for N. Simmons 1670. sm. 4to. Second Edition

———— The reasons of the christian religion. London, R. White, for F. Tyton 1667. sm. 4to. First Edition

[————] The saints everlasting rest. London, R. White for T. Underhil and F. Tyton 1650. sm. 4to. First Edition

Beale, Francis, tr. See Gioacchimo Greco

Beaumont, Francis, and John Fletcher. Bonduca. London, T. Sherlock 1778. 8vo. First Edition

———— Comedies and tragedies. London, for H. Robinson and H. Moseley 1647. fol.

Beaumont, Francis, *and* John Fletcher. Fifty comedies and tragedies. London, J. Macock 1679. fol.

Beaumont, Joseph. Psyche. London, J. Dawson 1648. fol. First Edition

[Beckford, William]. An Arabian tale. Tr. by S. Henley. London, for J. Johnson 1786. 8vo. First Edition. (Elizabeth Gulston)

[——— *tr.*]. *See* [Musaeus]

Bedford, Arthur. The evil and danger of stage-plays. London, W. Bonny ... 1706. 8vo. First Edition. (W. H. Cummings)

Bedloe, William. The examination of Captain William Bedlow deceased, relating to the Popish plot. London, Assigns of J. Bill, T. Newcomb and H. Hills 1680. fol. First Edition

——— A narrative ... of the horrid Popish plot. London, for R. Boulter, R. Smith and B. Harris 1679. fol. First Edition

Behn, Aphra. The city-heiress. London, for D. Brown ... 1682. 4to. First Edition. (Frederic Ouvry–Huth)

[———] The counterfeit bridegroom. London, for L. Curtiss 1677. 4to. First Edition. (Percy FitzGerald)

[———] The debauchee. London, for J. Amery 1677. 4to. First Edition

——— The Dutch lover. London, for T. Dring 1673. 4to. First Edition. (Huth)

——— The false count. London, M. Flesher 1682. 4to. First Edition. (Frederick Perkins–Huth)

——— The feign'd curtizans. London, for J. Tonson 1679. 4to. First Edition

——— The luckey chance. London, R. H. for W. Canning 1687. 4to. First Edition. (H. V. Jones)

——— A Pindarick on the death of our late sovereign. London, J. Playford 1685. fol. First Edition

——— Poems. London, for R. Tonson and J. Tonson 1684. 12mo. First Edition. (Purdy)

——— The roundheads. London, for D. Brown ... 1682. 4to. First Edition. (Huth)

[Behn, Aphra]. The rover. London, for J. Amery 1677. 4to. First Edition

———— Sir Patient Fancy. London, E. Flesher 1678. 4to. First Edition. (Huth)

———— The town-fopp. London, T. N. 1677. 4to. First Edition

———— The Widdow Ranter. London, for J. Knapton 1690. 4to. First Edition

———— The young king. London, for D. Brown 1683. 4to. First Edition. (Huth)

———— The younger brother. London, for J. Harris 1696. 4to. First Edition

———— *editor*. Miscellany, being A collection of poems by several hands. London, for J. Hindmarsh 1685. 8vo.

———— *tr. See Æsopus*

B[enlowes], E[dward]. Theophila. London, R. N. 1652. fol. First Edition. (Presentation copy, inscribed by the author, with his arms on sides. Bookplate of Ralph William Grey)

Bentley, Richard (1662-1742). A dissertation upon the Epistles of Phalaris. London, J. Leake 1697. 8vo. First Edition

———— A dissertation upon the Epistles of Phalaris. With an answer to the objections of . . . Charles Boyle. London, J. H. 1699. 8vo. First Edition

Bentley, Richard (1708-1782). Designs . . . for six poems by Mr. T. Gray. London, for J. Dodsley 1775. fol.

[Betterton, Thomas]. The amorous widow. London, for W. Turner 1706. 4to. First Edition. (Joseph Knight)

———— K. Henry IV. London, for R. W. 1700. 4to. First Edition

Bickerstaff, Isaac, *pseud. See* The Tatler

[Bickerstaffe, Isaac]. Lionel and Clarissa. London, for W. Griffin 1748. 8vo. First Edition

Bickham, George. The British monarchy. (London) G. Bickham 1748. fol. (Copy 1, Earl of Fife; 2, C. L. F. Robinson)

———— The musical entertainer. London, for C. Corbett [1734-9]. 2 v. in 1. fol. First Edition

Bickham, George.   The universal penman.   London, for H. Overton
     1733-43.   fol.   Second Edition

Billingsly, Nicholas.   Brachy-martyrologia.   London, J. C. 1657.
     12mo.   First Edition

Biochimo.   *See* Gioacchimo Greco

[Birkenhead, *Sir* John].   The assembly-man.   London, for R. Marriot
     166$\frac{2}{3}$ sm. 4to.   First Edition

Blackstone, William.   Commentaries.   Oxford, Clarendon Press 1765-9.
     4 v.   4to.   First Edition

Blair, Robert.   The grave.   London, for M. Cooper 1743.   4to.   First
     Edition, stitched

Blois, François Louis de.   A mirrour for monkes.   Paris 1676.   18mo.
     First Edition

Blome, Richard.   The gentlemans recreation.   London, S. Rotcroft
     1686.   fol.   First Edition

The bloody assizes.   London, for J. Dunton 1689.   sm. 4to.   (Thomas
     D. Bolton)

B[lount], T[homas].   Fragmenta antiquitatis.   London, Assigns of R.
     and E. Atkins 1679.   8vo.   First Edition

———— *tr.*   *See* Estienne

Blount, *Sir* Thomas Pope.   De re poetica.   London, R. Everingham
     for R. Bently 1694.   sm. 4to.   First Edition.   (H.V. Jones)

Blow, John.   Amphion Anglicus.   London, W. Pearson 1700.   fol.
     First Edition.   (James Ward–Bement)

Boccaccio, Giovanni.   The Decameron.   London, for R. Dodsley 1741.
     8vo.   (Francis Longe)

Bodley, *Sir* Thomas.   Reliquiae Bodleianae.   London, for J. Hartley
     1703.   8vo.   First Edition.   (Henry Wilson)

Boehme, Jacob.   The epistles of Jacob Behmen.   London, M. Sim-
     mons 1649.   sm. 4to.   First Edition

Boileau[-Despréaux, Nicolas].   Le lutrin. Tr. by N. O.   London, J. A.
     1682.   sm. 4to.   First Edition

Booth, G., *tr.*   *See* Diodorus Siculus

Boothby, Frances. Marcelia. London, for W. Cademan . . . 1670. 4to. First Edition. (H. V. Jones)

Boswell, James. The journal of a tour to the Hebrides. London, H. Baldwin for C. Dilly 1785. 8vo. First Edition

———— The life of Samuel Johnson. London, H. Baldwin 1791. 2 v. 4to. First Edition

Bovet, Richard. Pandaemonium. London, for J. Walthoe 1684. sm. 8vo. First Edition

[Boyle, Charles, *fourth Earl of Orrery*]. As you find it. London, for R. Parker 1603 [for 1703]. 4to. First Edition

———— Dr. Bentley's Dissertations . . . examin'd. London, for T. Bennet 1698. 8vo. First Edition

[Boyle], John [*fifth*] *Earl of Orrery*. Remarks on the life and writings of Dr. Jonathan Swift. London, for A. Millar 1752. 8vo. First Edition

[Brathwaite, Richard]. Astraea's teares. London, T. H. 1641. 12mo. First Edition

[————] A comment upon the Two tales of . . . Chaucer. London, W. Godbid 1665. 12mo. First Edition

[————] Drunken Barnaby's four journeys. London, for S. Illidge 1723. 12mo.

———— The English gentleman; and the English gentlewoman. London, J. Dawson 1641. fol. Third Edition

———— Lignum vitae. Londini, J. Grismond 1658. First Edition. sm. 8vo. (Corser–Gaisford)

[————] Mercurius Britanicus. n.p. 1641. sm. 4to. First Edition. (Buxton Forman)

———— Novissima tuba. Londini, J. Grismond 1658. 12mo. (Corser–Gaisford)

———— Panthalia. London, J. G. 1659. sm. 8vo. First Edition. (Haslewood–Mitford–Huth)

The bravo turn'd bully. London, for J. Purser 1740. 8vo. First Edition

[Bridges, John?]. A right pithy . . . comedy, entituled Gammer Gurtons needle. London, T. Johnson 1661. sm. 4to. (Halliwell Phillipps–Tite–McKee–Chew)

Brome, Alexander. A congratulatory poem, on the . . . return of . . . King Charls the II. London, for H. Brome 1660. sm. 4to.

Brome, Richard. Five nevv playes. London, for A. Crook . . . 1659. 8vo. First Edition

———— A joviall crew. London, J. Y[oung] for E. D[od] and N. E[lkins] 1652. 4to. First Edition. (A. C. Swinburne)

———— *editor*. Lachrymae musarum. London, T. N. 1650. 8vo. First Edition, Second Issue. (Lefferts)

Brooke, *Baron*. *See* Greville, Fulke

[Brooke, Frances Moore]. The history of Emily Montague. London, for J. Dodsley 1769. 4v. 12mo. First Edition. (Francis Longe)

Brooke, Henry. The fool of quality. London, for W. Johnston 1766-70. 5v. 8vo. First Edition

———— Gustavus Vasa. London, for R. Dodsley 1739. 8vo. First Edition

———— ———— Philadelphia, R. Bell 1778. 8vo.

Broome, William. Poems on several occasions. London, for B. Lintot 1727. 8vo. First Edition. (Lefferts–Purdy)

[Brown, John]. Barbarossa. London, for J. and R. Tonson and S. Draper 1755. 8vo. First Edition

Brown, Thomas. A collection of miscellany poems. London, for J. Sparks 1699. 8vo. First Edition. (I. B. Holroyd)

———— Physick lies a bleeding. London, for E. Whitlock 1697. sm. 4to. First Edition. (Cornelius Paine–Lefferts–Clawson–Hagen)

B[rowne], E[dward]. A description of an annuall world. London, E. G[riffin] 1641. sm. 8vo. First Edition

Browne, Edward (1644-1708). An account of several travels through a great part of Germany. London, for B. Tooke 1677. sm. 4to. First Edition. (Dunn)

———— A brief account of some travels. London, T. R. for B. Tooke 1673. sm. 4to. First Edition. (Dunn)

Browne, *Sir* Thomas. Christian morals. Cambridge, University-Press for C. Crownfield 1716. 12mo. First Edition

Browne, *Sir* Thomas. Hydriotaphia. London, for H. Brome 1658. sm. 8vo. First Edition

—— Pseudodoxia epidemica. London, T. H[arper] for E. Dod 1646. fol. First Edition. (Bement)

[——] Religio medici. [London] for A. Crooke 1642. sm. 8vo. First Unauthorized Edition

[——] —— London, E. Cotes for A. Crooke 1656. sm. 8vo. Fourth Authorized Edition

—— The works. London, for T. Basset, R. Chiswell, T. Sawbridge, C. Mearn, and C. Brome 1686. fol. First Edition

—— Posthumous works. London, for E. Curll and R. Gosling 1712. 8vo. First Edition

Brunt, Samuel. *See* A voyage to Cacklogallinia

Bucer, Martin. The judgement of Martin Bucer. London, M. Simmons 1644. sm. 4to. First Edition

Buck, George. The history of . . . Richard the third. London, W. Wilson 1646. fol. First Edition

Buck, Samuel, *and* Nathaniel Buck. Collection of views. Parts I-XIII (1721-38). 4v. obl. fol.

Buckingham, *Duke of*. *See* Villiers

B[ulwer], J[ohn]. Anthropometamorphosis. London, W. Hunt 1653. 4to. First Edition

—— Chirologia. London, T. Harper 1644. 8vo. First Edition. (Henry Perkins–Huth)

—— Philocophus. London, for H. Moseley 1648. 12mo. First Edition

Bunyan, John. Differences in judgment about water-baptism. London, for J. Wilkins 1673. sm. 8vo. First Edition. (Huth)

—— A discourse upon the pharisee and the publicane. London, for J. Harris 1685. 12mo. First Edition, Second Issue

—— The holy war. London, for D. Newman and B. Alsop 1682. 8vo. First Edition

—— The life and death of Mr. Badman. London, J. A. for N. Ponder 1680. 12mo. First Edition

Bunyan, John. One thing is needful. London [?1700]. 12mo. Fourth Edition

———— The pilgrim's progress. London, for N. Ponder 1680. 12mo. Fifth Edition

———— ———— London, for N. Ponder 1681. 12mo. Sixth Edition. (Huth)

———— ———— London, for N. Ponder 1683. 12mo. Ninth Edition

———— ———— London, A. W. for W. Johnston 1748. 12mo.

———— ———— The second part. London, for N. Ponder 1684. 12mo. First Edition

———— ———— Part II. [London] A.W. for W. Johnston 1748. 12mo.

———— ———— Part III (spurious). London, for C. Hitch 1749. 12mo.

———— Questions about the nature and perpetuity of the seventh-day-Sabbāth. London, for N. Ponder 1685. sm.12mo. First Edition

———— A relation of the imprisonment of Mr. John Bunyan. London, for J. Buckland 1765. 12mo. First Edition. (Learmont)

———— Seasonable counsel. London, for B. Alsop 1784. 12mo. First Edition

———— Voyage d'un Chrestien vers l'éternité. Amsterdam, J. Boekholt 1685. sm. 12mo. First French Edition

———— The works. London, for W. Johnston and E. and C. Dilly 1767-8. 2 v. fol. Third Edition. (John Caldwell–G. H. Watling–J. D. Collis)

[Burgoyne, John]. The maid of the Oaks. London, for T. Becket 1774. 8vo. First Edition

[Burke, Edmund]. A philosophical enquiry into the origin of our ideas of the sublime and the beautiful. London, for R. and J. Dodsley 1757. 8vo. First Edition

———— Reflections on the revolution in France. London, for J. Dodsley 1790. 8vo. First Edition, original boards, uncut

[Burnaby, Charles]. The modish husband. London, for J. Knapton ... 1702. 4to. First Edition

[————] The reform'd wife. London, for T. Bennet 1700. 4to. First Edition. (Huth)

Burnet, Gilbert. The history of the reformation of the Church of England. London, T. H. for R. Chiswell 1679-1715. 3 v. fol. First Edition. (Wrest Park–Earl of Kent)

———— Some passages of the life and death of . . . John Earl of Rochester. London, R. Chiswel 1680. 8vo. First Edition

Burns, Robert. Poems, chiefly in the Scottish dialect. Kilmarnock, J. Wilson 1786. 8vo. First Edition

———— ———— Edinburgh 1787. 8vo. Second Edition. First Edinburgh Edition

———— ———— London 1787. 8vo. Fourth Edition. First London Edition. (J. H. Shorthouse)

———— ———— Philadelphia, for P. Stewart and G. Hyde 1788. 12mo.

———— ———— Edinburgh 1798. 2 v. 8vo.

———— ———— New-York, J. Tiebout 1799. 8vo.

Burthogge, Richard. An essay upon reason. London, for J. Dunton 1694. 8vo. First Edition

[Burton, Robert]. The anatomy of melancholy. Oxford, R. W. for H. Cripps 1651. fol. Sixth Edition

[————] ———— London, for H. Cripps 1660. fol. Seventh Edition

[————] ———— Oxford, R.W. for Peter Parker 1676. fol. Eighth Edition. (Huth)

B[urton], R[obert or] R[ichard]. The English heroe. London, for N. Crouch 1687. sm. 12mo. First Edition. (John W. R. Crawford)

Bushell, Thomas. An extract by Mr. Bushell of his late abridgment of the Lord Chancellor Bacons philosophical theory in mineral prosecutions. London, T. Leach 1660. sm. 4to. First Edition

Butler, Joseph. The analogy of religion. London, for J., J. and P. Knapton 1736. 4to. First Edition

[Butler, Samuel]. Hudibras. The first part. London, J. G. 1663. 8vo. First Edition

[————] ———— The second part. London, T. R. 1664. 8vo. First Edition

[Butler, Samuel]. Hudibras. The third and last part. London, for S. Miller 1678. 8vo.

[———] ——— In three parts. London, T.W. 1726. 12mo.

[———] Hudibras, in three parts. Cambridge, J. Bentham 1744. 2 v. 8vo. (Mexborough)

——— The genuine remains. London, for J. and R. Tonson 1759. 2 v. 8vo. First Edition

Camoens, Luis de. The Lusiad. Tr. by R. Fanshawe. London, for H. Moseley 1655. fol. First Edition. (Earl of Arran–Earl of Ormonde and Ossory)

Camus, Jean Pierre. Nature's paradox. London, J. G. for E. Dod and N. Ekins 1652. sm. 4to. First Edition

[Capell, Edward]. Notes and various readings to Shakespeare. London, H. Hughs [1779-83]. 3 v. 4to.

Carew, Thomas. Poems. London, I. D. 1642. 8vo. Second Edition. (Lefferts–Purdy)

Carey, Henry. Poems on several occasions. London, E. Say 1729. 4to. Third Edition

[Carkesse, James]. Lucida intervalla. London 1679. sm. 4to. (H. B. Wheatley–Huth)

Carleton, George. The memoirs of an English officer. London, for E. Symon 1728. 8vo. First Edition. (Copy 1, Walter Wilson; 2, Bement)

Carlile, James. The fortune-hunters. London, for J. Knapton 1689. 4to. First Edition

Carpenter, Richard. A new play call'd The pragmatical Jesuit. London, for N. R., n.d. 4to. First Edition

Carter, Matthew. Honor rediviuus. London, E. Coates 1655. sm. 8vo. First Edition. (Huth)

——— A most true and exact relation of that ... expedition of Kent, Essex, and Colchester. By M. C. n.p. 1650. sm. 8vo. First Edition

Cartwright, William. Comedies, tragi-comedies, with other poems. London, for H. Moseley 1651. 12mo. First Edition

[Caryll, John].   The English princess.   London, for T. Dring 1667.
4to.   First Edition.   (Huth)

———— Sir Salomon.   London, for H. Herringman 1671.   4to.   First
Edition

The case and cure of persons excommunicated.   London, for J. R. 1682.
sm. 4to.   First Edition

Cats, Jacob.   Self-conflict. Tr. by J. Quarles.   London, for R. Sollers
1680.   8vo.   First Edition.   (Freeling–Huth)

The catterpillers of this nation anatomized.   London, for M. H. 1659.
sm. 4to.   First Edition

Cave, William.   Apostolici.   London, A. C. for R. Chiswell 1677.   fol.
First Edition

Cavendish, George.   The negotiations of Thomas Woolsey.   London,
for W. Sheares 1641.   sm. 4to.   First Edition

Cavendish, Margaret, *Duchess of Newcastle*.   The life of . . . William
Cavendish.   London, A. Maxwell 1667.   fol.   First Edition

———— ———— London, A. Maxwell 1675.   4to.   (Huth)

———— Orations of divers sorts.   London 1662.   fol.   First Edition.
(Presentation copy from the author to Mildmay Fane, Earl of
Westmoreland)

[————]   Playes.   London, A. Warren 1662.   fol.   First Edition

Cavendish, William, *Duke of Newcastle*.   A declaration . . . in answer
of . . . aspersions cast upon him by the Lord Fairefax.   York, S.
Bulkley 1642.   sm. 4to.   First Edition, stabbed

———— The humorous lovers.   London, J. M. 1677.   4to.   First Edition

———— The triumphant widow.   London, J. M. 1677.   4to.   First
Edition

[Centlivre, Susannah].   The gamester.   London, for W. Turner 1705.
4to.   First Edition

[————]   Love's contrivance.   London, for B. Lintott 1703.   4to.
First Edition

———— The man's bewitch'd.   London, for B. Lintott [1710].   4to.
First Edition.   (Huth)

Centlivre, Susannah. Mar-plot. London, for J. Tonson 1711. 4to. First Edition. (Huth)

[———] The perjur'd husband. London, for B. Banbury 1700. 4to. First Edition. (E. F. Leo–Huth)

——— The perplex'd lovers. London, for O. Lloyd . . . 1712. 4to. First Edition

[———] The platonick lady. London, for J. Knapton and E. Sanger 1707. 4to. First Edition

[———] The stolen heiress. London, for W. Turner and J. Nutt [1703]. 4to. First Edition

Ceriziers, René de. The triumphant lady. Tr. out of . . . French, by Sir William Lower. London, for G. Bedell and T. Collins 1656. sm. 8vo. First Edition

Cervantes Saavedra, Miguel de. The history . . . of . . . Don Quixote. Tr. by T. Smollett. London 1755. 2 v. 4to. First Edition

Chalkhill, John. Thealma and Clearchus. London, for B. Tooke 1683. 8vo. First Edition. (Wallace)

Chamberlayne, William. Loves victory. London, E. Cotes 1658. sm. 4to. First Edition. (Huth)

——— Pharonnida. London, for R. Clavell 1659. 8vo. First Edition. (William Tyas Harden)

[———] Wits led by the nose. London, for L. Curtis 1678. 4to. First Edition

Chapman, George. The tragedy of Alphonsus. London, for H. Moseley 1654. 8vo. First Edition

The character of a town-gallant. London, for W. L. 1675. sm. 4to. (Huth)

Charles I, *King of England*. Εἰκὼν Βασιλικὴ. The pourtraicture of his sacred Majestie. n.p. 1648. sm. 8vo. First Edition, First Issue

——— King Charls his speech made upon the scaffold. London, P. Cole 1649. sm. 4to. First Edition. (Hugh Perkins)

Charles II, *King of England*. Directions concerning preachers . . . 14 October 1662. London, J. Bill and C. Barker 1662. fol.

Charles II, *King of England*. His Majesties Declaration ... touching the causes & reasons that moved him to dissolve the two last parliaments. London, Assigns of J. Bill, T. Newcomb, and H. Hills 1681. fol. (2 copies)

────── Relation en forme de journal du voyage et sejour, que ... Charles II ... a fait en Hollande. A La Haye, chez A. Vlacq 1660. fol. First Edition. (Bement)

Charleton, Walter. Chorea gigantum. London, for H. Herringman 1663. sm. 4to. First Edition

[Chatterton, Thomas]. The execution of Sir Charles Bawdin. London, F. Newbery 1772. 4to. First Edition. (J. H. Ingram)

[──────] Poems, supposed to have been written at Bristol, by Thomas Rowley. London, for T. Payne 1777. 8vo. First Edition. (H. V. Jones)

[──────] ────── Cambridge, B. Flower 1794. 8vo.

────── The revenge. London, C. Rowarth 1795. 8vo. First Edition

Chaucer, Geoffrey. The works. Edited by T. Speght. London 1687. fol.

────── ────── By J. Urry. London, for B. Lintot 1721. fol. Eighth Edition. (Fountaine)

Chaucer's ghoast. London, T. Ratcliff & N. Thompson 1672. 12mo. in eights. First Edition. (Thomas Jolley)

Checkley, John. The speech of Mr. John Checkley, upon his tryall at Boston. London, J. Applebee 1738. 8vo. Second Edition. (Sabin 12365)

Chesterfield, *Earl of*. *See* Stanhope, Philip Dormer

Churchill, Charles. The author. London, for W. Flexney ... 1763. 4to. First Edition, stitched. (Buxton Forman)

────── The candidate. London, for the Author 1764. 4to. First Edition

────── The conference. London, for G. Kearsly ... 1763. 4to. First Edition, stitched. (Buxton Forman)

────── The duellist. London, for G. Kearsly ... 1764. 4to. First Edition

Churchill, Charles. The farewell. London, for the Author 1764.
4to. First Edition, stitched. (Buxton Forman)

——— Gotham. London, for the Author 1764. 4to. First Edition,
stitched. (Buxton Forman, with Churchill's autograph signature
in Book III)

[———] Independence. London, for the Author 1764. 4to. First
Edition. (Author's autograph signature on title)

[———] The Rosciad. London 1761. sm. 4to. First Edition

[———] The times. London, for the Author 1764. 4to. First Edition. (Author's autograph signature on title)

[Cibber, Colley]. Cinna's conspiracy. London, for B. Lintott 1713.
4to. First Edition

[———] The comical lovers. London, for B. Lintott [1707]. 4to.
First Edition

——— The double gallant. London, for B. Lintott [1707]. 4to.
First Edition

——— The lady's last stake. London, for B. Lintott [1708]. 4to.
First Edition

——— Love in a riddle. London, for J. Watts 1719. 8vo. First
Edition

——— Perolla and Izadora. London, for B. Lintott 1706. 4to. First
Edition

——— The rival fools. London, for B. Lintott [1709]. 4to. First
Edition

——— *See also* The tryall of Colley Cibber; Vanbrugh, *Sir* John, *and*
Colley Cibber

Cibber, Theophilus. The lover. London, for J. Watts 1730. 8vo.
First Edition

The citizen's companion. London, J. C. for B. Tooth 1673. 12mo. in
eights. (Huth)

[Citri de la Guette, Samuel]. The history of the triumvirates. Made
English by Tho. Otway. London, for C. Brome 1686. 8vo.

Clarendon, *Earl of*. *See* Hyde, Edward

Clavel, Robert. The general catalogue of books printed in England since the dreadful fire of London, 1666. London, A. Clark 1675. fol. First Edition

———— ———— [Supplements] Nos. 1-52. London 1674-94. fol. First Edition

[Cleveland, John]. The idol of the clownes. London 1654. sm. 8vo. First Edition. (Huth)

———— The works. London, R. Holt 1687. 8vo. First Edition. (John Mitford)

Clifford, M[artin]. Notes upon Mr. Dryden's poems. London 1687. sm. 4to. First Edition

Clive, Catherine. The rehearsal. London, for R. Dodsley 1753. 8vo. First Edition

Cocker, Edward. The pens triumph. London, R. Walton [1657]. obl. 8vo.

Codrington, Robert, *tr. See* Æsopus

Coffey, Charles. The beggar's wedding. London, for N. Rich[1729]. 8vo. First Edition

———— The female parson. London, for L. Gilliver and F. Cogan 1730. 8vo. First Edition

Cokayne, *Sir* Aston. The obstinate lady. London, W. Godbid 1657. sm. 4to. First Edition. (H.V. Jones)

Coleridge, Samuel Taylor. The fall of Robespierre. Cambridge, B. Flower 1794. 8vo. First Edition

———— The plot discovered. Bristol 1795. 8vo. First Edition. (Hagen)

———— Poems on various subjects. London, for G. G. and J. Robinsons, and F. Cottle 1796. 8vo. First Edition. (Hagen)

———— Poems ... To which are now added Poems by Charles Lamb, and Charles Lloyd. Bristol, N. Biggs 1797. 8vo. First Edition, but Second Edition of Coleridge's Poems

———— *tr. See* Schiller, Johann Friedrich Christoph von

A collection of loyal songs written against the Rump Parliament. London, for J. Stone ... 1731. 2 v. 8vo. First Edition. (W. L. Andrews)

A collection of state songs, poems, &c. London, for A. and W. Bell ... 1716. 8vo. First Edition. (Buxton Forman)

Collier, Jeremy. A defence of the Short view of the profaneness and immorality of the English stage. London, for S. Keble ... R. Sare ... and H. Hindmarsh 1699. 8vo. First Edition

———— A short view of the immorality, and profaneness of the English stage. London, for S. Keble ... R. Sare ... and H. Hindmarsh 1698. 8vo. First Edition

Collins, William. Odes on several descriptive and allegoric subjects. London, for A. Millar 1747. 8vo. First Edition

Collop, John. Poesis rediviva. London, for H. Moseley 1656. 8vo. First Edition. (Kershaw–Drinkwater)

Colman, George. Comus: a masque. Altered from Milton. London, for T. Lowndes ... 1772. 8vo. First Edition

[————] The Deuce is in him. London, for T. Becket ... 1763. 8vo. First Edition

———— The English merchant. London, for T. Becket ... 1767. 8vo. First Edition

[————] The fairy prince. London, for T. Becket 1771. 8vo. First Edition

[————] Man and wife. London, for T. Becket ... 1770. 8vo. First Edition

———— The man of business. London, for T. Becket 1774. 8vo. First Edition

[————] The musical lady. London, for T. Becket ... 1762. 8vo. First Edition

———— New brooms. London, for T. Becket 1776. 8vo. First Edition

[————] Polly Honeycombe. London, for T. Becket ... 1760. 8vo. First Edition

———— The spleen. London, for T. Becket 1776. 8vo. First Edition

———— *and* David Garrick. The clandestine marriage. London, for T. Becket ... 1766. 8vo. First Edition

Colman, George, *junior*. Ways and means. London, for G. G. J. and J. Robinson 1788. 8vo. First Edition

Comenius, John Amos. Orbis sensualium pictus. Tr. by C. Hoole. London, for C. Mearne 1685. 8vo. (Huth)

[Congreve, William]. Amendments of Mr. Collier's false and imperfect citations. London, for J. Tonson 1698. 8vo. First Edition

————— The double-dealer. London, for J. Tonson 1694. 4to. First Edition. (Groves)

————— The judgment of Paris. London, for J. Tonson 1701. 4to. First Edition. (Gosse)

————— Love for love. London, for J. Tonson 1695. 4to. First Edition

————— The mourning bride. London, for J. Tonson 1697. 4to. First Edition

————— The mourning muse of Alexis. London, for J. Tonson 1695. fol. First Edition

————— The old batchelour. London, for P. Buck 1693. 4to. First Edition

————— A Pindarique ode, humbly offer'd to the King. London, for J. Tonson 1695. fol. First Edition

————— A Pindarique ode, humbly offer'd to the Queen. London, for J. Tonson 1706. fol. First Edition

————— The tears of Amaryllis for Amyntas. London, for J. Tonson 1703. fol. First Edition

————— The way of the world. London, for J. Tonson 1700. 4to. First Edition

————— The works. Birmingham, J. Baskerville 1761. 3 v. 8vo.

The conquest of France. [London] A. M. for C. Bates [1700]. sm. 4to. (William Bedford)

Cook, John. King Charls his case. London, P. Cole 1649. sm. 4to.

Cooke, William, *attrib. author*. *See* Johnson, Samuel. The life . . .

Corbet, Richard. Certain elegant poems. London, R. Cotes 1647. 8vo. First Edition

Cornbury, *Viscount. See* Hyde, Henry

Corneille, Pierre. Horace. Tr. by C. Cotton. London, for H. Brome 1671. 4to. First Edition. (Percy FitzGerald)

[Corneille, Pierre]. Polyeuctes. Tr. by Sir William Lower. London,
T. Roycroft 1655. sm. 4to. First Edition

Cornwallis, *Sir* Charles.   A discourse of the most illustrious prince,
Henry. London, for I. Benson 1641. sm. 4to. (Huth)

Corolini, *Signor*.   *See* Swift, Jonathan: The Brobdingnagians

Corye, John. The generous enemies. London, H. Lloyd 1672. 4to.
First Edition. (Groves)

Costes, Gautier de, *Seigneur de La Calprenède*.   Cassandra. Tr. by C.
Cotterell.   London, for H. Moseley, W. Bentley, and T. Heath
1652. fol. First Complete Edition. (H. B. Wheatley)

Cotgrave, John. The English treasury of wit and language. London,
for H. Moseley 1655. 8vo. First Edition

Cotterell, Charles, *tr.* *See* Costes, Gautier de

[Cotton, Charles]. The confinement. London, for C. C. 1679. 8vo.
First Edition. (Chew)

———— The planters manual. London, for H. Brome 1675.   12mo.
First Edition

———— Poems on several occasions. London, for T. Basset . . . 1689.
12mo. First Edition

[————] The valiant knight. London, for J. Johnson 1663. sm. 4to.
First Edition. (Jolley–Huth)

———— The wonders of the peake. London, for J. Brome 1681. 8vo.
First Edition. Large paper. (Chew)

————*tr.* *See* Corneille, Pierre

Cotton, *Sir* Robert Bruce. An answer to such motives as were offer'd
by certain military-men to Prince Henry. London, for H. Mortlock 1675. 8vo.

———— A short view of King Henry the third's reign. London, for
H. Mortlock 1675. 8vo.

———— Cottoni posthuma . . . exposed to publick light . . . By J[ames]
H[owell]. London, M. C. for C. Harper 1679. 8vo.

The counters discourse. n.p. 1641. sm. 4to. (Huth)

Cowley, Abraham. Cutter of Coleman-Street. London, for H. Herringman 1663. sm. 4to. First Edition

Cowley, Abraham. The guardian. London, for J. Holden 1650. sm. 4to. First Edition

———— The mistresse. London, for H. Moseley 1647. 8vo. First Edition

———— A poem on the late Civil War. London 1679. sm. 4to. First Edition. (Lefferts–Hagen)

———— Poems. London, for H. Moseley 1656. fol. (Huth)

———— The works. London, J. M. for H. Herringman 1668. fol. First Edition

———— *tr.* *See* Anacreon

Cowley, Hannah. The belle's strategem. London, for T. Cadell 1782. 8vo. First Edition

[Cowper, William]. Olney hymns. London, W. Oliver 1779. 12mo. First Edition

———— Poems. London, for J. Johnson 1782, 1785. 2 v. 8vo. First Edition

———— *tr.* *See* Homerus

Cox, Robert. Actaeon and Diana. London, T. Newcomb [c. 1655]. sm. 4to. First Edition. (Bridgewater–Huth)

Crabbe, George. The village. London, for J. Dodsley 1783. sm. 4to. First Edition

[Craddock, Joseph]. Zobeide. London, for T. Cadell 1771. 8vo. First Edition

Crashaw, Richard. Carmen deo nostro. Paris, P. Targa 1652. 8vo. (Masterman Sykes–Leigh–Andrews)

———— Steps to the temple. London, for H. Moseley 1648. 12mo. Second Edition

Critical remarks on Capt. Gulliver's Travels. By Doctor Bantley. Printed at Cambridge, and sold by L. G. in London 1735. 8vo. First Edition

Croft, Herbert. Naked truth. The first part. n.p. 1680. fol.

Cromwell, Oliver. A copy of the letter . . . sent to the members of Parliament. London, M. S. for T. Jenner 1656. sm. 4to.

Cromwell, Richard. The happy sinner. London, for R. Clavell 1691. sm. 4to.

Crowne, John.   The ambitious statesman.   London, for W. Abington
 1679. 4to. First Edition. (H.V. Jones)

[———] Andromache.   London, T. Ratcliffe & N. Thompson 1675.
 4to. First Edition

——— Caligula. London, J. Orme 1698. 4to. First Edition

——— Calisto. London, T. Newcomb 1675. sm. 4to. First Edition. (Bridgewater)

——— City politiques. London, R. Bently and J. Hindmarsh 1683.
 sm. 4to. First Edition

——— The countrey wit. London, T. N. 1675. sm. 4to. First Edition. (Bridgewater)

——— Darius. London, for J. Knight and F. Saunders 1688. 4to.
 First Edition

——— The English frier. London, for J. Knapton 1690. 4to. First
Edition

——— Henry the sixth.   London, for R. Bentley and M. Magnes
 1681. 4to. First Edition

——— The history of Charles the eighth of France. London, T. R.
 and N. T. 1672. 4to. First Edition. (H.V. Jones)

——— Juliana. London, for W. Cademan . . . 1671. 4to. First
Edition

——— The married beau. London, for R. Bentley 1694. 4to. First
Edition

——— Regulus. London, for J. Knapton 1694. 4to. First Edition

——— Sir Courtly Nice. London, H. H. Jun. 1685. 4to. First Edition

——— Thyestes. London, for R. Bently and M. Magnes 1681. 4to.
 First Edition. (C. L. F. Robinson)

Cumberland, Richard.   The banishment of Cicero.   London, for J.
 Walter 1761. 4to. First Edition

[———] The battle of Hastings.   London, for E. and C. Dilly 1778.
 8vo. First Edition

[———] The Carmelite. London, for C. Dilly . . . 1784. 8vo. First
Edition

[Cumberland, Richard].　The fashionable lover.　London, for W. Griffin 1772.　8vo.　First Edition.　(C. L. F. Robinson)

―――― The mysterious husband.　London, for C. Dilly ... 1783.　8vo. First Edition

―――― The natural son.　London, for C. Dilly ... 1785.　8vo.　First Edition

[――――] The West Indian.　London, for W. Griffin 1771.　8vo. First Edition

―――― The wheel of fortune.　London, for C. Dilly 1795.　8vo.　First Edition

Davenant, Charles.　Circe.　London, for R. Tonson 1677.　4to.　First Edition.　(Lefferts)

[――――] An essay upon ways and means of supplying the war.　London, for J. Tonson 1695.　8vo.　First Edition

[――――] Essays.　London, for J. Knapton 1701.　8vo.

[Davenant, *Sir* William].　The cruelty of the Spaniards in Peru.　London, for H. Herringman 1658.　sm. 4to.　First Edition

―――― A discourse upon Gondibert ... with an answer to it by Mr. Hobbs.　Paris, chez M. Guillemot 1650.　sm. 12mo.　First Edition.　(A. B. Spingarn)

―――― The first days entertainment at Rutland-House.　London, J. M. for H. Herringman 1657.　sm. 8vo.　First Edition

―――― Gondibert.　London, T. Newcomb 1651.　4to.　First Edition.　(Sir Edward W. Watkin–John Dod)

[――――] The history of Sr Francis Drake.　London, for H. Herringman 1659.　sm. 4to.　First Edition

[――――] Love and honour.　London, for H. Robinson ... 1649.　sm. 4to.　First Edition.　(Newdigate)

―――― The man's the master.　(London) for H. Herringman 1669. 4to.　First Edition

―――― Poem, to the King's most sacred Majesty.　London, for H. Herringman 1663.　sm. 4to.　First Edition

[――――] The rivals.　London, for W. Cademan 1668.　sm. 4to.　First Edition

Davenant, *Sir* William.   The works.   London, T. N. for H. Herringman 1673.   fol.   First Collected Edition

Davenport, Robert.   The city-night-cap.   London, J. Cottrel 1661.
sm. 4to.   First Edition.   (Huth)

—— King Iohn and Matilda.   London, for A. Pennycuicke 1655.
sm. 4to.   First Edition.   (Bridgewater)

[Davies, John] (1627-1693).   The civil warres of Great Britain and Ireland.   Glasgow, R. Sanders 1664.   sm. 4to.   (Bulkeley Bandinel)

Day, John.   The blind-beggar of Bednal-Green.   London, for R. Pollard and T. Dring 1659.   sm. 4to.   First Edition

[Day, Thomas].   The desolation of America.   London, for G. Kearsly
...1777.   4to.   First Edition

[———] The history of Sandford and Merton.   London, for J. Stockdale 1783-9.   3 v.   12mo.   First Edition.   (Hoe)

[———] Liberty and patriotism.   London, for Fielding and Walker
1778.   4to.

Dee, John.   A true & faithful relation of what passed for many yeers
between Dr. John Dee ... and some spirits.   London, D. Maxwell
1659.   fol.   First Edition.   (Palmer)

[Defoe, Daniel].   The anatomy of Exchange-Alley.   London, for E.
Smith 1719.   8vo.   First Edition

[———] The case of Protestant dissenters in Carolina.   London 1706.
sm. 4to.   First Edition

[———] The chimera.   London, for T. Warner 1720.   8vo.   First
Edition

[———] The consolidator.   London, B. Bragg 1705.   8vo.   (Huth)

[———] A continuation of the life and adventures of Signor Rozelli.
London, for W. Taylor 1724.   8vo.

[———] The dumb philosopher.   London, for T. Bickerton 1719.
8vo.   First Edition.   (F. Grant–Purdy)

[———] An elegy on the author of The true-born-English-man.
London 1704.   sm. 4to.   First Edition

[———] Eleven opinions about Mr. H------y.   London, for J. Baker
1711.   8vo.   First Edition.   (Schweizer)

[Defoe, Daniel]. An essay on ... apparitions. London 1727. 8vo. First Edition. (Purdy)

[———] Flagellum. London, T. Warner 1723. 8vo. First Edition

[———] The fortunate mistress. London, for T. Warner 1724. 8vo. First Edition

[———] The fortunes and misfortunes of the famous Moll Flanders. London, for W. Chetwood MDDCXXI[sic]. 8vo. First Edition. (Clawson)

[———] The great law of subordination consider'd. London 1724. 8vo. First Edition. (John Croft Deverell–Schweizer)

[———] The history ... of ... Col. Jacque. London, J. Brotherton 1723. 8vo. First Edition. (B. C. Stephenson–Murray)

[———] The history of the life and adventures of Mr. Duncan Campbell. London, for E. Curll 1720. 8vo. First Edition

[———] The history of the press-yard. London, for T. Moor 1717. 8vo. First Edition

[———] A hymn to peace. London, for J. Nutt 1706. sm. 4to. First Edition

[———] An impartial history of ... Peter Alexowitz. London, for W. Chetwood 1723. 8vo. First Edition. (Huth–Adam–H.V. Jones–Schweizer)

[———] A journal of the plague year. London, for E. Nutt 1722. 8vo. First Edition

[———] A journey to the world in the moon. Edinburgh, Reprinted by J. Watson 1705. sm. 4to. (Huth)

[———] Jure divino. London 1706. fol. First Edition. (Viscount Bridport)

[———] The king of pirates. London, for A. Bettesworth 1720. 8vo. First Edition

[———] The life and adventures of Mrs. Christian Davies. London, for R. Montagu 1740. 8vo. First Edition. (Cathcart of Carbiston)

[———] The life ... of ... Captain Singleton. London, for J. Brotherton 1720. 8vo. First Edition. (Purdy)

[Defoe, Daniel]. The life . . . of Robinson Crusoe. London, for W. Taylor 1719-20. 3 v. 8vo. First Edition. (Ralph Clutton)

[———] The London ladies dressing-room. London 1725. 8vo. First Edition

[———] Memoirs of a cavalier. London, for A. Bell [c. 1720]. 8vo. First Edition

[———] Memoirs of the life and adventures of Signor Rozelli. London, for J. Morphew 1709. 8vo.

[———] Minutes of the negotiations of Monsr. Mesnager. London, for S. Baker 1717. 8vo. First Edition. (James Cowan of Ross Hall)

[———] The mock mourners. London 1702. sm. 4to. First Edition. (Huth–Bernheim–H.V. Jones–Schweizer)

[———] A new voyage round the world. London, for A. Bettesworth 1725. 8vo. First Edition. (James Gilpin–Hoe)

[———] The political history of the devil. London, for T. Warner 1726. 8vo. First Edition

[———] Reasons against the succession of the House of Hanover. London, for J. Baker 1713. 8vo. First Edition. (Bernheim–H.V. Jones–Schweizer)

[———] Reformation of manners. [London] 1702. sm. 4to. First Edition

[———] Religious courtship. London, for E. Matthews 1722. 8vo. First Edition. (Schweizer)

[———] A short narrative of the life and death of . . . Count Patkul. London, for T. Goodwin 1717. 8vo. First Edition

[———] Some account of the two nights court at Greenwich. Edinburgh, Re-printed 1716. sm. 8vo. (Schweizer)

[———] A speech without doors. London, for A. Baldwin 1710. 8vo. First Edition. (Schweizer)

[———] The storm. London, for G. Sawbridge 1704. 8vo. (Purdy)

[———] A system of magick. London 1727. 8vo. First Edition. (J. R. P. Forrest)

[Defoe, Daniel]. A tour thro' the whole island of Great Britain. London, G. Strahan 1724. 3 v. 8vo. First Edition. (Arthur Vaughan–James Cowan of Ross Hall)

[———] The true-born Englishman. [London] 1700. sm. 4to. First Edition

[———] A true collection of the writings of the author of The true born English-man. London 1703-5. 2 v. 8vo. (Huth)

[———] The villainy of stock-jobbers detected. London 1701. sm. 4to. First Edition

[Dekker, Thomas]. English villanies. London, E. P. for N. Gamage 1648. sm. 4to. (Lord George Lennox)

[Delap, John]. The royal suppliants. London, for J. Bowen 1781. 8vo. First Edition

Delaune, Henry. ΠΑΤΡΙΚΟΝ ΔΩΡΟΝ. London, A. M. for H. Seile 1657. 8vo. Second Edition. (Gaisford)

A delectable little history in metter. Glasgow 1695. 8vo. (Daniel–Huth)

Denham, *Sir* John. Poems and translations. London, for H. Herringman 1668. 8vo. First Collected Edition

Dennis, John. The court of death. London, for J. Knapton 1695. fol. First Edition

[———] A defence of Sir Fopling Flutter. London, for T. Warner 1722. 8vo. First Edition

——— An essay on the genius and writings of Shakespear. London, for B. Lintot 1712. 8vo. First Edition

——— The grounds of criticism in poetry. London, for G. Strahan and B. Lintot 1704. 8vo. First Edition

——— The impartial critick. London, for R. Taylor 1693. sm. 4to. First Edition

——— The monument. London, for D. Brown and A. Bell 1702. sm. 4to. First Edition, stitched

——— A plot, and no plot. London, for R. Parker [1697]. 4to. First Edition. (H. V. Jones)

——— Remarks on a book entituled, Prince Arthur. London, for S. Heyrick and R. Sare 1696. 8vo. First Edition

Dennis, John.   Remarks upon several passages in the preliminaries to the Dunciad.   London, for H. Whitridge 1729.   8vo.   First Edition

———— The usefulness of the stage.   London, for R. Parker 1698.   8vo. First Edition, stitched

———— Vice and luxury.   London, for W. Mears 1724.   8vo.   First Edition

———— *tr.   See* Ovidius Naso, Publius

A dialogue between Riches, Poverty, Godliness, Gravity, Labour, and Content.   London, for N. Bradford 1659.   sm. 4to.

[Dibdin, Charles].   The waterman.   London, for T. Becket 1776.   8vo. First Edition

Digby, *Sir* Kenelm.   The closet … opened.   London, E. C. & A. C. for H. Brome 1671.   8vo.

———— A late discourse … touching the cure of wounds by the powder of sympathy … Rendred … into English by R. White.   London, for R. Lownes and T. Davies 1658.   nar. 12mo.   First Edition

Dilke, Thomas.   The city lady.   London, for H. Newman 1697.   4to. First Edition.   (Kemble–Devonshire)

———— The lover's luck.   London, for H. Playford 1696.   4to.   First Edition.   (Kemble–Devonshire)

———— The pretenders.   London, for P. Buck 1698.   4to.   First Edition.   (Bridgewater)

Dillon, Wentworth, *fourth Earl of Roscommon*.   An essay on translated verse.   London, for J. Tonson 1684.   sm. 4to.   First Edition

The dilucidation of the late commotions of Turkey.   London, J. B. 1689.   sm. 4to.

Diodorus Siculus.   The historical library of Diodorus the Sicilian. Tr. by G. Booth.   London, E. Jones 1700.   fol.   First Edition

Disraeli, Isaac.   Romances.   London, for Cadell and Davies 1799.   8vo. First Edition

[Donaldson, James].   A pick-tooth for swearers.   Edinburgh, J. Reid 1698.   sm. 4to.   First Edition.   (Huth)

Donne, John.   Letters to severall persons of honour.   London, J. Flesher 1651.   sm. 4to.   First Edition

Donne, John. Paradoxes, problemes, essayes, characters. London, T. N. for H. Moseley 1652. 12mo. (Lefferts–Hagen)

Drummond, William. The most elegant, and elaborate poems. London, for W. Rands 1659. 8vo. (1656 title bound in)

———— The most elegant, and elabourate poems. London, for W. Rands 1659. 8vo. (E. Cooper–P. de Cardonnel–Horace Walpole–Hugh Perkins)

[Dryden, John]. Absalom and Achitophel [The first and] second part. London, for J. T. 1681-2. fol. First Edition

———— The address of John Dryden . . . to . . . the Prince of Orange. London, R. Taylor 1689. fol. First Edition. (Lefferts)

———— Albion and Albanus. London, for J. Tonson 1685. fol. First Edition

———— Alexander's feast. London, for J. Tonson 1697. fol. First Edition

———— All for love. (London) T. Newcomb 1678. 4to. First Edition. (H.V. Jones)

———— Amboyna. London, T. N. 1673. 4to. First Edition

———— Annus mirabilis. London, for H. Herringman 1667. 8vo. First Edition

———— The assignation. London, T. N. 1673. 4to. First Edition. (E. M. Cox–E. F. Leo)

———— Aurung-Zebe. London, T. N. 1676. 4to. First Edition

———— Britannia rediviva. London, for J. Tonson 1688. fol. First Edition

———— Cleomenes. London, for J. Tonson 1692. 4to. First Edition

———— The comedies, tragedies, and operas. London, for J. Tonson, T. Bennet and R. Wellington 1701. 2 v. fol. Large paper

———— The conquest of Granada. (London) T. N. 1672. 4to. First Edition

———— A dialogue . . . in The pilgrim. London, for B. Tooke 1700. 4to. First Edition

———— Don Sebastian. London, for J. Hindmarsh 1690. 4to. First Edition

Dryden, John.   The dramatick works.   London, for J. Tonson 1717.
6v.   8vo.   (Lefferts)

[————]   An elegy on the usurper O. C.   n.p. 1682.   sm. 4to.   (Lefferts)

———— Eleonora.   London, for J. Tonson 1692.   4to.   First Edition

———— An evening's love.   (London) T. N. 1671.   sm. 4to.   First
Edition

———— Fables.   London, for J. Tonson 1700.   fol.   First Edition

———— The fables.   London, T. Bensley 1797.   fol.   Large paper

———— The hind and the panther.   London, for J. Tonson 1687.   4to.
First Edition.   (Has three lines of errata on recto last leaf, and advertisement of books on verso. Has license leaf)

[————]   His Majesties declaration defended.   London, for T. Davies
1681.   fol.   First Edition

———— The kind keeper.   London, for R. Bentley and M. Magnes
1680.   4to.   First Edition

———— King Arthur.   London, for J. Tonson 1691.   4to.   First Edition

———— Love triumphant.   London, for J. Tonson 1694.   4to.   First
Edition

[————]   The Mall.   London, for W. Cademan 1674.   4to.   First
Edition.   (Lefferts)

———— Marriage a-la-mode.   London, T. N. 1673.   4to.   First Edition

[————]   The medall.   London, for J. Tonson 1682.   sm. 4to.   First
Edition, stitched

[————]   The mistaken husband.   London, for J. Magnes and R.
Bentley 1675.   4to.   First Edition.   (Lefferts)

———— Of dramatick poesie.   London, for H. Herringman 1668.   sm.
4to.   First Edition.   (Lefferts)

———— A poem upon the death of . . . Oliver, Lord Protector.   London, for W. Wilson 1659.   4to.   First Edition

———— Poems on various occasions.   London, for J. Tonson 1701.
fol.   First Collected Edition.   (H.V. Jones)

Dryden, John. Religiolaici. London, for J. Tonson 1682. 4to. First Edition

[———] The rival ladies. London, W. W. 1664. sm. 4to. First Edition

[———] Satyr to his muse. London, for T. W. 1682. 4to. (Lefferts)

[———] Sr Martin Mar-all. London, for H. Herringman 1668. 4to. First Edition. (Lefferts)

——— The Spanish fryar. London, for R. Tonson and J. Tonson 1681. 4to. First Edition. (Lefferts)

[———] The tempest. London, J. M. 1670. sm. 4to. First Edition

——— Threnodia Augustalis. London, for J. Tonson 1685. 4to. First Edition

——— To his sacred Maiesty, a panegyrick on his coronation. London, for H. Herringman 1661. fol. First Edition. (Lefferts)

——— Troilus and Cressida. London, for A. Swall and J. Tonson 1679. 4to. First Edition

——— Tyrannick love. London, for H. Herringman 1670. 4to. First Edition

——— The vindication. London, for J. Tonson 1683. sm. 4to. First Edition. (Robert Davies)

——— The wild gallant. (London) T. Newcomb 1669. 4to. First Edition

——— *See also* A panegyrick on the author of Absolom and Achitophel

——— *editor*. Examen poeticum. London, R. E. for J. Tonson 1693. 8vo. First Edition

[———] Miscellany poems. London, for J. Tonson 1684-1709. 6 v. in 5. 8vo. First Edition

[———] Sylvae. London, for J. Tonson 1685. 8vo. First Edition

——— *tr. See* Dufresnoy; Maimbourg; Juvenalis; Virgilius Maro

——— *and* Nathaniel Lee. The Duke of Guise. London, T. H. 1683. 4to. First Edition

——— Oedipus. London, for R. Bentley and M. Magnes 1679. 4to. First Edition

Dryden, John, *junior*. The husband his own cuckold. London, for J. Tonson 1696. 4to. First Edition. (McKee)

Duffet, Thomas. The mock-tempest. London, for W. Cademan 1675. sm. 4to. First Edition. (Bridgewater–Clawson)

—— New poems. London, for N. Woolfe 1676. 8vo. First Edition. (Hoe)

Dufresnoy, Charles Alphonse. De arte graphica. Tr. by Mr. Dryden. London, J. Heptinstall 1695. 4to. First Edition

Dugdale, *Sir* William. The antiquities of Warwickshire. London, T. Warren 1656. fol.

—— The history of St. Pauls Cathedral in London. London, T. Warren 1658. fol. (Charles Lilburn)

Dunton, John. The life and errors. London, for S. Malthus 1705. 12mo.

[D'Urfey, Thomas]. Butler's ghost. London, for J. Hindmarsh 1682. 8vo. First Edition

—— The campaigners. London, for A. Baldwin 1698. 4to. First Edition

—— An elegy upon the late blessed monarch King Charles II. London, for J. Hindmarsh 1685. fol. First Edition

—— The fool turn'd critick. London, for J. Magnes and R. Bentley 1678. 4to. First Edition

—— A fool's preferment. (London) for J. Knight and F. Saunders 1688. 4to. First Edition

—— Love for money. London, for A. Roper ... 1696. 4to. First Edition. (H.V. Jones)

—— Madam Fickle. London, T. N. 1677. 4to. First Edition

—— A new opera, call'd, Cinthia and Endimion. London, W. Onley 1697. 4to. First Edition. (Huth)

—— New opera's. London, for W. Chetwood 1721. 8vo. (Huth–H.V. Jones)

—— The royalist. London, for J. Hindmarsh 1682. 4to. First Edition

—— The siege of Memphis. London, for W. Cademan 1676. 4to. First Edition

D'Urfey, Thomas. Sir Barnaby Whigg. London, A. G. and J. P. 1681. 4to. First Edition. (Philip John Budworth)

———— Squire Oldsapp. London, for J. Magnes and R. Bentley 1679. 4to. First Edition

———— The virtuous wife. (London) T. N. 1680. 4to. First Edition. (Huth–H.V. Jones)

[————] The weesil trap'd. London, for A. Roper and J. Fox 1691. sm. 4to. First Edition, stitched

———— *See also* Shotterel, Robert, *and* Thomas D'Urfey

Eccleston, Edward. The cataclysm. London, for T. M. 1685. 4to. First Edition. (Bement)

Eden, *Sir* Frederic Morton. The state of the poor. London, J. Davis 1797. 3 v. 4to. First Edition

[Edwards, Henry]. A preparative to studie. London 1641. sm. 4to. First Edition. (Beaufoy)

Egan, Anthony. The Franciscan convert. London, for R. Clavel 1673. sm. 4to. (Huth)

Egerton, John. Egerton's theatrical remembrancer. London 1788. 12mo. First Edition

Egerton, Thomas, *Viscount Brackley*. The priviledges and prerogatives of the High Court of Chancery. London, for H. Sheapheard 1641. sm. 4to.

Enderbie, Percy, *tr.* *See* Pererius, Benedictus

England. *Parliament*. An Act for burying in wollen. London, J. Bill, C. Barker, T. Newcomb, and H. Hills 1678. fol.

———— An Act for the abolishing the kingly office in England. [London, E. Husband 1648]. fol.

———— An Act for the relief of creditors and poor prisoners . . . 5 October 1653. London, J. Field 1653. fol.

———— Certain Acts of Parliament appointed to be read yearly in parish churches. Oxford, L. L. 1681. fol.

———— A collection of . . . speeches and debates . . . relating to the horrid Popish plot. London, for F. Smith 1681. fol. First Edition

England. *Parliament.* An ordinance of the lords and commons . . . for, the utter suppression and abolishing of all stage-playes and interludes. London, for J. Wright 1647. sm. 4to. First Edition

———— The protestation of the Lords upon rejecting the impeachment of Mr. Fitz-Harris. March 28. 1681. London, for F. Smith 1681. 2 pp. fol. (2 copies, both imperfect)

———— Votes of the House of Commons 19 Nov. 1680. 2 pp. fol.

Erasmus, Desiderius. Witt against wisdom . . . Render'd into English [by White Kennett]. Oxford, L. Lichfield 1683. 8vo. First Edition

Essex, Robert Devereux, *third Earl of. See* The true mannor and forme . . .

Estcourt, Richard. The fair example. London, for B. Lintott 1706. 4to. First Edition. (Huth)

Estienne, Henri. The art of making devises. Tr. by T[homas] B[lount]. London, for R. Royston 1648. sm. 4to. (Comte de Caumont)

[Etherege, *Sir* George]. The comical revenge. London, for H. Herringman 1664. 4to. First Edition

———— The man of mode. London, J. Macock 1676. 4to. First Edition

———— She wou'd if she cou'd. London, for H. Herringman 1668. 4to. First Edition

———— The works. London 1704. 8vo.

Eugenius Theodidactus. *See* Heydon, John

Evans, Evan. Some specimens of the poetry of the antient Welsh bards. London, for R. and J. Dodsley 1764. 4to. First Edition

Evans, Thomas, *editor.* Old ballads. [London] for T. Evans 1784. 4 v. 8vo. (Hibbert)

Evelyn, John. Acetaria. London, for B. Tooke 1699. 8vo. First Edition

———— Fumifugium. London, W. Godbid 1661. sm. 4to. First Edition

[————] The history of the three late famous impostors. London, for H. Herringman 1669. 8vo. First Edition. (Groves)

Evelyn, John. Navigation and commerce. London, T. R. for B. Tooke 1674. 8vo. First Edition

———— Sylva. London, J. Martyn and J. Allestry 1664. fol. First Edition. (Bement)

———— *tr.* *See* La Quintinye, Jean de

Everard, John, *tr.* *See* Hermes Trismegistus

An exact collection of all orders, votes, debates . . . in the . . . late, and present Parliament relating to . . . Thomas Earl of Danby, and the other five lords in the Tower. London, for F. Smith 1679. fol. First Edition

An exact relation of the several engagements and actions of his Majesties fleet under . . . Prince Rupert . . . 1673. London, for J. B. 1673. sm. 4to. First Edition

(F., C.). Wit at a venture. London, for J. Edwin 1674. sm. 8vo. First Edition. (Huth)

Fairfax, Thomas, *third Baron Fairfax.* Short memorials. London, for R. Chiswell 1699. 8vo. First Edition. (Huth)

[Falconer, William]. The shipwreck. London, for the Author 1762. 4to. First Edition

Familiar forms of speaking. [London] J. R[edmayne] 1678. sm. 12mo. (Huth)

Fane, *Sir* Francis. Love in the dark. (London) T. N. 1675. 4to. First Edition. (H. V. Jones)

Fanshawe, Richard, *tr.* *See* Camoens, Luis de; Guarini, Giovanni Battista

Farquhar, George. Barcellona. London, for J. Smith . . . [1707]. 4to. First Edition

———— The beaux strategem. London, for B. Lintott [1707]. 4to. First Edition

———— The comedies. London, for J. Knapton . . . [1709]. 8vo.

———— The constant couple. London, for R. Smith 1700. 4to. First Edition

———— The inconstant. London, for J. Knapton . . . 1702. 4to. First Edition. (Huth)

Farquhar, George. Love and a bottle. London, for R. Standfast and F. Coggen 1699. 4to. First Edition

———— Love and business. London, for B. Lintott 1702. 8vo. First Edition

———— The recruiting officer. London, for B. Lintott [1705]. 4to. First Edition

———— Sir Harry Wildair. London, for J. Knapton 1701. 4to. First Edition

[Fell, John]. The life of . . . Dr. Thomas Fuller. London, for J. W. H. B. and H. M. 1661. sm. 8vo. First Edition. (W. L. Andrews)

Felltham, Owen. Resolves. London, for P. Dring 1661. fol. (Thomas Fuller)

Fénelon, François de Salignac de la Mothe-. The adventures of Telemachus. Tr. by T. Smollett. London, for S. Crowder . . . 1776. 2 v. 8vo. First Edition

———— ———— [Tr.] by Jn. Hawkesworth. New York, T. & J. Swords [1796]. 2 v. 8vo.

Fenton, Elijah. Mariamne. London, for J. Tonson 1723. 8vo. First Edition

[————] Poems on several occasions. London, for B. Lintot 1717. 8vo. First Edition. (Hoe)

Fielding, Henry. Amelia. London, for A. Millar 1752. 4 v. 12mo. First Edition. (William Harris Arnold)

[————] The author's farce. London, for J. Roberts 1730. 8vo. First Edition

———— A charge delivered to the Grand Jury. London, for A. Millar 1749. 8vo. First Edition

———— A clear state of the case of Elizabeth Canning. London, for A. Millar 1753. 8vo. First Edition. (Huth)

———— The coffee-house politician. London, for J. Watts 1730. 8vo. First Edition

[————] The Covent-Garden tragedy. London, for J. Watts 1732. 8vo. First Edition. (Bement)

Fielding, Henry.   Don Quixote in England.   London, for J. Watts 1734. 8vo. First Edition

——— An enquiry into the causes of the late increase of robbers. London, for A. Millar 1751. 8vo. First Edition. (Thomas Beach–R. H. Whitehurst–Huth)

——— Examples of the interposition of Providence in the detection ... of murder. London, for A. Millar 1752. sm.12mo. First Edition

[———] The fathers. London, for T. Cadell 1778. 8vo. First Edition

[———] The historical register. London, for J. Watts 1741. 8vo. First Edition

[———] The history of ... Joseph Andrews. London, for A. Millar 1742. 2 v. 8vo. First Edition

——— The history of Tom Jones. London, for A. Millar 1749. 6 v. 12mo. First Edition. (Sir Godfrey Webster)

[———] The lottery. London, for J. Watts 1732. 8vo. First Edition

——— Love in several masques. London, for J. Watts 1728. 8vo. First Edition. (H.V. Jones)

——— Miscellanies. London, for the Author 1743.   3 v.   8vo. First Edition. Large paper. Original boards, uncut

——— The miser. London, for J. Watts 1733. 8vo. First Edition

[———] Miss Lucy in town. London, for A. Millar 1742. 8vo. First Edition

——— The modern husband. London, for J. Watts 1732. 8vo. First Edition, wrappers, uncut

[———] An old man taught wisdom.   London, for J. Watts 1735. 8vo. First Edition, stitched, uncut

——— Pasquin. London, for J. Watts 1736. 8vo. First Edition

[———] Rape upon rape. London, for J. Wats 1730. 8vo. First Edition

[———] The Temple beau. London, for J. Watts 1730. 8vo. First Edition

[Fielding, Henry]. The tragedy of tragedies. London 1731. 8vo.
First Edition

―――― True state of the case of Bosavern Penlez. London, for A.
Millar 1749. sm. 4to. First Edition

―――― The wedding-day. London, for A. Millar 1743. 8vo. First
Edition

―――― *and* William Young. Plutus. London, for T. Waller 1742.
8vo.

[Fielding, Sarah]. The adventures of David Simple. London, for A.
Millar 1744. 2 v. 12mo. First Edition. (Richard Prime)

[Filmer, Edward]. A defence of dramatick poetry. London, for E.
Whitlock 1698. 8vo. First Edition. (Ambrose Holbech)

[――――] A farther defence of dramatick poetry. London, for E.
Whitlock 1698. 8vo. First Edition. (Ambrose Holbech)

[Finch, Heneage, *second Earl of Winchilsea*]. A true and exact relation of the late prodigious earthquake & eruption of Mount Ætna.
[London] T. Newcomb 1669. sm. 4to. First Edition

Fitz-Adam, Adam. *See* The World

Flaccus, Aulus Persius. *See* Juvenalis

Flatman, Thomas. On the death of . . . King Charles II. London, for
B. Tooke 1685. fol. First Edition

―――― A Pindarique ode on the death of . . . Thomas Earl of Ossory.
London, J. G. 1681. fol. First Edition

―――― Poems and songs. London, S. and B. G. for B. Took . . . 1674.
8vo. First Edition. (Lord Rockingham)

Flecknoe, Richard. Miscellania. London, T. Roycroft 1653. 8vo.
First Edition

―――― A relation of ten years travells. London, for the Author
[1656]. sm. 8vo.

Fletcher, John. The wild-goose chase. London, for H. Moseley 1652.
fol.

―――― *See also* Beaumont, Francis *and* John Fletcher

[Florando de Inglaterra]. The famous, pleasant, and delightful history
of Palladine of England. Tr. out of French by A[nthony] M[un-
day]. London, T. J. for A. Kembe 1664. sm. 4to. (Huth)

Foote, Samuel. The bankrupt. London, for C. Kearsly 1776. 8vo.
First Edition

———— The knights. London, for P. Vaillant 1754. 8vo. First
Edition

———— The maid of Bath. London, T. Sherlock 1778. 8vo. First
Edition. (Horace Walpole)

———— Taste. London, for R. Francklin 1752. 8vo. First Edition

Ford, *Sir* Edward. Experimented proposals how the King may have
money to pay and maintain his fleets. London, W. Godbid 1666.
sm. 4to.

[Forde, Emanuel]. The famous history of Montelion. London, A. P.
for W. Thackeray and T. Passinger 1673. sm. 4to.

Forde, Thomas. Fragmenta poetica. London, R. and W. Leybourn
1660. 8vo. First Edition. (H.V. Jones)

———— Love's labyrinth. London, R. and W. Leybourn 1660. 8vo.
First Edition. (H.V. Jones)

———— Virtus rediviva. [London] R. & W. Leybourn 1661. 8vo.
(2 copies: 1, Huth)

Foure fugitives meeting. n.p. 1641. sm. 4to. (Huth)

Fox, George. A primer for the schollers and doctors of Europe. London, for T. Simmons 1659. sm. 4to.

———— John Stubbs, *and* Benjamin Furly. A battle-door. London,
for R. Wilson 1660. fol. First Edition

[Francis, *Sir* Philip]. Junius. London, for H. S. Woodfall 1772. 2 v.
sm. 8vo. First Edition. (I. R. Hogarth)

[————] ———— London, T. Bensley 1799. 2 v. 8vo. (Hoe)

[————] ———— London, G. Woodfall 1812. 3 v. 8vo. (Arthur
Philip Lloyd, Leaton Knolls)

[Francklin, Thomas]. The Earl of Warwick. London, for T. Davies
... 1766. 8vo. First Edition

Free Masons. The constitutions of the Free-Masons. London, W.
Hunter 1723. 4to. First Edition

The French charity. Tr. . . . by F. S. J. E. London, for H. Mortlock
1665. 8vo.

Frowde, Philip.   The fall of Saguntum.   London, for J. Crokatt and
T. Wood 1727. 8vo. First Edition

Fuller, Thomas. Abel redevivus. London, T. Brudenell 1651. 4to.
First Edition. (Rev. John Brand–James Granger–Dogmersfield)

———— Anthologia. [London] sould by I. Stafford 1655. sm. 8vo.
First Edition. (Heber)

———— The appeal of iniured innocence. London, W. Godbid 1659.
fol. First Edition. (Amherst)

———— The church-history of Britain. London, for I. Williams 1655.
fol. First Edition. (Cecil Dunn Gardner)

———— The history of the worthies of England. London, J. G. W. L.
and W. G. for T. Williams 1662. fol. First Edition

———— A Pisgah-sight of Palestine. London, R. Davenport 1662.
fol. First Edition

Furly, Benjamin. *See* Fox, George, John Stubbs *and* Benjamin Furly

Gand, Louis de, *Baron de Brachey et de Romecour*. Parallelum olivae
nec non Olivarii . . . Angliae . . . Protectoris. Londini, ex typographia R. I. 1656. fol. First Edition

Garencieres, Theophilus de, *tr*.   *See* B., J., *Philalelos*; Nostradamus,
Michael

[Garrick, David].   Catharine and Petruchio.   London, for J. and R.
Tonson, and S. Draper 1756. 8vo. First Edition

[————] The country girl. London, for T. Becket . . . 1766. 8vo.
First Edition

[————] Cymon. London, for T. Becket . . . 1767. 8vo. First
Edition

[————] The enchanter. London, for J. and R. Tonson 1760. 8vo.
First Edition

———— Florizel and Perdita.   London, for J. and R. Tonson 1762.
8vo. First Edition

[————] The guardian. London, for I. Newbery 1759. 8vo. First
Edition

———— Lethe. London, for P. Vaillant 1749. 8vo. First Edition.
(J. F. Hinckley–H. V. Jones)

[Garrick, David]. Lilliput. London, for P. Vaillant 1757. 8vo. First Edition

[———] Love in a village. London, for T. Caslon . . . 1776. 8vo. First Edition

[———] The male-coquette. London, for P. Vaillant 1757. 8vo. First Edition

[———] May-day. London, for T. Becket 1775. 8vo. First Edition

[———] Miss in her teens. London, for J. and R. Tonson 1747. 8vo. First Edition

[———] Neck or nothing. London, for T. Becket 1766. 8vo. First Edition

[———] A new dramatic entertainment. London, for T. Becket 1774. 8vo. First Edition

[———] The tailors. London, T. Sherlock 1778. 8vo. First Edition. (Levy)

——— *See also* Colman, George, *and* David Garrick

Gay, John. Achilles. London, J. Watts 1733. 8vo. First Edition. (H. V. Jones)

——— The beggar's opera. London, for J. Watts 1728. 8vo. First Edition

——— Fables. London [I] for J. Tonson and J. Watts 1727; [II] for J. and P. Knapton and T. Cox 1738. 4to. First Edition

——— ——— London, for J. Stockdale 1793. 2 v. 8vo. (Sir Francis Hopkins)

——— The fan. London, for J. Tonson 1714. fol. First Edition

——— The petticoat. London, for R. Burleigh 1716. 8vo. First Edition. (Hoe–H. V. Jones)

——— Polly. London, for T. Thomson 1729. 8vo. First Edition

——— The shepherd's week. London, F. Burleigh 1714. 8vo. First Edition

——— Trivia. London, for B. Lintott [1730]. 8vo. First Edition. (H. V. Jones)

——— The what d'ye call it. London, for B. Lintott [1715]. 8vo. First Edition

[Gay, John]. Wine. London, for W. Keble 1708. fol. First Edition. (Hoe–H.V. Jones)

Gentili, Robert, *tr*. *See* Bacon, Francis: The naturall . . . history of winds

[Gentleman, Francis]. The Stratford jubilee. London, for T. Lowndes and J. Bell 1769. 8vo. First Edition

[———] The tobacconist. London, for J. Bell 1771. 8vo. First Edition

Gesta Romanorum. A record of ancient histories. London, T. H. for R. Scott 1681. 8vo. (Kershaw–Huth)

——— ——— London, for T. Basset 1689. 8vo.

The ghost or The woman wears the breeches. London, W. Bentley 1653. sm. 4to. First Edition. (Clawson)

Gibbon, Edward. An essay on the study of literature. London, for T. Becket and P. A. de Hondt 1764. 8vo. First Edition, original wrappers, uncut

——— The history of the decline and fall of the Roman empire. London, for W. Strahan and T. Cadell 1776-88. 6v. 4to. First Edition. (Lord Spencer)

——— Miscellaneous works. London, 1-2 for A. Strahan and T. Cadell jun. 1796; 3 for J. Murray 1815. 3v. 4to. First Edition. (Lord Spencer)

[———] A vindication. London, for W. Strahan and T. Cadell 1779. 8vo. First Edition, original wrappers

[Gifford, William]. The Baviad. London, for R. Faulder 1791. 8vo. First Edition

[Gildon, Charles]. A comparison between the two stages. London 1702. 8vo. First Edition

[———] Measure for measure. London, for D. Brown and R. Parker 1700. 4to. First Edition

——— *See also* Langbaine, Gerard

Gioacchimo Greco. The royall game of chesse-play . . . [Tr. by F. Beale]. London, for H. Herringman 1656. 12mo. First Edition. (Groves)

Giraffi, Alexander. An exact historie of the late revolutions in Naples
... rendred to English, by J[ames] H[owell]. London [I] R.A.
for R.Lowndes 1650; [II] A.M. for Abel Roper and T.Dring 1652.
2 v. 8vo. First Edition

Glanvill, Joseph. Plus ultra. London, J. Collins 1668. 8vo. First
Edition. (McBurney)

[Glasse, Hannah]. The art of cookery. London, for the Author
1747. fol. First Edition

Glover, Richard. Boadicia. London, for R. and J.Dodsley 1753. 8vo.
First Edition

Godolphin, Sidney, *tr. See* Virgilius Maro, Publius

Godwin, Mary Wollstonecraft. An historical and moral view of the
origin and progress of the French Revolution. London, for J.
Johnson 1794. 8vo. v. 1 (all published). First Edition

[———] Mary. London, for J. Johnson 1788. 8vo. First Edition

[———] Original stories. London, for J.Johnson 1788. 12mo. First
Edition

——— Thoughts on the education of daughters. London, for J.
Johnson 1787. 8vo. First Edition, paper boards

[———] Posthumous works. London, for J. Johnson 1798. 4 v.
8vo. First Edition

Godwin, William. An enquiry concerning political justice. London,
for G. G. J. and J. Robinson 1793. 2 v. 4to. First Edition.
(Henry Godfrey Godfrey Faussett Osborne)

——— Memoirs of the author of A vindication of the rights of woman.
London, for J. Johnson 1798. 8vo. First Edition

[Goethe, Johann Wolfgang von]. The sorrows of Werter [Tr. by
Richard Graves]. London, for J. Dodsley 1779. 2 v. 8vo. First
Edition

G[offe], T[homas]. The careles shepherdess. London, for R. Rogers
and W. Ley 1656. sm. 4to. First Edition

Goldsmith, Francis. *See* Groot, Hugo de

[Goldsmith, Oliver]. The art of poetry. London, for J. Newbery
1762. 2 v. 8vo.

[Goldsmith, Oliver].   The bee.   London, for J. Wilkie 1759.   8vo.
First Edition.   (H.V. Jones)

[————] The citizen of the world.   London, for J. Newbery 1762.
2 v.   8vo.   First Edition

[————] A description of Millenium Hall.   London, for J. Newbery
1762.   8vo.   First Edition

———— The deserted village.   London, for W. Griffin 1770.   4to.
First Edition

———— Essays.   London, for W. Griffin 1765.   8vo.   First Edition,
First Issue

———— The good natur'd man.   London, for W. Griffin 1768.   8vo.
First Edition

———— The Grecian history.   London, for J. and F. Rivington 1774.
2 v.   8vo.   First Edition

[————] An history of England.   London, for J. Newbery 1764.
2 v.   8vo.   First Edition

———— The history of England.   London, for T. Davies 1771.   4 v.
8vo.   First Edition

[————] The history of little Goody Two-Shoes.   London 1796.
24mo.

[————] The life of Richard Nash.   London, for J. Newbery 1762.
8vo.   First Edition.   (John Tattersall)

[————] The martial review.   London, for J. Newbery 1763.   12mo.
First Edition

[————] The memoirs of a Protestant.   London, for R. Griffiths and
E. Dilly 1758.   2 v.   12mo.   First Edition

———— Poems and plays.   Dublin 1777.   8vo.

———— ———— London, for B. Newbery and T. Johnson 1780.   12mo.

[————] Poems for young ladies.   London, for J. Payne 1767.   12mo.
First Edition.   (H.V. Jones)

———— The poetical and dramatic works.   London, H. Goldney 1780.
2 v.   8vo.

———— She stoops to conquer.   London, for F. Newbery 1773.   8vo.
First Edition, First Issue

Goldsmith, Oliver.   The traveller.   London, for J. Newbery 1765.
4to.   First Edition

[———] The vicar of Wakefield.   Salisbury, B. Collins 1766.   2 v.
8vo.   First Edition.   (Francis Longe)

[———] ——— Dublin, for W. and W. Smith 1766.   2 v.   12mo.
(v. 1 undated)

——— *and* Thomas Parnell.   Poems.   London, W. Bulmer 1795.   4to.
First Edition.   (Kern)

[Goring, Charles].   Irene.   London, for J. Bayley 1708.   4to.   First
Edition.   (H. V. Jones)

Gothofredus, Jacobus.   The history of the united provinces of Achaia
. . . rendred into English . . . by H. Stubbe.   London, A. Clark
1673.   sm. 4to.

Gould, Robert.   The laurel.   London, for B. Tooke 1685.   4to.   First
Edition.   (Lefferts)

——— Poems.   London 1689.   8vo.   First Edition

[Granville, George, *Baron Lansdowne*].   The British enchanters.
London, for J. Tonson 1706.   4to.   First Edition

——— Heroick love.   London, for F. Saunders . . . 1698.   4to.   First
Edition

[———] The Jew of Venice.   London, for B. Lintott 1701.   4to.
First Edition.   (H. B. Wheatley)

[———] Poems upon several occasions.   London, for J. Tonson 1712.
8vo.   First Edition

Graves, Richard, *tr.   See* Goethe, Johann Wolfgang von

The Graves-End tilt-boat.   London 1699.   8vo.

[Gray, Thomas].   An elegy wrote in a country church yard.   London, for R. Dodsley 1751.   4to.   First Edition

[———] ——— London, for R. Dodsley 1751.   4to.   Second Edition

[———] An elegy written in a country church yard.   London, for
R. Dodsley 1751.   4to.   Third Edition

[———] ——— London, for R. Dodsley 1751.   4to.   Fourth Edition

[Gray, Thomas]. An elegy written in a country church yard. London, for R. Dodsley 1751. 4to. Sixth Edition

———— Ode performed in the Senate-House at Cambridge, July 1, 1769. Cambridge, J. Archdeacon 1769. 4to. First Edition, wrappers. (H.V. Jones)

———— Odes. Strawberry-Hill 1757. 4to. First Edition

———— Poems. London, for J. Dodsley 1768. 8vo. First Collected Edition

Great Britain's glory. London, W. O., n.d. 4to.

Greene, Alexander. The polititian cheated. London, for R. Crofts 1663. sm. 4to. First Edition. (Newdigate)

Greville, Fulke, *Baron Brooke.* The remains. London, T. N. 1670. 8vo. First Edition. (Lefferts–Poor)

Groot, Hugo de. Hugo Grotius his Sophompaneas. Edited by F. Goldsmith. London, W. H. [1652]. 8vo. First Edition. (Heber)

[Guarini, Giovanni Battista]. Il pastor fido. Tr. by R. Fanshawe. London, for H. Moseley 1648. 4to. First Edition. (Samuel Wegg)

[————] Pastor fido. Tr. by R. Fanshawe. Dramatized by E. Settle. London, for W. Cademan 1677. 4to. First Edition

Gulliver decypher'd. London, for J. Roberts, n.d. 8vo. First Edition

Guzman, Hinde and Hannam outstript. London 1657. sm. 8vo. First Edition. (Sir Charles Bagot–Beaufoy–Huth)

H., J., *Esq. See* Harington, John

Hainam, Richard. *See* The witty rogue

Hale, *Sir* Matthew. The primitive origination of mankind. London, W. Godbid 1677. fol. First Edition. (Groves)

[Hale, Thomas]. An account of several new inventions. London, for J. Astwood 1691. 12mo.

Hall, John. Poems. Cambridge, R. Daniel 1646. 8vo. First Edition. (Frederic Ouvry)

H[all], J[oseph]. Satans fiery darts quenched. London, M. F. for N. Butter 1647. 12mo. First Edition. (Mark P. Robinson)

Hall, Thomas.   Funebria florae.   London, for H. Mortlock 1660. sm. 4to.   First Edition

Hamilton, Anthony.   Memoirs of Count Grammont.   London, for S. and E. Harding [1793].   4to.

Hamilton, William.   Poems on several occasions.   Edinburgh, for W. Gordon 1760.   8vo.   First Edition.   (Hoe)

H[ammond], W[illiam].   Poems.   London, for T. Dring 1655.   8vo. First Edition.   (Steeves–Huth)

H[arington], J[ohn].   The Grecian story.   London, for W. Crook 1684.   4to.   First Edition.   (Bement)

[Harrington, James].   The common-wealth of Oceana.   London, J. Streater 1656.   sm. fol.   First Edition

Hartley, J., *and another*.   History of the Westminster election.   London 1784.   4to.   First Edition

[Harvey, Christopher].   The school of the heart.   London, for L. Lloyd 1676.   8vo.   Third Edition.   (Joseph Cooper Walker)

[———] The synagogue.   London, J. L. for P. Stephens 1647.   nar. 12mo.   Second Edition

[Havard, William].   King Charles the First.   London, for J. Watts 1737.   8vo.   First Edition

——— Regulus.   London, H. Woodfall, jun. 1744.   8vo.   First Edition

Hawkesworth, John, *tr*.   *See* Fénelon: Telemachus [1796]

Hawkins, William.   Cymbeline.   London, for J. Rivington and J. Fletcher 1759.   8vo.   First Edition

——— Henry and Rosamond.   London, for W. Owen 1749.   8vo. First Edition

Hayne, Thomas.   The life and death of Martin Luther.   London, I. L. for I. Stafford 1641.   sm. 4to.   First Edition.   (H. V. Jones)

[Head, Richard].   Proteus redivivus.   London, W. D. 1675.   12mo. First Edition.   (Sir Francis C. M. Boileau)

Heath, James.   A brief chronicle of the late intestine warr.   London, J. B. for W. Lee 1663.   8vo.   (Huth)

[———] Flagellum: or The life and death ... of Oliver Cromwel.   By S. T.   London, for L. R. 1663.   sm. 8vo.   First Edition.   (Hoe)

Heath, Robert. Clarastella. London, for H. Moseley 1650. 12mo. First Edition. (Gaisford–McKee–Poor)

Henley, Samuel, *tr. See* Beckford, William

Henry VIII, *King of England.* Assertio septem sacramentorum. Tr. into English by T. W. London, N. Thompson 1687. sm. 4to.

Herbert, Edward, *Baron Herbert of Cherbury.* The life and raigne of King Henry the eighth. London, E. G. for T. Whitaker 1649. fol. First Edition

———— The life of Edward Lord Herbert of Cherbury. Strawberry-Hill 1764. 4to. First Edition. (Lord John Townshend)

———— Occasional verses. London, T. R. for T. Dring 1665. 8vo. (Walpole–Utterson–John Dunn Gardner–Purdy)

Herbert, George. Herbert's remains. London, for T. Garthwait 1652. 12mo. First Edition

Herle, Charles. Worldly policy, and Moral prudence. London, for S. Gellibrand 1654. 12mo. First Edition

Hermes Trismegistus. The divine pymander. Tr. . . . by [J.] Everard. London, R. White 1650. sm. 8vo. First Edition. (Sinckler Porter)

Herrick, Robert. Hesperides. London, for John Williams, and Francis Eglesfield 1648. 8vo. First Edition. (Marsh–Steeves–Locker-Lampson)

[Heydon, John]. Advice to a daughter. By Eugenius Theodidactus. London, T. J. for F. Cossinet 1659. 12mo. Second Edition. (W. Richardson–Huth)

Heyrick, Thomas. Miscellany poems. Cambridge, J. Hayes 1691. 4to. First Edition

———— The submarine voyage. Cambridge, J. Hayes 1691. 4to. First Edition

[Heywood, Thomas]. The generall history of women. London, W. H. 1657. 12mo. First Edition. (Huth)

[————] The life of Merlin. London, J. Okes 1641. 4to. First Edition. (Huth)

———— Reader, here you'l plainly see iudgement perverted by these three. n.p. 1641. sm. 4to. First Edition

Hickeringill, Edmund. The naked truth. The second part. London, for F. Smith 1681. fol. Second Edition

H[ickes], W[illiam]. Grammatical drollery. London, for T. Fox 1682. 8vo. First Edition. (Huth)

[Hiffernan, Paul]. The heroine of the cave. London, for T. Evans 1775. 8vo. First Edition

Hill, Aaron. Elfrid. London, for B. Lintott and E. Sanger [1710]. 4to. First Edition

[————] The fatal vision. London, for E. Nutt [1716]. 4to. First Edition

———— Merope. London, for A. Millar 1749. 8vo. First Edition

[————] The walking statue. n.p. 1709. 8vo. First Edition

Hill, John. Eden. London 1757. fol. First Edition

———— The story of Elizabeth Canning considered. London, for M. Cooper 1753. 8vo. First Edition. (Huth)

[Hippisley, John]. Flora. London, for T. Wood 1729. 8vo. First Edition

An historical description of the glorious conquest of the city of Buda. London, for R. Clavell 1686. sm. 4to.

Hoadly, Benjamin. The suspicious husband. London, for J. and R. Tonson 1747. 8vo. First Edition

Hobbes, Thomas. The answer of Mr. Hobbs to Sir William D'Avenant's Preface before Gondibert. Paris, chez M. Guillemot 1650. sm. 12mo. First Edition. (A. B. Spingarn)

———— Leviathan. London, for A. Crooke 1651. fol. First Edition

———— tr. See Homerus

Holcroft, Thomas. Duplicity. London, for G. Robinson 1781. 8vo. First Edition

———— The road to ruin. London, for J. Debrett 1792. 8vo. First Edition

Holland, Philemon, tr. See Livius, Titus

Holyday, Barten, tr. See Juvenalis

[Home, John]. Alfred. London, for T. Becket 1778. 8vo. First Edition

[178]

[Home, John]. Douglas. London, for A. Millar 1757. 8vo. First Edition

[————] The siege of Aquileia. London, for A. Millar 1760. 8vo. First Edition

Homerus. Homer's Iliads. Tr. by T. Hobbes. London, J. C. for W. Crook 1676. 12mo. First Edition

———— Homer's Odysses. Tr. by T. Hobbes. London, J. C. for W. Crook 1675. 12mo. First Edition

———— The Iliad. Tr. by Mr. Pope. London, W. Bowyer 1715-20. 6v. fol. First Edition

———— ———— London, C. Rivington 1760. 6v. 8vo. (William Fullerton)

———— The Iliad and Odyssey. Tr. by W. Cowper. London, for J. Johnson 1791. 2v. 4to. First Edition

———— The Odyssey. Tr. by Mr. Pope. London, for B. Lintot 1725-6. 5v. fol. First Edition

———— ———— London, C. Rivington 1760. 5v. 8vo. (William Fullerton)

Hooker, Richard. The works. London, for R. Scot ... 1682. fol. Large paper. (Thomas Zouch)

Hoole, Charles. *See* Comenius

Hoole, John. Cyrus. London, for T. Davies 1768. 8vo. First Edition

Hope, *Sir* William, *tr. See* Solleysell, Jacques de

[Hopkins, Charles]. Niglected virtue. London, for H. Rhodes ... 1696. 4to. First Edition

———— Pyrrhus. London, for S. Briscoe ... 1695. 4to. First Edition

Horatius Flaccus, Quintus. Horace's Art of poetry. Tr. by the Earl of Roscommon. London, for H. Herringman 1680. sm. 4to. First Edition. (Chew)

———— The poems ... rendred in English verse by several persons. London, E. Cotes 1666. 12mo. First Edition. (Purdy)

———— *See also* Pope, Alexander; Swift, Jonathan

Horsley, John. Britannia Romana. London 1732. fol.

[Howard, Edward]. Caroloiades. London, J. B. 1689. 8vo. First Edition

———— The usurper. London, for H. Herringman 1668. 4to. First Edition

———— The womens conquest. London, J. M. 1671. 4to. First Edition

Howard, James. All mistaken. London, H. Brugis 1672. 4to. First Edition. (Huth)

Howard, John. An account of the principal lazarettos in Europe. Warrington, W. Eyres 1789. 4to. First Edition. (2 copies, one a presentation)

———— The state of the prisons in England and Wales. Warrington, W. Eyres 1777. 4to. First Edition

Howard, *Sir* Robert. Four new plays. London, for H. Herringman 1665. fol. First Edition. (Huth)

———— The great favourite. (London) for H. Herringman 1668. 4to. First Edition

———— Poems. London, for H. Herringman 1660. 8vo. First Edition. (William Harris Arnold)

Howell, James. ΔΕΝΔΡΟΛΟΓΙΑ Dodona's grove. [London] 1644. sm. 4to. Second Edition

———— Epistolae Ho-Elianae. London, for H. Moseley 1645. 4to. First Edition

[————] Florus Hungaricus. London, W. G. for H. Marsh 1664. sm. 8vo. First Edition

———— A German diet. London, for H. Moseley 1653. fol. First Edition

[————] The history of the life and death of Oliver Cromwell. London, for F. Coles 1663. sm. 4to.

[————] Instructions for forreine travell. London, T. B. for H. Mosley 1642. nar. 12mo. First Edition

———— Londinopolis. London, J. Streater 1657. fol. First Edition

[————] Poems on several choice and various subjects. London, J. Cottrel 1663. 8vo. First Edition. (Huth)

Howell, James. ΠΡΟΕΔΡΙΑ-ΒΑΣΙΛΙΚΗ. London, J. Cottrel 1664. fol. First Edition

―――― S. P Q. V. A survay of the signorie of Venice. London, for R. Lowndes 1651. fol. First Edition

―――― Twelve several treatises, of the late revolutions. London, J. Grismond 1661. sm. 8vo. First Edition

―――― tr. See Giraffi, Alexander

[Hunt, Thomas]. The great and weighty considerations relating to the Duke of York. London 1680. fol. First Edition

Hunter, John. An historical journal. London, for J. Stockdale 1793. 4to. First Edition

Hyde, Edward, first Earl of Clarendon. A brief view ... of the ... errors to church and state, in Mr. Hobbes's book, entitled Leviathan. Oxon: Printed at the Theater 1676. 4to.

―――― The history of the Rebellion ... in England. Oxford, Printed at the Theater 1707, 1704. 3 v. fol.

―――― The life of Edward Earl of Clarendon. Oxford, Clarendon Printing-House 1759. 3 v. 8vo. First Edition

[Hyde, Henry, Viscount Cornbury]. The mistakes. London, S. Richardson 1758. 8vo. First Edition

An impartial account of divers remarkable proceedings the last sessions of Parliament relating to the horrid Popish plot. London 1679. fol. First Edition

The indictment, arraignment, tryall, and judgment ... of twenty-nine regicides. London, for J. Walthoe 1713. 8vo.

Ireland, Samuel. Picturesque views on the upper ... Avon. London 1795. fol. Large paper

[Jackman, Isaac]. The divorce. London, for G. Kearsly 1781. 8vo. First Edition

Jacob, Hildebrand. The works. London, for W. Lewis 1735. 8vo. First Edition. (Presentation copy from the author to the Earl of Orrery)

James I, King of England. The narrative history of King James. London, for M. Sparke 1651. sm. 4to. First Edition. (Lefferts–Bement)

Jenkins, Elijah, *pseud.* *See* Mottley, John

Jephson, Robert. Braganza. London, for T. Evans and T. Davies 1775. 8vo. First Edition

―――― The law of Lombardy. London, for T. Evans 1779. 8vo. First Edition. (H. Cavendish)

―――― Love at first sight. London, for T. Becket ... 1763. 8vo. First Edition. (H. Cavendish)

Johnson, Charles. The force of friendship. London, for E. Sanger 1710. 4to. First Edition. (H.V. Jones)

[――――] Fortune in her wits. London, for B. Lintott 1705. 4to. First Edition

[――――] The gentleman-cully. London, for A. Bettesworth and R. Wellington 1702. 4to. First Edition

―――― Love and liberty. London, for B. Lintott 1709. 4to. First Edition. (John Genest)

―――― The successful pyrate. London, for B. Lintott 1713. 4to. First Edition

―――― The tragedy of Medaea. London, for R. Francklin 1731. 8vo. First Edition

―――― The victim. London 1714. 8vo. First Edition

―――― The village opera. London, for J. Watts 1729. 8vo. First Edition

Johnson, James. The Scots Musical Museum. Edinburgh, J. Johnson [1787-1803]. 6v. in 2. 8vo. (Sir John Stainer)

Johnson, Richard. The crown garland of golden roses. London, J. M. for W. and T. Thackeray 1662. 8vo.

Johnson, Samuel (1691-1773). The blazing comet. London, for J. Crokatt 1732. 8vo. First Edition

[Johnson, Samuel] (1709-1784). An account of the life of Mr. Richard Savage. London, for J. Roberts 1744. 8vo. First Edition. (W.F. Prideaux)

[――――] The Adventurer. London, for J. Payne 1753-4. fol. First Edition, as published, in parts

[Johnson, Samuel] (1709-1784). A dictionary of the English language. London, W. Strahan 1755. 2 v. fol. First Edition

[————] The Idler. London, J. Newbery 1761. 2 v. 12mo. First Edition. (J. C. Levi)

———— Irene. London, for R. Dodsley 1749. 8vo. First Edition. (G. W. Steeves)

[————] A journey to the Western Islands of Scotland. London, for W. Strahan and T. Cadell 1775. 8vo. First Edition, First Issue. (Paul Panton)

———— Letters to and from the late Samuel Johnson. Published . . . by Hester Lynch Piozzi. London, for A. Strahan and T. Cadell 1788. 2 v. 8vo. First Edition. (Wm. Priestman)

———— The life of Samuel Johnson. London, for G. Kearsley 1785. 12mo. Second Edition. (Attrib. author, William Cooke)

———— The lives of the most eminent English poets. London, for C. Bathurst . . . 1781. 4 v. 8vo. First Edition. (H. V. Jones)

[————] London. London, for R. Doddesley 1738. fol. First Edition

[————] Marmor Norfolciense. London, for J. Brett 1739. 8vo. First Edition

———— Mr. Johnson's Preface to his edition of Shakespear's Plays. London, for J. and R. Tonson . . . 1765. 8vo. First Edition

[————] The plan of a dictionary. London, for J. and P. Knapton 1747. 8vo.

[————] The prince of Abissinia. London, for R. and J. Dodsley 1759. 2 v. sm. 8vo.

[————] The Rambler. London, for J. Payne and J. Bouquet 1751-2. 2 v. fol. First Edition, as published, in parts. (Sir William Augustus Fraser–Hagen)

[————] ———— London, for J. Payne 1753. fol. First Edition as published, in parts, but with the 1753 title

———— The vanity of human wishes. London, for R. Dodsley 1749. 4to. First Edition. (R. J. Collier)

Johnstone, John. An history of the wonderful things of nature. Tr. by J. Rowland. London, J. Streater 1657. fol. First Edition

Jones, Henry. The Earl of Essex. London, for R. Dodsley 1753. 8vo. First Edition

Jones, Inigo. The most notable antiquity of Great Britain, vulgarly called Stone-Heng. London, J. Flesher 1655. fol. First Edition. (Earl of Jersey–W. L. Andrews)

Jonson, Benjamin. Catiline. London, for A. C. 1669. 4to. (H. B. Wheatley)

—— Every man in his humour. London, for J. and R. Tonson and S. Draper 1752. 8vo.

[Jordan, Thomas]. Death dis-sected. Printed by authority for the use of the author 1649. 8vo. First Edition

—— Rules to know a royall king. London, for R. Wood and E. Christopher 1642. sm. 4to. First Edition

Joyner, William. The Roman empress. (London) T. N. 1671. 4to. First Edition

Juvenalis, Decimus Junius. Juvenal's sixteen satyrs. Tr. by Sir R. Stapylton. London, for H. Moseley 1647. 8vo. First Edition

—— Mores hominum . . . By Sir R. Stapylton. London, R. Hodgkinsonne 1660. fol. First Edition. Large paper

—— The satires. Tr. by J. Dryden. London, for J. Tonson 1693. fol. First Edition. Large paper

—— The tenth satyr. The English by T. Shadwell. London, D. Mallet 1687. 4to. First Edition

—— *and* Aulus Persius Flaccus. Tr. by Barten Holyday. Oxford, W. Downing 1673. fol. First Edition. (Chevalier de Chatelain)

Kelly, Hugh. False delicacy. London, for R. Baldwin 1768. 8vo. First Edition

Kemble, John Philip. Fugitive pieces. York, W. Blanchard 1780. 8vo. First Edition. (John Pritt Harley)

Killigrew, Anne. Poems. London, for S. Lowndes 1686. 4to. First Edition. (Chew)

Killigrew, Thomas. Comedies, and tragedies. London, for H. Herringman 1664. fol. First Edition. (Cornelius Paine–Charles Lilburn)

Killigrew, Thomas. The prisoners and Claracilla. London, T. Cotes 1641. 12mo. First Editions of both plays, 1640 and 1641 respectively, with general title 1641

Killigrew, *Sir* William. Four new playes. Oxford, H. Hall 1666. fol.

———— Mid-night and daily thoughts. London, for Thomas Bennet, at the Half-Moon ... 1694. 8vo. ([-]²; B-F⁸; G⁶). (Haslewood–Corser–Huth)

———— ———— London, for Randal Taylor ... 1694. 8vo. ([-]²; B-F⁸; G⁶; H⁴; I²)

[————] Pandora. London, T. Mabb 1664. 8vo. First Edition. (Lefferts)

[King, Henry]. Poems, elegies, paradoxes, and sonnets. London, J. G. for R. Marriot 1657. 8vo. First Edition

King, Josiah. The examination and tryal of old Father Christmas. London, for H. Brome ... 1678. 8vo. First Edition

Kinnaston, Sir Francis. Leoline & Sydanis. London, R. Hearne 1642. sm. 4to. First Edition. (Bindley–Gaisford)

Knight, Samuel. The life of Erasmus. Cambridge, C. Crownfield 1726. 8vo. First Edition. (Samuel Prince–Hoe)

LaCalprenède. *See* Costes, Gautier de

Lacy, John. Sr. Hercules Buffoon. London, for J. Hindmarsh 1684. 4to. First Edition

Lamb, Charles. *See* Coleridge, Samuel Taylor

[Landor, Walter Savage]. Gebir. London 1798. 8vo. First Edition, wrappers, uncut. (John Drinkwater)

———— The poems. London, for T. Cadell, junr. and W. Davies 1795. 8vo. First Edition, original boards, uncut

[————] Poems from the Arabic and Persian. Warwick, H. Sharpe 1800. 4to. First Edition, stabbed, uncut

Langbaine, Gerard. An account of the English dramatick poets. Oxford, L. L. 1691. 8vo. First Edition

———— The lives and characters of the English dramatick poets ... continued ... [by Charles Gildon]. London, for T. Leigh and W. Turner [1699]. 8vo. First Edition

Lansdowne, *Baron.* *See* Granville, George

LaQuintinye, Jean de.   The compleat gard'ner. Tr. by J. Evelyn. London, for M. Gillyflower and J. Partridge 1693. fol. First Edition. (Sir John Cope)

Law, John. Money and trade. London, for W. Lewis 1720. 8vo.

Law, William. A serious call to a devout and holy life. London, for W. Innys 1729. 8vo. First Edition. (Anne Pollen)

[Leanerd, John]. The rambling justice. London, E. F. 1678. 4to. First Edition

Lee, Nathaniel. Caesar Borgia. London, R. E. 1680. 4to. First Edition

——— Constantine the Great. London, H. Hills Jun. 1684. 4to. First Edition

——— Gloriana. London, for J. Magnes and R. Bentley 1676. 4to. First Edition

——— Lucius Junius Brutus. London, for R. Tonson and J. Tonson 1681. 4to. First Edition

——— The massacre of Paris. London, for R. Bentley and M. Magnes 1690. 4to. First Edition

——— Mithridates. London, R. E. 1678. 4to. First Edition

——— The Princess of Cleve. London 1689. 4to. First Edition

——— The rival queens. London, for J. Magnes and R. Bentley 1677. 4to. First Edition

——— Sophonisba. London, for J. Magnes and R. Bentley 1676. 4to. First Edition

——— The tragedy of Nero. London, T. R. and N. T. 1675. 4to. First Edition

——— *See also* Dryden, John, *and* Nathaniel Lee

Lennox, Charlotte. The sister. London, for J. Dodsley 1769. 8vo. First Edition

[LeSage, Alain René]. The adventures of Gil Blas. Tr. by T. Smollett. London, for J. Osborn 1750. 4v. 12mo.

[Leslie, Charles]. A short and easie method with the deists. London, J. Applebee 1723. 8vo. Eighth Edition

A letter from a clergyman to his friend, with an account of the travels of Capt. Lemuel Gulliver. London, for A. Moore 1726. 8vo. First Edition

Lewis, John. A complete history of the several translations of the Holy Bible...in English. London, H. Woodfall 1739. 8vo. Second Edition

———— The life of mayster Wyllyam Caxton. London 1737. 8vo. First Edition. (White Knights)

The life and death of . . . Henrietta Maria de Bourbon. London, for S. Speed 1669. 12mo. (Purdy)

Lindsay, *Sir* David. The works. Glasgow, R. Sanders 1665. 8vo. (Lord Willoughby de Broke)

Livius, Titus. The Roman history. Tr. by P. Holland. London, for A. Churchill 1686. fol.

Lloyd, Charles. *See* Coleridge, Samuel Taylor

Lloyd, Robert. The capricious lovers. London, for R. Withy and W. Griffin 1764. 8vo. First Edition

Lobo, Jerome. A short relation of the river Nile. Tr. by Sir P. Wyche. London, for J. Martyn, Printer to the Royal Society 1669. 8vo. First Edition. (George de Ligné Gregory)

Lock, Matthew. The English opera. London, T. Ratcliff and N. Thompson 1675. 4to. First Edition. (Sir Francis Fust)

[Locke, John]. A collection of several pieces. London, J. Bettenham 1720. 8vo. First Edition

———— An essay concerning humane understanding. London, E. Holt 1690. fol. First Edition

———— A letter to . . . Edward Lord Bishop of Worcester. London, H. Clark 1697. 8vo. First Edition

[————] Some thoughts concerning education. London, for A. and J. Churchill 1693. 8vo. First Edition. (Bement)

[Longus]. Daphnis and Chloe. By G. Thornley. London, for J. Garfeild 1657. 8vo. First Edition

A looking-glasse for sope-patentees. London 1646. sm. 4to. First Edition

Lovelace, Richard. Lucasta. London, T. Harper 1649. 8vo. First Edition. (Hugh Perkins)

Lower, *Sir* William, *tr.* *See* Ceriziers; Corneille, Pierre

Lucretius Carus, Titus. An essay on the first book. Tr. by J. Evelyn. London, for G. Bedle and T. Collins 1656. 8vo. First Edition

Lunardi, Vincent. An account of five aerial voyages in Scotland. London, for the Author, and sold by J. Bell 1786. 8vo. First Edition

M., G. *See* Miege, Guy

M., J. *See* Marsh, John

[Mackenzie, Henry]. The man of feeling. London, for T. Cadell 1771. 12mo. First Edition. (Huth)

Macleod, Donald. Memoirs of the . . . old Highlander, Serjeant Donald Macleod. London, Peterborough–House Press 1791. 8vo. Second Edition

Macpherson, James, *tr.* *See* Ossian

Madox, Thomas. The history and antiquities of the exchequer. London, for W. Owen 1769. 2 v. 4to. Second Edition. (Thomas M. Lowndes)

Magnus, Olaus. A compendious history of the Goths, Swedes, & Vandals. London, J. Streater 1658. fol. First Edition

Maimbourg, Louis. The history of the League. Tr. by J. Dryden. London, M. Flesher 1684. 8vo. First Edition

[Mallet, David]. Elvira. London, for A. Millar 1763. 8vo. First Edition

[———] Eurydice. London, for A. Millar 1731. 8vo. First Edition

[———] Mustapha. London, for A. Millar 1739. 8vo. First Edition

[——— *and* James Thomson]. Alfred. London, for A. Millar 1740. 8vo. First Edition

Mallet, *Sir* John. Concerning penal laws. London, for T. Cockeril 1680. fol. First Edition

[Malthus, Thomas Robert]. An essay on the principle of population. London, for J. Johnson 1798. 8vo. First Edition

[Mandeville, Bernard]. The fable of the bees. London, for J. Roberts 1714. 12mo. First Edition

Mandeville, *Sir* John. The voiage and travaile of Sir John Maundevile. London, for J. Woodman ... 1725. 8vo. First Edition. (Huth)

Manley, Mary. The lost lover. London, for R. Bently ... 1696. 4to. First Edition

―――― The royal mischief. London, for R. Bentley ... 1696. 4to. First Edition

[Manning, Francis]. All for the better. London 1703. 4to. First Edition

―――― The generous choice. London, for R. Wellington ... 1700. 4to. First Edition

[Manuche, Cosmo]. The bastard. London, for M. M. ... 1652. 4to. First Edition

Marmion, Shakerley. The antiquary. London, F. K. 1641. sm. 4to. First Edition

M[arsh], J[ohn]. An argument or, debate in law ... By J. M. London, T. Paine and M. Simmons 1642. sm. 4to. First Edition. (Buxton Forman)

Martialis, Marcus Valerius. Ex otio negotium. Or, Martiall his epigrams. Tr. by R. Fletcher. London, T. Mabb for W. Shears 1656. 8vo. First Edition. (Morgan Thomas)

Marvell, Andrew. Miscellaneous poems. London, for R. Boulter 1681. fol. First Edition

―――― The rehearsal transpros'd. London, A. B. for the Assigns of J. Calvin and T. Beza 1672. 8vo. First Edition

―――― ―――― The second part. London, for N. Ponder 1673. 8vo. First Edition

―――― *and others*. A collection of poems on affairs of state. London 1689. sm. 4to. (Hoe–R. J. Collier–Groves)

Massinger, Philip. Three new playes. London, for H. Moseley 1655. 8vo. First Edition

―――― Thomas Middleton, *and* William Rowley. The excellent comedy, called The old law. London, for E. Archer 1656. sm. 4to. First Edition. (Huth)

Matthew, *Sir* Tobie.   A collection of letters.   London, for H. Herringman 1660.   8vo.   First Edition

May, Thomas.   The old couple.   London, J. Cottrel 1658.   sm. 4to.
First Edition.   (Huth)

[Mayne, Jasper].   The amorous warre.   n.p. 1648.   sm. 4to.   First
Edition

Mead, Robert.   The combat of love and friendship.   London, for M.
M.... 1654.   sm. 4to.   First Edition.   (Bridgewater)

Medbourne, Matthew.   Tartuffe.   London, H. L. and R. B. 1670.   4to.
First Edition

M[ennes] *Sir* J[ohn], *and* Ja[mes] S[mith].   Musarum deliciae.   London, for H. Herringman 1656.   8vo.   First Edition.   (H.V. Jones)

[———]   Recreation for ingenious head-pieces.   London, M. Simmons 1654.   8vo.

Mercurius Menippeus.   The loyal satyrist.   London, for J. Hindmarsh
1682.   sm. 4to.   First Edition

Meriton, Thomas.   Love and war.   London, for C. Webb 1658.   sm.
4to.   First Edition.   (Mitford)

———   The wandring lover.   London, T. L. 1658.   sm. 4to.   First
Edition.   (Hoe)

Middleton, Thomas.   Any thing for a quiet life.   London, T. Johnson
1662.   sm. 4to.   First Edition.   (Huth)

———   The mayor of Quinborough.   London, for H. Herringman
1661.   sm. 4to.   First Edition.   (McKee)

———   No $\begin{Bmatrix} \text{wit} \\ \text{help} \end{Bmatrix}$ like a womans.   London, for H. Moseley 1657.
8vo.   First Edition

———   A tragi-coomodie, called The witch.   London, J. Nichols
1778.   8vo.   First Edition

———   Two new playes.   London, for H. Moseley 1657.   8vo.   First
Edition.   (Stirling Maxwell–Locker-Lampson–Church–Clawson)

———   Women beware women.   London, for H. Moseley 1657.   8vo.
First Edition.   (J. Payne Collier–Groves)

———   *See also* Massinger, Philip, Thomas Middleton *and* William
Rowley

Middleton, Thomas, *and* William Rowley. The changeling. London, for H. Moseley 1653. 4to. First Edition. (Kern)

M[iege], G[uy]. Delight and pastime. By G. M. London, for J. Sprint and G. Conyers 1697. 16mo. First Edition. (John Nicoll–Carnavon–Huth)

[Miller, James]. Art and nature. London, for J. Watts 1738. 8vo. First Edition

[———] The coffee-house. London, for J. Watts 1737. 8vo. First Edition. (Edward Hailstone)

[———] An hospital for fools. London, for J. Watts 1739. 8vo. First Edition

[———] The humours of Oxford. London, for J. Watts 1730. 8vo. First Edition

[———] Mahomet the impostor. London, for J. Watts 1744. 8vo. First Edition

[———] The man of taste. London, for J. Watts 1735. 8vo. First Edition

[———] The mother-in-law. London, for J. Watts 1734. 8vo. First Edition

[———] The universal passion. London, for J. Watts 1737. 8vo. First Edition

Milton, John. Areopagitica. London 1644. sm. 4to. First Edition. (Robert J. Collier)

——— A brief history of Moscovia. London, M. Flesher 1682. 8vo. First Edition. (Elton)

——— Colasterion. [London] 1645. sm. 4to. First Edition

——— Considerations touching the likeliest means to remove hirelings out of the church. London, T. N. 1659. 12mo. First Edition. (H.V. Jones)

——— A defence of the people of England. n.p. 1692. 8vo. First Edition. (H.V. Jones)

——— The doctrine and discipline of divorce. London, T. P[ayne] and M. S[immons] 1643. sm. 4to. First Edition

——— ΕΙΚΟΝΟΚΛΑΣΤΗΣ. London, M. Simmons 1649. sm. 4to. First Edition

Milton, John. The history of Britain. London, J. M. 1670. sm. 4to.
First Edition

———— Joannis Miltoni Angli Pro populo Anglicano defensio. Londini, Typis DuGardianis 1651. sm. 4to. First Edition. (Scrope
Berdmore–Henry C. Compton–James Boswell)

———— Joannis Miltoni Angli Pro populo Anglicano defensio secunda.
Londini, Typis Neucomianis 1654. 8vo. First Edition. (Lefferts–Poor–Wallace)

———— Joannis Miltoni Angli Pro se defensio. Londini, Typis Neucomianis 1655. 8vo. First Edition. (Winans–Lefferts–Hagen)

———— Joannis Miltoni Londinensis poemata. Londini, W. R. 1673.
8vo.

———— Letters of state. London 1694. 12mo. First Edition

———— Literae pseudo-senatus Anglicani, Cromwellii. London 1676.
sm. 12mo. First Edition. (Winans–Poor–Wallace)

———— Mr John Miltons Character of the Long Parliament. London,
for H. Brome 1681. sm. 4to. First Edition

———— Of reformation touching church-discipline in England. [Lon-
don] for T. Underhill 1641. sm. 4to. First Edition. (H.V.
Jones)

———— Of true religion. London 1673. sm. 4to. First Edition

———— Paradise lost. London, Printed, and are to be sold by Peter
Parker . . . Robert Boulter . . . and Matthias Walker 1667. 8vo.
First Edition, second title-page. (Groves)

———— ———— London, Printed, and are to be sold by P. Parker . . .
R. Boulter . . . and M. Walker . . . 1668. sm. 4to. First Edition,
third title-page

———— ———— London, S. Simmons, and to be sold by S. Thomson
. . . H. Mortlack . . . M. Walker . . . and R. Boulter . . . 1668. sm.
4to. First Edition, fourth title-page

———— ———— London, S. Simmons, and are to be sold by T. Helder
1669. sm. 4to. First Edition, seventh title-page

———— ———— London, S. Simmons 1674. 8vo. Second Edition

———— ———— London, M. Flesher 1688. fol. First Illustrated Edition

Milton, John. Paradise lost. Birmingham, J. Baskerville 1759. 4to. (Griswold–Ives)

———— Paradise regain'd. London, J. M. for J. Starkey 1671. 8vo. First Edition

———— ———— London, for J. Starkey 1680. 8vo. Second Edition. (Kalbfleisch)

———— ———— Birmingham, J. Baskerville 1759. 4to. (Griswold–Ives)

———— Poems. London, R. Raworth 1645. 8vo. First Edition. (Hugh Perkins)

———— Poems, &c. upon several occasions. London, for T. Dring 1673. 8vo.

———— The poetical works. London, W. Bulmer 1794. 3 v. fol.

———— The reason of church-governement urg'd against prelaty. London, E. G. 1641. sm. 4to. First Edition

———— The tenure of kings and magistrates. London, M. Simmons 1649. sm. 4to. First Edition

———— Tetrachordon. London 1645. sm. 4to. First Edition

———— A treatise of civil power. London, T. Newcomb 1659. 12mo. First Edition

———— See also Bucer, Martin; Colman, George: Comus

Miscellaneous poems and translations. By several hands. London, for B. Lintott 1712. 8vo. (John Hervy–W. F. Prideaux)

Montagu, Charles. See Prior, Matthew, and Charles Montagu

[Montagu, Elizabeth]. An essay on the writings and genius of Shakespear. Dublin, for H. Saunders ... 1769. 12mo.

Montagu, Walter. The accomplish'd woman. London, for G. Bedell and T. Collins 1656. 12mo. First Edition

———— The shepheard's paradise. London, for T. Dring 1629 [1659]. 8vo. First Edition, First Issue. (Randall Hatfield)

Montalvan, Perez de. See Perez de Montalvan, Juan

Montesquieu, M. de Secondat, Baron de. The spirit of laws. London, for J. Nourse and P. Vaillant 1750. 2 v. 8vo.

Moore, Edward. The foundling. London, for R. Francklin 1748. 8vo. First Edition

[———] The gamester. London, for R. Francklin 1753. 8vo. First Edition

——— Gil Blas. London, for R. Francklin 1751. 8vo. First Edition

Moore, *Sir* Thomas (d. 1735). Mangora. London, for W. Harvey and E. Nutt 1718. 8vo. First Edition

[More, Henry]. Divine dialogues. London, J. Flesher 1668. 8vo. First Edition. (Groves)

More, *Sir* Thomas. The historie of the pitifull life . . . of Edward the fifth. London, T. Payne 1641. 12mo. First Edition

Morgan, Matthew. A poem upon the late victory over the French fleet. London 1692. sm. 4to. First Edition

Morgan, Sylvanus. The sphere of gentry. London, W. Leybourn 1661. fol. First Edition. Large paper. (Sir Henry Hope Edwardes)

Morison, David. Poems, chiefly in the Scottish dialect. Montrose, D. Buchanan 1790. 8vo.

Morland, Samuel. The history of the evangelical churches of the valleys of Piemont. London, H. Hills 1658. fol. First Edition. (Thomas Western, Felix Hall)

[Morris, Robert]. Fatal necessity. London, for R. Dodsley . . . 1742. 8vo. First Edition

Morton, Thomas. Columbus. London, for W. Miller 1792. 8vo. First Edition

[Motteux, Peter Anthony]. The amorous miser. London 1705. 4to. First Edition. (Lefferts)

——— Beauty in distress. London, for D. Brown and R. Parker 1698. 4to. First Edition

——— Love's a jest. London, for P. Buck . . . 1696. 4to. First Edition

——— The loves of Mars and Venus. London 1697. 4to. First Edition

Motteux, Peter Anthony. Thomyris. London, for J. Tonson 1707. 4to. First Edition. (Lefferts–Hoe–H.V. Jones)

[——— editor]. The gentleman's journal. January 1692-November 1694. London 1692-4. 3 v. sm. 4to. First Edition. (W. H. Cummings)

——— tr. See Rabelais, François

[Mottley, John]. Joe Miller's jests. London, T. Read 1739. 8vo. First Edition

Mountfort, William. Greenwich-Park. London, for J. Hindmarsh ... 1691. 4to. First Edition. (Huth)

——— The injur'd lovers. London, for S. Manship 1688. 4to. First Edition

[———] King Edward the third. London, for J. Hindmarsh ... 1691. 4to. First Edition

Mumford, Joseph. The Catholic-scripturist. [Edinburgh] Holy-Rood-House 1687. Third Edition. 8vo. (J. R. P. Forrest)

Mun, Thomas. England's treasure by forraign trade. London, J. G. 1664. 8vo. First Edition

Munday, Anthony, tr. See Florando de Inglaterra

Murphy, Arthur. All in the wrong. London, for P. Vaillant 1761. 8vo. First Edition. (Hoe–H.V. Jones)

——— The apprentice. London, for P. Vaillant 1756. 8vo. First Edition. (Hoe–H.V. Jones)

——— The old maid. London, for P. Vaillant 1761. 8vo. First Edition. (Hoe–H.V. Jones)

[———] What we must all come to. London, for P. Vaillant 1764. 8vo. First Edition. (Hoe–H.V. Jones)

[———] Zenobia. London, for W. Griffin 1768. 8vo. First Edition

Musaeus. Musaeus, on the loves of Hero and Leander. By Sir R. Stapylton. London, F. B. for H. Mosley 1647. 12mo. First Edition. (Huth)

[———] Popular tales of the Germans. Tr. . . . [by William Beckford?]. London, for J. Murray 1791. 2 v. 12mo. First Edition

Mylne, James. Poems. Edinburgh, for W. Creech 1790. 8vo. First Edition. (Pauncefort Duncombe)

Napier, John. Napiers narration. London, R. O[ulton] and G. D[exter] 1641. sm. 4to. First Edition. (Clawson–H.V. Jones)

Naps upon Parnassus. London, for N. Brook 1658. 8vo. First Edition. (Sykes–Mitford–Gaisford)

Naunton, *Sir* Robert. Fragmenta regalia. [London] 1641. sm. 4to.

Nedham, Marchamont, *tr. See* Selden, John

Neville, Robert. The poor scholar. London, T. Johnson 1662. sm. 4to. First Edition. (Cornelius Paine–Huth)

The new Atlantis. n.p. 1687. 4to. First Edition. (Lefferts)

A new miscellany of original poems. London, for P. Buck . . . and G. Strahan 1701. 8vo. First Edition

Newcastle, Margaret, *Duchess of. See* Cavendish, Margaret

Newcastle, William, *Duke of. See* Cavendish, William

[Norris, Henry]. The royal merchant. London, for H. N. 1706. 4to. First Edition

[North, Francis, *first Baron Guilford*]. A philosophical essay of musick. London, for J. Martyn 1677. sm. 4to. First Edition. (W. H. Cummings)

Nostradamus, Michael. The true prophecies or prognostications. Tr. by Theophilus de Garencieres. London, T. Ratcliffe and N. Thompson 1672. fol. First Edition. (Earl of Kent–Earl de Grey)

———— *See also* B., J., *Philalelos*

O., N., *tr. See* Boileau[-Despréaux, Nicolas]

Oates, Titus. An exact discovery of the mystery of iniquity. London, T. James 1679. sm. 4to. First Edition

———— The memoires of Titus Oates. London, for T. Graves 1685. sm. 4to.

———— A true narrative of the horrid plot . . . of the Popish party. London, for T. Parkhurst and T. Cockerill 1679. fol. First Edition

Odell, Thomas. The patron. London, W. Pearson [1729]. 8vo. First Edition

Ogilby, John, *tr.* *See* Virgilius Maro, Publius

Oldham, John. Poems and translations. London, for J. Hindmarsh 1683. 8vo. First Edition

———— Remains. London, for J. Hindmarsh 1684. 8vo. First Edition

[————] Some new pieces. London, M. C. for J. Hindmarsh 1681. 8vo. First Edition

———— *tr.* *See* Anacreon

Oldmixon, John. The grove. London, for R. Parker 1700. 4to. First Edition

[Oldys, William]. The British librarian. London, for T. Osborne 1738. 8vo. First Edition

The Order of the hospitalls 1557. [London, c. 1690]. 8vo.

Ossian. Fingal. Tr. by J. Macpherson. London, for T. Becket and P. A. DeHondt 1762. 4to. First Edition. (Charles Francis Wyatt–Charles Richard Summers, Bp. of Winchester)

Otway, Thomas. Alcibiades. London, for W. Cademan 1675. 4to. First Edition. (Hoe–H.V. Jones)

———— ———— London, for R. Bentley and S. Magnes 1687. 4to.

———— The atheist. London, for R. Bentley and J. Tonson 1684. 4to. First Edition. (Hoe–H.V. Jones)

———— Friendship in fashion. London, E. F. 1678. 4to. First Edition. (Hoe–H.V. Jones)

———— Heroick friendship. London, for R. King 1719. 4to. First Edition

———— The history and fall of Caius Marius. London, for R. Bentley 1692. 4to. First Edition

———— The orphan. London, for R. Bentley and M. Magnes 1680. 4to. First Edition. (Hoe–H.V. Jones)

———— The souldiers fortune. London, for R. Bentley and M. Magnes 1681. 4to. First Edition. (Hoe–H.V. Jones)

———— Titus and Berenice. London, for R. Tonson 1677. 4to. First Edition. (Hoe–H.V. Jones)

Otway, Thomas. Venice preserv'd. London, for J. Hindmarsh 1682. 4to. First Edition. (Hoe–H.V. Jones)

——— Windsor Castle. London, for C. Brome 1685. 4to. First Edition

——— *tr. See* Citri de la Guette

Ovidius Naso, Publius. The passion of Byblis. Tr. by J. Dennis. London, for R. Parker 1692. sm. 4to. First Edition

Owen, John. John Owen's Latine epigrams Englished by T. Harvey. London, R. White 1677. 12mo. First Edition

Oxford University. The judgment and decree . . . July 21. 1683, against certain pernicious books. (Oxford) Printed at the Theater 1683. fol. First Edition

P., H. *See* Peacham, Henry

P., R. *See* Paltock, Robert

P., W. The history of witches and wizards. London, for C. Hitch . . . n.d. nar. 12mo. (Daniel–Huth)

Palaeopolitanus, Franciscus. *See* More, Henry

Palladine of England. *See* Florando de Inglaterra

Palladio, Andrea. The four books of architecture. Tr. by I. Ware. London (1737). fol.

[Paltock, Robert]. The life and adventures of Peter Wilkins. London, for J. Robinson and R. Dodsley 1751. 2 v. 12mo. First Edition. (Mexborough)

Pamela's conduct in high life. London, for Ward and Chandler 1741. 12mo. First Edition

A panegyrick on the author of Absolom and Achitophel. n.p. Reprinted in the year 1682. fol. (Lefferts)

[Park, James]. A warning to England. [London] 1679. sm. 4to. First Edition

[———] A warning to London. [London] 1679. sm. 4to. First Edition

[Parker, Martin]. The king, and a poore northerne man. London, A. Clark 1673. 8vo. (Utterson–Daniel–Huth)

Parker, Martin.   The poet's blind mans bough.   London, F. Leach 1641. sm. 4to. First Edition.   (Bibl. Anglo Poetica–Midgeley–Corser–Huth)

Parliament.   *See* England. *Parliament*

Parnell, Thomas.   *See* Goldsmith, Oliver, *and* Thomas Parnell

[Pascal, Blaise].   Les provinciales . . . faithfully rendred into English. London, J. G. 1657. 12mo. First Edition

[Patrick, Simon].   A friendly debate between a conformist and a non-conformist. London, for R. Royston 1669. 8vo. First Edition

Pattison, William.   The poetical works.   London, for H. Curll 1728. 2 v. 8vo. First Edition

[Payne, Henry Neville].   The fatal jealousie.   London, for T. Dring 1673. 4to. First Edition

[———] The morning ramble.   London, for T. Dring 1673.   4to. First Edition. (Huth)

[———] The siege of Constantinople.   London, for T. Dring 1675. 4to. First Edition

P[eacham], H[enry].   A paradox in the praise of a dunce, to Smec-tymnuus. London, for T. Paybody 1642. sm. 4to. First Edition

Pecuniae obediunt omnia.   York, J. White 1696. 8vo. First Edition

[Pepys, Samuel].   Memoires relating to the state of the Royal Navy of England. [London] 1690. 8vo. First Edition

[Percy, Thomas, *editor*].   Reliques of ancient English poetry. London, for J. Dodsley 1765. 3 v. 8vo. First Edition

Pererius, Benedictus.   The astrologer anatomiz'd. Tr. by P. Enderbie. London 1674. 12mo. First Edition

Perez de Montalvan, Juan.   Aurora Ismenia and The prince. Tr. by T. Stanley.   London, W. Wilson 1650. 8vo. (Purdy)

Philalethes, Eugenius, *pseud*.   *See* Vaughan, Thomas

Philip, Arthur.   The voyage of Governor Philip to Botany Bay. London, for J. Stockdale 1789. 4to. First Edition. (John Trevenen, Helston)

Philipot, Thomas, *tr*.   *See* Æsopus

Philips, Ambrose.   The Briton.   London, for B. Lintott 1722.   8vo. First Edition

Philips, Ambrose. The distrest mother. London, for S. Buckley and J. Tonson 1712. 4to. First Edition

———— Hibernia freed. London, for J. Bowyer 1722. 8vo. First Edition

[———— *editor*]. A collection of old ballads. London, for J. Roberts ...1727, 1726, 1725. 3 v. 8vo. I, Third Edition; II, Second Edition; III, First Edition. (Alexander I. Beresford–Hope)

[Philips, John]. Cyder. London, for J. Tonson 1708. 8vo. First Edition. (Charles Lilburn)

[Philips, Katherine]. Poems. London, J. G. for R. Marriott 1664. 8vo. First Edition

———— ———— London, J. M. for H. Herringman 1667. fol. First Authorized Edition

[Philips, William]. Hibernia freed. London, for J. Bowyer 1722. 8vo. First Edition

———— The revengeful queen. London, for P. Buck 1698. sm. 4to. First Edition. (Jolley–Huth)

Phillips, Edward. Theatrum poetarum. London, for C. Smith 1675. 12mo. First Edition

Phillips, John, *tr.* *See* Scarron, Paul

Piozzi, Hester Lynch. *See* Johnson, Samuel: Letters

Pix, Mary. Ibrahim the thirteenth. London, for J. Harding and R. Wilkin 1696. 4to. First Edition

———— The innocent mistress. London, J. Orme 1697. 4to. First Edition

———— Queen Catharine. London, for W. Turner and R. Basset 1698. 4to. First Edition

[————] The Spanish wives. London, for R. Wellington 1696. 4to. First Edition

Plowden, Dorothea. Virginia. London, J. Barker 1800. 8vo. First Edition

Polly Peachum's jests. London, for J. Roberts 1728. 8vo. First Edition. (J. P. Collier–W. F. Prideaux)

[Polwhele, Richard]. The unsex'd females. London, for Cadell and Davies 1798. 8vo. First Edition. (W. F. Prideaux)

Poole, Joshua. The English Parnassus. London, for T. Johnson 1657.
8vo. First Edition. (Henry James Pye)

———— ———— London, for H. Brome ... 1677. 8vo.

[Pope, Alexander]. The Dunciad, variorum. London, for A. Dod
1729. 4to.

———— An epistle from Mr. Pope to Dr. Arbuthnot. London, J.
Wright 1734. fol. First Edition

———— An epistle to ... Viscount Cobham. Of the knowledge and
characters of men. London, for L. Gilliver 1733. fol. First
Edition

[————] An essay on criticism. London, for W. Lewis 1711. 4to.
First Edition

[————] An essay on man. London, for J. Wilford [1733-4]. 4 pts.
fol. First Edition, First Issue

———— The First Epistle of the First book of Horace imitated. London, for R. Dodsley 1737. fol. First Edition. (Hagen)

[————] The First Epistle of the Second book of Horace, imitated.
London, for T. Cooper 1737. fol. First Edition, stitched

———— The First Satire of the Second book of Horace, imitated. London, L. G. 1733. fol. First Edition, stitched

———— Horace his Ode to Venus. Lib. IV. Ode I. Imitated by Mr. Pope.
London, for J. Wright 1737. fol. First Edition, stitched

———— Of the characters of women. London, J. Wright 1735. fol.
First Edition. (2 copies)

———— One thousand seven hundred and thirty eight. London, for
T. Cooper, n.d. fol. First Edition

———— One thousand seven hundred and thirty eight. Dialogue II.
London, for R. Dodsley 1738. fol. First Edition

———— The rape of the locke. [London] for B. Lintott 1712. 8vo.
First Edition

———— The Second Epistle of the Second book of Horace, imitated.
London, for R. Dodsley 1737. fol. First Edition, stitched

———— The Sixth Epistle of the First book of Horace imitated. London, for L. Gilliver 1737. fol. First Edition. (Hagen)

Pope, Alexander.   The temple of fame.   London, for B. Lintott 1715.
8vo.   First Edition.   (W. F. Prideaux)

———— Windsor-Forest.   London, for B. Lintot 1713.   fol.   First
Edition

———— The works.   London, W. Bowyer, for J. Tonson and B. Lintot 1717.   fol.

———— ———— London [I] W. Bowyer for B. Lintot 1717; II, J.
Wright for L. Gilliver 1735; [III], J. Wright for J. Knapton . . .
1737.   4to.   (Mexborough)

———— tr.   See Homerus; Statius

[Pordage, Samuel].   Herod and Mariamne.   London, for W. Cademan 1673.   4to.   First Edition.   (Huth)

[————] The medal revers'd.   London, for C. Lee 1682.   sm. 4to.
First Edition.   (Lefferts)

[————] The siege of Babylon.   London, for R. Tonson 1678.   4to.
First Edition.   (Huth)

Porter, Thomas.   The carnival.   London, for H. Herringman 1664.
4to.   First Edition.   (Bridgewater)

———— The villain.   London, for H. Herringman and S. Speed 1663.
sm. 4to.   First Edition.   (Bridgewater)

Powell, George.   Alphonso.   London, for A. Roper and T. Bever
1691.   4to.   First Edition.   (Huth)

[————] A new opera; called, Brutus of Alba.   London, W. Onley
1697.   4to.   First Edition

———— The treacherous brothers.   London, for J. Blackwell 1690.
4to.   First Edition.   (Huth)

[————] A very good wife.   London, for S. Briscoe 1693.   4to.
First Edition.   (Hoe–H.V. Jones)

Prance, Miles.   A true narrative and discovery of several . . . passages
relating to the horrid Popish plot.   London, for D. Newman 1679.
fol.   First Edition

Preti, Girolamo.   Oronta. Tr. by T. Stanley.   London, W. Wilson
1650.   8vo.   (Purdy)

[Prior, Matthew].   An ode humbly inscrib'd to the Queen.   London,
for J. Tonson 1706.   fol.   First Edition

Prior, Matthew. An ode, in imitation of the Second ode of the Third book of Horace. London, for J. Tonson 1692. fol. First Edition

———— A second collection of poems. London, for J. Roberts 1716. 8vo. First Edition

———— To the King, an ode. London, for J. Tonson 1695. fol. First Edition. (Halsey)

[———— *and* Charles Montagu]. The hind and the panther transvers'd. London, for W. Davis 1687. 4to. First Edition

The prison-breaker. London, for A. Moore 1725. 8vo. First Edition

Probus Britanicus. *See* John, Samuel

The proceedings and tryal in the case of William Lord Archbishop of Canterbury, and [the bishops of St. Asaph, Ely, Chichester, Bath and Wells, Peterborough, Bristol] ... 1688. London, for T. Basset and T. Fox 1689. fol. First Edition

A prospect of Hungary, and Transylvania. London, for W. Miller 1664. sm. 4to. First Edition

The Protestants vade mecum. London, for D. Browne ... 1680. 8vo. First Edition. (Huth)

[Puckle, James]. The club. London 1711. 12mo. First Edition

Pudding and dumpling burnt to pot. London, A. Dodd 1727. 8vo. First Edition

Puleston, Hamlet. Historical essaies & observations. Oxon 1664. sm. 4to. First Edition. (Huth)

Pye, Henry James. Poems on various subjects. London, for J. Stockdale 1787. 2 v. 8vo. First Edition. (Earl of Sydney)

Quarles, Francis. Observations concerning princes and states. London, for J. Sweeting 1642. sm. 4to. First Edition. (C. L. deLuc)

———— The virgin widow. London, for R. Royston 1649. 4to. First Edition. (Charles Robert Scott Murray)

Quarles, John. Gods love. London, for J. Stafford 1651. 8vo. First Edition. (Huth)

———— The history of the most vile Dimagoras. London, J. M. for J. Stafford 1658. 8vo. (Strettell–Huth)

———— *tr. See* Cats, Jacob

R., W.   The arbitrary punishments and cruel tortures inflicted on prisoners for debt.   London, F. Watson 1729.   8vo.   First Edition.
(Huth)

Rabelais, François.   The works. Bks. 1-3 tr. by Sir T. Urquhart; 4-5 by
P. Motteux.   London 1653-94.   5 v.   12mo.   First Edition

[Radcliffe, Anne].   The romance of the forest.   London, for T. Hookham and J. Carpenter 1791.   3 v.   8vo.   First Edition.   (Bunbury)

Ralegh, *Sir* Walter.   All is not gold that glisters.   London, for G. Horton 1651.   sm. 4to.   First Edition.   (Huth).   (Attrib. to Ralegh)

———— The cabinet-council.   London, T. Newcomb 1658.   12mo.
First Edition.   (John Gurdon Rebow)

———— Judicious and select essayes and observations.   London, T. W.
1650.   8vo.   First Edition

———— The prince.   London 1642.   sm. 4to.   First Edition

———— Three discourses.   London, for B. Barker 1702.   8vo.   First
Edition

Ramsay, Allan, *editor*.   The ever green.   Edinburgh, T. Ruddiman
1724.   2 v.   8vo.   First Edition.   (Huth)

Randolph, Thomas.   Πλουτοφθαλμία πλουτογαμία.   London 1651.
sm. 4to.   First Edition

[Raspe, Rudolph Erich].   The singular travels ... of Baron Munnik-
houson, commonly pronounced Munchausen.   Oxford, The Booksellers 1786.   12mo.   Second Edition

Ravenscroft, Edward.   The anatomist.   London 1697.   4to.   First
Edition

———— The careless lovers.   London, for W. Cademan 1673.   4to.
First Edition

———— The citizen turn'd gentleman.   London, for T. Dring 1672.
4to.   First Edition

———— Dame Dobson.   London, for J. Hindmarsh 1684.   4to.   First
Edition

———— The English lawyer.   London, J. M. 1678.   4to.   First Edition

———— The Italian husband.   London, for I. Cleave 1698.   4to.   First
Edition

Ravenscroft, Edward. King Edgar and Alfreda. London, for M. Turner 1677. 4to. First Edition

────── Titus Andronicus. London, J. B. 1687. 4to. First Edition

────── The wrangling lovers. London, for W. Crook 1677. sm. 4to. First Edition, stitched

The reasons and narrative of proceedings betwixt the two Houses . . . touching the trial of the Lords in the Tower. On Monday the 26th. of May, 1679. London 1679. fol. First Edition

Reeve, Clara. The old English baron. London, for E. and C. Dilly 1778. 8vo. Second Edition, but first under this title. (Bement)

[Revet, Edward]. The town-shifts. London, for T. Dring 1671. sm. 4to. First Edition

The revolter. London 1687. sm. 4to. First Edition. (John Genest)

Reynard the Fox. The most delectable history. London, A. M. and R. R. for E. Brewster 1681. sm. 4to.

────── The most delightful history of Reynard the Fox . . . [By John Shirley]. London, for T. Passinger . . . 1681. 4to. First Edition

────── The most pleasant and delightful history. London, A. M. and R. R. for E. Brewster 1681. sm. 4to.

────── The most pleasing and delightful history. London, W. Onley 1697. 2 pts. 8vo.

────── The shifts of Reynardine. London, T. J. for E. Brewster 1684. sm. 4to.

[Richardson, Samuel]. Clarissa. London, for S. Richardson 1748. 7 v. 12mo. First Edition

[──────] The history of Sir Charles Grandison. London, for S. Richardson 1754. 7 v. 12mo. First Edition. (Richard Prime)

[──────] Pamela. London, for C. Rivington 1741. 4 v. 8vo. First Edition

Richardson, Thomas. Richardson's new battledore. Derby, T. Richardson [1790]. 16mo. (H.V. Jones)

────── Richardson's new royal battledore. Derby, T. Richardson [1790]. 16mo. (H.V. Jones)

Rider, Cardanus. Rider's British Merlin: for . . . 1768. London, H. Woodfall 1768. 12mo.

[Rivers, John Abbott]. The sad condition of a distracted kingdom.
London, B. A. 1645. sm. 4to. First Edition. (Freeling–Bulkeley Bandinel–Huth)

Roche, Regina Maria. The children of the abbey. London, for W.
Lane, at the Minerva-Press 1796. 4v. 12mo. First Edition

Rochester, *Earl of*. *See* Wilmot, John, *second Earl of Rochester*

Rogers, Nehemiah. The figg-less figg-tree. London, J. S. 1659. 4to.
First Edition

Roscommon, *Earl of*. *See* Dillon, Wentworth

Ross, John. *See* Rous, John

Round about our coal-fire: or, Christmas entertainments. London, for
J. Roberts [c. 1730]. 8vo. First Edition. (Daniel–Huth)

Rous, John. Joannis Rossi . . . historia regum Angliae. Oxonii, e Theatro Sheldoniano 1745. 8vo. Second Edition

[Rowe, Elizabeth]. Poems on several occasions. London, for J. Dunton 1696. 8vo. First Edition

Rowe, John. Tragi-comoedia. Oxford, L. Lichfield 1653. sm. 4to.
First Edition

[Rowe, Matthew]. An exact and full relation of the great victory . . .
at Dungons-Hill in Ireland, August 8. 1647. London, for E. Husband 1647. sm. 4to. First Edition

Rowe, Nicholas. The ambitious step-mother. London, for P. Buck
1701. 4to. First Edition

——— The biter. London, for J. Tonson 1705. 4to. First Edition.
(Huth)

——— The fair penitent. London, for J. Tonson 1703. 4to. First
Edition

——— The royal convert. London, for J. Tonson 1708. 4to. First
Edition

——— Tamerlane. London, for J. Tonson 1702. 4to. First Edition

——— The tragedy of Jane Shore. London, for B. Lintott [1713].
4to. First Edition

——— The tragedy of the Lady Jane Gray. London, for B. Lintott
1715. 4to. First Edition

Rowe, Nicholas. Ulysses. London, for J. Tonson 1706. 4to. First Edition

Rowland, John, *tr.* *See* Johnstone, John

R[owley], A[lexander]. Sodalis discipulus. The schollers companion. London, M. Bell 1648. 8vo. First Edition

R[owley], W[illiam]. The Christmas ordinary. London, for J. Courtney 1682. sm. 4to. First Edition

―――― *See also* Massinger, Philip, Thomas Middleton *and* William Rowley; Middleton, Thomas, *and* William Rowley; Shakespeare, William, *and* William Rowley

Rupert, *Prince.* Letter to the Earl of Arlington . . . the XXIXth of May, 1673. [London] T. Newcomb 1673. sm. fol. First Edition

―――― Letter to the Earl of Arlington . . . June 5. [1673]. [London] T. Newcomb 1673. sm. fol. First Edition

―――― *See also* An exact relation . . . 1673

Rushworth, John. Historical collections [Pt. I]. London, T. Newcomb 1659. fol. First Edition

―――― Historical collections. London, for D. Browne . . . 1721. 8 v. fol. Second Edition. (Amherst)

Rymer, Thomas. A short view of tragedy. London, R. Baldwin 1693. 8vo. First Edition

Sad and deplorable news from Fleet-Street. London, D. M. 1674. sm. 4to. First Edition. (Huth)

Sadducismus debellatus. London, for H. Newman and A. Bell 1698. 4to. First Edition. (Huth)

Sancroft, William, *Archbishop of Canterbury.* *See* The proceedings and tryal

Saunders, Charles. Tamerlane. London, for R. Bentley and M. Magnes 1681. 4to. First Edition

Savage, Richard. The tragedy of Sir Thomas Overbury. London, for S. Chapman 1724. 8vo. First Edition

Scarron, Paul. Scarron's comical romance. Tr. by J. Phillips? London, J. C. for W. Crooke 1676. fol. First Edition

Scheffer, John.   The history of Lapland.   At the theater in Oxford 1674.   fol.   First Edition

Schiller, Johann Friedrich Christoph von.   The death of Wallenstein. Tr. by S. T. Coleridge.   London, G. Woodfall 1800.   8vo.   First Edition.   (J. Hookham Frere–Hagen)

——— The Piccolomini. Tr. by S. T. Coleridge.   London [G. Woodfall] 1800.   8vo.   First Edition.   (J. Hookham Frere–Hagen)

Scot, Reginald.   The discovery of witchcraft.   London, for A. Clark 1665.   fol.   Third Edition

Scott, John.   The poetical works.   London, for J. Buckland 1782.   8vo. First Edition

Scott, Thomas.   The mock-marriage.   London, for H. Rhodes . . . 1696.   4to.   First Edition

——— The unhappy kindness.   London, for H. Rhodes . . . 1697. 4to.   First Edition

The secret history of the reigns of K. Charles II, and K. James II.   n.p. 1690.   12mo.   First Edition

Sedley, *Sir* Charles.   Antony and Cleopatra.   London, for R. Tonson 1677.   4to.   First Edition.   (W. F. Prideaux)

——— Bellamira.   London, D. Mallet 1687.   4to.   First Edition

——— The miscellaneous works.   London, J. Nutt 1702.   8vo.

——— The mulberry-garden.   London, for H. Herringman 1668. 4to.   First Edition.   (Bridgewater)

Selden, John.   Of the dominion, or ownership of the sea. Tr. by M. Nedham.   London, W. Du-Gard 1652.   fol.   First Edition.   (C. L. F. Robinson)

——— Opera omnia.   Londini, Typis G. Bowyer 1726.   3 v.   fol.

——— Table-talk.   London, for E. Smith 1689.   sm. 4to.   First Edition.   (Hoe–Learmont)

——— Tracts.   London, for T. Basset and R. Chiswell 1683.   fol.

Seneca, Lucius Annaeus.   Medea. Tr. by E. Sherburne.   London, for H. Moseley 1648.   8vo.   First Edition.   (Chew)

——— Seneca's answer to Lucilius. Tr. by E. Sherburne.   London, for H. Moseley 1648.   8vo.   First Edition.   (Chew)

Seneca, Lucius Annaeus. Troades. Tr. by E. Sherburne. London, A. Godbid and J. Playford 1679. 8vo. First Edition. (Chew)

———— Troas. Tr. by J. Talbot. London, for J. Tonson 1686. 4to. First Edition

[Settle, Elkanah]. The character of a Popish successour. London, for T. Davies 1681. fol. First Edition

[————] The character of a Popish successour compleat. London, for J. Graves 1681. fol. First Edition

[————] The city-ramble. London, for B. Lintott and E. Sanger [1712]. 4to. First Edition

———— The Empress of Morocco. London, for W. Cademan 1673. 4to. First Edition

[————] Eusebia triumphans. London, for the Author 1704. fol.

———— Love and revenge. London, for W. Cademan 1675. 4to. First Edition. (Bridgewater)

———— *See also* Guarini, Giovanni Battista

Sewel, William. The history of the rise . . . of the . . . Quakers. London, Assigns of J. Sowle 1722. fol. First Edition in English. (H. V. Jones)

[Shadwell, Charles]. The fair Quaker of Deal. London, for J. Knapton . . . 1710. 4to. First Edition

———— The humours of the army. London, for J. Knapton 1713. 4to. First Edition

Shadwell, Thomas. Bury-Fair. London, for J. Knapton 1689. 4to. First Edition

———— The dramatick works. London, for J. Knapton and J. Tonson 1720. 4v. 8vo. First Edition. (Sir John Cope)

———— Epsom-Wells. London, J. M. 1673. 4to. First Edition

———— The humorists. London, for H. Herringman 1671. 4to. First Edition

———— The Lancashire witches. London, for J. Starkey 1682. 4to. First Edition. (Lefferts–Hagen)

———— The libertine. London, T. N. 1676. 4to. First Edition. (Huth)

[Shadwell, Thomas]. The medal of John Bayes. London, for R. Janeway 1682. sm. 4to. First Edition. (Lefferts–Hailstone)

—— Psyche. London, T. N. 1675. 4to. First Edition. (Halsey)

[——] The royal shepherdess. London, for H. Herringman 1669. 4to. First Edition. (Huth)

—— The scowrers. London, for J. Knapton 1691. 4to. First Edition

—— The Squire of Alsatia. London, for J. Knapton 1688. 4to. First Edition

—— A true widow. London, for B. Tooke 1679. 4to. First Edition

—— Upon his Majesties late declarations for toleration. London, J. C. for S. Heyrick 1672. fol. First Edition. (Bement)

—— The virtuoso. London, T. N. 1676. 4to. First Edition

—— The volunteers. London, for J. Knapton 1693. 4to. First Edition

—— The woman-captain. London, for S. Carr 1680. 4to. First Edition

Shakespeare, William. Comedies, histories, & tragedies. London, for P. Chetwinde 1663. fol. (C. C. Harrison–G. L. Harrison–Mary McMillan Norton)

—— —— London, for P. C[hetwinde] 1664. fol.

—— —— London, for H. Herringman, E. Brewster, & R. Bentley 1685. fol. (C. C. Harrison–G. L. Harrison–Mary McMillan Norton)

—— Julius Caesar. London, H. H. Jun., n.d. 4to. Fifth Quarto Edition

—— —— London, for H. Herringman and R. Bentley 1691. 4to. Sixth Quarto Edition

—— Othello. London, for R. Bentley 1695. 4to.

—— The plays and poems. Collected . . . by S. Johnson. Philadelphia, Bioren & Madan 1795-6. 8 v. 12mo. First American Edition

Shakespeare, William.   The tragedy of Hamlet.   London, for R. Wellington and E. Rumball 1703.   4to.

———— The works . . . Revis'd . . . by N. Rowe.   London, for J. Tonson 1709.   6v.   8vo.   First Illustrated Edition.   Large paper

———— ———— With notes . . . by Mr. Theobald.   London, for A. Bettesworth . . . 1733.   7 v.   8vo.

———— *and* William Rowley.   The birth of Merlin.   London, T. Johnson 1662.   sm. 4to.   First Edition.   (Hoe–H.V. Jones)

[Shenstone, William].   The judgment of Hercules.   London, for R. Dodsley 1741.   8vo.   First Edition

[————]   Poems upon various occasions.   Oxford, L. Lichfield 1737.   8vo.   First Edition.   (Erasmus Wilson)

Sherburne, *Sir* Edward.   Salmacis, Lyrian & Sylvia.   London, W. Hunt 1651.   8vo.   First Edition

———— *tr.   See* Seneca, Lucius Annaeus

Sheridan, Richard Brinsley.   The critic.   London, for T. Becket 1781.   8vo.   First Edition

———— The duenna.   London, G. Woodfall 1794.   8vo.   First Edition

———— Pizarro.   London, for J. Ridgway 1799.   8vo.   First Edition

[————]   The rivals.   London, for J. Wilkes 1775.   8vo.   First Edition

[————]   The school for scandal.   Dublin, for J. Ewling [? 1778].   8vo.   First Edition

[————]   A trip to Scarborough.   London, for G. Wilkie 1781.   8vo.   First Edition

[————]   Verses to the memory of Garrick.   London, T. Evans . . . 1779.   4to.   First Edition

Shipman, Thomas.   Carolina.   London, for S. Heyrick 1683.   8vo.   First Edition.   (Bridgewater)

———— Henry the third of France.   London, B. G. 1678.   4to.   First Edition

Shirley, James.   The contention of Ajax and Ulysses.   London, for J. Crook [1659].   8vo.   First Edition.   (Purdy)

Shirley, James. Honoria and Mammon. London, T.W. [1659]. 8vo. First Edition. (Purdy)

[———] Love will finde out the way. By J. B. London, J. Cottrel 1661. sm. 4to. (A reprint of Shirley's "The constant maid")

——— Poems &c. London, for H. Moseley 1646. 8vo. First Edition

——— Six new playes. London, for H. Robinson and H. Moseley 1653. 8vo. First Edition. (John Carruthers)

Shirley, John. *See* Reynard the Fox

A short and serious narrative of Londons fatal fire. London, for P. Dring 1667. sm. 4to. First Edition. (Huth)

A short explication of such foreign words, as are made use of in musick books. London, for J. Brotherton 1724. 12mo. First Edition. (W. H. Cummings)

Shotterel, Robert, *and* Thomas D'Urfey. Archerie reviv'd. London, T. Roycroft 1676. 8vo. First Edition

Sidney, *Sir* Philip. The Countess of Pembroke's Arcadia. London, H. Lloyd 1662. fol. (Mark P. Robinson)

Sillar, David. Poems. Kilmarnock, J. Wilson 1789. 8vo. First Edition. (Andrew J. Kirkpatrick)

Skelton, John. Pithy pleasaunt and profitable workes of Maister Skelton. London, for C. Davis 1736. 8vo. 12mo.

Smith, Adam. An inquiry into the nature and causes of the wealth of nations. London, for W. Strahan and T. Cadell 1776. 2 v. 4to. First Edition

Smith, Edmund. Phaedra and Hippolitus. London, for B. Lintott, n.d. 4to. First Edition. (H.V. Jones)

Smith, James. *See* Mennes, *Sir* John, *and* James Smith

[Smollett, Tobias]. The adventures of Ferdinand Count Fathom. London, for W. Johnston 1753. 2 v. 12mo. First Edition. (Francis Longe)

[———] The adventures of Peregrine Pickle. London, for the Author 1751. 4v. 12mo. First Edition

[———] The adventures of Roderick Random. London, for J. Osborn 1748. 2 v. 12mo. First Edition

Smollett, Tobias. An essay on the external use of water. London, for M. Cooper 1752. 4to. First Edition

[————] The expedition of Humphry Clinker. London, for W. Johnston 1671 [1771]. 3 v. 12mo. First Edition

[————] The history and adventures of an atom. London, for Robinson and Roberts 1749 [1769]. 2 v. 12mo. First Edition. (Church)

———— Plays and poems. London, for T. Evans 1777. 8vo. First Edition. (Hoe)

[————] The regicide. London, Printed by subscription 1749. 8vo. First Edition, stabbed. (H.V. Jones). (Lacks last 8 leaves)

[————] The reprisal. London, for R. Baldwin 1757. 8vo. First Edition

———— *tr. See* Cervantes Saavedra; Fénelon: Telemachus. 1776; LeSage

Solleysell, Jacques de. The compleat horseman. Tr. by Sir William Hope. London, for M. Gillyflower ... 1696. fol.

Somerville, William. The chace. London, for G. Hawkins 1735. 4to. First Edition

Sophocles. Electra. Tr. by C. Wase. The Hague, for S. Brown 1649. 8vo. First Edition

Southerne, Thomas. The disappointment. London, for J. Hindmarsh 1684. 4to. First Edition

———— The fatal marriage. London, for J. Tonson 1694. 4to. First Edition. (Hagen)

———— The fate of Capua. London, for B. Tooke 1700. 4to. First Edition

———— The maids last prayer. London, R. Bentley and J. Tonson 1693. 4to. First Edition. (Percy FitzGerald)

———— Oroonoko. London, for H. Playford ... 1696. 4to. First Edition

———— Sir Anthony Love. London, for J. Fox and A. Roper 1691. 4to. First Edition. (Percy FitzGerald)

———— The wives excuse. London, for S. Brisco 1692. 4to. First Edition

Southey, Robert. Joan of Arc. Bristol, Bulgin and Rosser 1796. 4to.
 First Edition

——— Poems. Bristol, N. Biggs 1797. 8vo. in fours. First Edition

A specimen of a true dissenting catechism. [London, J. Applebee
 1738?]. 1 page. 8vo.

Speed, John. The theatre of the Empire of Great Britain. London
 1676. fol.

Speed, Samuel. Fragmenta carceris. London, J. R. for T. Rooks 1675.
 sm. 4to. First Edition. (Purdy)

Speght, Thomas, *editor*. *See* Chaucer, Geoffrey

Spenser, Edmund. The works. London, H. Hills for J. Edwin 1679.
 fol.

Spinoza, Benedict. A treatise partly theological, and partly political.
 London 1689. 8vo. First Edition

Spottiswood, John. The history of the Church of Scotland. London,
 J. Flesher 1655. fol.

Sprat, Thomas. The history of the Royal-Society of London. London, T. R. 1667. 4to. First Edition. (Sir Thomas Hanmer–
 Bunbury)

Sprigg, Joshua. Anglia rediviva. London, R.W. for I. Partridge 1647.
 fol. First Edition. (Presentation copy from the publisher)

Stanhope, Philip Dormer, *Earl of Chesterfield*. Letters . . . to his son.
 London, for J. Dodsley 1774. 2 v. 4to. First Edition

——— ——— I, Boston, for J. Boyle and J. D. M'Dougall 1779;
 II, Newbury-port, J. Mycall 1779. 2 v. 8vo.

Stanley, Thomas. Europa. Cupid crucified. Venus vigils. London,
 W. W[ilson] 1649. 8vo. (Purdy)

——— Poems. [London] 1651. 8vo. (Park–Mitford)

——— *tr.* *See* Perez de Montalvan, Juan; Preti, Girolamo

Stapleton, *Sir* Robert. The slighted maid. London, for T. Dring
 1663. sm. 4to. First Edition. (Clawson)

——— The step-mother. London, J. Streater 1664. sm. 4to. First
 Edition

——— *tr.* *See* Juvenalis; Musaeus

English 1641-1800

Statius, Publius Papinius. The first book of Statius his Thebais. Tr. by Mr. Pope. (London, for B. Lintott 1712). 8vo. First Edition

Steele, *Sir* Richard. The conscious lovers. London, for J. Tonson 1723. 8vo. First Edition. (Groves)

———— The crisis. London, S. Buckley 1714. sm. 4to. First Edition. (2 copies: 1, Sussex)

———— The Englishman. London, for F. Burleigh 1714. sm. 4to. Second Edition. (Sussex)

———— The funeral. London, for J. Tonson 1702. 4to. First Edition

———— The importance of Dunkirk consider'd. London, for A. Baldwin 1713. 8vo. Fourth Edition. (Sussex)

———— A letter to a member of Parliament. London 1714. sm. 4to. Second Edition. (Sussex)

———— Mr. Steele's apology for himself and his writings. London 1714. sm. 4to. First Edition. (Sussex)

———— The tender husband. London, for J. Tonson 1705. 4to. First Edition

———— *See also* The Tatler

Sterne, Laurence. The case of Elijah and the widow of Zerephath, consider'd. York, for J. Hildyard 1747. 8vo. First Edition

[————] Letters from Eliza to Yorick. London, for the Editor 1775. 8vo. First Edition

[————] Letters from Yorick to Eliza. London, for G. Kearsley and T. Evans 1775. 8vo. First Edition

———— Letters . . . to his most intimate friends. London, for T. Becket 1775. 3 v. 8vo. First Edition

[————] The life and opinions of Tristram Shandy. I-II [York, J. Hinxham] 1760; III-IV, London, for R. and J. Dodsley, 1761; V-IX, London, for T. Becket and P. A. DeHondt 1762-7. 8vo. First Edition. (Sterne's autograph signature in V, VII, IX)

[————] A sentimental journey through France and Italy. London, for T. Becket and P. A. DeHondt 1768. 2 v. 8vo. First Edition. Large paper

[Sterne, Laurence]. The sermons of Mr. Yorick. London, I-II, for R. and J. Dodsley, n.d.; III-IV, for T. Becket and P. A. DeHondt 1766; V-VII, for W. Strahan, T. Cadell and T. Beckett 1769. 7 v. in 3. 8vo. First Edition

———— Sterne's letters to his friends. London, for G. Kearsly and J. Johnson 1775. 8vo. First Edition

Stewart, James. Plocacosmos. London 1782. fol. First Edition

Stothard, Thomas. Shakespeares Seven ages of man illustrated. Hammersmith 1799. fol. First Edition

Strode, William. The floating island. London, T. C. 1655. sm. 4to. First Edition

Stubbe, Henry. A justification of the present war. London, for H. Hills and J. Starkey 1673. 4to. First Edition

———— tr. See Gothofredus, Jacobus

Stubbs, John. See Fox, George, John Stubbs and Benjamin Furly

Stukeley, William. Itinerarium curiosum. London 1776. 2 v. in 1. fol. Second Edition. (Sir Laurence Gomme)

Suckling, Sir John. Fragmenta aurea. London, for H. Moseley 1646. 8vo. First Edition

———— The works. London, for J. Tonson 1709. 8vo.

Swift, Jonathan. Bounce to Fop. Dublin, Printed, London, Reprinted for T. Cooper 1736. fol.

———— The Brobdingnagians [By Signor Corolini]. London 1726. 8vo. First Edition

[————] Cadenus and Vanessa. Dublin 2726[sic]. 8vo. First Edition

[————] A complete collection of genteel and ingenious conversation . . . By Simon Wagstaff. London, for B. Motte and C. Bathurst 1738. 8vo. First Edition

[————] A discourse of the contests and dissensions between the nobles and the commons in Athens and Rome. London, for J. Nutt 1701. sm. 4to. First Edition

[————] Essays divine, moral, and political. London 1714. 8vo. First Edition

[Swift, Jonathan]. The First Ode of the Second book of Horace para-phras'd. London, for A. Dodd 1714. sm. 4to. First Edition

[———] The flying island, &c. [By Signor Corolini]. London 1726. 8vo. First Edition

[———] A full and true account of the battell ... between the antient and the modern books. London [for J. Nutt] 1704. 8vo. First Edition. (Mynderse)

[———] The history of the four last years of the Queen. London, for A. Millar 1758. 8vo. First Edition. (David, Earl of North-esk)

[———] A key, being observations ... upon the travels of Lemuel Gulliver. By Signor Corolini. London 1726. 8vo. First Edition

[———] The kingdom of horses [By Signor Corolini]. London 1726. 8vo. First Edition

——— A libel on Dr. D———ny. Printed at Dublin: and Re-printed at London, for A. Moore 1730. 8vo.

——— The life and genuine character of Doctor Swift. London, for J. Roberts 1733. fol. First Edition

[———] Miscellanies in prose and verse. London, for J. Morphew 1711. 8vo. First Edition

[———] A modest proposal for preventing the children of poor peo-ple from being a burthen. Dublin, S. Harding 1729. 8vo. First Edition

[———] The most wonderful wonder. London, for A. More 1726. sm. 4to. First Edition

[———] Part of the Seventh Epistle of the First book of Horace imi-tated. London, for A. Dodd 1713. sm. 4to. First Edition

[———] The publick spirit of the Whigs. London, for J. Morphew 1714. 4to. First Edition

[———] The reasons which induc'd her Majesty to create ... Robert Harley, Esq: a peer of Great-Britain. London, for J. Morphew 1711. sm. 4to. First Edition, stitched

[———] Some remarks on the Barrier Treaty. London, for J. Mor-phew 1712. 8vo. First Edition

[Swift, Jonathan]. The story of the injured lady. London, for M. Cooper 1746. 8vo. First Edition

[———] A tale of a tub. London, for J. Nutt 1704. 8vo. First Edition. (Mynderse)

——— Three sermons. London, for R. Dodsley 1744. 4to. First Edition. (H.V. Jones)

[———] Tory annals. London 1712. 8vo. First Edition, stitched

[———] Travels into several remote nations of the world. London, for B. Motte 1726. 2 v. 8vo. I, Second Edition; II, First Edition

——— *See also* the following anonymous pamphlets on Gulliver's Travels: Critical remarks on Capt. Gulliver's Travels; Gulliver de-cypher'd; A letter from a clergyman; Pudding and dumpling burnt to pot

Swinhoe, Gilbert. The tragedy of the unhappy fair Irene. London, J. Streater 1658. sm. 4to. First Edition. (H.V. Jones)

T., S. *See* [Heath, James]: Flagellum

T[albot], J., *tr. See* Seneca, Lucius Annaeus

Tate, Nahum. Cuckolds-haven. London, for J. H. 1685. 4to. First Edition. (Bridgewater–Clawson)

——— The history of King Lear. London, for E. Flesher 1681. 4to. First Edition

——— The history of King Richard the second. London, for R. Tonson and J. Tonson 1681. 4to. First Edition. (Bridgewater–Clawson)

——— The ingratitude of a common-wealth. London, T. M. 1682. 4to. First Edition

——— Injur'd love. London, for R. Wellington 1707. 4to. First Edition. (Huth–Clawson)

——— The island-princess. London, R. H. 1687. 4to. First Edition

——— Mausolaeum. London, for B. Aylmer . . . W. Rogers . . . R. Baldwin 1695. fol. First Edition

——— Poems. London, T. M. for B. Tooke 1677. 8vo. First Edition

[Tatham, John]. The Scots Figgaries. London, W. H. 1652. sm. 4to. First Edition. (Bridgewater)

The Tatler. London, April 12, 1709-January 2, 1711. Nos. 1-271 [With spurious nos. [274]-330, dated January 6-March 29, 1710; March 31-May 19, 1711, lacking nos. 272, 273, 276, 281]. First Edition. (William Gott)

[Taverner, William]. The artful husband. London, for E. Sawbridge, n.d. 4to. First Edition

—— The artful wife. London, for J. Roberts 1718. 8vo. First Edition

[——] The female advocates. London, for J. Baker 1713. 4to. First Edition

[Taylor, Francis]. Grapes from Canaan. London, T. L. 1658. 8vo. First Edition. (Nassau–Sykes–Hugh Perkins)

Taylor, Jeremy, *Bp.* A choice manual. London, J. Flesher 1667. 12mo. First Edition

—— The great exemplar. London, R. N. 1649. 3 v. sm. 4to. First Edition

—— The rule and exercises of holy dying. London, for R. Royston 1651. 12mo. First Edition

—— The rule and exercises of holy living. London, for R. Royston 1650. 12mo. First Edition

—— ΘΕΟΛΟΓΙΑ ’ΕΚΛΕΚΤΙΚΗ. A discourse of the liberty of prophesying. London, for R. Royston 1647. 4to. First Edition

Tempest, Pierce. The cryes of the City of London. (London 1711). 2 v. in 1. fol. 74 proof impressions. (Purdy)

Temple, *Sir* John. The Irish rebellion. London, R. White 1646. 4to. First Edition

Theobald, Lewis. Double falshood. London, J. Watts 1728. 8vo. First Edition

—— Orestes. London, for J. Watts 1731. 8vo. First Edition

—— The perfidious brother. London, J. Brown 1715. 4to. First Edition

—— The Persian princess. London, for J. Browne 1717. sm. 4to. First Edition

Thomas, *à Kempis.* The following of Christ. [Edinburgh] Holy-Rood-House 1687. nar. 12mo. (W. Moir Bryce)

[Thompson, Edward]. The courtesan. London, for J. Harrison 1765. 4to. First Edition

Thomson, James. Agamemnon. London, for A. Millar 1738. 8vo. First Edition

[———] Britannia. London, for T. Warner 1729. fol. First Edition

——— The castle of indolence. London, for A. Millar 1748. 4to. First Edition

——— Coriolanus. London, for A. Millar 1749. 8vo. First Edition

——— Edward and Eleonora. London 1739. 8vo. First Edition

——— A poem, to the memory of ... the Lord Talbot. London, for A. Millar 1737. 4to. First Edition

——— The seasons. London 1730. 4to. First Complete Edition

——— Spring. London 1728. 8vo. First Edition, original wrappers, uncut

——— Tancred and Sigismunda. London, for A. Millar 1745. 8vo. First Edition

——— The tragedy of Sophonisba. London, for A. Millar 1730. 8vo. First Edition

——— *See also* Mallet, David, *and* James Thomson

[Tracy, John]. Periander. London, for J. Watts 1731. 8vo. First Edition. Large paper. (Dogmersfield)

Tragicum theatrum actorum, & casuum tragicorum Londini. Amstelodami, apud J. Jansonium 1649. 8vo. First Edition

[Trapp, Joseph]. Abra-mule. London, for J. Tonson 1704. 4to. First Edition

Treby, *Sir* George, *editor*. A collection of letters ... relating to the horrid Popish plott. London, for S. Heyrick, T. Dring and J. Wickins 1681. fol. First Edition

[Trotter, Catharine]. Agnes de Castro. London, for H. Rhodes ... 1696. 4to. First Edition. (Huth)

[———] Fatal friendship. London, for F. Saunders 1698. 4to. First Edition

[———] Love at a loss. London, for W. Turner 1701. 4to. First Edition. (Cornelius Paine–Stainforth–Huth)

[Trotter, Catharine]. The unhappy penitent. London, for W. Turner 1701. 4to. First Edition. (Cornelius Paine–Stainforth–Huth)

A true and impartial relation of the informations against three witches. London, F. Collins 1682. sm. 4to. First Edition

A true catalogue, or, an account of the several places and most eminent persons . . . where, and by whom Richard Cromwell was proclaimed Lord Protector. n.p. 1659. sm. 4to. First Edition

The true mannor and forme of the proceeding to the funerall of . . . Robert Earle of Essex. London, for H. Seale 1646. sm. 4to. First Edition. (Huth)

A true relation of strange and wonderful sights seen in the air, at the time the moon was in the eclipse, January 1, 1655/6. London, for L. Chapman 1656. sm. 4to. First Edition. (Huth)

The tryal of Colley Cibber. London, for the Author 1740. 8vo. First Edition. (Edward Hailstone). (Preface signed "T. Johnson")

[Tuke, Sir Samuel]. The adventures of five hours. London, for H. Herringman 1663. 8vo. First Edition

Twenty four country dances for the year 1759, 1760. London, n.d. 4 pts. 12mo. (McBurney)

Urquhart, Sir Thomas, tr. See Rabelais, François

[Vanbrugh, Sir John]. The confederacy. London, for J. Tonson 1705. 4to. First Edition. (C. L. F. Robinson)

[———] The false friend. London, for J. Tonson 1702. 4to. First Edition. (Hoe)

[———] The mistake. London, for J. Tonson 1706. 4to. First Edition. (Halsey)

[———] The pilgrim. London, for B. Tooke 1700. 4to. First Edition, First Issue

[———] The relapse. (London) for S. Briscoe 1697. 4to. First Edition

[——— and Colley Cibber]. The provok'd husband. London, for J. Watts 1728. 8vo. First Edition

Vaughan, Henry. Olor Iscanus. London, T. W. for H. Moseley 1651. 8vo. First Edition

——— Silex scintillans. London, T. W. 1650. 8vo. First Edition

Vaughan, Thomas. Anima magica abscondita. London, T. W. 1650. 12mo. First Edition

[———] Anthroposophia theomagica. London, T. W. 1650. 12mo. First Edition

——— A breif natural history. London, for M. Smelt 1669. 8vo. First Edition

——— Euphrates. London, for R. Boulter 1671. 8vo. First Edition

[———] Lumen de lumine. London, for H. Blunden 1651. 8vo. First Edition

[Venables, Robert]. The experienc'd angler. London, for R. Marriot 1662. 8vo. First Edition. (Huth)

——— ——— London, B. W. 1683. 8vo. Fifth Edition

Vere, *Sir* Francis. The commentaries. Cambridge, J. Field 1657. fol. First Edition

[Villiers, George, *second Duke of Buckingham*]. The rehearsal. London, for T. Dring 1672. 4to. First Edition

Virgilius Maro, Publius. The passion of Dido for Æneas. Tr. by E. Waller & S. Godolphin. London, for H. Moseley 1658. 8vo. First Edition. (C. B. Foote)

——— Virgil's Æneis. Tr. by G. Douglas. Edinburgh, A. Symson and R. Freebairn 1710. fol.

——— The works. Tr. by J. Ogilby. London, T. Maxey 1650. 8vo. (Hoe)

——— ——— Tr. by J. Dryden. London, for J. Tonson 1697. fol. First Edition. (Martha Shorte)

A voyage to Cacklogallinia. By Captain Samuel Brunt. London, J. Watson 1727. 8vo. First Edition

Vox regis. London, for F. Smith 1681. sm. 4to. First Edition

Vyner, Robert. A very long, curious and extraordinary sermon, preached . . . March 14, 1732. London, for H. Fitz-Drug 1733. sm. fol. Second Edition. (Bateman)

W., T., *tr. See* Henry VIII, *King of England*: Assertio. 1687

Wagstaff, Simon. *See* Swift, Jonathan: A complete collection . . .

[Wake], William, *Archbishop of Canterbury*. The genuine epistles of the apostolical Fathers. London, for A. Bettesworth ... 1737. 8vo. Fourth Edition. (Huth)

[Waller, Edmund]. On the park at St. Jamese's. [London] for T. Dring [1660]. fol. First Edition

———— A panegyrick to my Lord Protector. London, for R. Lowndes 1655. sm. 4to. First Edition

———— Poems, &c. London, I. N. for H. Moseley 1645. 8vo. Fourth Edition, but first to be authorized by Waller

———— ———— London, for J. Tonson 1711. 8vo. Eighth Edition. Large paper

[————] To the King, upon his Majesties happy return. [London] for R. Marriot [1660]. fol. First Edition

———— The workes. London, for T. Walkley 1645. 8vo. First Edition, First Issue. (Hagen)

———— *tr. See* Virgilius Maro, Publius

Walpole, Horace, *Earl of Orford*. Anecdotes of painting in England. I-II, Strawberry-Hill, T. Farmer 1762; III, Strawberry-Hill 1763; IV, Strawberry-Hill, T. Kirgate 1771. 4v. 4to. First Edition. (Presentation copy, inscribed, from Walpole to Isabella Carlisle)

———— A catalogue of engravers ... in England. Strawberry-Hill 1763. 4to. First Edition. (Presentation copy, inscribed, from Walpole to Isabella Carlisle)

———— The mysterious mother. Strawberry-Hill 1768. 8vo. First Edition

[Walsingham, *Sir* Francis]. Arcana aulica. London, T. C. 1655. 8vo. First Edition

Walton, Brian. The considerator considered. London, T. Roycroft 1659. 8vo. First Edition. (H. A. Simcoe)

[Walton, Izaak]. The compleat angler. London, T. Maxey 1653. 8vo. First Edition. (William Gott)

[————] ———— London, T. M. 1655. 8vo. Second Edition

[————] ———— London, J. G. 1661. Third Edition, First Issue

[————] ———— London, for R. Marriot 1668. 8vo. Fourth Edition. (McKee)

Walton, Izaak.   The life of Mr. George Herbert.   London, T. New-comb 1670.   8vo.   First Edition

———— The lives of Dr. John Donne, Sir Henry Wotton, Mr. Richard Hooker, Mr. George Herbert.   London, T. Newcomb 1670.   8vo. First Edition

———— Charles Cotton *and* Robert Venables.   The universal angler. London, for R. Marriott 1676.   8vo.   (T. Gosden–Joseph Craw-hall)

Wantner, Abel.   [Prospectus of his History of ... Gloucester].   n.p. n.d.   3 pp.   fol.

[Ward, Edward].   The history of the Grand Rebellion.   London, for J. Morphew 1713.   3 v.   8vo.   First Edition.   (Sir Henry Hope Edwardes–Bement)

Ward, John.   An encouragement to warre.   [London 1642].   sm. 4to.

Ware, Isaac, *tr.*   *See* Palladio, Andrea

Wase, Charles, *tr.*   *See* Sophocles

Watts, Isaac.   Catechisms.   London, for E. Matthews 1730.   12mo. First Edition.   (Presentation copy, inscribed, from the author to Mr. Tatnall)

———— Divine and moral songs.   Worcester, Massachusetts, I. Thomas 1788.   12mo.

———— A guide to prayer.   London, for E. Matthews 1715.   12mo. First Edition

———— Horae lyricae.   London, S. and D. Bridge 1706.   8vo.   First Edition.   (Presentation copy, inscribed, from Watts to John Hart)

———— Hymns and spiritual songs.   London, J. Humfreys 1707. 12mo.   First Edition

———— ———— Worcester (Massachusetts) I. Thomas 1786.   12mo.

W[eaver], T[homas].   Plantagenets tragicall story.   London, M. F. for R. Tomlins 1649.   8vo.   First Edition.   (John Gibbs)

———— Songs and poems of love and drollery.   n.p. 1654.   8vo.   First Edition.   (Simon Williams–Groves)

Webster, John.   The displaying of supposed witchcraft.   London, J. M. 1677.   fol.   First Edition.   (Brinley)

Wecker, John.   Eighteen books of the secrets of art & nature.   London, for S. Miller 1660.   fol.   (Verney)

Wesley, Charles.   Hymns and sacred poems.   Bristol, F. Farley 1749. 2 v.   12mo.   First Edition

—— Hymns for the use of families.   Bristol, W. Pine 1767.   12mo. First Edition

—— Short hymns.   Bristol, E. Farley 1762.   2 v.   12mo.

—— *See also* Wesley, John, *and* Charles Wesley

Wesley, John.   A collection of hymns.   London, J. Paramore 1780. 12mo.   First Edition

—— *and* Charles Wesley.   Hymns and sacred poems.   London, W. Strahan 1739.   12mo.   First Edition

Wesley, Samuel.   The history of the Old and New Testament.   London, for C. Harper [1701]-1704.   3 v.   12mo.   (Weston–Heber–F. S. Ellis–Bement)

Weston, Joseph.   The Amazon queen.   London, for H. Herringman 1667.   4to.   First Edition.   (Joseph Knight)

Whincop, Thomas.   Scanderbeg.   London, for W. Reeve 1747.   8vo. First Edition

White, John.   Journal of a voyage to New South Wales.   London, for I. Debrett 1790.   4to.   First Edition

White, R.   *See* Digby, *Sir* Kenelm: A late discourse

Whitehead, William.   The Roman father.   London, for R. Dodsley 1750.   8vo.   First Edition

—— The school for lovers.   London, for R. and J. Dodsley 1762. 8vo.   First Edition.   (H. Cavendish)

[Wild, Robert].   The benefice.   London 1689.   4to.   First Edition

[Wilkes, John].   The fall of Mortimer.   London, for G. Kearsley 1763.   8vo.   First Edition

Wilkins, Richard.   The sope-patentees.   London, I. F. 1646.   sm. 4to. First Edition

Wilkinson, Richard.   Vice reclaim'd.   London, for B. Lintott 1703. 4to.   First Edition

Willan, Leonard.   Astraea.   London, R. White 1651.   8vo.   First Edition

Willis, Francis, *tr.   See* Anacreon

[Wilmot], John [*second*] *Earl of Rochester.*   Poems, &c. on several occasions: With Valentinian.   London, for J. Tonson 1691.   8vo.

[————]   Valentinian.   London, for T. Goodwin 1685.   4to.   First Edition

Wilson, John.   Belphegor.   London, J. Leake 1691.   4to.   First Edition

Wine, beer, ale, and tobacco.   London, J. B.   1658.   sm. 4to.   First Edition, stitched

Winstanley, William.   England's worthies.   London, J. C. and F. C. 1684.   8vo.   First Edition

————   The honour of the taylors.   London, A. Milbourn 1687.   4to. (Purdy)

Wiseman, Jane.   Antiochus the Great.   London, for W. Turner 1702. 4to.   First Edition

[Wither, George].   Ecchoes from the sixth trumpet.   n.p. 1666.   8vo. First Edition.   (Mitford)

————   Fides-Anglicana.   London 1660.   8vo.   First Edition.   (Lefferts–Bement)

————   An improvement of imprisonment.   London 1661.   8vo. First Edition

————   Meditations upon the Lords Prayer.   London 1665.   8vo. First Edition

————   Opobalsamum Anglicanum.   [London] 1646.   4to.   First Edition

————   Speculum speculativum.   London 1660.   8vo.   First Edition

————   Vaticinium causuale.   London, for T. Ratcliffe and E. Mottershed 1655.   sm. 4to.   First Edition

The witty rogue . . . or, the history of . . . Richard Hainam.   London, for E. S. 1656.   sm. 4to.   First Edition

The woman turn'd bully.   London, J. C. 1675.   4to.   First Edition.
(Hoe)

Wood, Thomas, *tr.   See* Anacreon

Woodhouse, James.   Poems on sundry occasions.   London, W. Richardson and S. Clark 1764.   4to.   First Edition

Wordsworth, William.   Descriptive sketches.   London, for J. Johnson 1793.   4to.   First Edition

[——— *and* Samuel Taylor Coleridge].   Lyrical ballads.   [I] London, for J. & A. Arch 1798; II, London, for T. N. Longman and O.
Rees . . . by Biggs and Co. Bristol 1800.   2 v.   8vo.   I, First Edition, Second Issue; II, First Edition, First Issue.   (D. Laing–Mac-
George)

The World.   By Adam Fitz-Adam.   London, for R. and J. Dodsley
[1753-6].   4v.   fol.   First Edition

Wortley, *Sir* Francis.   Characters and elegies.   n.p. 1646.   sm. 4to.
First Edition.   (Chew)

Wotton, *Sir* Henry.   Reflections upon ancient and modern learning.
London, J. Leake 1697.   8vo.   Second Edition

——— Reliquiae Wottonianae.   London, T. Maxey 1651.   12mo.
First Edition.   (J. D. Brodie)

Wright, James.   Sales epigrammatum.   London, T. R. for C. Eccleston 1663.   8vo.   First Edition

Wright, Thomas.   The female vertuoso's.   London, J. Wilde 1693.
4to.   First Edition

Wyche, *Sir* Peter, *tr.   See* Lobo, Jerome

Wycherley, William.   The country-wife.   London, for T. Dring 1675.
4to.   First Edition

——— The gentleman dancing-master.   London, J. M. 1673.   4to.
First Edition.   (Purdy)

——— Love in a wood.   London, J. M. 1672.   4to.   First Edition

——— Miscellany poems.   London, for C. Brome, J. Taylor, and B.
Tooke . . . 1704.   fol.   (Sir Thomas Woollaston White)

——— The plain-dealer.   London, T. N. 1677.   4to.   First Edition

English 1641-1800

Yarranton, Andrew. England's improvement by sea and land. London, R. Everingham 1677. 4to. First Edition

Young, Arthur. Travels. Bury St. Edmund's, J. Rackham 1792. 4to. First Edition. (Viscount Sydney)

[Young, Edward]. The brothers. London, for R. Dodsley 1753. 8vo. First Edition

Young, William. *See* Fielding, Henry, *and* William Young

Books Printed in England, Scotland & Ireland, and English Books and Books by English Authors Printed Abroad after 1800

This list does *not* include Americana, Bibles and liturgical books and Science, which will be found in the lists *Americana*; *Bibles*; and *Science*

A'Beckett, Gilbert Abbott. The comic Blackstone. London, Punch Office 1846. 8vo. First Edition

——— The comic history of England. (London) Punch Office 1847-8. 2 v. 8vo.

——— The comic history of Rome. (London) Bradbury and Evans [1848]. 8vo. First Edition

Ainsworth, William Harrison. Ballads... To which is added The combat of the thirty. London, G. Routledge (1872). 8vo. (Presentation copy, inscribed, from the author to his cousin)

——— James the second. London, H. Colburn 1848. 3 v. 8vo. First Edition

——— The life and adventures of Mervyn Clitheroe. London, G. Routledge 1857-8. 12 pts. in 11. Second Edition of I-IV; First Edition of V-XII, wrappers

[———] Poems. By Cheviot Ticheburn. (London, J. Arliss) [1822]. 8vo. First Edition, stitched

——— The Tower of London. London, R. Bentley 1840. 13 pts. in 12. 8vo. First Edition, First Issue, wrappers

——— Windsor Castle. London, H. Colburn 1844. 11 pts. in 10. 8vo. First Edition in parts, wrappers

Albert, *Prince Consort of England*. The principal speeches and addresses. London, J. Murray 1862. 8vo. First Edition. (Presentation copy, inscribed, from Queen Victoria to Viscount Sydney)

Alken, Henry. Symptoms of being amused. London, Thos. McLean 1822-5. obl. fol. First Edition

[Apperley, Charles James]. The life of a sportsman. By Nimrod. London, R. Ackermann 1842. 8vo. First Edition

[229]

[Apperley, Charles James]. Memoirs of the life of . . . John Mytton. London, R. Ackermann 1851. 8vo. Third Edition

[Arblay, Frances Burney, *Madame* d']. The wanderer. London, for Longman . . . 1814. 5 v. 8vo. First Edition

Aristophanes. The Acharnians. The Birds and The Knights. Tr. by J. H. Frere. London [W. Pickering] 1840. 4to.

Arnold, *Sir* Edwin. Poems narrative and lyrical. Oxford, F. Macpherson 1853. 12mo. First Edition

[Arnold, Matthew]. Alaric at Rome. Rugby, Combe and Crossley 1840. 8vo. First Edition, wrappers. (E. H. Butler–Kern)

———— Cromwell. Oxford, J. Vincent 1843. 8vo. First Edition, wrappers

———— ———— Oxford, for T. and G. Shrimpton 1863. 8vo. Second Edition, wrappers

———— ———— Oxford, A. T. Shrimpton 1891. 8vo. Third Edition, wrappers

———— Empedocles on Etna. London, B. Fellowes 1852. 12mo. First Edition

———— England and the Italian question. London, Longman . . . 1859. 8vo. First Edition. (Presentation copy)

———— On translating Homer. London, Longman . . . 1861. 8vo. First Edition. (Presentation copy, inscribed, from Arnold to M. Nisard. James T. Fields copy)

———— ———— Last words. London, Longman 1862. 8vo. First Edition. (Presentation copy, inscribed, from Arnold to M. Nisard. James T. Fields copy)

———— Poems. London, Macmillan 1869. 2 v. 8vo.

———— Saint Brandan. London, E. W. & A. Skipworth 1867. 8vo. First Edition, wrappers. (Carter & Pollard p. 161)

———— The strayed reveller. London, B. Fellowes 1849. 12mo. First Edition

Arthur, *King*. The birth, life and acts of King Arthur. London, J. M. Dent 1893. 2 v. 4to.

———— Le morte d'Arthur. London, Riccardi Press 1910-11. 4 v. 4to.

English after 1800

Arthur, *King*. Le morte d'Arthur. Chelsea, Ashendene Press 1913. fol. (One of an edition of 145 copies)

Aspin, Jehoshaphat. The naval and military exploits which have distinguished the reign of George the third. London, for S. Leigh 1820. 12mo. First Edition. (Bement)

Astle, Thomas. The origin and progress of writing. London, T. Bensley 1803. fol. Second Edition

Aucassin & Nicolette. Tr. by A. Lang. London, D. Nutt 1887. 8vo. First Edition. Large paper. (No. 59 of an edition of 63 copies)

[Austen, Jane]. Emma. London, for J. Murray 1816. 3 v. 8vo. First Edition

[———] Mansfield Park. London, for T. Egerton 1814. 3 v. 12mo. First Edition

[———] Northanger Abbey: and Persuasion. London, J. Murray 1818. 4 v. 8vo. First Edition

[———] Pride and prejudice. London, for T. Egerton 1813. 3 v. 8vo. First Edition

[———] Sense and sensibility. London, for the Author 1811. 3 v. 8vo. First Edition

Barham, Richard Harris. The Ingoldsby legends. First, Second, Third series. London, R. Bentley 1840, 1842, 1847. 3 v. 8vo. First Edition, First Issue

[Barrie, *Sir* James Matthew *and* H. B. Marriott Watson]. Richard Savage. [London, Privately printed 1891]. 12mo. First Edition, wrappers

Beaconsfield, *Earl of*. *See* Disraeli, Benjamin

Beardsley, Aubrey. A book of fifty drawings. London, Leonard Smithers 1897. 4to. First Edition

——— The early work. London, John Lane 1899. 4to. First Edition

——— The later work. London, John Lane 1901. 4to. First Edition

——— A second book of fifty drawings. London, Leonard Smithers 1899. 4to. First Edition

Beaumont, Francis *and* John Fletcher. Songs and lyrics from the plays. Edited by E. H. Fellowes. London, F. Etchells & H. Macdonald 1928. fol. (Haslewood books. No. 172 of an edition of 345 copies)

Bede, Cuthbert. *See* Bradley, Edward

Beerbohm, Max. Caricatures of twenty-five gentlemen. London, L. Smithers 1896. 8vo. First Edition

——— The poets' corner. London, William Heinemann 1904. fol.

Bell, Currer, Ellis *and* Acton. *See* Brontë, Charlotte, Emily *and* Anne

Bellasis, George Hutchins. Views of Saint Helena. London, John Tyler 1815. obl. fol.

Benson, Arthur Christopher. Babylonica. Eton, G. New 1895. 4to. First Edition. (One of 75 copies)

——— Le cahier jaune. Eton, G. New 1892. 8vo. First Edition, wrappers. (No. 84 of an edition of 200 copies, privately printed). (Presentation copy inscribed by the author)

——— The myrtle bough. Eton, Spottiswoode 1903. 8vo. First Edition

Birnbaum, Martin. Oscar Wilde. New York, J. F. Drake 1914. 8vo. First Edition. (No. 29 of an edition of 50 copies signed by the author)

Blackmore, Richard Doddridge. Lorna Doone. London, S. Low ... 1869. 3 v. 8vo. First Edition

[———] Poems by Melanter. London, R. Hardwicke 1854. 8vo. First Edition

——— *tr. See* Virgilius Maro, Publius

Blake, William. Illustrations of the Book of Job. London, Published by the Author, and J. Linnell 1826. fol. First Edition

Blunt, Wilfrid Scawen. The poetry of Wilfrid Blunt selected ... by W. E. Henley and G. Wyndham. London, W. Heinemann 1898. 8vo. First Edition. (Presentation copy, inscribed, from Blunt to his cousin Alfred Douglas)

——— Sonnets and songs. By Proteus. London, J. Murray 1875. 8vo. First Edition

Borrow, George.   The Bible in Spain.   London, for J. Murray 1843.
3 v. 8vo.   First Edition

———— Embéo e Majaró Lucas. (Translation of Gospel of St. Luke
into dialect of Spanish gypsies). [Madrid] 1837. 8vo. First Edition

———— An English gypsy word-book.   [London] Taylor and Francis 1889. 8vo.   First Edition

———— Lavengro.   London, for J. Murray 1851.   3 v.   8vo.   First
Edition

———— Romano Lavo-Lil.   London, for J. Murray 1874.   8vo.   First
Edition

———— Romantic ballads.   Norwich, S. Wilkin 1826.   8vo.   First
Edition, First Issue

———— Wild Wales.   London, for J. Murray 1862.   3 v.   8vo.   First
Edition

———— tr.   See Klinger, Friedrich Maximilian von; Wyn, Elis

Bowers, Georgiana.   Leaves from a hunting journal.   London, Chatto
& Windus 1880. obl. fol.   First Edition

———— A month in the midlands.   (London) Bradbury, Evans (1868).
obl. 4to.   First Edition

Bradford, William.   Sketches of the country, character, and costume
in Portugal and Spain.   London, for John Booth (1814).   fol.

[Bradley, Edward].   The adventures of Mr. Verdant Green.   London, N. Cooke 1853. 8vo.   First Edition

[————] The further adventures of Mr. Verdant Green.   London,
H. Ingram 1854. 8vo.   First Edition

[————] Little Mr. Bouncer and his friend, Verdant Green.   London, J. Blackwood [1873]. 8vo.   First Edition

[————] Love's provocations.   London, Ward and Lock 1855. 8vo.
First Edition

[————] Mr. Verdant Green married and done for.   London, J.
Blackwood 1857. 8vo.   First Edition

[————] Photographic pleasures. By Cuthbert Bede.   London, T.
McLean 1855. 8vo.   First Edition.   (Presentation copy, inscribed, from the author to George F. Pardon)

[Bradley, Edward]. The white wife. London, S. Low . . . 1865. 8vo. First Edition

[Bridges, Robert]. Eight plays. London, E. Bumpus 1885-94. 8v. 4to. First Editions, wrappers

[———] The growth of love. Portland, Maine, T. B. Mosher 1894. 8vo. (No. 70 of an edition of 400 copies)

——— Milton's prosody. Oxford, Clarendon Press 1893. 4to. (No. 97 of an edition of 250 copies on large paper). (Inscribed by the author)

——— The necessity of poetry. Oxford, Clarendon Press 1918. 12mo. First Edition, stitched

[———] On the elements of Milton's blank verse in Paradise Lost. [? Oxford 1887]. 8vo. First Edition. (Presentation copy, inscribed by Bridges to Sir Edmund Gosse)

[———] On the prosody of Paradise Regained and Samson Agonistes. Oxford, B. H. Blackwell 1889. 8vo. First Edition. (Presentation copy, inscribed by Bridges to Sir Edmund Gosse)

——— Poems. London, B. M. Pickering 1873. 8vo. First Edition

——— ——— ——— Large paper. (Presentation copy, inscribed and with A.L.S. from the author to Andrew Lang)

The British gallery of pictures [described] by . . . Henry Tresham and William Young Ottley. London, Bensley 1818. fol.

[Brontë, Charlotte]. Jane Eyre. London, Smith, Elder 1847. 3 v. 8vo. First Edition

[———] Shirley. London, Smith, Elder 1849. 3 v. 8vo. First Edition

[———] Villette. London, Smith, Elder 1853. 3 v. 8vo. First Edition

[Brontë, Charlotte, Emily *and* Anne]. Poems by Currer, Ellis, and Acton Bell. London, Aylott and Jones 1846. 12mo. First Edition. (Francis Hessey)

Brooke, Rupert. 1914 and other poems. London, Sidgwick & Jackson 1915. 8vo. First Edition

——— Poems. London, Sidgwick & Jackson 1911. 8vo. First Edition

Brough, Robert B.   The life of Sir John Falstaff.   London, Longman
...1857.   10 pts.   8vo.   First Edition, wrappers

[Browning, Elizabeth Barrett].   An essay on mind.   London, J. Duncan 1826.   8vo.   First Edition.   (Stephen G. Holland)

[———] Prometheus bound.   London, A. J. Valpy 1833.   8vo.   First
Edition

———— The runaway slave at Pilgrim's Point.   London, E. Moxon
1849.   8vo.   First Edition, wrappers.   (Carter & Pollard p. 169)

———— Sonnets.   Reading 1847.   8vo.   (Carter & Pollard p. 167)

———— *and* R. H. Horne.   Psyche Apocalypté.   London, Hazell ...
1876.   8vo.   First Edition.   (Presentation copy, inscribed, from
Horne to E. W. Gosse. With A.L.S. from Robert Browning to
Gosse)

Browning, Robert.   Bells and pomegranates. No. I-VIII.   London, E.
Moxon 1841-6.   8vo.   First Edition of all except No. V

———— Letters. Edited by T. J. Wise.   London 1895-6.   2 v.   8vo.
First Edition

———— ———— Second Series.   London 1907-8.   2 v.   8vo.   First
Edition

———— Men and women.   London, Chapman and Hall 1855.   2 v.
8vo.   First Edition

———— Paracelsus.   London, E. Wilson 1835.   8vo.   First Edition

———— The ring and the book.   London, Smith, Elder 1868.   4 v.   8vo.
First Edition.   (Alfred A. Bethune–Baker)

———— Sordello.   London, E. Moxon 1840.   8vo.   First Edition.
(T. Tileston Wells)

———— Strafford.   London, for Longman ... 1837.   8vo.   First Edition, wrappers

Buchanan, Robert.   The fleshly school of poetry.   London, Strahan
1872.   8vo.   First Edition

Bulwer-Lytton, Edward George.   *See* Lytton, Edward George Bulwer

Burghclere, Herbert Coulston Gardner, *first Baron, tr.   See* Virgilius
Maro, Publius

Burns, Robert. Letters addressed to Clarinda. Glasgow, Niven, Napier and Khull 1802. 8vo. First Edition

———— Poems ascribed to Robert Burns. Glasgow, Chapman & Lang 1801. 8vo. First Edition, Second Issue

Burton, *Sir* Richard Francis. Camoens: his life and his Lusiads. London, B. Quaritch 1881. 2 v. 8vo. First Edition. (Geo. Evelyn Cower)

———— *tr*. *See* Camoens, Luis de

Bury, Richard de. Philobiblon. Tr. by J. B. Inglis. London, for T. Rodd 1832. 8vo. First Edition. (S. P. Avery)

———— ———— Tr. by A. F. West. New York, Grolier Club 1889. 3 v. 4to. (One of an edition of 297 copies)

[Butler, Samuel]. Erewhon. London, Trübner 1872. 8vo. First Edition

———— Erewhon revisited. London, G. Richards 1901. 8vo. First Edition

———— The way of all flesh. London, G. Richards 1903. 8vo. First Edition

Byron, George Gordon, *Lord*. Childe Harold's pilgrimage [Cantos I-II]. London, for J. Murray 1812. 4to. First Edition

———— ———— Canto III. London, for J. Murray 1816. 8vo. First Edition, wrappers

———— ———— Canto IV. London, J. Murray 1818. 8vo. First Edition. (2 copies)

———— The deformed transformed. London, for J. and H. L. Hunt 1824. 8vo. First Edition, wrappers

[————] Don Juan. London, T. Davison 1819; London, for J. Hunt 1823. 2 v. 8vo. (Cantos I-VIII)

[————] ———— London, T. Davison 1820-21. 2 v. 8vo. (Cantos I-V). First Edition of v. 2

[————] ———— London, for J. Hunt 1823. 3 v. 8vo. (Cantos VI-XIV). First Edition

[————] ———— London, for J. and H. L. Hunt 1824. 8vo. (Cantos XV-XVI). First Edition

[Byron, George Gordon, *Lord*]. English bards, and Scotch reviewers. London, for J. Cawthorn [1809]. 8vo. First Edition

———— The Giaour. London, T. Davison 1813. 8vo. First Edition, wrappers

———— Hebrew melodies. London, for J. Murray 1815. 8vo. First Edition, wrappers

———— Hours of idleness. Newark, S. and J. Ridge 1807. 8vo. First Edition

[————] Lara. London, for J. Murray 1814. 8vo. First Edition. (William Williamson Willink–John Drinkwater)

———— Letters and journals . . . with notices of his life, by Thomas Moore. London, J. Murray 1830. 2 v. 4to. First Edition. (John Drinkwater)

———— Manfred. London, J. Murray 1817. 8vo. First Edition, First Issue, wrappers

———— Marino Faliero. The prophecy of Dante. London, J. Murray 1821. 8vo. First Edition, First Issue

———— Mazeppa. London, J. Murray 1819. 8vo. First Edition, wrappers

[————] Parisina. London, for J. Murray 1816. 8vo. First Edition, wrappers

———— The prisoner of Chillon. London, for J. Murray 1816. 8vo. First Edition, wrappers

———— Sardanapalus. The two Foscari. Cain. London, J. Murray 1821. 8vo. First Edition

[————] The siege of Corinth. London, for J. Murray 1816. 8vo. First Edition, wrappers

[————] Waltz. By Horace Hornem. London, W. Clark 1821. 8vo. Second Edition, wrappers

———— Werner. London, J. Murray 1823. 8vo. First Edition, First Issue, wrappers

Calderón de la Barca, Pedro. *See* FitzGerald, Edward

[Calverley, Charles Stuart]. Christ's College. Christmas, 1857. The posthumous papers of the Pickwick Club. 8vo. Leaflet, 4 pp.

Cambridge University. Cantabrigia depicta. Cambridge, Harraden & Son 1809. fol.

———— A history of the University of Cambridge. London, for R. Ackermann 1815. 2 v. fol. First Edition

Camoens, Luis de. The lyricks. Tr. by R. F. Burton. London, B. Quaritch 1844. 2 v. 8vo. First Edition. (Geo. Evelyn Cower)

———— Os Lusiadas. Tr. by R. F. Burton. London, B. Quaritch 1880. 2 v. 8vo. First Edition. (Presentation copy, inscribed by Burton. With bookplate of Geo. Evelyn Cower)

———— *See also* Burton, *Sir* Richard Francis

Campbell, Thomas. Gertrude of Wyoming. London, T. Bensley 1809. 4to. First Edition

Carey, David. Life in Paris. London, for J. Fairburn 1822. 8vo.

Carpenter, Edward. Moses. London, E. Moxon [1875]. 8vo. First Edition. (Presentation copy, inscribed)

[————] Towards democracy. Manchester, J. Heywood 1885. 8vo. Second Edition. (Presentation copy, inscribed, from the author to Edward Maitland)

Carroll, Lewis. Alice's adventures in Wonderland. London, Macmillan 1866. 8vo.

———— Sylvie and Bruno. London, Macmillan 1889. 8vo. First Edition

———— Sylvie and Bruno concluded. London, Macmillan 1893. 8vo. First Edition

———— Through the looking-glass. London, Macmillan 1872. First Edition

Cavendish, George. The life of Cardinal Wolsey. Edited by S. W. Singer. Chiswick, C. Whittingham 1825. 2 v. 8vo. (Beckford (Hamilton Palace)–Purdy)

Caxton, William. *See* Lefèvre, Raoul; Ovidius Naso, Publius; Reynard the Fox; Tasso, Torquato; Voragine, Jacobus de

Challoner, *Sir* Thomas, *tr. See* Erasmus, Desiderius

Chatterton, Thomas. The Rowley poems. London, Vale Press 1898. 2 v. 8vo. (One of an edition of 210 copies)

English after 1800

Chaucer, Geoffrey. The works. Hammersmith, Kelmscott Press 1896. 4to. (One of an edition of 425 copies)

Clare, John. Madrigals & chronicles. London, Beaumont Press 1924. 8vo. (No. 109 of an edition of 310 copies)

———— Poems. London, R. Cobden-Sanderson (1920). 8vo.

———— Poems descriptive of rural life and scenery. London, for Taylor and Hessey 1820. 8vo. First Edition

———— The rural muse. London, Whittaker 1835. 8vo. First Edition

———— The shepherd's calendar. London, for J. Taylor 1827. 8vo. First Edition. (Graham Pollard)

———— The village minstrel. London, for Taylor and Hessey 1821. 2 v. 8vo. First Edition. (Presentation copy, inscribed, from Clare to J. C. Burkhardt)

Coleridge, Samuel Taylor. Aids to reflection. London, for Taylor and Hessey 1825. 8vo. First Edition

———— "Blessed are ye that sow beside all waters!" A lay sermon. London, for Gale and Fenner 1817. 8vo. First Edition

———— The Friend. 28 parts (No. 1, June 1, 1809 – No. 27, March 15, 1810, with unnumbered issue, January 11, 1810, between Nos. 20 and 21). Penrith, J. Brown 1809-10. 8vo. First Edition. (John Waugh)

———— ———— London, for Gale and Curtis 1812. 8vo. First Edition in complete volume form with both half-title and title

———— Remorse. London, for W. Pople 1813. 8vo. First Edition, wrappers

———— The rime of the ancient mariner. Edinburgh, A. Hill 1837. fol.

———— Sibylline leaves. London, Rest Fenner 1817. 8vo. First Edition. Large paper

———— Specimens of the table talk. London, J. Murray 1835. 2 v. 8vo. First Edition

———— Zapolya. London, for Rest Fenner 1817. 8vo. First Edition, wrappers

Collins, William Wilkie. Antonina. London, R. Bentley 1850. 3 v. 8vo. First Edition

———— *See also* Dickens, Charles

[Combe, William]. The dance of life. London, R. Ackermann 1817. 8vo. First Edition

[————] The English dance of death. London, J. Diggens 1815-16. 2 v. 8vo.

[————] The history of Johnny Quae Genus. London, R. Ackermann 1822. 8vo. First Edition. (Joseph Neeld–H. K. Boldero)

[————] The tour of Doctor Syntax in search of the picturesque. [London, R. Ackermann 1812]. 8vo. First Edition

[————] The second tour of Doctor Syntax, in search of consolation. London, R. Ackermann 1820. 8vo. First Edition

[————] The third tour of Doctor Syntax, in search of a wife. London, R. Ackermann (1821). 8vo. First Edition

Congreve, William. The complete works. London, Nonesuch Press 1923. 4 v. 4to. (No. 850)

Conrad, Joseph. Almayer's folly. London, T. Fisher Unwin 1895. 8vo. First Edition

Cowper, William. Memoir of the early life of William Cowper. London, for R. Edwards 1816. 8vo. First Edition

———— *tr. See* Milton, John

Crabbe, George. Tales of the Hall. London, J. Murray 1819. 2 v. 8vo. First Edition

———— Readings in Crabbe [Edited by Edward FitzGerald]. London, B. Quaritch 1883. 8vo. First Edition. (Thomas Hutchinson)

Craig, Edward Gordon. The marionnette. Florence (Tipografia Giuntina) 1918. I: 1-12. 12mo. First Editions, wrappers

———— The mask. Florence (Tipografia Giuntina) 1918. 8: 1, 6-8, 11. 8vo. First Editions

———— The three men of Gotham. Florence 1919. 16mo. First Edition, wrappers. (Quinn)

[Craik, Dinah Maria Mulock]. John Halifax, gentleman. London, Hurst and Blackett 1856. 3 v. 8vo. First Edition

Cruikshank, George. Vol. I of My sketch book. (London) 1834-6. obl. fol. First Edition

Dana. A magazine of independent thought. Dublin, Hodges, Figgis 1904-5. Nos. 1-12, May 1904-April 1905. 8vo. First Edition, wrappers

Dante Alighieri. The Purgatory of Dante Alighieri. Tr. by C. L. Shadwell. With an introduction by Walter Pater. London, Macmillan 1892. 8vo. First Edition

[Davidson, John]. Plays. Greenock, J. Davidson 1889. 8vo. First Edition. (Presentation copy, inscribed, from the author to Julian Marshall)

Davies, William Henry. The autobiography of a super-tramp. London, A. C. Fifield 1908. 8vo. First Edition

———— The soul's destroyer. London, The Author [1905]. 8vo. First Edition, wrappers. (Presentation copy with A.L.S. from Davies to C. J. Stewart)

A defence of the character and conduct of the late Mary Wollstonecraft Godwin. London, for J. Wallis 1803. 8vo. First Edition

Defoe, Daniel. The life and strange surprizing adventures of Robinson Crusoe. London, F. Etchells & H. Macdonald 1929. 4to. (Haslewood books. No. 92 of an edition of 535 copies)

DeMorgan, Augustus. A budget of paradoxes. London, Longmans, Green 1872. 8vo. First Edition

DeMorgan, William. Joseph Vance. London, W. Heinemann 1906. 8vo. First Edition. (Charles H. Moore)

[DeQuincey, Thomas]. Confessions of an English opium-eater. London, for Taylor and Hessey 1822. 8vo. First Edition, uncut

[————] Walladmor. London, for Taylor and Hessey 1825. 2 v. 8vo. First Edition, uncut

Dibdin, Thomas Frognall. Here begyneth a littel tome and hathe to name The Lincolne Nosegay. [London 1811]. 8vo. First Edition. (Thomas Westwood copy, with A.L.S. from Dibdin)

Dickens, Charles. The battle of life. London, Bradbury & Evans 1846. 8vo. First Edition

———— Bleak House. London, Bradbury & Evans 1852-3. 20 pts. in 19. 8vo. First Edition

Dickens, Charles.   The chimes.   London, Chapman and Hall 1845.
8vo.   First Edition, First Issue

———— A Christmas carol.   London, Chapman & Hall 1843.   8vo.
First Edition, First Issue

———— The cricket on the hearth.   London, Bradbury and Evans
1846. 8vo.   First Edition

———— Dealings with the firm of Dombey and Son.   London, Bradbury & Evans 1846-8.   20 pts. in 19.   8vo.   First Edition

———— Doctor Marigold's prescriptions.   London, Chapman & Hall
1865. 8vo.   First Edition, wrappers.   (All the year round. Christmas number)

———— Great expectations.   London, Chapman and Hall 1861.   3 v.
8vo.   First Edition.   (Samuel Henry Austin)

———— The haunted house.   London, Chapman & Hall 1859.   8vo.
First Edition, stitched.   (All the year round. Christmas number)

———— The haunted man.   London, Bradbury & Evans 1848.   8vo.
First Edition

———— The life and adventures of Martin Chuzzlewit. London, Chapman & Hall 1843-4.   20 pts. in 19.   8vo.   First Edition, First Issue,
wrappers

———— The life and adventures of Nicholas Nickleby. London, Chapman and Hall 1838-9.   20 pts. in 19.   8vo.   First Edition, wrappers

———— Little Dorrit.   London, Bradbury & Evans 1855-7.   20 pts. in
19. 8vo.   First Edition

———— Master Humphrey's clock. London, Chapman and Hall 1840-
41. 88 pts. 4to.   First Edition, wrappers

———— Memoirs of Joseph Grimaldi.   London, R. Bentley 1838.   2 v.
8vo.   First Edition, First Issue

———— Mrs. Lirriper's legacy.   London, Chapman & Hall 1864.   8vo.
First Edition, wrappers.   (All the year round. Christmas number)

———— Mrs. Lirriper's lodgings.   London, Chapman & Hall 1863.
8vo.   First Edition, wrappers.   (All the year round. Christmas
number)

English after 1800

Dickens, Charles. Mugby Junction. London, Chapman & Hall 1866. 8vo. First Edition, wrappers. (All the year round. Christmas number)

———— The mystery of Edwin Drood. London, Chapman & Hall 1870. 6 pts. 8vo. First Edition, wrappers

———— The mystery of Edwin Drood. Complete. Brattleboro, Vt., T. P. James 1874. 8vo. First Edition, wrappers

———— Oliver Twist. London, R. Bentley 1838. 3 v. 8vo. First Edition, First Issue

———— Our mutual friend. London, Chapman and Hall 1864-5. 20 pts. in 19. 8vo. First Edition, wrappers

———— The personal history . . . of David Copperfield. London, Bradbury & Evans 1849-50. 20 pts. in 19. 8vo. First Edition, wrappers

———— The posthumous papers of the Pickwick Club. London, Chapman & Hall 1836-7. 20 pts. in 19. 8vo. First Edition, wrappers

———— Sketches by "Boz." London, J. Macrone 1836. 2 v. 12mo. First Edition

———— Somebody's luggage. London, Chapman & Hall 1862. 8vo. First Edition, stitched. (All the year round. Christmas number)

———— A tale of two cities. London, Chapman and Hall 1859. 8 pts. in 7. 8vo. First Edition, First Issue

———— Tom Tiddler's ground. London, Chapman & Hall 1861. 8vo. First Edition, stitched. (All the year round. Christmas number)

———— The uncommercial traveller. London, Chapman and Hall 1861. 8vo. First Edition

———— and Wilkie Collins. A message from the sea. London, Chapman & Hall 1860. 8vo. First Edition, stitched. (All the year round. Christmas number)

———— No thoroughfare. London, Chapman & Hall 1867. 8vo. First Edition, wrappers. (All the year round. Christmas number)

[Disraeli, Benjamin, *first Earl of Beaconsfield*]. The letters of Runnymede. London, J. Macrone 1836. 8vo. First Edition

[————] Vivian Grey. London, H. Colburn 1826. 5 v. 8vo. First Edition

Dobson, Austin.   Four Frenchwomen.   London, Chatto & Windus 1890.   4to.   First Edition.   (No. 31 of an edition of 50 copies on large paper)

Dodgson, Charles Lutwidge.   *See* Carroll, Lewis

Donne, John.   The poems.   New-York, Grolier Club 1895.   2 v. 12mo.   (One of an edition of 380 copies)

Dowson, Ernest.   Decorations.   London, Chiswick Press 1899.   8vo. First Edition

—— The Pierrot of the minute.   London, L. Smithers 1897.   4to. First Edition

—— Verses.   London, Chiswick Press 1896.   8vo.   First Edition

Drinkwater, John.   Abraham Lincoln.   London, Sidgwick & Jackson 1918.   8vo.   First Edition, wrappers.   (Presentation copy, inscribed, from the author to William Daunt)

—— Rupert Brooke.   London, Chiswick Press 1916.   8vo.   First Edition.   (No. 72 of an edition of 115 copies)

Dryden, John.   All for love.   San Francisco, J. H. Nash 1929.   fol. (No. 161 of an edition of 250 copies)

Edgeworth, Maria.   Harrington . . . and Ormond.   London, for R. Hunter . . . 1817.   3 v.   8vo.   First Edition

—— Harry and Lucy concluded.   London, for R. Hunter . . . 1825. 4 v.   8vo.   First Edition.   (Presentation copy, inscribed by the author, June 13, 1825)

—— Helen.   London, R. Bentley 1834.   3 v.   8vo.   First Edition

—— Leonora.   London, for J. Johnson 1806.   2 v.   8vo.   First Edition

Edgeworth, Richard Lovell *and* Maria Edgeworth.   Essay on Irish bulls.   London, for J. Johnson 1802.   8vo.   First Edition

Egan, Pierce.   Life in London.   London, for Sherwood, Neely and Jones 1821.   8vo.   First Edition

—— The life of an actor.   London, for C. S. Arnold 1825.   8vo. First Edition

—— Pierce Egan's anecdotes.   London, for Knight & Lacey 1827. 8vo.   First Edition

Egan, Pierce.   Real life in London.   London, for Jones 1821-2.   2 v. 8vo.   First Edition.   (2 extra plates)

———— *See also* Real life in Ireland

Eliot, George.   Adam Bede.   Edinburgh, W. Blackwood 1859.   3 v. 8vo.   First Edition

———— Agatha.   London, Trübner 1869.   8vo.   Second Edition, folded, but not stitched.   (Buxton Forman).   (Carter & Pollard p. 194)

———— Brother and sister.   London 1869.   8vo. wrappers.   (Carter & Pollard p. 191)

———— Daniel Deronda.   Edinburgh, W. Blackwood 1876.   8 pts. 8vo.   First Edition, wrappers

———— Felix Holt the radical.   Edinburgh, W. Blackwood 1866.   3 v. 8vo.   First Edition

———— Impressions of Theophrastus Such.   Edinburgh, W. Blackwood 1879.   8vo.   First Edition

———— Middlemarch.   Edinburgh, W. Blackwood 1871.   8 pts.   8vo. First Edition

———— The mill on the Floss.   Edinburgh, W. Blackwood 1860.   3 v. 8vo.   First Edition

———— Romola.   London, Smith, Elder 1863.   3 v.   8vo.   First Edition

———— Scenes of clerical life.   Edinburgh, W. Blackwood 1858.   2 v. 8vo.   First Edition

———— Silas Marner.   Edinburgh, W. Blackwood 1861.   8vo.   First Edition

———— *tr.   See* Feuerbach, Ludwig

Erasmus, Desiderius.   The praise of folie. Tr. by Sir T. Challoner.   London, Essex House Press 1901.   4to.

Erskine, Thomas, *first Baron Erskine*.   The speeches of . . . Thomas Erskine.   London, for J. Ridgway, I-III, 1813, Second Edition; IV, 1810, First Edition; V, 1812, First Edition.   8vo.   (Presentation copy from the author to William Mansel)

Fellowes, Edmund Horace, *editor.   See* Beaumont, Francis, *and* John Fletcher

Fellowes, W. D.   A visit to the monastery of La Trappe.   London, for
T. M'Lean 1823.   8vo.   Fourth Edition.   Large paper.   (Mc-
Burney)

Feuerbach, Ludwig.   The essence of Christianity. Tr. by Marian Evans.
London, J. Chapman 1854.   8vo.   First Edition

[FitzGerald, Edward].   Agamemnon.   [London 1865].   8vo.   First
Edition, wrappers.   (Presentation copy to Charles Eliot Norton,
with corrections in the author's hand)

[———]   The downfall and death of King Œdipus.   (Guildford)
[1880-81].   2 v.   8vo.   First Edition, wrappers.   (One of 50
copies)

[———]   Euphranor.   London, W. Pickering 1851.   8vo.   First Edition

[———]   The mighty magician.   [London 1853].   8vo.   First Edition, wrappers

[———]   Polonius.   London, W. Pickering 1852.   8vo.   First Edition

[———]   Salámán and Absál.   London, J. W. Parker 1856.   4to.   First
Edition.   (Presentation copy, inscribed, from the author to George
Borrow)

———   Six dramas of Calderon. Freely translated.   London, W. Pickering 1853.   8vo.   First Edition

———   See also Crabbe, George; Omar Khayyám

Fletcher, John.   See Beaumont, Francis, and John Fletcher

Frere, John Hookham, tr.   See Aristophanes

[Galsworthy, John].   From the four winds. By John Sinjohn.   London, T. Fisher Unwin 1897.   8vo.   First Edition

[———]   A man of Devon. By John Sinjohn.   Edinburgh, W. Blackwood 1901.   8vo.   First Edition.   (With A.L.S. from the author
laid in)

———   Plays.   London, Duckworth 1909.   8vo.   First Edition.
(Signed quotation from "Strife" in author's hand)

[Galt, John].   The Ayrshire legatees.   Edinburgh, for W. Blackwood
1821.   8vo.   First Edition.   (With A.L.S. from the author to
W. E. Johnston laid in)

Galt, John. Bogle Corbet. London, H. Colburn and R. Bentley [1831].
3 v. 8vo. First Edition

[Gaskell, Elizabeth Cleghorn]. The moorland cottage. London,
Chapman & Hall 1850. 8vo. First Edition

[————] Ruth. London, Chapman & Hall 1853. 3 v. 8vo. First
Edition. (Presentation copy, inscribed by the author)

The Germ. London, Aylott & Jones 1850. 1-4, Jan.-April 1850. 8vo.
First Edition, wrappers. Single sheet of announcement

Gilbert, *Sir* William Schwenk. The "Bab" ballads. London, G. Routledge [1869]. sm. 4to. First Edition. (J. A. Chamberlain)

Gillray, James. The life of William Cobbett. London, H. Humphrey
1809. fol.

Gissing, George. Born in exile. London, A. and C. Black 1892. 3 v.
8vo. First Edition

———— By the Ionian Sea. London, Chapman and Hall 1901. 4to.
First Edition

———— Charles Dickens. A critical study. London, Blackie 1898.
8vo. First Edition. (Victorian era series)

———— Critical studies of the works of Charles Dickens. New York,
Greenberg 1924. 8vo. First Edition

———— The crown of life. London, Methuen 1899. 8vo. First Edition

[————] Demos. London, Smith, Elder 1886. 3 v. 8vo. First
Edition

———— Denzil Quarrier. London, Lawrence & Bullen 1892. 8vo.
First Edition. (Quinn)

———— The emancipated. London, R. Bentley 1890. 3 v. 8vo.
First Edition

———— Eve's ransom. London, Lawrence & Bullen 1895. 8vo. First
Edition

———— The house of cobwebs. London, Archibald Constable 1906.
8vo. First Edition

———— Human odds and ends. London, Lawrence and Bullen 1898.
8vo. First Edition

Gissing, George. In the year of jubilee. London, Lawrence and Bullen 1894. 3 v. 8vo. First Edition

———— Isabel Clarendon. London, Chapman and Hall 1886. 2 v. 8vo. First Edition

———— Letters. London, Archibald Constable 1927. 8vo.

———— Letters to Edward Clodd. London, for private circulation 1914. 8vo. First Edition, wrappers

———— A life's morning. London, Smith, Elder 1888. 3 v. 8vo. First Edition

———— The nether world. London, Smith, Elder 1889. 3 v. 8vo. First Edition

———— New Grub Street. London, Smith, Elder 1891. 3 v. 8vo. First Edition

———— The odd women. London, Lawrence & Bullen 1893. 3 v. 8vo. First Edition

———— Our friend the charlatan. London, Chapman and Hall 1901. 8vo. First Edition

———— The paying guest. London, Cassell 1895. 8vo. First Edition. (Cassell's pocket library)

[————] The private life of Henry Maitland. London, Eveleigh Nash 1912. 8vo. First Edition

———— The private papers of Henry Ryecroft. Westminster, Archibald Constable 1903. 8vo. First Edition

———— Sins of the fathers. Chicago, P. Covici 1924. 8vo. First Edition

———— Sleeping fires. London, T. Fisher Unwin 1895. 8vo. First Edition. (Autonym library)

———— Thyrza. London, Smith, Elder 1887. 3 v. 8vo. First Edition

———— The town traveller. London, Methuen 1898. 8vo. First Edition

———— The unclassed. London, Chapman and Hall 1884. 3 v. 8vo. First Edition

———— Veranilda. London, Archibald Constable 1904. 8vo. First Edition. (Laurence A. Waldron)

Gissing, George. The whirlpool. London, Lawrence and Bullen 1897. 8vo. First Edition

——— Will Warburton. London, Archibald Constable 1905. 8vo. First Edition

——— Workers in the dawn. London, Remington 1880. 3 v. 8vo. First Edition

Godwin, Mary Wollstonecraft. *See* A defence of the character and conduct . . .

Godwin, William. Fleetwood. London, for R. Phillips 1805. 3 v. 8vo. First Edition

——— Mandeville. I-III, Edinburgh, for Archibald Constable 1817; IV, London, for Effingham Wilson 1818. 4 v. 8vo. First Edition

Goldsmith, Oliver. The vicar of Wakefield. London, R. Ackermann 1817. 8vo.

[Gordon, Adam Lindsay]. Bush ballads and galloping rhymes. Melbourne, Clarson, Massina 1870. 8vo. First Edition

[Gosse, Edmund]. Father and son. London, W. Heinemann 1907. 8vo. First Edition

Gradus ad Cantabrigiam. London, for J. Hearne 1824. 8vo. First Edition

Gray, Thomas. An elegy written in a country church-yard. San Francisco, J. H. Nash 1925. fol. (No. 175 of an edition of 200 copies)

Greenaway, Kate. Kate Greenaway's album. London, G. Routledge [1880]. 24mo. First Edition

——— Kate Greenaway's almanack for 1883-95. London, G. Routledge. 13 v. 24mo., 32mo. First Editions

——— Kate Greenaway's almanack for 1897. London, J. M. Dent. 32mo. First Edition

——— Kate Greenaway's calendar for 1896. London, Wells Gardner, Darton. 12mo. First Edition

Gregory, R. A. *and* H. G. Wells. Honours physiography. London, J. Hughes 1893. 8vo. First Edition

Grimm, Ludwig Jakob *and* Wilhelm Karl.   German popular stories. London [I] C. Baldwyn 1823; II, J. Robins . . . 1826.   2 v.   12mo. First Edition, First Issue.   (J. W. R. Crawford)

Guy's porridge pot.   London, for the Author 1808.   8vo.   First Edition

Hall, Charles.   The effects of civilization on the people in European states.   London, for the Author 1805.   8vo.   First Edition

——— Observations on the principal conclusion in Mr. Malthus's Essay on population.   London, for the Author 1805.   8vo.   First Edition

Hamilton, *Lady* Anne.   Secret history of the court of England.   London, W. H. Stevenson 1832.   2 v.   8vo.   First Edition

Hardy, Thomas.   A changed man.   London, Macmillan 1913.   8vo. First Edition

[———] Desperate remedies.   London, Tinsley 1871.   3 v.   8vo. First Edition.   (Stephen George Holland)

——— The dynasts.   London, Macmillan 1904-1908.   3 v.   8vo. 1, First Edition, Second Issue; 2-3, First Issue

——— The famous tragedy of the Queen of Cornwall.   London, Macmillan 1923.   4to.   First Edition

——— Far from the madding crowd.   London, Smith, Elder 1874. 3 v.   8vo.   First Edition.   (Charles Hope Willis)

——— The return of the native.   London, Smith, Elder 1878.   3 v. 8vo.   First Edition.   (Edward Joseph Dent)

——— The trumpet-major.   London, Smith, Elder 1880.   3 v.   8vo. First Edition

[———] Under the greenwood tree.   London, Tinsley 1872.   2 v. 8vo.   First Edition.   (Earl of Sheffield–M. L. Parrish)

——— The well-beloved.   London, Osgood, McIlvaine 1897.   8vo. First Edition

——— Wessex tales.   London, Macmillan 1888.   2 v.   8vo.   First Edition

——— The woodlanders.   London, Macmillan 1887.   3 v.   8vo. First Edition

[Harrison, Mary St. Leger]. The history of Sir Richard Calmady. London, Methuen 1901. 2 v. 8vo. First Edition. (Presentation copy, inscribed to Charles E. Kingsley by the author)

[Hayward, Abraham]. Verses of other days. London 1847. 8vo. First Edition. (Presentation copy, inscribed by the author)

Hazlitt, William. Liber amoris. London, for J. Hunt 1823. 8vo. First Edition

[Helps, *Sir* Arthur]. Essays written in the intervals of business. London, W. Pickering 1841. 8vo. First Edition

[———] Thoughts in the cloister and the crowd. London, for H. Wix 1835. 8vo. First Edition

Helyas. The history of Helyas, Knight of the Swan. Tr. by R. Copland. New York, Grolier Club 1901. 4to.

Henley, William Ernest. A book of verses. London, D. Nutt 1888. 8vo. First Edition. Large paper

——— *and* R. L. Stevenson. Three plays. London, D. Nutt 1892. 12mo. First Edition. (Autographed by Henley)

Heron-Allen, Edward, *tr. See* Omar Khayyám

Herrick, Robert. Selections from the poetry of Robert Herrick. New York, Harper 1882. 4to.

Hewlett, Maurice. Earthwork out of Tuscany. London, J. M. Dent 1895. 8vo. First Edition

——— The forest lovers. London, Macmillan 1898. 8vo. First Edition

——— Little novels of Italy. London, Chapman & Hall 1899. 8vo. First Edition

——— A masque of dead Florentines. London, J. M. Dent 1895. obl. 4to. First Edition

——— The wreath. London, for the Author 1914. 8vo. First Edition. (Presentation copy, inscribed by the author)

The history and adventures of little Henry. London, D. N. Shury for S. and J. Fuller 1810. 16mo.

Hobson, Bulmer. A short history of the Irish Volunteers. Dublin, The Candle Press 1918. I. 8vo. First Edition

Hogg, James. The pilgrims of the sun. London, for J. Murray 1815. 8vo. First Edition. (Presentation copy, inscribed by the author)

Homerus. The Odyssey. Tr. by W. Morris. London, Reeves & Turner 1887. 2 v. 4to. First Edition. Large paper. (Buxton Forman)

Hood, Thomas. Memorials. London, E. Moxon 1860. 2 v. 8vo. First Edition. (Presentation copy, inscribed by the author's daughter to Lady Hill)

——— National tales. London, W. H. Ainsworth 1827. 2 v. 8vo. First Edition

——— The plea of the midsummer fairies. London, for Longman ... 1827. 8vo. First Edition

——— Poems. London, E. Moxon 1846. 2 v. 8vo. First Edition

——— Poems of wit and humour. London, E. Moxon 1847. 8vo. First Edition. (Mark Pattison)

Horne, Richard Hengist, *editor*. A new spirit of the age. London, Smith, Elder 1844. 2 v. 8vo. First Edition

——— *See also* Browning, Elizabeth Barrett

Hornem, Horace. *See* Byron, George Gordon, *Lord*

Hort, J. J. The embroidered banner. London, J. & D. A. Darling 1850. 8vo. First Edition. (Thomas Parkin)

Housman, Alfred Edward. Last poems. London, G. Richards 1922. 8vo. First Edition

——— A Shropshire lad. London, Kegan Paul ... 1896. 8vo. First Edition

[Hughes, Thomas]. Tom Brown at Oxford. Cambridge, Macmillan 1861. 3 v. 8vo. First Edition

[———] Tom Brown's school days. Cambridge, Macmillan 1857. 8vo. First Edition

Hunt, Leigh. Amyntas. London, for T. and J. Allman 1820. 8vo. First Edition

——— Bacchus in Tuscany. London, for J. and H. L. Hunt 1825. 8vo. First Edition

——— Captain Sword and Captain Pen. London, C. Knight 1835. sm. 4to. First Edition. (William Rapley)

Hunt, Leigh.   The descent of liberty.   London, for Gale, Curtis and Fenner 1815.   8vo.   First Edition

——— A jar of honey from Mount Hybla.   London, Smith, Elder 1848.   8vo.   First Edition

——— The Old Court suburb.   London, Hurst and Blackett 1855. 2 v.   8vo.   First Edition

——— The palfrey.   London, How and Parsons 1842.   8vo.   First Edition, wrappers

——— The poetical works.   London, E. Moxon 1832.   8vo.   First Edition, First Issue.   (Mark P. Robinson)

——— Stories from the Italian poets.   London, Chapman and Hall 1846.   2 v.   8vo.   First Edition

——— The Town.   London, Smith, Elder 1848.   2 v.   8vo.   First Edition

——— Ultra-crepidarius.   London, for J. Hunt 1823.   8vo.   First Edition, wrappers

Huxley, Aldous.   The burning wheel.   Oxford, B. H. Blackwell 1916. 8vo.   First Edition, wrappers.   ("Adventurers all" series. No. 7)

Inglis, John Bellingham, *tr. See* Bury, Richard de

Irish insurrection. Tracts for the times. Nos. [1]-13.   Dublin 1915-16. 8vo.

Jefferies, Richard.   Bevis.   London, Sampson Low ... 1882.   3 v.   8vo. First Edition

——— Jack Brass.   London, T. Pettit 1873.   8vo.   First Edition

——— Reporting; editing & authorship.   London, J. Snow [1872]. 8vo.   First Edition

——— The story of my heart.   London, Longmans, Green 1883. 8vo.   First Edition

——— Suez-Cide!!   London, J. Snow 1876.   8vo.   First Edition

——— T.T.T.   Wells, A. Young 1896.   8vo.   First Edition

Johnson, Samuel.   A diary of a journey into North Wales. Edited by R. Duppa.   London, for R. Jennings 1816.   8vo.   First Edition

Jones, Ebenezer.   Studies of sensation and event.   London, C. Fox 1843.   8vo.   First Edition

Jones, John. Attempts in verse ... and an introductory essay ... by R. Southey. London, J. Murray 1831. 8vo. First Edition

Jones, Owen. The grammar of ornament. London, Day 1856. fol.

——— Plans ... of the Alhambra. London, Owen Jones 1842-5. fol.

Keats, John. Endymion. London, for Taylor and Hessey 1818. 8vo. First Edition

——— Lamia, Isabella, The eve of St. Agnes. London, for Taylor and Hessey 1820. 8vo. First Edition

——— Poems. London, for C. & J. Ollier 1817. 12mo. First Edition. (W. K. Bixby)

[Keble, John]. The christian year. Oxford, W. Baxter 1827. 2 v. 8vo. First Edition

Kennedy, Margaret. The ladies of Lyndon. London, W. Heinemann (1923). 8vo. First Edition

Kingsley, Charles. Andromeda. London, J. W. Parker 1858. 8vo. First Edition

——— Hereward the Wake. London, Macmillan 1866. 2 v. First Edition

Kipling, Rudyard. Collah-Wallah and the poison stick. New York 1925. 8vo. First Edition. (No. 28 of an edition of 66 numbered copies)

——— Departmental ditties and other verses. Lahore, The Civil and Military Gazette Press [1886]. 8vo. First Edition, wrappers

——— The five nations. London, Methuen 1903. 8vo. First Edition. (Autographed by Kipling)

——— "If." London, Macmillan, n.d. Folio broadside, signed by Kipling

——— The jungle book. London, Macmillan 1894. 8vo. First Edition

——— Plain tales from the hills. Calcutta, Thacker, Spink 1888. 8vo. First Edition

——— The potted princess. New York 1925. 8vo. First Edition. (No. 28 of an edition of 66 numbered copies)

——— Schoolboy lyrics. Lahore, "Civil and Military Gazette" Press 1881. 12mo. First Edition, wrappers. (Ram Singh)

Kipling, Rudyard. The second jungle book. London, Macmillan 1895. 8vo. First Edition

——— Soldiers three. Allahabad, The "Pioneer" Press 1888. 8vo. First Edition, First Issue. (Indian railway library, No. 1)

[——— *and* Beatrice Kipling]. Echoes. Lahore, "Civil and Military Gazette" Press [1884]. 12mo. First Edition, wrappers

[Klinger, Friedrich Maximilian von]. Faustus. Tr. by G. Borrow. London, W. Simpkin and R. Marshall 1825. 8vo. First Edition. (Lionel Johnson)

[Laing, David]. Select remains of the ancient popular poetry of Scotland. Edinburgh 1822. 8vo.

Lamb, Charles. Album verses. London, E. Moxon 1830. 8vo. First Edition

[———] Elia. London, for Taylor and Hessey 1823. 8vo. First Edition, First Issue

[———] ——— ——— First Edition, Second Issue

[———] Elia. Second series. Philadelphia, Carey, Lea and Carey 1828. 8vo. First Edition

——— John Woodvil. London, T. Plummer 1802. 8vo. First Edition

[———] The last essays of Elia. London, E. Moxon 1833. 8vo. First Edition

Landor, Walter Savage. Andrea of Hungary, and Giovanna of Naples. London, R. Bentley 1839. 8vo. First Edition

——— Antony and Octavius. London, Bradbury & Evans 1856. 8vo. First Edition. (Presentation copy from the author)

[———] Count Julian. London, for J. Murray 1812. 8vo. First Edition

——— Dry sticks, fagoted. Edinburgh, J. Nichol 1858. 8vo. First Edition

——— Fra Rupert. London, Saunders and Otley 1840. 8vo. First Edition. (Augustus Hare)

——— Idyllia heroica decem. Pisis, apud S. Nistrium 1820. 8vo. First Edition. (Presentation copy from Landor to Robert Southey)

Landor, Walter Savage. Imaginary conversations of Greeks and Romans. London, E. Moxon 1853. 8vo. First Edition

———— The last fruit off an old tree. London, E. Moxon 1853. 8vo. First Edition. (Presentation copy from the author to J. T. Fields, with annotations by the former)

———— Letter ... to R. W. Emerson. Bath, E. Williams [1856]. 8vo. First Edition. (Presentation copy, inscribed, from Landor to Mrs. Andrew Crosse)

———— The letters of a conservative. London, Saunders and Otley 1836. 8vo. First Edition. (Presentation copy from the author)

[————] The Pentameron and Pentalogia. London, Saunders and Otley 1837. 8vo. First Edition

[————] Poems from the Arabic & Persian. Warwick, H. Sharpe 1800. 4to. First Edition, stitched

———— Popery: British and foreign. London, Chapman & Hall 1851. 8vo. First Edition

[———— *and others*]. Literary hours. (Liverpool, G. Smith) 1837. 8vo. (Sidney Colvin)

Lang, Andrew. The household of Mary Queen of Scots. Glasgow, J. Maclehose 1905. 8vo. First Edition, wrappers

———— *tr. See* Aucassin & Nicolette

Lawrence, D. H. The white peacock. London, W. Heinemann 1911. 8vo. First Edition

Lefèvre, Raoul. The recuyell of the historyes of Troye. Tr. by W. Caxton. Hammersmith, Kelmscott Press 1892. 4to.

[Leigh, Percival]. The comic English grammar. London, R. Bentley 1840. 8vo.

[————] The comic Latin grammar. London, C. Tilt 1840. 8vo.

Leolinus Siluriensis. *See* Machen, Arthur

[Lever, Charles James]. Arthur O'Leary. London, H. Colburn 1844. 3 v. 8vo. First Edition. (Presentation copy, inscribed, from the author. Hoe copy)

[————] Our mess. Dublin, W. Curry 1843-4. 35 pts. in 32. 8vo. First Edition, wrappers

Lewis, Matthew Gregory.   Tales of wonder.   London, W. Bulmer
1801. 2 v. 8vo. Large paper

———— Timour the Tartar. London, Lowndes & Hobbs [1811]. 8vo.
First Edition, wrappers

Lloyd, Charles. Desultory thoughts in London. London, C. and H.
Baldwyn 1821. 8vo. First Edition

———— The Duke d'Ormond . . . and Beritola. London, Longman . . .
1822. 8vo. First Edition

———— Poems. London, Longman . . . 1823. 8vo. First Edition

The looking glass. London, Thomas McLean 1830-32. 3 v. fol.
(Plates by R. Seymour and W. Heath)

[Lytton, Edward George Bulwer, *first Baron Lytton*]. Eugene Aram.
London, H. Colburn 1832. 3 v. 8vo. First Edition

[————] Harold. London, R. Bentley 1848. 3 v. 8vo. First Edition

[————] Ismael. London, for J. Hatchard 1820. 12mo. First
Edition

[————] Kenelm Chillingly. London, W. Blackwood 1873. 3 v.
8vo. First Edition

[————] The last days of Pompeii. London, R. Bentley 1834. 3 v.
8vo. First Edition

[————] The last of the barons. London, Saunders and Otley 1843.
3 v. 8vo. First Edition

[————] Pelham. London, H. Colburn 1828. 3 v. 8vo. First Edition

[————] Rienzi. London, Saunders and Otley 1835. 3 v. 8vo.
First Edition

[————] Sculpture. [Cambridge 1825]. 8vo. First Edition,
wrappers

Macaulay, Thomas Babington. Pompeii. [Cambridge 1819]. 8vo.
First Edition, wrappers

McCrae, John. In Flanders fields. New York, G. P. Putnam's Sons
1919. 8vo. First Edition

[Machen, Arthur]. The anatomy of tobacco. By Leolinus Siluriensis.
(London) for G. Redway 1884. 8vo. First Edition

Mackail, John William. William Morris. London, Vail & Co., n.d. 8vo. (City Branch pamphlets, 5)

[Mahony, Francis Sylvester]. The reliques of Father Prout. London, J. Fraser 1836. 2 v. 8vo. First Edition

Malet, Lucas. *See* Harrison, Mary St. Leger

Malory, *Sir* Thomas, *tr. See* Arthur, *King*

Manners, *Lord* John. England's trust. London, for J. G. F. & J. Rivington 1841. 12mo. First Edition. (H. W. Closson)

Manning trial. The Bermondsey murder. London, W. M. Clark 1849. 8vo. First Edition

———— A full report of the trial of Manning and his wife. London, E. Lloyd 1849. 8vo. First Edition

———— The only correct account of the confession and execution of Frederick George Manning and Maria Manning. London, W. M. Clark (1849). 8vo. First Edition

———— Verbatim report of the trial of George & Maria Manning, for the murder of Patrick O'Connor. London, G. Vickers 1849. 8vo. First Edition

Marlowe, Christopher, *tr. See* Ovidius Naso, Publius

[Marryat, Frederick]. The King's Own. London, H. Colburn and R. Bentley 1830. 3 v. 8vo. First Edition

———— Masterman Ready. London, Longman . . . 1841. 3 v. 8vo. First Edition

———— Olla perdrida. London, Longman . . . 1840. 3 v. 8vo. First Edition

———— Percival Keene. London, H. Colburn 1842. 3 v. 8vo. First Edition

[————] Peter Simple. London, Saunders and Otley 1834. 3 v. 8vo. First Edition. (Locker-Lampson)

———— The phantom ship. London, H. Colburn 1839. 3 v. 8vo. First Edition

[————] Snarleyyow. London, H. Colburn 1837. 3 v. 8vo. First Edition

———— The travels and romantic adventures of Monsieur Violet. London, Longman . . . 1843. 3 v. 8vo. First Edition. (Conyngham)

Marryat, Frederick. Valerie. London, H. Colburn 1849. 2 v. 8vo. First Edition

Masefield, John. Ballads. London, E. Mathews 1903. sm. 4to. First Edition, wrappers

———— On the Spanish main. London, Methuen (1906). 8vo. First Edition

———— Reynard the fox. London, W. Heinemann 1919. 8vo. First Edition. Large paper

———— Salt-water ballads. London, G. Richards 1902. 8vo. First Edition

Mason, Finch. The run of the season. London, Anthony Treherne (1885). obl. 4to. First Edition

Mason, George Henry. The costume of China. London, William Bulmer 1804. fol.

May, Philip William. Phil May's sketch-book. London, Chatto & Windus 1895. fol.

Melanter. *See* Blackmore, Richard Doddridge

Meredith, George. The adventures of Harry Richmond. London, Smith, Elder 1871. 3 v. 8vo. First Edition. (Morris L. Parrish)

———— Beauchamp's career. London, Chapman and Hall 1876. 3 v. 8vo. First Edition

———— Diana of the Crossways. London, Chapman and Hall 1885. 3 v. 8vo. First Edition

———— The egoist. London, C. Kegan Paul 1879. 3 v. 8vo. First Edition

———— Emilia in England. London, Chapman & Hall 1864. 3 v. 8vo. First Edition

———— Modern love. London, Chapman & Hall 1862. 8vo. First Edition

———— The ordeal of Richard Feverel. London, Chapman and Hall 1859. 3 v. 8vo. First Edition

———— Poems. London, J. W. Parker (1851). 8vo. First Edition. (R. H. Stoddard)

———— The tragic comedians. London, Chapman and Hall 1880. 2 v. 8vo. First Edition

Merrick, Leonard. The man who was good. London, Chatto & Windus 1892. 2 v. 8vo. First Edition. (Presentation copy from the author)

——— Violet Moses. London, R. Bentley 1891. 3 v. 8vo. First Edition

Meyrick, *Sir* Samuel Rush. A critical inquiry into antient armour. London, Henry G. Bohn 1842. 3 v. 4to.

The microcosm of London. London, R. Ackermann (1808). 3 v. 4to.

Middleton, Richard. The day before yesterday. London, T. Fisher Unwin 1912. 8vo. First Edition

——— The ghost ship & other stories. London, T. Fisher Unwin 1912. 8vo. First Edition

——— Monologues. London, T. Fisher Unwin (1913). 8vo. First Edition

——— Poems & songs. [First and] second series. London, T. F. Unwin 1912. 2 v. 8vo. First Edition

Milne, Alan Alexander. When we were very young. London, Methuen (1924). 8vo. First Edition

Milton, John. Latin and Italian poems. Tr. by W. Cowper. Chichester, J. Seagrave 1808. 4to. First Edition

Mitford, John. The adventures of Johnny Newcome in the navy. London, Sherwood, Neely and Jones 1819. 8vo. First Edition

Moleville, Bertrand de. The costume of the hereditary states of the House of Austria. London, William Bulmer 1804. fol.

Montaigne, Michel Eyquem de. Essays. Tr. by John Florio. Boston, Houghton Mifflin 1902. 3 v. fol. (No. 182 of an edition of 265 copies printed at the Riverside Press)

Moore, George. Confessions of a young man. London, Swan Sonnenschein 1888. 8vo. First Edition

——— A drama in muslin. London, Vizetelly 1886. 8vo. First Edition. (Emily Morris Gallatin)

——— Esther Waters. London, W. Scott 1894. 8vo. First Edition. (Emily Morris Gallatin)

Moore, George. Evelyn Innes. London, T. Fisher Unwin 1898. 8vo. First Edition. (Emily Morris Gallatin)

——— Flowers of passion. London, Provost 1878. sm. 4to. First Edition

——— 'Hail and farewell!' Ave. London, W. Heinemann 1911. 8vo. First Edition

——— ——— Salve. London, W. Heinemann 1912. 8vo. First Edition

——— ——— Vale. London, W. Heinemann (1914). 8vo. First Edition

——— Impressions and opinions. New York, C. Scribner's Sons 1891. 8vo. First American Edition

——— Letters . . . to Ed. Dujardin 1886-1922. New York, Crosby Gaige 1929. 8vo. First Edition. (No. 9, signed by the author)

——— Memoirs of my dead life. London, W. Heinemann 1906. 8vo. First Edition

——— ——— New York, D. Appleton 1907. 8vo. First American Edition

——— Mike Fletcher. London, Ward and Downey 1889. 8vo. First Edition. (Emily Morris Gallatin)

——— Modern painting. London, W. Scott 1893. 8vo. First Edition

——— A mummer's wife. London, Vizetelly 1885. 8vo. First Edition. (Emily Morris Gallatin)

——— Pagan poems. London, Newman 1881. 8vo. First Edition. (Emily Morris Gallatin)

——— Sister Teresa. London, T. Fisher Unwin 1901. 8vo. First Edition. (Emily Morris Gallatin)

Moore, Thomas. The epicurean, a tale . . . and Alciphron, a poem. London, J. Macrone 1839. 12mo. First Edition

——— The loves of the angels. London, for Longman . . . 1823. 8vo. First Edition. (John Drinkwater)

——— The poetical works of the late Thomas Little, Esq. London, for J. and T. Carpenter 1801. 8vo. First Edition

[Moore, Thomas]. Tom Crib's memorial to Congress. London, for Longmans ... 1819. 8vo. First Edition

—— *See also* Byron. Letters and journals

Morris, William. Address delivered in the Town Hall, Birmingham, on the 19th of February, 1879. Birmingham, E. C. Osborne (1879). 8vo. First Edition

—— Address on the collection of paintings of the English Pre-Raphaelite school ... October 2nd, 1891. Birmingham, E. C. Osborne (1891). 8vo.

—— Address to trades' unions. London, Socialist League office 1885. 8vo. (The Socialist platform, 1)

—— The aims of art. London, "The Commonweal" 1887. sq. 12mo. First Edition

—— Art and socialism. London, W. Reeves 1884. 24mo. Large paper

—— Chants for socialists. London, Socialist League office 1885. 12mo. First Edition

—— Concerning Westminster Abbey. London, The Society for the protection of ancient buildings, n.d. 8vo.

—— The day is coming. London, Reeves, n.d. 8vo. (Chants for socialists, 1)

—— The decorative arts. London, Ellis and White 1878. 8vo.

—— The earthly paradise. London, F. S. Ellis 1868. 6v. 8vo. First Edition. (One of 20 copies on large paper). (Hoe–Quinn)

—— The God of the poor. London, Office of "Justice," n.d. 8vo.

—— Hopes and fears for art. London, Ellis & White 1882. 8vo. First Edition. (One of 25 copies on large paper)

—— A king's lesson. Aberdeen, J. Leatham 1891. 16mo. sq. 12mo.

—— Labour and pleasure. Birmingham, Cund Bros. (1880). 8vo. First Edition

—— The labour question from the socialist standpoint. Edinburgh, Co-operative Printing Company 1886. 8vo. (Claims of labour lectures, 5)

—— The legend of "The Briar Rose." n.p. 1890. sq. 12mo.

Morris, William.   The life and death of Jason.   Hammersmith, Kelmscott Press 1895.   4to.

———— The Manifesto.   London, Socialist League office 1885.   8vo.

———— Monopoly.   London, "The Commonweal" 1890. 8vo. (The Socialist platform, 7)

———— The reward of labour.   (Hammersmith Socialist Society, n.d.). 8vo.   (Hammersmith Socialist Library, 1).   First Edition

———— A short account of the Commune of Paris. By E. B. Bax, Victor Dave and William Morris.   London, Socialist League office 1886. 8vo.   (The Socialist platform, 4)

———— The socialist ideal of art.   London, Reprinted from "The New Review," January, 1891.   8vo.

———— Socialists at play.   South Place Institute 1885.   sq. 12mo.

———— A summary of the principles of socialism. By H. M. Hyndman & William Morris.   London, The Modern Press 1884.   12mo.

———— The tables turned.   London, Office of "The Commonweal" 1887.   12mo.

———— Textile fabrics.   London, W. Clowes 1884.   8vo.   First Edition.   (2 copies)

———— True and false society.   London, Socialist League office 1888. 8vo.   (The Socialist platform, 6)

———— ———— Hammersmith, The Hammersmith Socialist Society 1893.   8vo.

———— Under an elm-tree.   Aberdeen, J. Leatham 1891.   16mo. First Edition

———— Useful work versus useless toil.   London, Socialist League office 1886.   8vo.   (The Socialist platform, 2)

———— The voice of toil: All for the cause. Two chants of socialists. London, Reprinted from "Justice," n.d.   8vo.

———— tr.   See Homerus; The tale of Beowulf

Morrison, Arthur.   A child of the Jago.   London, Methuen 1896. 8vo.   First Edition

———— Tales of mean streets.   London, Methuen 1894.   8vo.   First Edition

Morrison, Arthur. To London Town. London, Methuen 1899. 8vo.
First Edition

Moulton, Louise Chandler. Arthur O'Shaughnessy. Cambridge,
Stone & Kimball 1894. 8vo. First Edition. (Presentation copy,
inscribed, from the author)

Munro, Neil. Children of tempest. Edinburgh, W. Blackwood 1903.
8vo. First Edition

——— The daft days. Edinburgh, W. Blackwood 1907. 8vo. First
Edition

——— Doom Castle. Edinburgh, W. Blackwood 1901. 8vo. First
Edition

——— Fancy Farm. Edinburgh, W. Blackwood 1910. 8vo. First
Edition

——— Gilian the dreamer. London, Isbister 1899. 8vo. First Edition

——— John Splendid. Edinburgh, W. Blackwood 1898. 8vo. First
Edition

——— The Lost Pibroch. Edinburgh, W. Blackwood 1896. 8vo.
First Edition

——— The new road. Edinburgh, W. Blackwood 1914. 8vo. First
Edition

——— The shoes of fortune. London, Isbister 1901. 8vo. First
Edition

New numbers. Ryton, Dymock, Gloucester 1914. 1: 1-4. 4to.
First Edition, wrappers

Newman, John Henry. Apologia pro vita sua. London, Longman,
Green ... 1864. 8vo. First Edition. (Quinn)

Nicholson, William. The history of the wars occasioned by the French
Revolution. London, Richard Evans 1816. fol.

Nimrod. *See* Apperley, Charles James

Noyes, Alfred. Poems. Edinburgh, W. Blackwood 1904. 4to. First
Edition. (Evelyn Anthony Woodd)

Omar Khayyám. Rubáiyát of Omar Khayyam. Tr. by E. FitzGerald.
London, B. Quaritch 1859. 4to. First Edition, wrappers

Omar Khayyám. Rubáiyát of Omar Khayyam. Tr. by E. FitzGerald. London, B. Quaritch 1868. 4to. Second Edition, wrappers

———— ———— London, B. Quaritch 1872. 4to. Third Edition

———— ———— Reproduced from a manuscript written and illuminated by F. Sangorski & Sutcliffe. London, Siegle, Hill (1910). 4to. (No. 118 of an edition of 550 copies)

———— ———— Edward Fitzgerald's Rubâ'iyât . . . with their original Persian sources collated . . . and literally translated by E. Heron-Allen. 8vo. London, B. Quaritch 1899

———— The quatrains. Tr. by J. Payne. London, for the Villon Society 1898. 8vo. (No. 466)

O'Shaughnessy, Arthur William Edward. An epic of women. London, J. C. Hotten 1870. 8vo. First Edition

———— Lays of France. London, Ellis and Green 1872. 8vo. First Edition. (Presentation copy, inscribed, from the author to Swinburne)

———— Music and moonlight. London, Chatto and Windus 1874. 8vo. First Edition

———— Songs of a worker. London, Chatto and Windus 1881. 8vo. First Edition

———— *See also* Moulton, Louise Chandler

———— *and* Eleanor O'Shaughnessy. Toyland. London, Daldy, Isbister 1875. 8vo. First Edition

Otway, Thomas. The works. London, Nonesuch Press 1927. 3 v. 4to. (No. 450)

Ovidius Naso, Publius. All Ovids elegies. Tr. by C. Marlowe. London, F. Etchells & H. Macdonald 1925. 8vo. (Haslewood books. No. 364 of an edition of 625 copies)

———— Ovyde hys booke of Methamorphose. Books X-XV. Tr. by W. Caxton. Oxford, Shakespeare Head Press 1924. fol. (No. 307 of an edition of 375 copies)

Oxberry, William, *editor*. The new English drama. London, W. Simpkin and R. Marshall 1818-24. 22 v. 8vo. (W. L. Andrews)

Oxford University. A history of the University of Oxford. London, for R. Ackermann 1814. 2 v. fol. First Edition

Pater, Walter Horatio.   Appreciations.   London, Macmillan 1889.
8vo.   First Edition

———— Essays from the "Guardian."   London, Chiswick Press 1896.
8vo.   First Edition.   (No. 25 of an edition of 100 copies)

———— ———— London, Macmillan 1901.   8vo.

———— Gaston de Latour.   London, Macmillan 1896.   8vo.   First
Edition

———— Greek studies.   London, Macmillan 1895.   8vo.   First Edition

———— An imaginary portrait.   Oxford, H. Daniel 1894.   8vo.   First
Edition.   (No. 211 of an edition of 250 copies)

———— Imaginary portraits.   London, Macmillan 1887.   8vo.   First
Edition

———— Marius the Epicurean.   London, Macmillan 1885.   2 v.   8vo.
First Edition

———— Miscellaneous studies.   London, Macmillan 1895.   8vo.   First
Edition

———— Plato and Platonism.   London, Macmillan 1893.   8vo.   First
Edition

———— Studies in the history of the Renaissance.   London, Macmillan
1873.   8vo.   First Edition

———— *See also* Studies in European literature

———— *editor*.   *See* Dante Alighieri

Patmore, Coventry.   The angel in the house.   London, J. W. Parker
1854.   8vo.   First Edition.   (Presentation copy, inscribed, from
the author to E. W. Gosse)

Payne, John.   The descent of the dove.   London, for the Author 1902.
8vo.   First Edition, folded, but not stitched.   (One of 25 copies)

———— Intaglios.   London, B. M. Pickering 1871.   8vo.   First Edition.   (Murray. Presentation copy, inscribed, from the author to
W. B. Scott)

———— Lautrec.   London, Pickering 1878.   8vo.   First Edition,
wrappers

———— New poems.   London, Newman 1880.   8vo.   First Edition.
(Presentation copy, inscribed, from the author)

Payne, John. Songs of life and death. London, H. S. King 1872. 8vo.
First Edition

———— Vigil and vision. London, The Villon Society 1903. 8vo.
First Edition

———— *tr. See* Omar Khayyám; Villon, François

[Peacock, Thomas Love]. The Round Table. London, J. Arliss
[1817]. 12mo. First Edition

[————] Sir Hornbook. London, for Sharpe and Hailes 1814. 12mo.
First Edition, wrappers

Phillips, Stephen. Endymion. London, Privately printed [1905].
8vo. First Edition. (No. 5 of an edition of 30 copies)

———— Grief and God. London, Privately printed 1905. sm. 4to.
First Edition, wrappers

———— Nero. London, Macmillan 1906. 8vo.

———— New poems. London, J. Lane 1908. 8vo.

———— Orestes. London, for private circulation 1884. sm. 4to.
First Edition, wrappers

———— The sin of David. London, Macmillan 1904. 8vo.

———— Ulysses. London, J. Lane 1902. 8vo.

[Polidori, John William]. The vampyre. London, for Sherwood,
Neely and Jones 1819. 8vo. First Edition, First Issue

Pope, Alexander. An essay on criticism. San Francisco, J. H. Nash
1928. fol. (No. 178 of an edition of 250 copies)

———— The rape of the lock. London, F. Etchells & H. Macdonald
1925. 8vo. (Haslewood books. No. 174 of an edition of 725
copies)

Porter, Jane. The Scottish chiefs. London, for Longman . . . 1810.
5 v. 8vo. First Edition

———— *and* Anna Maria Porter. Tales round a winter hearth. London, for Longman . . . 1826. 2 v. 8vo. First Edition

Praed, Winthrop Mackworth. Athens. [Cambridge 1824]. 8vo.
First Edition, wrappers. (E. W. Gosse–C. B. Foote)

Proteus. *See* Blunt, Wilfrid Scawen

Prout, *Father. See* Mahony, Francis Sylvester

The punishments of China. London, W. Bulmer 1801. fol. First Edition

Reade, Charles. Christie Johnstone. London, R. Bentley 1853. 8vo. First Edition. (Halsey)

——— The cloister and the hearth. London, Trübner 1861. 4 v. 8vo. First Edition

——— The eighth commandment. London, Trübner 1860. 8vo. First Edition. (Buxton Forman)

——— Hard cash. London, S. Low 1863. 3 v. 8vo. First Edition

——— "It is never too late to mend." London, R. Bentley 1856. 3 v. 8vo. First Edition

——— Peg Woffington. London, R. Bentley 1853. 8vo. First Edition. (Halsey)

——— A perilous secret. London, R. Bentley 1884. 2 v. 8vo. First Edition

——— Put yourself in his place. London, Smith, Elder 1870. 3 v. 8vo. First Edition

——— Singleheart and doubleface. London, Chatto & Windus 1884. 8vo. First Edition

——— White lies. London, Trübner 1857. 3 v. 8vo. First Edition

——— A woman-hater. Edinburgh, W. Blackwood 1877. 3 v. 8vo. First Edition

Real life in Ireland. London, J. L. Marks 1821. 8vo. First Edition. (C. Jeaffreson). [Ascribed to Pierce Egan]

Reid, Mayne. The headless horseman. London, Chapman & Hall [1866-7]. 20 parts. 8vo. First Edition

——— The quadroon. London, G. W. Hyde 1856. 3 v. 8vo. First Edition

——— The rifle rangers. London, W. Shoberl 1850. 2 v. 8vo. First Edition

——— The scalp hunters. London, C. J. Skeet 1851. 3 v. 8vo. First Edition

——— The wild huntress. London, R. Bentley 1861. 3 v. 8vo. First Edition

English after 1800

Reynard the Fox.   The history of Reynard the foxe. By W. Caxton. Edited by H. H. Sparling.   Hammersmith, Kelmscott Press 1892. 4to.

Ritchie, Leitch.   Beauty's costume.   London, Longman, Orme, Brown, Green, and Longmans 1838.   4to.   First Edition

Rogers, Samuel.   Jacqueline.   London, for J. Murray 1814.   8vo. First Edition.   (William Williamson Willink–John Drinkwater)

Rossetti, Dante Gabriel.   Sir Hugh the Heron.   London, G. Polidori's private press 1843.   4to.   First Edition, wrappers.   (Clawson)

Ruskin, John.   Modern painters.   London, Smith, Elder 1848-60.   5 v. 8vo.   I, 1848, Fourth Edition; II, 1849, Second Edition; III-V, 1856, 1860, First Edition.   (Collin Armstrong)

———— Poems. Collected 1850.   12mo.   First Edition.   (W. H. Harrison–R. B. Adam–Kern)

———— Salsette and Elephanta.   Oxford, J. Vincent 1839.   8vo.   First Edition, wrappers.   (Presentation copy, inscribed by Ruskin)

———— Seven lamps of architecture.   London, Smith, Elder 1849.   8vo. First Edition.   (Collin Armstrong)

———— The stones of Venice.   London, Smith, Elder 1858-67.   3 v. 8vo.   Second Edition.   (Collin Armstrong)

Ryley, Samuel William.   The itinerant.   I-III, London, for Taylor and Hessey 1808; IV-VI, for Sherwood, Neely and Jones 1816-17; VII-IX, for Sherwood 1827.   9 v.   12mo.   First Edition

[Scott, Michael].   The cruise of the Midge.   Edinburgh, W. Blackwood 1836.   2 v.   8vo.   First Edition

[————] Tom Cringle's log.   Edinburgh, W. Blackwood 1833.   2 v. 8vo.   First Edition

[Scott, *Sir* Walter].   The abbot.   Edinburgh, for Longman . . . 1820. 3 v.   8vo.   First Edition

[————] Anne of Geierstein.   Edinburgh, for Cadell 1829.   3 v.   8vo. First Edition

———— Ballads and lyrical pieces.   Edinburgh, J. Ballantyne 1806. 8vo.   First Edition

[————] Border antiquities.   London, Longman [1812-15].   2 v. 4to.   First Edition.   (James Fletcher)

[Scott, *Sir* Walter].   The bride of Lammermoor.   Edinburgh, for A. Constable 1819.   3 v.   8vo.   First Edition.   (Tales of my landlord. Third Series)

[———] Chronicles of the Canongate.   Edinburgh, for Cadell 1827. 2 v.   8vo.   First Edition.   (Charles Lilburn)

[———] The fortunes of Nigel.   Edinburgh, for A. Constable 1822. 3 v.   8vo.   First Edition

[———] Guy Mannering.   Edinburgh, J. Ballantyne 1815.   3 v. 8vo.   First Edition

——— Halidon Hill.   Edinburgh, for A. Constable 1822.   8vo.   First Edition, wrappers

[———] The heart of Mid-Lothian.   Edinburgh, for A. Constable 1818.   4 v.   8vo.   First Edition.   (Tales of my landlord. Second Series)

[———] Ivanhoe.   Edinburgh, for A. Constable 1820.   3 v.   8vo. First Edition

[———] Kenilworth.   Edinburgh, for A. Constable 1821.   3 v. 8vo.   First Edition

——— The lay of the last minstrel.   London, for Longman . . . 1805. 4to.   First Edition

[———] A legend of Montrose.   Edinburgh, for A. Constable 1819. 2 v.   8vo.   First Edition.   (Tales of my landlord. Third Series)

——— Letters on demonology and witchcraft.   London, J. Murray 1830.   8vo.   First Edition

[———] The monastery.   Edinburgh, for Longman . . . 1820.   3 v. 8vo.   First Edition.   (Robert William Duff)

[———] Peveril of the Peak.   Edinburgh, for A. Constable 1822. 4 v.   8vo.   First Edition

[———] The pirate.   Edinburgh, for A. Constable 1822.   3 v.   8vo. First Edition

[———] Quentin Durward.   Edinburgh, for A. Constable 1823.   3 v. 8vo.   First Edition

[———] Redgauntlet.   Edinburgh, for A. Constable 1824.   3 v.   8vo. First Edition

[Scott, *Sir* Walter]. Rob Roy. Edinburgh, J. Ballantyne 1818. 3 v. 8vo. First Edition

———— Rokeby. Edinburgh, J. Ballantyne 1813. 4to. First Edition

[————] St Ronan's well. Edinburgh, for A. Constable 1824. 3 v. 8vo. First Edition

[————] Tales of the crusaders. Edinburgh, for A. Constable 1825. 4 v. 8vo. First Edition

———— The vision of Don Roderick. Edinburgh, J. Ballantyne 1811. 4to. First Edition

[————] Waverley. Edinburgh, J. Ballantyne 1814. 3 v. 8vo. First Edition

[————] Woodstock. Edinburgh, for A. Constable 1826. 3 v. 8vo. First Edition

Shadwell, Charles Lancelot, *tr.* *See* Dante Alighieri

The Shanachie. Dublin, Maunsel [1906-1907]. 6 pts. 4to. First Edition, wrappers

[Shelley, Mary Wollstonecraft]. Frankenstein. London, for Lackington...1818. 3 v. 8vo. First Edition

Shelley, Percy Bysshe. Adonais. Pisa, with the types of Didot 1821. 4to. First Edition, wrappers preserved

———— Alastor. London, for Baldwin, Cradock, and Joy ... 1816. 8vo. First Edition. (D. F. Appleton–Hagen)

———— The Cenci. Italy, for C. and J. Ollier 1819. 8vo. First Edition

———— Epipsychidion. Montagnola di Lugano, Officina Bodoni 1923. 4to.

———— Hellas. London, C. and J. Ollier 1822. 8vo. First Edition. (Roxburghe)

———— Laon and Cythna. London, for Sherwood, Neely, & Jones 1818. 8vo. First Edition. (Huth)

———— Letters. London, E. Moxon 1852. 8vo. First Edition. (McKee–Poor)

———— The masque of anarchy. London, E. Moxon 1832. 12mo. First Edition. (David Robert Clark)

Shelley, Percy Bysshe. Note books. Edited by H. B. Forman. Boston, Bibliophile Society 1911. 3 v. 8vo. (One of an edition of 465 copies)

———— Posthumous poems. London, for J. and H. L. Hunt 1824. 8vo. First Edition

———— Prometheus unbound. London, C. and J. Ollier 1820. 8vo. First Edition

———— Queen Mab. London, P. B. Shelley 1813. 8vo. First Edition

———— ———— London, W. Clark 1821. 8vo. First Published Edition

———— The revolt of Islam. London, for J. Brooks 1829. 8vo. (Original Laon and Cythna sheets with new title)

———— Rosalind and Helen. London, for C. and J. Ollier 1819. 8vo. First Edition. (W. B. Tegetmeier–Buxton Forman)

———— Zastrozzi. London, for G. Wilkie and J. Robinson 1810. 12mo. First Edition. (Kenealy)

Sheridan, Richard Brinsley. Clio's protest. London, for J. Arnould 1819. 8vo. (Halsey)

———— An ode to scandal. London, for W. Wright 1819. 8vo. First Edition. (Halsey)

[Shorthouse, Joseph Henry]. John Inglesant. Birmingham, Cornish 1880. 8vo. First Edition. (Presentation copy, inscribed by the author)

Sinjohn, John. See Galsworthy, John

Skinner, Joseph. The present state of Peru. London, for Richard Phillips 1805. 4to.

Smith, Albert. The wassail-bowl. London, R. Bentley 1843. 2 v. 8vo. First Edition

Southey, Robert. Chronicle of the Cid. London, for Longmans . . . 1808. 4to. First Edition. (John Hughes)

———— Essays, moral and political. London, J. Murray 1832. 2 v. 8vo. First Edition. (Presentation copy)

———— The expedition of Orsua; and The crimes of Aguirre. London, for Longman . . . 1821. 8vo. First Edition

Southey, Robert. Thalaba the destroyer. London, for T. N. Longman and O. Rees 1801. 2 v. 8vo. First Edition

———— *See also* Jones, John

Spenser, Edmund. The faerie queene. Cambridge, University Press 1909. 2 v. 4to. (One of an edition of 350 copies)

———— ———— Chelsea, Ashendene Press 1924. fol. (One of an edition of 180 copies)

———— The minor poems. Chelsea, Ashendene Press 1925. fol. (One of an edition of 200 copies)

Stephens, James. The adventures of Seumas Beg. The rocky road to Dublin. London, Macmillan 1915. 8vo. First Edition

———— Arthur Griffith. Dublin, Wilson, Hartnell, n.d. 8vo. First Edition, wrappers

———— The charwoman's daughter. London, Macmillan 1912. 8vo. First Edition

———— The crock of gold. London, Macmillan 1912. 8vo. First Edition

———— Deirdre. London, Macmillan 1923. 8vo. First Edition

———— The demi-gods. London, Macmillan 1914. 8vo. First Edition

———— Five new poems. London, A. T. Stevens 1913. 8vo. First Edition, wrappers

———— Green branches. Dublin, Maunsel 1916. 8vo. First Edition, wrappers

———— Here are ladies. London, Macmillan 1913. 8vo. First Edition

———— The hill of vision. Dublin, Maunsel 1912. 8vo. First Edition

———— Hunger. Dublin, The Candle Press 1918. 8vo. First Edition, wrappers

———— In the land of youth. London, Macmillan 1924. 8vo. First Edition

———— The insurrection in Dublin. Dublin, Maunsel 1916. 8vo. First Edition

Stephens, James. Insurrections. Dublin, Maunsel 1909. 8vo. First Edition

———— Irish fairy tales. London, Macmillan 1920. 8vo. First Edition

———— Little things. Freelands, Privately printed 1924. 8vo. First Edition, wrappers

———— Reincarnations. London, Macmillan 1918. 8vo. First Edition

Stevenson, Robert Louis. A child's garden of verses. London, Longmans, Green 1885. 8vo. First Edition

———— Father Damien. Sydney 1890. 8vo. First Edition

———— ———— San Francisco, J. H. Nash 1930. fol. (No. 156 of an edition of 250 copies)

———— An inland voyage. London, C. Kegan Paul 1878. 8vo. First Edition

[————] The Pentland rising. Edinburgh, A. Elliot 1866. 16mo. First Edition

———— Strange case of Dr Jekyll and Mr Hyde. London, Longmans, Green 1886. 8vo. First Edition

———— Travels with a donkey in the Cevennes. London, C. Kegan Paul 1879. 8vo. First Edition

———— Treasure Island. London, Cassell 1883. 8vo. First Edition

———— Virginibus puerisque. London, C. Kegan Paul 1881. 8vo. First Edition

———— *See also* Henley, William Ernest *and* R. L. Stevenson

Studies in European literature, being the Taylorian lectures 1889-1899 delivered by . . . S. Mallarmé, W. Pater, E. Dowden, W. M. Rossetti. Oxford, Clarendon Press 1900. 8vo. First Edition

[Surtees, Robert Smith]. The analysis of the hunting field. London, R. Ackermann 1846. First Edition

[————] "Ask Mamma." London, Bradbury and Evans 1858. 8vo. First Edition

[————] Handley Cross; or Mr. Jorrocks's hunt. London, Bradbury and Evans 1854. 8vo. First Edition

[Surtees, Robert Smith].   Hillingdon Hall.   London, J. C. Nimmo 1888.   8vo.

[———] Mr. Facey Romford's hounds.   London, Bradbury and Evans 1865.   8vo.   First Edition

[———] Mr. Sponge's sporting tour.   London, Bradbury and Evans 1853.   8vo.   First Edition

[———] "Plain or ringlets?"   London, Bradbury and Evans 1860. 8vo.   First Edition

Swinburne, Algernon Charles.   Laus Veneris.   London, E. Moxon 1866.   8vo.   Folded, but not stitched.   (Carter & Pollard p. 272)

——— Love's cross-currents. London, Chatto & Windus 1905. 8vo. First Edition

——— Mary Stuart.   London, Chatto & Windus 1881.   8vo.   First Edition.   (With author's initials and corrections)

——— Poems and ballads.   London, E. Moxon 1866.   8vo.   First Edition, First Issue

——— The queen-mother. Rosamond.   London, B. M. Pickering 1860.   8vo.   First Edition

Symonds, John Addington.   The Renaissance.   Oxford, H. Hammans 1863.   8vo.   First Edition

Symons, Arthur.   Aubrey Beardsley.   London, J. M. Dent 1905.   4to.

The tale of Beowulf. Tr. by W. Morris.   Hammersmith, Kelmscott Press 1895.   4to.

Tasso, Torquato.   The history of Godefrey of Boloyne. Tr. by W. Caxton.   Hammersmith, Kelmscott Press 1893.   4to.

[Tennyson, Alfred, *Lord*].   In memoriam.   London, E. Moxon 1850. 8vo.   First Edition.   (Francis Grant–Locker-Lampson)

——— Maud, and other poems. London, E. Moxon 1855. 8vo. First Edition

——— The new Timon and the poets. Privately printed 1876. 12mo. First Edition, stitched

——— Poems. London, E. Moxon 1833. 8vo. First Edition

——— ——— ———1842. 2 v. 8vo. First Edition

English after 1800

Tennyson, Alfred, *Lord*. Poems, chiefly lyrical. London, E. Wilson 1830. 8vo. First Edition

——— Timbuctoo. (*In* Prolusiones academicae . . . Cantabrigiae . . . J. Smith) (1829). 8vo. First Edition, wrappers. (Edward K. Butler)

[——— *and* Charles]. Poems, by two brothers. London, for W. Simpkin and R. Marshall 1827. 12mo. First Edition. (Sir William A. Fraser)

Thackeray, William Makepeace. The book of snobs. London, Punch Office 1848. 8vo. First Edition, wrappers

[———] Doctor Birch and his young friends. London, Chapman and Hall 1849. 4to. First Edition

[———] An essay on the genius of George Cruikshank. (London) H. Hooper 1840. 8vo. First Edition

——— ——— Illustrated by 250 etchings from his works from 1810 to 1870. [London 1840]. 4to. (Frederick Burgess)

[———] The history of Henry Esmond, Esq. London, for Smith, Elder 1852. 3 v. 8vo. First Edition. (C. E. Richardson)

——— The history of Pendennis. London, Bradbury & Evans 1848-50. 24 pts. in 23. 8vo. First Edition, wrappers

——— The history of Samuel Titmarsh and the great Hoggarty diamond. London, Bradbury & Evans 1849. 4to. First Edition

[———] The Kickleburys on the Rhine. London, Smith, Elder 1850. 4to. First Edition

——— Miscellaneous papers and sketches. Boston, Houghton Mifflin 1889. 8vo. (G. B. McCutcheon)

——— Miscellanies. London, Bradbury & Evans 1855-7. 4 v. 8vo. First Edition

[———] Mrs Perkins's ball. (London) Chapman & Hall (1847). 4to. First Edition, First Issue

——— The new sketch book. London, A. Rivers 1906. 8vo. First Edition. (G. B. McCutcheon)

——— The Newcomes. London, Bradbury and Evans 1853-5. 24 pts. in 23. 8vo. First Edition, wrappers

English after 1800

Thackeray, William Makepeace. Novels by eminent hands. London, Bradbury & Evans 1856. 8vo. First Edition

[———] "Our street." London, Chapman and Hall 1848. 4to. First Edition

[———] Rebecca and Rowena. London, Chapman and Hall 1850. 4to. First Edition

[———] The rose and the ring. London, Smith, Elder 1855. 4to. First Edition

——— Stray papers. London, Hutchinson 1901. 8vo. First Edition. (G. B. McCutcheon)

——— Thackeray in the United States . . . By J. G. Wilson. New York, Dodd, Mead 1904. 2 v. 8vo. (G. B. McCutcheon)

——— Vanity Fair. London, Punch Office 1847-8. 20 pts. in 19. 8vo. First Edition, wrappers

——— The Virginians. London, Bradbury and Evans 1857-9. 24 pts. in 23. 8vo. First Edition, wrappers

Theocritus. Sixe idillia. Manchester, Cloister Press 1922. 4to. (No. 152 of an edition of 380 copies)

Thompson, Francis. [A collection of 51 contributions in prose and verse to the magazine "Merry England"]. London 1888-95. 8vo. First Edition

——— The hound of Heaven. London, Burns and Oates (1909). 8vo.

——— Poems. London, E. Mathews 1893. 4to. First Edition. (Elkin Mathews)

——— Shelley. London, Burns & Oates 1909. 8vo. First Edition. Large paper. (Hubert Greville Palmer)

——— Songs wing-to-wing. London, Westminster Press (for private circulation) 1895. 4to. First Edition, First Issue. (Everard Meynell copy, autographed by the author)

——— The works. London, Burns & Oates (1913). 3 v. 8vo. First Edition

Ticheburn, Cheviot. *See* Ainsworth, William Harrison

Trollope, Anthony. Framley Parsonage. London, Smith, Elder 1861. 3 v. 8vo. First Edition

Trollope, Anthony. He knew he was right. London, Virtue [1868-9]. 32 pts. 8vo. First Edition, wrappers

—————— How the "Mastiffs" went to Iceland. London, Virtue 1878. 4to. First Edition

—————— The last chronicle of Barset. London, Smith, Elder [1866-7]. 32 pts. 8vo. First Edition, wrappers

—————— The life of Cicero. London, Chapman and Hall 1880. 2 v. 8vo. First Edition

—————— The noble jilt. London, Constable 1923. 8vo. First Edition

—————— Orley Farm. London, Chapman & Hall [1861-2]. 20 pts. 8vo. First Edition, wrappers

—————— The prime minister. London, Chapman & Hall 1876. 4 v. 8vo. First Edition

—————— Ralph the heir. London, Hurst and Blackett 1871. 3 v. 8vo. First Edition

—————— The struggles of Brown, Jones, and Robinson. London, Smith, Elder 1870. 8vo. First Edition

—————— Tales of all countries. [First and] second series. London, Chapman and Hall 1861, 1863. 2 v. 8vo. First Edition

Trollope, Frances. The life and adventures of Michael Armstrong, the factory boy. London, H. Colburn 1839-40. 12 pts. 8vo. First Edition

[Utterson, Edward Vernon, *editor*]. Select pieces of early popular poetry. London, W. Pickering 1825. 2 v. 8vo.

Vanbrugh, *Sir* John. The works. London, Nonesuch Press 1927. 4 v. 4to. (No. 879)

Villon, François. The poems. Tr. by J. Payne. London, for the Villon Society 1878. sm. 4to. First Edition. (No. 41 of an edition of 157 copies)

Virgilius Maro, Publius. The Aeneids. Tr. by W. Morris. London, Ellis and White 1876. 2 v. 8vo. First Edition. Large paper. (One of 25 copies). (Hoe–Quinn)

—————— The Georgics. Tr. by R. D. Blackmore. London, S. Low, Son, and Marston 1871. 8vo. First Edition

English after 1800

Virgilius Maro, Publius. The Georgics. Tr. by Lord Burghclere. London, J. Murray 1904. 4to. First Edition

Voragine, Jacobus de. The golden legend. Tr. by W. Caxton. Hammersmith, Kelmscott Press 1892. 3 v. 4to.

[Walmsley, Edward]. Physiognomical portraits. London, J. Major, R. Jennings and R. Triphook 1824. 2 v. 4to. First Edition. Large paper. (C. A. Tulk–J. S. Virtue)

[Warren, Samuel]. Ten thousand a-year. Edinburgh, W. Blackwood 1841. 3 v. 8vo. First Edition

Wathen, James. A series of views illustrative of the Island of St. Helena. London, T. Clay 1821. 4to.

Watson, Henry Brereton Marriott. *See* Barrie, *Sir* James Matthew *and* H. B. Marriott Watson

Watson, *Sir* William. Epigrams of art, life, and nature. Liverpool, G. G. Walmsley 1884. sm. 4to. First Edition

———— Excursions in criticism. London, E. Mathews 1893. 8vo. First Edition

———— The father of the forest. London, J. Lane 1895. 8vo. First Edition

———— Lachrymae musarum. London, for private distribution 1892. 8vo. First Edition, folded, but not stitched

———— New poems. London, J. Lane 1909. 8vo. First Edition

———— Odes and other poems. London, J. Lane 1894. 8vo. First Edition

———— The prince's quest. London, E. Mathews and J. Lane 1893. 8vo. First Edition

———— Sable and purple. London, E. Nash 1910. 8vo. First Edition

———— Wordsworth's grave. London, T. F. Unwin 1890. 8vo. First Edition

Webster, John. Love's graduate. Oxford, Daniel Press 1885. 4to. (No. 20 of an edition of 150 copies)

Wells, Herbert George. Text-book of biology. London, W. B. Clive (1892-3). 2 v. 8vo. First Edition

———— *See also* Gregory, R. A. *and* H. G. Wells

English after 1800

West, Andrew Fleming, *tr.*   *See* Bury, Richard de

[Westmacott, Charles Molloy].   The English spy.   London, Sherwood, Jones 1825-6.   2 v.   8vo.   First Edition

Whibley, Charles, *editor.*   In cap and gown.   London, Kegan Paul, Trench 1889.   8vo.   First Edition.   (Presentation copy)

Whistler, James Abbott McNeill.   Eden versus Whistler.   Paris, Louis-Henry May [1899].   4to.   First Edition.   Large paper.   (No. 96 of an edition of 250 copies)

—— The etched work.   New York, Grolier Club 1910.   6 v.   4to.

—— The gentle art of making enemies.   Paris, Delabrosse 1890. 12mo.   First Edition, wrappers

—— —— London, W. Heinemann 1890.   4to.   First Authorized Edition.   Large paper.   (No. 55 of an edition of 250 copies)

—— Mr. Whistler's "Ten o'clock."   London (Spottiswoode) 1888. sm. 4to.   First Edition, wrappers

[White, William Hale].   The autobiography of Mark Rutherford. London, Trübner 1881.   8vo.   First Edition

[——] Mark Rutherford's deliverance.   London, Trübner 1885. 8vo.   First Edition

[——] The revolution in Tanner's Lane.   London, Trübner 1887. 8vo.   First Edition

Wilde, Oscar.   The ballad of Reading Gaol.   London, L. Smithers 1898.   8vo.   First Edition

—— De profundis.   London, Methuen [1905].   8vo.   First Edition.   (One of 50 copies on Japanese vellum)

—— For love of the king.   London, Methuen (1922).   8vo.   First Edition.   (Quinn)

—— The happy prince.   London, D. Nutt 1888.   8vo.   First Edition.   Large paper.   (No. 48 of an edition of 75 copies, signed by author and publisher)

—— A house of pomegranates.   London, J. R. Osgood, McIlvaine 1891.   4to.   First Edition.   (Edward and Marianna Heron–Allen)

—— An ideal husband.   London, L. Smithers 1899.   4to.   First Edition

Wilde, Oscar. The importance of being earnest. London, L. Smithers 1899. 4to. First Edition

———— Lady Windermere's fan. London, E. Mathews and J. Lane 1893. 4to. First Edition

———— Poems. London, D. Bogue 1881. 8vo. First Edition

———— Ravenna. Oxford, T. Shrimpton 1878. 8vo. First Edition, wrappers

———— Salomé. Paris, Librairie de l'art indépendant 1893. sm. 4to. First Edition, wrappers

———— Vera. Privately printed 1902. 4to. First Edition, wrappers. (No. 180 of an edition of 200 copies)

———— A woman of no importance. London, J. Lane 1894. 4to. First Edition. (R. Strathern)

Wise, Thomas James, *editor*. *See* Browning, Robert

Wolfe, Charles. Remains. Dublin, for A. and W. Watson 1825. 2 v. 12mo. First Edition

Wordsworth, William. Ecclesiastical sketches. London, for Longman ... 1822. 8vo. First Edition. (Wallace)

———— The excursion. London, for Longman 1814. 4to. First Edition

———— Memorials of a tour on the continent, 1820. London, for Longman 1822. 8vo. First Edition. (Groves)

———— Peter Bell. London, Strahan and Spottiswoode 1819. 8vo. First Edition, wrappers

———— Poems. London, for Longman ... 1801. 2 v. 8vo. First Edition

———— The prelude. London, E. Moxon 1850. 8vo. First Edition

———— The river Duddon. London, for Longman ... 1820. 8vo. First Edition. (Hagen)

———— The waggoner. London, Strahan and Spottiswoode 1819. 8vo. First Edition, wrappers

———— The white doe of Rylstone. London, for Longman ... 1815. 4to. First Edition. (J. T. Beer)

Wordsworth, William. Yarrow revisited. London, for Longman ... 1835. 12mo. First Edition. (Wallace)

Wycherley, William. The complete works. London, Nonesuch Press 1924. 4v. 4to. (No. 577)

Wyn, Elis. The sleeping bard. Tr. by G. Borrow. London, J. Murray 1860. 8vo. First Edition

Yeats, William Butler. Mosada. Dublin, Sealy, Bryers and Walker 1886. 8vo. First Edition. (Presentation copy, inscribed, from the author to Charles Johnston)

Young, Francis Brett. Cold harbour. London, W. Collins (1924). 8vo. First Edition

—— My brother Jonathan. London, W. Heinemann (1928). 8vo. First Edition

—— Portrait of Clare. London, W. Heinemann (1927). 8vo. First Edition

—— Sea horses. London, Cassell (1925). 8vo. First Edition

—— *and* E. Brett Young. Undergrowth. London, M. Secker (1913). 8vo. First Edition

English Broadside Ballads

BL = Black Letter; IL = Italic Letter; RL = Roman Letter

An answer to Moggy's misfortune. Tune of Robin Cushe. PrInted [sic] for P. Brooksby, J. Deacon, J. Blare, J. Back. 4 col. 3 wdcts. BL

A ballad of the cloak's knavery. To an excellent new tune, much in request. 3 col. 1 wdct. IL & RL

Barbara Allen's cruelty. To the tune of Barbara Allen. Printed and sold at the Printing-Office in Bow-Church-Yard, London. 4 col. 2 wdcts. IL & RL

Bateman's tragedy. Printed and sold at the Printing-Office in Bow Church Yard, London. 4 col. 3 wdcts. IL

The beggers delight. To a pleasant new tune. 3 col. 2 wdcts. BL

The Berkshire lady. Printed and sold in Bow-Church Yard, London. 5 col. 1 wdct. RL

Bonny Dundee. To an excellent tune, called Bonney Dundee. Printed and sold in Bow-Church Yard, London. 3 col. 1 wdct. IL & RL

The bonny Scottish lad. To an excellent new tune ... The Liggan waters. Printed for J. Conyers at the Black Raven in Holborn. 4 col. 3 wdcts. BL

The bride's burial. Tune of The lady's fall. 4 col. 1 wdct. RL

Captain Hind's progress and ramble. Tune of Robin Hood revived. 4 col. 2 wdcts. RL

The children in the wood. Printed and sold at the Printing-Office in Bow-Church-Yard, London. 5 col. 6 wdcts. IL & RL

Constance and Anthony. 4 col. 2 wdcts. IL & RL

The couragious plow-man. To the tune of, Dick and Nan. London, Printed for F. Coles, T. Vere, J. Wright, and J. Clark. 5 col. 2 wdcts, wdct headpiece. BL

The cruel knight. Printed and sold at the Printing-Office in Bow-Church-Yard, London. 4 col. RL

The cruel step-mother. Printed and sold at the Printing-Office in Bow-Church-Yard, London. 4 col. 2 wdcts. RL

Cupid's revenge. Printed and sold at the Printing-Office in Bow-Church-Yard, London. 4 col. 2 wdcts. IL & RL

————— [another issue]. 4 col. 1 wdct. RL

The dame of honour: Or, Hospitality. Sung by Mrs. Willis, in the opera call'd, The kingdom of the birds. 3 col. 3 wdcts. IL & RL

The description of a town miss. To the tune of, Amarilli. Printed for F. Coles, T. Vere, J. Wright, and J. Clarke. 4 col. 2 wdcts. BL

The dispairing youths grief. To the tune of, Black and sullen hour. Printed for P. Brooksby, in Pye-Corner. 3 col. 2 wdcts. BL & RL

The distressed mother. To the tune of, Let Cesar live long. Printed for P. Brooksby, J. Deacon, J. Blare, J. Back. 3 col. 3 wdcts. BL

The Dorset-shire damosel. To the tune of, Fond boy, &c. Or, Love's a sweet passion, &c. Printed for J. Deacon, at the Angel in Guilt-spur-street. 3 col. 2 wdcts. BL & RL

The Dutchess of Suffolk's calamity. To the tune of Queen Dido. 4 col. 2 wdcts. IL & RL

An excellent ballad of a dreadful combat fought between Moore of Moore Hall and the dragon of Wantley. Printed and sold at the Printing-Office in Bow-Church-Yard, London. 4 col. 1 wdct. RL

An excellent ballad, of a Prince of England's courtship to the King of France's daughter. 5 col. 2 wdcts. RL

The fair lady of the west. Tune of, A gallant damosel in Bristol-City, &c. or, William the weaver. London, Printed for W. Thackeray, T. Passenger, and W. Whitwood. 4 col. 3 wdcts. BL

Fair Margaret's misfortunes. Printed and sold by William and Cluer Dicey, at the Printing-Office in Bow-Church-Yard, London. 4 col. 2 wdcts. IL & RL

Fair Maudlin. Printed and sold in Bow-Church-Yard, London. 4 col. RL

Faithful Damon. To the tune of, The doubting virgin. Printed for J. Deacon, at the Angel in Guiltspur-street, without Newgate. 4 col. 4 wdcts. BL & RL

The faithful shepherd. To a new Scotch tune: Or, There was an a bonny young lad, &c. Printed for P. Brooksby at the Golden Ball in Pye Corner. 3 col. 2 wdcts. BL & RL

A famous sea-fight between Captain Ward and the Rainbow. Tune, Captain Ward. Printed and sold at the Printing-Office in Bow-Church-Yard, London. 4 col. 1 wdct. RL

A godly guide of directions. Tune is, Aim not too high, by Robert Tipping. Printed for P. Brooksby at the golden ball in Pye-Corner. 3 col. 1 wdct. BL

A godly warning to all young maidens. Printed and sold in Bow-church Yard, London. 4 col. 1 wdct. RL

The golden bull. Printed and sold at the Printing Office in Bow-Church-Yard, London. 4 col. RL. (2 issues)

The great boobee. To the tune of, Salleeger's round. 4 col. 2 wdcts. IL & RL

The great messenger of mortality. Printed and sold at the Printing-Office in Bow Church-Yard, London. 3 col. 1 wdct. RL

The Hamstead-Fair ramble. London, Printed for J. Bland, near Holborn, 1708. 2 col. IL & RL

The hasty virgin. To an excellent new tune, much in request. Printed for J. Deacon, at the Sign of the Angel in Guiltspur-Street, without Newgate. 3 col. 2 wdcts. BL & RL

Hind's progress and ramble. Tune of, Robin Hood reviv'd. 4 col. 1 wdct. IL & RL

The honour of a London 'prentice. Printed and sold in Bow-Church Yard, London. 4 col. 1 wdct. RL

The humours of Bow Fair. 1 col. 1 wdct. RL

The hunting of the hare. Printed and sold in Bow Church-Yard, London. 4 col. 1 wdct. IL & RL

Innocent country maids. Set to an excellent country dance. Printed for P. Brooksby, at the Golden-Ball in Pye-Corner. 4 col. 4 wdcts. BL & RL

An invitation to Lubberland. To the tune of, Billy and Molly. Or, The journey-man shooemaker. Printed for J. Deacon, at the Angel in Guiltspur-street. 4 col. 5 wdcts. BL

Johnny Armstrong's last goodnight.   Printed and sold at the Printing-Office in Bow-Church-Yard, London.   4 col.   1 wdct.   RL

The kind lady. To a new tune. Or, Heyboys up we go, the charming Nymph, or Jenny Gin.   Printed for J. Conyers at the Black Raven in Duck Lane.   4 col.   4 wdcts.   BL & RL

King John and the Abbot of Canterbury.   Printed and sold in Bow-Church-Yard, London.   4 col.   2 wdcts.   IL & RL

The lady Isabella's tragedy. Tune of, The lady's fall.   Printed in Bow-Church-Yard, London.   4 col.   1 wdct.   RL

The lady's policy.   5 col.   2 wdcts.   RL

A lamentable ballad of the tragical end of a gallant lord and virtuous lady. To the tune of, The lady's fall, &c.   Printed and sold at the Printing-Office in Bow Church-yard, London.   5 col.   1 wdct.   RL

The languishing swain. Tune of, Charon make haste.   Printed for J. Deacon, at the Angel in Guilt-Spur-ftreet without Newgate.   3 col.   2 wdcts.   BL & RL

The late bloody fight in Flanders. To the tune of, Let Mary live long.   Printed for P. Brooksby at the Golden-Ball in Pye-Corner.   4 col.   1 wdct.   BL

The life and death of fair Rosamond.   Printed and sold at the Printing-Office in Bow-Church-Yard, London.   4 col.   1 wdct.   RL

The maiden's lamentation. To the tune of, I am a sturdy beggar, &c.   London: Printed for E. Randal near Aldgate.   2 col.   IL & RL

Maids lamentation. The tune is, The Lass that comes to Bed to me, Or, Sawney is gone.   Printed for P. Brooksby at the Golden Bull in Pye-Corner.   3 col.   1 wdct.   BL & RL

The merchant's son and the beggar-wench of Hull.   Printed and sold at the Printing-Office in Bow Church Yard, London.   4 col.   2 wdcts.   IL & RL

Neptune's raging fury. Tune of, When the stormy winds do blow, &c.   London: Printed for A. M. W. O. and T. Thackeray, at the Angel in Duck-lane.   4 col.   1 wdct.   BL & RL

A new summons to all the merry wagtail jades to attend Horn-Fair.   Printed and sold in Stonecutter's-Street, near the Fleet-Market.   3 col.   1 wdct.   RL

A new summons to Horn-Fair. Printed in Stone-Cutter-Street. 3 col. 1 wdct. RL

The noble gallant. To a pleasant new tune: called, the German Princesses farewel. Printed for I. H. and sold by F. Coles, T. Vere, I. Wright, and I. Clarke. 4 col. 4 wdcts. BL

The northern ditty. To a new Scots tune. Printed and sold at the Printing-Office in Bow-Church-Yard, London. 4 col. 1 wdct. IL & RL

The northern lord. Printed and sold at the Printing-Office in Bow-Church-Yard, London. 4 col. RL

The old ballad of the three jolly butchers and ten highwaymen. Sold at the Printing-Office in Bow-Church-Yard, London. 3 col. 3 wdcts. IL & RL

An old ballad of Whittington and his cat. Tune of, Come thou to me. Printed and sold in Bow-Church Yard, London. 4 col. 4 wdcts. RL

The old man's wish. To a new playhouse tune. Printed and sold at the Printing-Office in Bow-Church-Yard, London. 4 col. 2 wdcts. IL & RL

The Oxfordshire tragedy. Printed and sold in Bow Church-yard. 4 col. RL

Patient Grissell. Printed and sold at the Printing-Office in Bow Church-yard. 5 col. 1 wdct. RL

A pleasant ballad of King Hery [sic] II. and the miller of Mansfield. 4 col. IL & RL

A pleasant ballad of Tobias. Printed and sold in Bow-Church-Yard, London. 4 col. 1 wdct. IL & RL

A pleasant jigg. Tune of Mary live long. Printed for J. Deacon, at the Angel in Guilt-spur-street without New-Gate. 4 col. 4 wdcts. BL

A pleasant song of the valiant deeds atchieved by . . . Sir Guy of Warwick. Tune, Was ever man, &c. Printed and sold at the Printing-Office in Bow-Church-Yard. 4 col. 1 wdct. IL & RL

The poor mans prayer for peace. To the tune of Game at cards. Printed for P. Brooksby at the Golden-Ball in Pye-Corner. 4 col. 4 wdcts. BL & RL

Poor Robin's dream. Tune, The new pack of cards. Printed and sold at the Printing-Office in Bow-Church-Yard, London. 3 col. 3 wdcts. IL

Queen Eleanor's confession. Printed and sold at the Printing-Office in Bow-Church-Yard, London. 4 col. 2 wdcts. IL

The rarest old ballad that ever was seen, Of the blind beggar's daughter of Bednal-Green. Printed and sold at the Printing Office in Bow Church Yard, London. 4 col. IL & RL

Roman charity. Printed and sold in Bow-Church-Yard, London. 5 col. 1 wdct. RL

The saylors departure. To a new tune of, Adieu my pretty one. Printed for J. Wright, J. Clarke, W. Thackeray, and T. P. 5 col. 4 wdcts. BL & RL

A sea-fight, between Sir George Byng, and the Spaniards. Printed and sold in Bow-church-yard, London. 4 col. 1 wdct. RL

A song in praise of the leather bottel. To the tune of, The bottelmaker's delight, &c. Printed by Tho. Norris, at the Looking-glass on London-bridge. 4 col. 1 wdct. IL & RL

The Spanish lady's love to an English sailor. Printed and sold at the Printing-Office in Bow Church Yard, London. 4 col. 1 wdct. RL

The squire's grief crown'd with comfort. To the tune of, Let the soldiers rejoyce. Printed for P. Brooksby, J. Deacon, J. Blare, J. Back. 4 col. 3 wdcts. BL

A third merry ditty of cold and raw. Printed for J. Deacon, at the Angel in Guiltspur-street. 4 col. 4 wdcts. BL

Tom and Will. 4 col. 2 wdcts. IL & RL

The tragical ballad: Or, The nobleman's cruelty to his son. Printed and sold at the Printing-Office in Bow-Church-Yard. 4 col. RL

True love requited! Or, The bailiffs daughter of Islington. Printed and sold in Aldermary Church-Yard, Bow-Lane, London. 3 col. 1 wdct. RL

The two constant lovers. To a pleasant new tune. Printed by and for A. M., and sold by the Booksellers of London. 5 col. 3 wdcts. BL

The two faithful lovers. To the tune of, Franklin is fled away, &c. London: Printed for A. M. W. O. and T. Thackeray, at the Angel in Duck-lane. 4 col. 3 wdcts. BL

The unfortunate concubine. Printed and sold in Bow-Church-Yard, London. 5 col. 1 wdct. IL

The unfortunate lovers. Printed and sold at the Printing-Office in Bow-Church-Yard, London. 4 col. 2 wdcts. RL

An unhappy memorable song of the hunting of Chevy-Chase. Printed and sold at the Printing-Office in Bow-Church-Yard, London. 5 col. 1 wdct. IL & RL. (2 issues)

The wandering Jew. Printed and sold at the Printing-Office in Bow-Church-Yard, London. 4 col. 1 wdct. IL & RL

The wandering young gentlewoman. 4 col. IL & RL

The wanton wife of Bath. Printed and sold at the Printing-Office in Bow Church-yard, London. 4 col. 1 wdct. IL & RL

A weeks loving, wooing, and wedding. To the tune of Billy and Molly. Printed for P. Brooksby at the Golden Ball in Pye-Corner, J. Deacon at the Angel in Gilt-spur-street, J. Blare at the Looking-glass on London-bridge near the Church, J. Back at the Black Boy on London-bridge near the Draw Bridge. 4 col. 3 wdcts. BL

The west country nymph. Tune, Young Jammy. Printed for P. Brooksby. 4 col. 4 wdcts. BL

The Winchester wedding. To a new country dance: Or The king's jigg. 4 col. 2 wdcts. IL & RL

The woeful lamentation of Jane Shore. Printed and sold in Bow-Church-Yard. 5 col. RL

The woody choristers. Printed and sold in Bow-Church Yard, London. 4 col. 1 wdct. RL

A young man put to his shifts. To the tune of, Cupids Trappan. London Printed for W. Thackeray, T. Passenger, and W. Whitwood. 4 col. 3 wdcts. BL & RL

The young-mans resolution. To the tune of, In summer time. Printed for C. Pasinger, at the Seven-Stars, on London-bridge. 4 col. 3 wdcts. BL & RL. (Ballad signed "J. S.")

Miscellaneous English Broadsides

Bellman's verses; Carols; Dyers' Company verses; Elegies; Lamplighter's verses; Manuscripts; Newman's verses; Proclamations, etc.

Army of the Irish Republic (Dublin Command). Order, 24 April 1916. Signed by James Connelly, Commandant-General, Dublin Division. 1 p. Typed. 4to.

Bellman's verses. 1705. A copy of verses humbly presented to all my worthy masters and mistresses in the precinct of St. Katherines Tower, By George Wright, Bell-man. London Printed by R. How, at the Seven-Stars, in Talbot-Court, in Grace-church-street, 1705. 3 col. Wdct. pictorial border. IL & RL

———— 1710. A copy of verses humbly presented to all my worthy masters and mistresses in the Bridge-Ward, London. By John Guy, Bell-man. London, Printed by R. How, in the year, 1710. 3 col. 1 wdct. IL & RL

———— 1714. A copy of verses humbly presented to all my worthy masters and mistresses in the Ward of Bridge within, London. By John Guy, Bell-man. London: Printed for John Guy, 1714. 3 col. 1 wdct. IL & RL

———— 1745. A copy of verses humbly presented to all my worthy masters and mistresses in the Ward of Bridge: By Daniel Archer, Bell-man. London: Printed by M. Ellis and R. Jellyman, in Elliots-Court in the Little Old Baily, 1745. 3 col. Wdct. pictorial border. RL

———— 1783. A copy of verses humbly presented to all my worthy masters and mistresses, in the Parish of St. Mary, Islington, By John Green, beadle and bellman. London: Printed by Thomas Bayley, in Petticoat Lane, near Whitechapel Bars, for the year 1783. 3 col. Wdct. headpiece, 18 wdcts. forming border. RL

———— 1799. A copy of verses, humbly presented to all my masters and mistresses, in the Parish of St. Mary-Le-Strand, By John Wotton, beadle and bellman, for the year 1799. London: Printed by H. Reynell (No. 21,) Piccadilly, near the Hay-Market. 3 col. Wdct. headpiece, 18 wdcts. forming border, 1 wdct. signed "I. Bell Sct." otherwise the 18 as in 1783 Verses. RL

Miscellaneous English Broadsides

Bellman's verses. n.d.   A copy of verses, humbly presented to all my worthy masters and mistresses in the Parish of St. Mary-Le-Strand, By John Wotton, beadle and bellman.   London: Printed by H. Reynell (No. 21,) Piccadilly, near the Hay-Market.   3 col.   Wdct. headpiece, 18 wdcts. forming border, as in 1799 Verses.   RL

———— 1800.   A copy of verses, humbly presented to all my worthy masters and mistresses, in the Parish of St. Mary-Le-Strand, By John Wotton, beadle and bellman, for the year 1800.   London: Printed by H. Reynell (No. 21,) Piccadilly, near the Hay-Market.   3 col. Wdct. headpiece, 18 wdcts. forming border, as in 1799 Verses.   RL

———— 1801.   A copy of verses, humbly presented to all my worthy masters and mistresses, in the Parish of St. Mary-Le-Strand, By John Wotton, beadle and bellman, for the year 1801.   London: Printed by H. Reynell, (No. 21,) Piccadilly, near the Hay-Market.   3 col. Wdct. headpiece, 18 wdcts. forming border, as in 1799 Verses.   RL

———— 1803.   A copy of verses, humbly presented to all my worthy masters and mistresses, in the Parish of St. Mary-Le-Strand, By John Wotton, beadle and bellman, for the year 1803.   London: Printed by H. Reynell, (No. 21,) Piccadilly, near the Black Bear.   3 col. Wdct. headpiece, 18 wdcts. forming border, as in 1799 Verses.   IL & RL

———— 1805.   A copy of verses, humbly presented to all my worthy masters and mistresses, in the Parish of St. Mary-Le-Strand, By John Wotton, beadle and bellman, for the year 1805.   London: Printed by Henry Reynell, No. 21, Piccadilly, near the Black Bear.   3 col. Wdct. headpiece, 18 wdcts. forming border, as in 1803 Verses.   IL & RL

———— 1806.   A copy of verses, humbly presented to all my worthy masters and mistresses, in the Parish of St. Mary-Le-Strand, By John Wotton, beadle and bellman, for the year 1806.   London: Printed by Henry Reynell, No. 21, Piccadilly, near the Black Bear.   3 col. Wdct. headpiece, 18 wdcts. forming border, as in 1803 & 1805 Verses.   IL & RL

———— 1807.   A copy of verses, humbly presented to all my worthy masters and mistresses, of the Parish of St. Mary, Islington, in the County of Middlesex, By Nelson Stratton, beadle and bellman, for the year 1807.   London: Printed by Henry Reynell, No. 21, Piccadilly, near the Black Bear.   3 col.   Wdct. headpiece, 18 wdcts. forming border, as in 1803, 1805, 1806 Verses.   IL & RL

Bellman's verses. 1834. A copy of verses for the year 1834. Humbly presented to all the worthy inhabitants of the Parish of St. Mary, Islington, by Robert Brown, beadle and bellman.   Engraved, printed, and sold by J. V. Quick, Bowling Green Lane, Clerkenwell; and Little Paternoster Row, Spitalfields, London.   3 col. Wdct. head- and tailpieces, 14 wdcts. forming border.   RL

Burnet, D.   A new elegy on the much lamented death of . . . Prince George of Denmark, who departed this life . . . the 28th of October, 1708. London: Printed by J. Read, behind the Green-Dragon-Tavern in Fleetstreet, 1708. 2 col. Broad pictorial wdct. border, 2 wdcts. IL & RL

Carol. Christus natus est.   London, Printed and sold by J. Bradford, in Little Britain, the Corner House over against the Pump, 1701.   4 col.   2 wdcts.   BL, IL & RL

—————— Christmas drawing near at hand.   Printed and sold by T. Batchelar, 115, Long Alley, Moorfields, London.   4 carols.   2 col. 17 wdcts.   RL

—————— Divine mirth.   Batchelar, printer, Long Alley.   3 carols.   3 col.   9 wdcts.   RL

—————— The divine poem, and A new Christmas carol.   Printed and sold by T. Bachelar, 115, Long Alley, Moorfields, London.   2 col. 13 wdcts.   RL

—————— Three new Christmas carols.   Printed and sold in Aldermary Church Yard, London.   2 col.   3 wdcts., wdct. border.   IL & RL

Charles II, *King of England*.   [Letter to Gilbert, Archbishop of Canterbury, concerning an Act for establishing an additional revenue . . . 4 November 1674].   London 1674.   fol.

—————— [Proclamation concerning times and seasons for the curing of the Kings-Evil].   London, Assigns of J. Bill deceas'd: and H. Hills and T. Newcomb 1683.   fol.

—————— A proclamation for calling in, and suppressing of two books written by John Milton; the one intituled, Johannis Miltoni Angli pro populo Anglicano defensio . . . and the other in answer to a book intituled The pourtraicture of his sacred Majesty . . . And also a third book, intituled, The obstructors of justice, written by John Goodwin.   Whitehall the 13th day of August . . . 1660. London, J. Bill and C. Barker 1660.   fol.   (Bibl. Lindesiana Cat. of Proclamations No. 3241)

Miscellaneous English Broadsides

Charles II, *King of England*. A proclamation for apprehension of Edward Whalley and William Goffe . . . for their execrable treasons in sentencing to death . . . our late . . . father . . . Whitehall, the two and twentieth day of September, in the twelfth year of our reign. London, C. Barker and J. Bill 1660. fol.

Colledge, Stephen. A letter from Mr. Stephen Colledge to a person of quality . . . Tower, 15 Aug. 1681. Printed for Francis Smith at the Elephant and Castle in Cornhill, 1681. 2 pp. fol.

——— A true copy of the dying words of Mr. Stephen Colledge, left in writing under his own hand, and confirmed by him at the time of execution, August 31, 1681 at Oxford. London, Printed for Edith Colledge, 1681. 2 pp. fol.

Copy of a letter written by our Blessed Saviour, Jesus Christ. Printed and sold by T Bachelar, 115, Long Alley, Moorfields, London. 2 col. 1 wdct.

D., *Sir* W. An elegy on the much lamented death of . . . Queen Anne: who departed this mortal life . . . the 1st of . . . August, 1714. London: Printed by J. Read in White-Fryers. 2 col. Broad pictorial wdct. border, 2 wdcts. IL & RL

Dickens, Charles. A.L.S. To G. P. R. James. (London) Devonshire Terrace Jan. 31, 1850. 3 pp. 12mo.

The drunken mistake. Publish'd Octr. 11th. 1784, by J. Wallis, No. 16, Ludgate Street, London. Copper engraving. 3 col., 11 stanzas, with music. IL

Dyers' Company. 1804. Song composed for the Dyers' Company: and sung at their annual dinner 1804. S. Gosnell, Printer, Little Queen Street, Holborn. 1 col. RL

An elegy on the much lamented death of Sir Thomas De Veil, Knt. who departed this life . . . the seventh of October. 2 col. Wdct. pictorial border, 1 wdct. RL

An elegy to the memory of the Right Honorable Thomas Earl of Ossory, who departed this life, July the 30th. 1680. 2 col. Wdct. mourning border. RL

Englands obligations to Captain William Bedloe, the grand discoverer of this most horrid plot. Part I. The second impression. London, T. Dawks 1679. fol.

Miscellaneous English Broadsides

The following is a copy of a bill, written by the late Rev. Rowland Hill which was stuck up at Richmond on Saturday, 4th of June, 1774, close to the play bill for that day. 4th Edition. Printed & published by W. C. Pearse, 2, Queen-street, Cheapside

Frost Fair. [Copper engraving showing frozen river, with booths, etc., inscribed] Frost Fair printed upon the Ice on the River Thames Jan' 23d. 1739/40. [Below, woodcut compartment, footmen at sides, medallion at top enclosing inscription] [type ornaments] George Beacher, Whitehall-Stairs, 173-40. [type ornaments] [and below] Elizabeth-Frances Baynham. [row of type ornaments] Printed on the River of Thames when Frozen over, January 24, 1739-40

———— A view of Frost Fair, on the Thames, February 1814. Published by T. Batchelar, 115, Long Alley, Moorfields. Large wdct. IL & RL

A full and exact description of the surrender of ... Lille. To the tune of, For the honour of great Queen Anne. London: Printed by J. Bradford, at the Bible in Fetter-lane near Fleetstreet, 1708. 3 col. 3 wdcts. IL & RL

Gloucester. [Letter of Robert, Lord Bishop of Gloucester, to the diocese...] 20 January 1681. [Gloucester 1681]. fol.

———— [Letter of John, Lord Bishop of Gloucester, to the diocese...] 1679. [Gloucester 1679]. fol.

———— Orders and instructions to the ministers and church-wardens of the diocese of Gloucester concerning the making of terriers, and keeping their register booke ... 14 October 1679. [Gloucester 1679]. fol.

———— [Proclamation against rogues and vagabonds]. [Gloucester 1677]. fol.

Irish War News. Dublin, April 25, 1916. 1:1. 4 pp. 4to.

Jenner, Edward. A.L.S. To Lyman Spalding. Cheltenham Nov. 10, 1801. 3 pp. 8vo.

Lamp-lighter's poems. 1742. The lamp-lighter's poem: humbly presented, to all his worthy masters and mistresses. Compos'd by a Lamp-lighter. Printed for the subscribers, by L. How, in Petticoat-Lane, near White-Chappel-Bars, 1742. 3 col. Wdct. of Guild Hall, type ornament border. IL & RL

Miscellaneous English Broadsides

Lamp-lighter's poems. 1744. The lamp-lighter's poem: humbly presented, to all his worthy masters and mistresses. Compos'd by a Lamp-lighter. Printed for the subscribers, by L. How, in Petticoat-Lane, near White-Chappel-Bars, 1744. 2 col. Wdct. of Guild Hall, type ornament border. IL & RL

———— n.d. The lamp-lighter's poem, humbly presented to all his worthy masters and mistresses. Compos'd by a Lamp-lighter. Printed and sold at No. 81, Shoe Lane, Fleet Street. 2 col. 2 wdcts. of Lord Mayor's Show, 4 wdcts. of lamp-lighter at work. RL

———— n.d. The lamp-lighter's poem, humbly presented to all his worthy masters and mistresses. Printed and sold by Sabine and Son, 81, Shoe Lane, Fleet Street, London. 2 col. Wdct. of St. Paul's Church, 4 wdcts. of lamp-lighter at work. RL

London. The right of electing sheriffs of London and Middlesex briefly stated and declared. London, for R. Dew 1682. fol.

Newsman's verses. 1788. Newsman's present to his worthy masters and mistresses, on the New Year, 1788. 2 col. 1 wdct., type ornament border. IL & RL

———— 1792. The newsman's present to his worthy customers, on the New Year, 1792. 2 col. 1 wdct., type ornament border. RL

———— 1796. The newsman's humble gift, to his indulgent customers, for the year 1796. 2 col. 1 wdct., type ornament border. RL

———— 1800. The newsman's present to his worthy customers, for the year 1800. 2 col. 1 wdct., type ornament border. RL

———— 1846. The newsman's address to his master's customers. Christmas 1846. Printed and sold by John Mc.Shee, 22, Wellington Place, Wellington Street, Blackfriars Road. 2 col. Ornamental border. RL

The nurse's song. 1 col., 5 stanzas. Ornamental border. RL

Parker, Matthew, *Archbishop*. Degrees of marriage. London, for B. Griffin, and S. Keble 1696. fol.

[Play bill] 1795. Theatre Royal, Drury Lane . . . Friday, November 13. 1795. (London) C. Lowndes (1795)

———— 1824. New Surrey Theatre Thursday March 18, 1824. W. Glendinning, Printer, 25, Hatton Garden, London

Miscellaneous English Broadsides

Play bill 1847. Theatre Royal Margate ... 9th August, 1847. [C. D. Dixon, Printer, Margate]. Wdct. pictorial border

Poblacht na H Eireann. The Provisional Government of the Irish Republic to the people of Ireland. [Dublin 1916]. [Proclamation]. fol.

A poem upon Mr. Tytus Oates, the first discoverer of the late Popish plot. London, for H. Brome and R. Chiswell 1679. fol.

Proposals, for printing by subscription, the Poetical Works of Dr. Oliver Goldsmith ... June 1, 1785. Dublin, for H. Whitestone ... (1785). 4 pp. 4to.

The Provisional Government to the citizens of Dublin. [Dublin 1916]. [Proclamation]. 8vo.

The righteous man's exhortations. Pinted[sic] for P. Brooksby, J. Deacon, J. Blare, and J. Back. 1691. 3 col. 3 wdcts. RL

Shelley, Mary Wollstonecraft. A.L.S. To —— Kentish Town, 16 Jan.

Southey, Robert. A.L.S. To J. A. Heraud, Junior. Keswick, March 20, 1827. 2 pp. 4to.

To each gentleman soldier in the company of the Honourable Paul Ferris, Esq; Lieut. Col. of the Blue Regiment of Train'd Bands of the City of London, whereof the Honourable Sir William Billers, Kt. & Adm. is Colonel. [Signed] Anthony Huggins, Marshal. 1 col. Wdct. pictorial border, with "GR" at top. IL & RL

Americana

This list includes all items of American interest except books in Science, and Bibles and liturgical books, which appear in the lists *Science* and *Bibles*.

1471

Mela, Pomponius. Cosmographia. Milan [P. Castaldi] 25 September 1471. 8vo. (H 11014)

1475

Ptolemaeus, Claudius. Cosmographia. Vicenza, H. Liechtenstein, 13 September 1475. fol. (Huth). (H*13536)

1478

Mela, Pomponius. Cosmographia. Venice, B. Maler, E. Ratdolt, P. Löslein, 1478. 4to. (La Vallière–Wodhull–Andrews). (H *11016)

1482

Mela, Pomponius. Cosmographia. Venice, E. Ratdolt, 18 July 1482. 4to. (H*11019)

Ptolemaeus, Claudius. Cosmographia. Ulm, L. Holle, 16 July 1482. fol. (H*13539)

1490

Ptolemaeus, Claudius. Cosmographia. Rome, P. de Turre, 4 November 1490. fol. (C. L. F. Robinson). (H*13541)

1493

Carvajal, Bernardinus. Oratio super praestanda solenni obedientia. [Rome, S. Plannck, after 19 June 1493]. 4to. (GW 6145)

Colombo, Christoforo. Epistola de insulis nuper inventis. [Rome, S. Plannck, after 29 April 1493]. 4to. (H*5489; GW 7177)

Ortiz, Alfonso. Los tratados. Sevilla, por tres Alemanes cōpañeros, 1493. fol. (Huth). (H 12109)

1494

Colombo, Christoforo. De insulis nuper in mari Indico repertis. [Basel, J. Bergmann de Olpe, 1494]. 4to. (Marquis d'Adda–Murray). (H*15942)

Americana

Verardus, Carolus.   Historia Baetica.   [Basel] J. Bergmann de Olpe 1494.   4to.   (Marquis d'Adda–Murray).   (H*15942)

1498

Mela, Pomponius.   Cosmographia.   Salamanca 1498.   4to.   (H11021)

1507

Gesta proxime per Portugalenses ī India.   Impressum colonie . . . 1507 prima die mensis Februarii p me Joannem Landen.   sm. 4to. (Huth)

Waldseemüller, Martin.   Cosmographiae introductio.   Vrbs Deodate, iiij.kl. Septēbris (29 Aug. 1507).   sm. 4to.   Third Edition

1508

Fracan, Montalboddo.   Itinerariū Portugallēsiū.   [Mediolani?] 1508. fol.   (C. L. F. Robinson–Kalbfleisch)

1511

Martyr, Peter.   Opera.   Legatio babilonica. Occeanea decas. Poemata. Hispali, Jacobū corumberger, 11 April 1511.   fol.   First Edition

Ptolemaeus, Claudius.   Liber geographiae.   Venetiis, Iacobum Pentium de leucho, 20 March 1511.   fol.   (2 copies)

1513

Ptolemaeus, Claudius.   Geographie opus.   (Strassburg) I. Schott, 12 March 1513.   fol.

1515

Schöner, Johann.   Luculentissima quaedā terrae totius descriptio. Noribergae . . . officina Ioannis Stuchssen 1515.   sm. 4to.   (S. L. M. Barlow–Andrews)

1516

Martyr, Peter.   De orbe novo decades.   Alcala, in contubernio Arnaldi Guillelmi, nonis Novēbris (5 Nov.) 1516.   fol.   First Edition. (Church)

1517

[Vespuccius-Waldseemüller].   Cosmographiae introductio.   [Lyons] Iohanem de la Place [c. 1517].   sm. 4to.   (Sorbonne dup.–S. L. M. Barlow)

Americana

1519

Fernando de Enciso, Martin. Suma de geographia. Seuilla, por Iacobo crōberger 1519. fol.

1520

Solinus, Julius. Ioannis Camertis ... in C. Iulii Solini ΠΟΛΥΙΣΤΩΡΑ enarrationes. Viennae Austriae, per Ioannē Singreniū 1520. fol. (W. H. Crawford)

1522

Mela, Pomponius. De orbis sitv. Basileae, apud Andream Cratandrum, Jan. 1522. fol. (W. H. Crawford)

Ptolemaeus, Claudius. Opus geographie. Strassburg, Ioannes Grieninger, 12 March 1522. fol. (Huth)

1524

Apianus, Petrus. Cosmographicus liber. Excusum Landshutae typis ... Joannis Weyssenburgers 1524. sm. 4to. First Edition. (Inscribed below colophon: "Anno eod. p. Auctore Pet. Api ... datus sum Fuchspergero")

Cortes, Hernando. La preclara narratione della Nuoua Hispagna del mare oceano. Venetia, Bernardino de Viano de Lexona, 20 Aug. 1524. sm. 4to. (Church)

1528

Bordone, Benedetto. Libro ... nel qual si ragiona di tutte l'isole del mondo. Vinegia, Nicolo d'Aristotile, June 1528. fol. First Edition

1532

Cortes, Hernando. De insvlis inventis. Coloniae, ex officina Melchioris Nouesiani ... Decimo kalendas mensis Septembris (23 Aug.) 1532. fol.

Martyr, Peter. Extraict ov recveil des isles. Paris, Simon de Colines 1532. sm. 4to. (E. N. Crane)

1534

Bordone, Benedetto. Isolario. Vinegia, Nicolo d'Aristotile, June 1534. fol. Second Edition

Fernandez de Oviedo y Valdés, Gonzalo. Libro secondo delle Indie Occidentali. Vinegia, December 1534. sm. 4to. (Wodhull)

Americana

Martyr, Peter, *and others*. Libro primo della Historia de l'Inde Occidentali; Libro secondo delle Indie Occidentali; Libro vltimo del Svmmario delle Indie Occidentali. Vinegia, October 1534. sm. 4to.

1535

Fernandez de Oviedo y Valdés, Gonzalo. La historia general de las Indias. Seuilla, Juam Cromberger, September 1535. fol. First Edition

Ptolemaeus, Claudius. Geographicae enarrationis. Libri octo. Lvgdvni, M. et G. Trechsel 1535. fol.

[Xeres, Francisco de]. Libro primo de la conquista del Perv. Vinegia, Stephano da Sabio, March 1535. sm. 4to. (Wodhull)

1544

Gemma, Reinerus, *Frisius*. De principiis astronomiae. Antuerpiae, Ioannes Richard 1544. sm. 8vo.

1547

Bordone, Benedetto. Isolario. Vinegia, Federico Toresano 1547. fol.

1548

Ptolemaeus, Claudius. La geografia . . . ridotta in uolgare Italiano da Pietro Andrea Mattiolo. Venetia, Gioā. Baptista Pedrezano 1548. sm. 8vo.

1550

Cortes, Hernando. Von dem Newen Hispanien. Augspurg, Philipp Vlhart 1550. fol.

[Ramusio, Giovanni Battista]. Delle navigationi et viaggi. Venetia, Gli heredi di Lucantonio Giunti 1550. v. 1. fol. First Edition

1551

[Borrhaus, Martin]. Elementale cosmographicum. Parisiis, G. Cauellat 1551. sm. 8vo.

Waldseemüller, Martin. Cosmographiae introductio. Parisiis, G. Cauellat 1551. sm. 8vo.

1552

Casas, Bartolomé de las. Breuissima relacion de la destruycion de las Indias. Seuilla, S. Trugillo 1552. sm. 4to. (Tract No. 1)

Americana

Casas, Bartolomé de las.   Lo que se signe es vn pedaço de vna carta. [Seuilla, S. Trugillo 1552].   sm. 4to.   (Tract No. 2)

———— Entre los remedios . . . para reformaciõ de las Indias.   Seuilla, Jacome Crõberger 1552.   sm. 4to.   (Tract No. 3)

———— Este es vn tratado . . . sobre la materia de los Yndios.   Seuilla, S. Trugillo 1552.   sm. 4to.   (Tract No. 4)

———— Tratado cõprobatorio del imperio soberano.   Seuilla, S. Trugillo 1552.   sm. 4to.   (Tract No. 5)

———— Aqui se cõtienẽ treynta proposiciones.   Seuilla, S. Trugillo 1552.   sm. 4to.   (Tract No. 6)

———— Aqui se cotiene vna disputa . . . entre el obispo . . . y el doctor Gines de Sepulueda.   Seuilla, S. Trugillo 1552.   sm. 4to.   (Tract No. 7)

———— Aqui se cõtienẽ vnos auisos y reglas para los confessores.   Seuilla, S. Trugillo 1552.   sm. 4to.   (Tract No. 8)

———— Principia quedã ex quibus procedendum.   Hispali, in edibus S. Trugilli [1552].   sm. 4to.   (Tract No. 9)

1554

Aristoteles.   Dialectica resolutio.   Mexici, Ioannes paulus 1554.   fol.

[Ramusio, Giovanni Battista].   Delle navigationi et viaggi.   Venetia, nella stamperia de Givnti 1554.   v. 1.   fol.   Second Edition.   (Vernon)

Vespuccius, Americus.   Mundus nouus.   Augsburg, J. Otmar 1554.   sm. 4to.   (Huth)

1555

Martyr, Peter.   The decades of the new worlde. Tr. by R. Eden.   Londini, in aed. G. Powell (by E. Sutton) 1555.   sm. 4to.   (Huth). (STC 647)

Nuñez Cabeza de Vaca, Alvar.   La relacion y comentarios.   Valladolid, Francisco fernandez de Cordoua 1555.   sm. 4to.

1556

Polo, Marco.   La description geographique . . . de l'Inde Orientale . . . en vulgaire François (par François Gruget).   Paris, pour Estienne Groulleau 1556.   sm. 4to.   (Lancelot Holland–Lord James Butler)

Americana

1557

Fernandez de Oviedo y Valdés, Gonzalo. Libro. XX. Dela segunda parte de la general historia delas Indias. Valladolid, Francisco Fernandez de Cordoua 1557. fol.

1558

Thevet, André. Les singvlaritez de la France Antarctique. Anvers, Christophle Plantin 1558. sm. 8vo. (Baron Pichon–C. L. F. Robinson)

Zeno, Caterino. De i commentarii del viaggio. Venetia, Francesco Marcolini 1558. sm. 8vo.

1559

Ramusio, Giovanni Battista. Delle navigationi et viaggi. Venetia, nella stamperia de Givnti 1559. v. 2. fol. First Edition

1561

Ptolemaeus, Claudius. La geografia . . . tradotta . . . in Italiano, da Girolamo Rvscelli. Venetia, Vincenzo Valgrisi 1561. sm. 4to. (2 copies)

1563

Ramusio, Giovanni Battista. Delle navigationi et viaggi. Venetia, nella stamperia de Givnti 1563. v. 1. fol. Third Edition

1565

Benzoni, Girolamo. La historia del mondo nvovo. Venetia, Francesco Rampazetto 1565. sm. 8vo. First Edition. (E. N. Crane–C. L. F. Robinson)

[Ramusio, Giovanni Battista]. Delle navigationi et viaggi. Venetia, nella stamperia de Givnti 1565. v. 3. fol. Second Edition. (2 copies)

1566

Ledesma, Bartolomé de. De septem novae legis sacramentis summarium. Mexici, Antonius de Espinosa 1566. 8vo.

1568

Thevet, André. The new founde vvorlde. Tr. by T. Hacket. London, H. Bynneman 1568. sm. 4to. (STC 23950)

Americana

1571

Colombo, Fernando.   Historie . . . de' fatti dell' Ammiraglio D. Christoforo Colombo . . . tradotte nell' Italiana dal S. Alfonso Vlloa.   Venetia, Francesco de Franceschi Sanese 1571.   sm. 8vo.   First Edition.   (Hubbard)

Fernandez, Diego, *of Palencia*.   Primera, y segvnda parte, de la historia del Perv.   Seuilla, en casa de Hernando diaz 1571.   fol.

Molina, Alonso de.   Vocabulario en lengva Castellana y Mexicana.   Mexico, en casa de Antonio de Spinosa 1571.   fol.   (Huth)

1574

Martyr, Peter.   De rebvs oceanicis et novo orbe.   Coloniae, apud Geruinum Calenium & haeredes Quentelios 1574.   8vo.   (Robert Southey–Montino–H.V. Jones)

1576

Porcacchi, Tommaso.   L'isole piv famose del monde.   Venetia, Simon Galignani & Girolamo Porro 1576.   fol.   Second Edition

1577

Belleforest, François.   L'histoire vniverselle dv monde.   Paris, Geruais Mallot 1577.   4to.

Martyr, Peter.   The history of trauayle. Tr. by R. Eden.   London, R. Iugge 1577.   sm. 4to.   (STC 649)

1578

Benzoni, Girolamo.   Novae novi orbis historiae (Tr. into Latin by Urbain Chauveton).   [Genevae] apvd Evstathivm Vignon 1578.   sm. 8vo.   (Has errata leaf).   (Huth)

—— Novae novi orbis.   Genevae, apvd Evstathivm Vignon 1578.   sm. 8vo.   (Has "Genevae" on title, but lacks errata leaf, although errors have not been corrected).   (Beaufoy)

Léry, Jean de.   Histoire d'vn voyage fait en la terre dv Bresil.   [La Rochelle] Antoine Chuppin 1578.   sm. 8vo.   First Edition.   (Mark P. Robinson)

Americana

1580

Frobisher, *Sir* Martin.   De Martini Forbisseri Angli navigatione . . . in Latinum translata per D. Joan. Tho. Freigivm.   Noribergae, in officina Catharinae Gerlachin & Haeredum Iohannis Montani 1580. sm. 8vo.

1581

Memorabilis historia persecutionum . . . in Waldensem . . . M.D.LXII, Gallice primum in lucem aedita, nunc vero a Christophero Richardo Biturige, Latinitate donata.   Genevae, E. Vignon 1581.   sm. 8vo.   (Beaufoy)

1583

Casas, Bartolomé de las.   The Spanish colonie. Tr. by M. M. S.   London [T. Dawson] 1583.   sm. 4to.   (Britwell).   (STC 4739)

[Ramusio, Giovanni Battista].   Delle navigationi et viaggi.   Venetia, appresso i Giunti 1583.   v. 2.   fol.   Third Edition

1586

Gonzalez de Mendoza, Juan.   Dell'historia della China . . . tradotta . . . dal . . . Francesco Avanzo.   Venetia, A. Muschio 1586.   sm. 4to.

Laudonnière, René de.   L'histoire notable de la Floride.   Paris, G. Auuray 1586.   sm. 8vo.

1587

Martyr, Peter.   De orbe novo.   Paris, G. Auvray 1587.   sm. 8vo. (Sir Arthur Helps)

1588

[Gonzalez de Mendoza, Juan].   The historie of the great and mightie kingdome of China. Tr. by R. Parke.   London, I. Wolfe 1588. sm. 4to.   (F. Ouvry–Ives).   (STC 12003)

1589

Hakluyt, Richard.   The principall navigations, voiages and discoveries of the English nation.   London, G. Bishop and R. Newberie 1589. fol.   First Edition.   (STC 12625)

1590

Bry, Théodore de.   Admiranda narratio fida, tamen, de commodis et incolarum ritibus Virginiae.   Francofurti ad Moenum, I. Wechel 1590.   fol.   First Edition, First Issue.   (America. Great voyages. Latin. I).   (W. L. Andrews)

[304]

Americana

1594

Bry, Théodore de. America. Great voyages. Latin. I-XI. Francofurti ad Moenum, I. Wechel 1594-1620. 3 v. fol. (John Ord)

1596

Acosta, José de. Historia naturale, e morale delle Indie ... tradotta ... nella Italiana da Gio. Paolo Galucci. Venetia, B. Basa 1596. sm. 4to. (C. L. F. Robinson)

[Lopez de Gomara, Francesco]. The pleasant historie of the conquest of the West India. Tr. by T. Nicholson. London, T. Creede 1596. sm. 4to. (STC 16808)

Ralegh, *Sir* Walter. The discoverie of the large, rich and bevvtifvl empire of Gviana. London, R. Robinson 1596. sm. 4to. First Edition. (STC 20635)

1598

Acosta, José de. Histoire naturelle et moralle des Indes. Paris, M. Orry 1598. sm. 8vo. (E. M. Satow)

Bry, Théodore de. India. Small voyages. Latin. I-X. Francofurti, W. Richter 1598-1613. 3 v. fol. (John Ord)

Casas, Bartolomé de las. Narratio regionum Indicarum. Francofurti, Sumptibus Theodori de Bry 1598. sm. 4to. (Bridgewater)

Hakluyt, Richard. The principal navigationes, voiages . . . and discoveries of the English nation. London, G. Bishop, R. Newberie and R. Barker 1598-1600. 3 v. in 2. fol. (STC 12626)

Hulsius, Levinus. Kurtze warhafftige beschreibung der newen reyse. Nürnberg, C. Lochner 1598. sm. 4to.

Linschoten, Jan Huygen van. Iohn Hvighen van Linschoten. His discours of voyages. Tr. by W. Phillip. London, I. Wolfe [1598]. fol. (STC 15691)

1600

Bry, Théodore de. America. Great voyages. German. I-XIII. Franckfort 1600-1624. 2 v. fol.

1601

Galvam, Antony. The discoveries of the world. Londini, G. Bishop 1601. sm. 4to. (STC 11543)

Americana

1603

Bry, Théodore de. India. Small voyages. German. I-XI. Franckfort am Mayn 1603-75. fol.

1604

Acosta, José de. The naturall and morall historie of the East and West Indies. Tr. by E. Grimston. London, V. Simmes 1604. sm. 4to. (G. Robinson–J. Lancaster). (STC 94)

1605

Vega, Garcilaso de la, *El Inca*. La Florida del Ynca. En Lisbona ... por P. Crasbeeck 1605. 8vo. First Edition. (C. L. F. Robinson)

1606

[Ramusio, Giovanni Battista]. Delle navigationi et viaggi. Venetia, nella stamperia di Givnti 1606. fol. v. 2-3. 2, Fourth Edition; 3, Third Edition. (Vernon)

1607

Gonzalez Holguin, Diego. Vocabulario. Lima 1607-8. sm. 4to. (title lacking)

Nicholl, John. An houre glasse of Indian newes. London, for N. Butter 1607. sm. 4to. First Edition. (Huth). (STC 18532)

1609

Lescarbot, Marc. Histoire de la Nouvelle France. Paris, I. Milot 1609. 8vo. First Edition. (E. N. Crane)

Soto, Ferdinando de. Virginia richly valued. London, F. Kyngston 1609. sm. 4to. (STC 22938)

Symonds, William. Virginia. London, I. Windet 1609. sm. 4to. First Edition. (Marshall). (STC 23594)

[Veer, Gerrit de]. The true ... description of three voyages. Tr. by W. Phillip. London, T. Pavier 1609. sm. 4to. (Dogmersfield–John Jay Paul). (STC 24628)

Vega, Garcilaso de la, *El Inca*. Primera parte de los commentarios reales. En Lisboa, P. Crasbeeck 1609. First Edition

1610

Lescarbot, Marc. Les muses de la Nouvelle France. Paris, I. Millot 1610. 8vo. (E. N. Crane)

Americana

1611

Lescarbot, Marc. Histoire de la Nouvelle-France. Paris, I. Millot 1611. 8vo.

West, Thomas, *Baron De La Warre*. The relation of the Right Honourable the Lord De-La-Warre. London, W. Hall 1611. sm. 4to. First Edition. (Halsey). (STC 25266)

1612

Hudson, Henry, *and others*. Descriptio ac delineatio geographica detectionis freti. Amsterodami, ex officina H. Gerardi 1612. sm. 4to. (C. L. F. Robinson)

Lescarbot, Marc. Les muses de la Nouvelle France. Paris, I. Millot 1612. 8vo.

Smith, John. A map of Virginia. Oxford, J. Barnes 1612. sm. 4to. (Huth). (STC 22791). (4th state of map)

1613

Champlain, Samuel de. Les voyages. Paris, J. Barjon 1613. 4to. First Edition

Hulsius, Levinus. Eylffter [-neuntzehende schiffarth] ander theil. Franckfurt am Mayn, E. Kempffer 1613 [-26]. 8 v. sm. 4to.

Ramusio, Giovanni Battista. Delle navigationi et viaggi. Venetia, appresso I. Givnti 1613. v. 1. fol. Sixth Edition

1614

Colombo, Fernando. Historie . . . della vita . . . dell' . . . Christoforo Colombo. Milano, G. Bordoni [1614]. sm. 8vo.

1615

Barros, Juan de. Quarta decada da Asia. Em Madrid, na Impressao Real 1615. fol. First Edition. For the first three Decades see 1628

1616

Smith, John. A description of New England. London, H. Lownes 1616. sm. 4to. (Huth). (STC 22788). (6th state of map)

1617

Vega, Garcilaso de la, *El Inca*. Historia general del Peru. Cordova, por la viuda de A. Barrera 1617. fol. First Edition

Americana

Lescarbot, Marc.   Histoire de la Nouvelle-France.   Paris, A. Perier 1618.   12mo.   (DePuy)

———— Les muses de la Nouvelle France.   Paris, A. Perier 1618.   12mo. (DePuy)

1620

Champlain, Samuel de.   Voyages et descouvertures.   Paris, C. Collet 1620.   sm. 8vo.   (E. N. Crane–H. LeRoy Edgar)

A declaration of the state of the colonie and affaires in Virginia.   London, T. S[nodham] 1620.   sm. 4to.   First Edition, Second Issue. (Ives).   (STC 24835)

Whitbourne, Richard.   A discourse and discovery of Nevv-Found-Land.   London, F. Kyngston 1620.   sm. 4to.   First Edition. (STC 25372)

1621

Ordonnez, Pedro de Cevallos.   Eyghentlijcke beschryvinghe van West Indies.   Amsterdam, M. Coliin 1621.   fol.

Philoponus, Honorius.   Nova typis transacta navigatio.   [Venice] 1621.   fol.   (M. A. Elton)

1622

A briefe relation of the discovery . . . of New England.   London, J. Haviland 1622.   sm. 4to.   (Huth).   (STC 18483)

[Brinsley, John].   A consolation for oure grammar schooles.   London, R. Field 1622.   sm. 4to.   (White Kennett).   (STC 3767)

[Cushman, Robert].   A sermon preached at Plimoth . . . December 9. 1621.   London, I. D[awson] 1622.   sm. 4to.   First Edition. (Britwell).   (STC 6149)

Hawkins, *Sir* Richard.   The observations of Sir Richard Havvkins. London, I. D[awson] 1622.   fol.   (STC 12962)

Herrera, Antonio de.   Nievvve werelt, anders ghenaempt VVest-Indien.   Amsterdam, M. Colijn 1622.   fol.

———— Novvs orbis.   Amstelodami, M. Colin 1622.   fol.   First Edition.   (Huth)

LeMaire, Jacob.   Spieghel der Avstralische navigatie.   Amsterdam, M. Colijn 1622.   fol.

Americana

[Mourt, G., *editor*]. A relation or iournall. London, for I. Bellamie 1622. sm.4to. First Edition, First Issue. (Britwell). (STC 20074)

Smith, John. New Englands trials. London, W. Iones 1622. sm.4to. Second Edition. (STC 22793)

Wassenaer, Nicolaes van. Historisch verhael alder ghedenck-weer-dichste geschiedenissē. t'Amstelredam, Jan Evertss. Cloppen-burgh an't Water 1622-35. 21 pts. in 5 v. 4to. (Pts. 18-21 by Barend Lampe)

Whitbourne, Richard. A discourse containing a loving invitation to adventurers. London, F. Kyngston 1622. sm.4to. First Edition. (STC 25375a)

1624

Donne, John. A sermon vpon the eighth verse of the first chapter of the Acts of the Apostles. London, for T. Iones 1624. sm.4to. (STC 7052)

Smith, John. The generall historie of Virginia. London, I. D[awson] and I. H[aviland] 1624. fol. (Calthorpe). (Sabin-Eames 82824: 7; STC 22790)

1625

Martyr, Peter. The historie of the VVest-Indies. London, for A. Hebb [?1625]. sm.4to. (STC 651)

Robinson, John. A iust and necessarie apologie of certain Christians ... called Brownists. [?Leyden] 1625. sm.4to. (STC 21108)

1626

Casas, Bartolomé de las. Istoria ò breuissima relatione della distrvttione dell' Indie Occidentali . . . Con la traduttione in Italiano di F. Bersabita [Giacomo Castellani]. Venetia, M. Ginammi 1626. sm.4to. First Edition of first Italian translation

[Vaughan, William]. The golden fleece. London, for F. Williams 1626. sm.4to. First Edition. (Barlow–Church). (STC 24609)

1628

Barros, Juan de. Decada primeira [segunda, terceira] da Asia. Em Lisboa, I. Rodriguez 1628. fol. For the fourth Decade see 1615

Americana

1630

Alexander, William, *Earl of Stirling*. The mapp and description of New-England. London, for N. Butter 1630. sm. 4to. (W. O. Massingberd). (STC 342)

Casas, Bartolomé de las. Istoria ò breuissima relatione della distrvttione dell' Indie Occidentali . . . Tradotta . . . dall' . . . Giacomo Castellani. Venetia, M. Ginammi 1630. sm. 4to. Second Edition of first Italian translation

[Higginson, Francis]. New Englands plantation. London, T. C[otes] and R. C[otes] 1630. sm. 4to. (Church). (STC 13449)

Laet, Joannes de. Beschrijvinghe van West-Indien. Leyden, bij de Elzeviers 1630. sm. fol. (Andrews)

Vryheden by de vergaderinghe van de negenthiene . . . aen allen den ghenen die eenighe colonien in Nieu-Nederlandt sullen planten. Amstelredam, M. I. Brandt 1630. sm. 4to. (Huth)

[White, John, *of Dorchester*]. The planters plea. London, W. Iones 1630. sm. 4to. First Edition. (Church). (STC 25399)

1631

Smith, John. Advertisements for the unexperienced planters. London, I. Haviland 1631. sm. 4to. (Hoe–Vail). (STC 22787). (6th state of map)

1632

Champlain, Samuel de. Les voyages. Paris, P. LeMur 1632. 4to.

Diaz del Castillo, Bernal. Historia verdadera de la conqvista de la Nueva-España. Madrid, en la Imprenta del Reyno 1632. fol. First Edition

Sagard-Théodat, Gabriel. Le grand voyage du pays des Hurons. Paris, D. Moreau 1632. 8vo.

Smith, John. The generall historie of Virginia. London, I. D[awson] and I. H[aviland] 1632. fol. (Sabin-Eames 82829, with maps of Ould Virginia, Virginia and Summer Ils. in the 4th state; map of New England in the 8th). (STC 22790d)

1633

James, Thomas, *Captain*. The strange and dangerous voyage of Captaine Thomas Iames. London, I. Legatt 1633. sm. 4to. (STC 14444)

Americana

Laet, Joannes de.   Novvs orbis seu descriptiones Indiae Occidentalis.
Lvgd. Batav., apud Elzevirios 1633.   fol.   (John Innys–Robert
Southey)

1634

[Abbot], George.   A briefe description of the whole world.   London,
for W. Sheares 1634.   12mo.   (STC 31)

Wood, William.   Nevv Englands prospect.   London, T. Cotes 1634.
sm. 4to.   First Edition.   (STC 25957).   (2 copies)

1635

Foxe, Luke.   North-vvest Fox.   London, B. Alsop and T. Fawcet 1635.
sm. 4to.   First Edition.   (Lenox–W. T. Emmet).   (STC 11221)

Wood, William.   Nevv Englands prospect.   London, T. Cotes 1635.
sm. 4to.   Second Edition.   (Church).   (STC 25958)

1636

Casas, Bartolomé de las.   Il svpplice schiavo Indiano. Tradotto in Italiano per ... M. Ginammi.   Venetia 1636.   sm. 4to.

Sagard-Théodat, Gabriel.   Histoire dv Canada.   Paris, C. Sonnivs
1636.   sm. 8vo.   (Huth)

1637

Brébeuf, Jean de.   Relation de ce qvi s'est passé dans le pays des Hvrons
... 1636.   Paris, S. Cramoisy 1637.   12mo.   (Wrest Park)

Le Jeune, Paul.   Relation de ce qvi s'est passé en la Novvelle France ...
1636.   Paris, S. Cramoisy 1637.   12mo.   (Wrest Park)

Morton, Thomas.   New English Canaan.   Amsterdam, J. F. Stam
1637.   sm. 4to.   (STC 18202)

1638

Le Jeune, Paul.   Relation de ce qvi s'est passé en la Novvelle France ...
1638.   Paris, S. Cramoisy 1638.   sm. 8vo.   Second Edition

LeMercier, François.   Relation de ce qvi s'est passé ... dans le pays des
Hurons ... 1637 & 1638.   Paris, S. Cramoisy 1638.   sm. 8vo.

Underhill, John.   Nevves from America.   London, J. D[awson] 1638.
sm. 4to.   (Pembroke).   (STC 24518)

[Vincent, Philip]. A trve relation of the late battell. London, T. Harper 1638. sm. 4to. Second Edition. (STC 24760)

1640

Casas, Bartolomé de las. La liberta pretesa dal supplice schiavo Indiano. Tradotto in Italiano per . . . M. Ginammi. Venetia, M. Ginammi 1640. sm. 4to.

1641

An appeale to every impartiall . . . reader. London, for F. Coules and H. Twyford 1641. sm. 4to.

Castell, William. A petition of W. C. . . . for the propagating of the Gospel in America. [London] 1641. sm. 4to. (White Kennett)

Cotton, John. An abstract of the lawes of New England. London, for F. Coules and W. Ley 1641. sm. 4to.

—— A coppy of a letter. [London] 1641. sm. 4to.

—— The way of life. London, M. F. for L. Fawne and S. Gellibrand 1641. sm. 4to. (H.V. Jones)

Hook, William. Nevv Englands teares. London, T. P. for I. Rothwell and H. Overton 1641. sm. 4to. Second Edition

[Palafox y Mendoza, Juan de]. Regla, y constitvtiones. [Puebla de Los Angeles, Mexico] 1641. sm. 4to.

Roberts, Lewes. The treasure of traffike. London, E. P. for N. Bourne 1641. sm. 4to. (Huth)

1642

Cotton, John. The churches resurrection. London, R. O. & G. D. for H. Overton 1642. sm. 4to. First Edition. (H.V. Jones)

—— The powring ovt of the seven vials. London, for R. S. 1642. sm. 4to. First Edition

Lechford, Thomas. Plain dealing. London, W. E. and I. G. for N. Butter 1642. sm. 4to. (White Kennett)

1643

Casas, Bartolomé de las. Istoria, ò breuissima relatione della distrvttione dell' Indie Occidentali . . . Tradotta in Italiano . . . G. Castellani. Venetia, M. Ginammi 1643. sm. 4to. Third Edition of first Italian translation

Goodwin, Thomas, *and others.* An apologeticall narration of some ministers formerly exiles. London, for R. Dawlman 1643. sm. 4to.

Herle, Charles. The independency on Scriptures of the independency of churches. London, T. Brudenell for N. A. 1643. sm. 4to.

Huit, Ephraim. The whole prophecie of Daniel explained. [London] for H. Overton 1643. sm. 4to.

Lalemant, Jérôme. Relation de ce qvi s'est passé en la mission des Hvrons... 1641. jusques... 1642. Paris, S. Cramoisy 1643. sm. 8vo. First Issue

New Englands first fruits. London, R. O. and G. D. for H. Overton 1643. sm. 4to. (Eliot's Indian tracts No. 1). (White Kennett)

[Steuart, Adam]. Some observations and annotations upon the Apologeticall Narration. London, for C. Meredith 1643. sm. 4to.

Vimont, Barthelemy. Relation de ce qvi s'est passé en la Novvelle France ... 1642. Paris, S. Cramoisy 1643. sm. 8vo. Second Issue

Williams, Roger. A key into the language of America. London, G. Dexter 1643. sm. 8vo.

1644

Castell, William. A short discoverie of the coasts and continent of America. London 1644. sm. 4to. First Edition, First Issue. (Britwell)

A coole conference between the Cleared Reformation and the Apologeticall Narration. [London 1644]. sm. 4to.

Cotton, John. The keyes of the Kingdom of Heaven. [London] M. Simmons for H. Overton 1644. sm. 4to.

The covenanter vindicated from periurie. London, T. Paine 1644. sm. 4to.

A declaration against the Antinomians. London, for I. Iones 1644. sm. 4to.

Dury, John. An epistolary discourse. London, for C. Greene 1644. sm. 4to.

Edwards, Thomas. Antapologia. London, G. M. for R. Smith 1644. sm. 4to.

[Field, John, *and* Thomas Wilcox].   An advertisement to the Parliament of England.   London, for M. Walbancke 1644.   sm. 4to.

[Forbes, Alexander].   An anatomy of independency.   London, for R. Bostock 1644.   sm. 4to.

[Goodwin, John].   M. S. to A. S. with a plea for libertie of conscience. London, F. N. for H. Overton 1644.   sm. 4to.

[Henderson, Alexander].   Reformation of church-government in Scotland.   [London] for R. Bostock 1644.   sm. 4to.

Mather, Richard, *and* William Thompson.   A modest and brotherly ansvver to Mr. Charles Herle.   London, for H. Overton 1644. sm. 4to.

Rutherford, Samuel.   The due right of presbyteries.   London, E. Griffin for R. Whittaker and A. Crook 1644.   sm. 4to.

The saints apologie.   London, A. C. 1644.   sm. 4to.

Steuart, Adam.   An ansvver to a libell intituled, A coole conference. London 1644.   sm. 4to.

1645

Baylie, Robert.   A dissvasive from the errours of the time.   London, for S. Gellibrand 1645.   sm. 4to.

A brief narration of the practices of the churches in New-England. London, M. Simmons for J. Rothwell 1645.   sm. 4to.   (White Kennett)

Casas, Bartolomé de las.   Conqvista dell' Indie Occidentali. Tradotta in Italiano per ... M. Ginammi.   Venetia, M. Ginammi 1645.   sm. 4to.

Cotton, John.   The powring out of the seven vials.   London, for R. S. 1645.   sm. 4to.   Second Edition

——— The way of the churches of Christ in New-England.   London, M. Simmons 1645.   sm. 4to.

Great Britain. *Parliament.* Two ordinances of the Lords and Commons ... whereby Robert Earle of Warwick is made Governor ... of America.   London, for J. Wright 1645.   sm. 4to.

Hook, William.   New-Englands sence.   London, J. Rothwell 1645. sm. 4to.   (Church)

Americana

Lalemant, Jérôme. Relation de ce qvi s'est passé dans le pays des Hvrons ... 1642 ... iusqu' ... 1643. Paris, S. & G. Cramoisy 1645. 12mo.

Vicars, John. The pictvre of independency. London, J. Macock 1645. sm. 4to.

Vimont, Barthelemy. Relation de ce qvi s'est passé en la Novvelle France ... 1643 & 1644. Paris, S. & G. Cramoisy 1645. 12mo.

1646

Cornwell, Francis. A description of the spirituall temple. London, J. Dawson 1646. sm. 8vo. (With running headline "The difference between the Christian and Antichristian church"). (Thomas Park)

Cotton, John. A conference Mr. John Cotton held at Boston. London, J. Dawson 1646. sm. 8vo. (Thomas Park)

———— The controversie concerning liberty of conscience. London, for T. Banks 1646. sm. 4to. First Edition. (White Kennett)

Winslow, Edward. Hypocrisie vnmasked. London, R. Cotes for J. Bellamy 1646. sm. 4to. (H. LeRoy Edgar)

1647

Baylie, Robert. Anabaptism. London, M. F. for S. Gellibrand 1647. sm. 4to.

Child, John. New-Englands Jonas cast up at London. London, for T. R. and E. M. 1647. sm. 4to. (White Kennett)

Cotton, John. The bloudy tenant, washed. London, M. Symmons for H. Allen 1647. sm. 4to. (Menzies–Ives–Church)

[Lalemant, Jérôme]. Relation de ce qvi s'est passé ... 1645 & 1646. Paris, S. & G. Cramoisy 1647. 12mo. (Lenox)

Mather, Richard. A reply to Mr. Rutherford. London, for J. Rothwell and H. Allen 1647. sm. 4to.

Ragueneau, Paul. Relation de ce qvi s'est passé ... aux Hvrons ... 1645 iusqu' ... 1646. Paris, S. & G. Cramoisy 1647. 12mo. (Lenox)

[Shepard, Thomas]. The day-breaking, if not the sun rising of the Gospell. London, R. Cotes for F. Clifton 1647. sm. 4to. (Eliot's Indian tracts No. 2)

Ward, Nathaniel. The simple cobler of Aggawam. London, J[ohn]
D[ever] & R[obert] I[bbitson] for S. Bowtell 1647. sm. 4to.
First Edition. (E. N. Crane)

1648

Cotton, John. The way of Congregational churches cleared. London,
M. Simmons for J. Bellamie 1648. sm. 4to.

Hooker, Thomas. A survey of the summe of church-discipline. London, A. M. for J. Bellamy 1648. sm. 4to. (John Russell–William
Partrigg–John Partridge–David D. Field)

Plantagenet, Beauchamp. A description of the province of New-
Albion. [London] 1648. sm. 4to. First Edition

Rutherford, Samuel. A survey of the spirituall Antichrist. London,
J. D. & R. I. for A. Crooke 1648. sm. 4to.

Shepard, Thomas. The clear sun-shine of the Gospel. London, R.
Cotes for J. Bellamy 1648. sm. 4to. (Eliot's Indian tracts No. 3)

1649

Breeden-Raedt aende vereenichde Nederlandsche provintien. Antwerp, F. van Duynen 1649. sm. 4to.

Bullock, William. Virginia impartially examined. London, J. Hammond 1649. sm. 4to. First Edition

Cotton, John. The controversie concerning liberty of conscience.
London, R. Austin for T. Banks 1649. sm. 4to. Second Edition

Great Britain. *Parliament.* An Act for promoting and propagating the
Gospel . . . in New England. London, for E. Husband 1649. sm.
fol.

[Lalemant, Jérôme, *and others*]. Relation de ce qvi s'est passé . . . 1647
& 1648. Paris, S. & G. Cramoisy 1649. 12mo.

A perfect description of Virginia. London, for R. Wodenorth 1649.
sm. 4to. First Edition. (Bridgewater)

Ragueneau, Paul. Relation de ce qvi s'est passé . . . aux Hvrons . . .
1647 & 1648. Paris, S. & G. Cramoisy 1649. 12mo.

Steendam, Jacob. Den distelvink. Eerste [twede] deel. Amsterdam,
P. Dircksz 1649. sm. 4to. (W. L. Andrews). For pt. III see
1650

Winslow, Edward. The glorious progress of the Gospel. London, for H. Allen 1649. sm. 4to. (Eliot's Indian tracts No. 4)

1650

Donck, Adriaen van der. Vertoogh van Nieu-Neder-Land. In's Graven-Hage, M. Steel 1650. sm. 4to.

Steendam, Jacob. Den distelvink. Darde deel. Amsterdam, P. Dircksz 1650. sm. 4to. (W. L. Andrews). For pts. I-II see 1649

Thorowgood, Thomas. Iewes in America. London, W. H. for T. Slater 1650. sm. 4to.

1651

Bulkeley, Peter. The Gospel-covenant. London, M. Simmons 1651. sm. 4to. Second Edition

Whitfield, Henry. The light appearing more and more towards the perfect day. London, T. R. & E. M. for J. Bartlett 1651. sm. 4to. First Edition, First Issue. (Eliot's Indian tracts No. 5). (Church)

1652

Whitfield, Henry. Strength out of weakness. London, M. Simmons for J. Blague and S. Howes 1652. sm. 4to. (Eliot's Indian tracts No. 6). (White Kennett)

[Williams, Roger]. The fourth paper, presented by Major Butler, to Parliament. London, for G. Calvert 1652. sm. 4to.

1653

Bressani, Francesco Gioseppe. Breve relatione. In Macerata, per gli heredi d'Agostino Grisei 1653. sm. 4to.

Drake, *Sir* Francis. Sir Francis Drake revived. London, for N. Bourne 1653. sm. 4to. (Heber–Church)

Eliot, John, *and* Thomas Mayhew. Tears of repentance. London, P. Cole 1653. sm. 4to. (Eliot's Indian tracts No. 7). (White Kennett)

Mendez Pinto, Fernando. The voyages . . . done into English by H[enry] C[ogan]. London, J. Macock for H. Cripps and L. Lloyd 1653. fol. First Edition. (E. M. Satow)

A platform of church-discipline . . . agreed upon . . . at Cambridge. London, for P. Cole 1653. sm. 4to.

Americana

[Johnson, Edward]. A history of New-England. London, for N.
Brooke 1654. sm. 4to. First Edition. (Britwell)

Pyncheon, William. The time when the first Sabbath was ordained.
London, R. I. 1654. sm. 4to.

1655

Baylie, Robert. The disswasive from the errors of the time. London,
E. Tyler for S. Gellibrand 1655. sm. 4to.

Eliot, John. A late and further manifestation of the progress of the
Gospel. London, M. S. 1655. sm. 4to. (Eliot's Indian tracts
No. 8). (White Kennett)

[Gage, Thomas]. A new survey of the West-Indies. London, E. Cotes
1655. fol. (John Archer)

[Hartlib, Samuel]. The reformed common-wealth of bees. London,
for G. Calvert 1655. sm. 4to.

—— The reformed Virginian silk-worm. London, J. Streater for
G. Calvert 1655. sm. 4to.

Le Mercier, François. Relation de ce qvi s'est passé . . . en la Novvelle
France . . . 1653 & 1654. Paris, S. et G. Cramoisy 1655. sm. 8vo.

N., N. America. London, R. Hodgkinsonne for E. Dod 1655. sm.
8vo.

Rosaccio, Giuseppe. Prospectus mvndi. Weltblick . . . in das teutsch
vbergesetzt von I. C. G. C. N. Augspurg, A. Aperger 1655. sm.
4to.

S., I. A brief and perfect journal of the late proceedings . . . of the English army in the West-Indies. London 1655. 8vo.

1656

Cotton, John. A practical commentary . . . upon the First Epistle Generall of John. London, R. I. and E. C. for T. Parkhurst 1656. fol.
(2 copies)

Donck, Adriaen van der. Beschryvinge van Nieuvv-Nederlant.
Aemsteldam, E. Nieuwenhof 1656. sm. 4to. Second Edition.
(H. C. Bernheim)

Americana

Donck, Adriaen van der. Conditien, die door de heeren bvrgermeeste-
ren gepresenteert werden aen alle de gene, die als coloniers na
Nieuw-Nederlant willen vertrecken. Amsterdam, J. Banning
1656. sm. 4to. (H. C. Bernheim)

Hammond, John. Leah and Rachel. London, T. Mabb 1656. sm.
4to. (White Kennett)

1657

[De Quen, Jean]. Relation de ce qvi s'est passé ... 1655 & 1656. Paris,
S. et G. Cramoisy 1657. sm. 8vo.

Ligon, Richard. A trve & exact history of ... Barbados. London, for
H. Moseley 1657. fol.

1659

[Norton, Humphrey]. New-England's ensigne. London, T. L. for
G. Calvert 1659. sm. 4to. (Huth)

1660

[Burroughs, Edward]. A declaration of the sad and great persecution
... of ... Quakers. London, for R. Wilson [1660]. sm. 4to.

[Fox, George]. An epistle general to them who are of the royal priest-
hood. London, for T. Simmons 1660. sm. 4to.

LeBlanc, Vincent. The world surveyed ... rendred into English by
F[rancis] B[rooke]. London, for J. Starkey 1660. sm. fol.

Norton, John. The heart of New-England rent. London, J. H. for
J. Allen 1660. 16mo. Second Edition. (Rice–Ives)

Penington, Isaac. An examination of the grounds ... which ... induce
the court of Boston ... to make that order ... against the Quakers.
London, for L. Lloyd 1660. sm. 4to.

[Stephenson, Marmaduke]. A call from death to life. London, for
T. Simmons 1660. sm. 4to.

Thorowgood, Thomas. Jews in America. London, for H. Brome
1660. sm. 4to.

1661

Pagan, Blaise François de, *Comte*. An historical ... description of the
great country & river of the Amazones. London, for J. Starkey
1661. sm. 8vo.

Americana

1662

Kort verhael van Nieuw-Nederlants gelegentheit. [Amsterdam] 1662. sm. 4to. (DePuy–Church)

1664

[Boucher, Pierre]. Histoire veritable et natvrelle . . . de la Novvelle France. Paris, F. Lambert 1664. 12mo.

Du Creux, François. Historiae Canadensis. Parisiis, S. Cramoisy et S. Mabre-Cramoisy 1664. sm. 4to. (Jeremiah Milles)

Norton, John. A copy of the letter returned by the ministers of New-England to Mr. John Dury. Cambridge, S. G. and M. I. for H. Usher 1664. sm. 4to.

—— Three choice and profitable sermons. Cambridge, S. G. and M. I. for H. Usher 1664. sm. 4to.

Verklaringe van hare ho. mogende de heeren Staten Generael, op de declaratie van syne Majesteyt van Groot Bretagne. Vytrecht, J. de Bal 1664. sm. 4to.

1665

[Lalemant, Jérôme]. Relation de ce qvi s'est passé . . . 1663 & 1664. Paris, S. Cramoisy & S. Mabre-Cramoisy 1665. 12mo.

Ruyter, Michiel de. Journael. Amsterdam, P. la Burgh 1665. sm. 4to.

1666

Alsop, George. A character of the province of Mary-Land. London, T. J. for P. Dring 1666. sm. 8vo. First Edition

1667

Fage, Robert. Cosmography. London, S. Griffin for J. Overton 1667. sm. 8vo.

Great Britain. Articles of peace & alliance, between . . . Charles II . . . and . . . the States General of the United Netherlands. [London] Assigns of J. Bill and C. Barker 1667. sm. 4to.

Kort en bondigh verhael. Amsterdam, M. Willemsz, Doornick 1667. sm. 4to. (Copy 1, C. L. F. Robinson; 2, A. C. Bernheim)

Netherlands. *States General.* Articulen van Vrede. In 's Graven-Hage, H. van Wouw 1667. sm. 4to.

Americana

1668

P[enn], W[illiam]. The sandy foundation shaken. London 1668. sm. 4to. First Edition

1669

Morton, Nathaniel. New-Englands memoriall. Cambridge, S. G. and M. S. for J. Vsher 1669. sm. 4to. First Edition. (John Evelyn–Lefferts–Hoe–Vail)

Robinson, William, *and* William Leddra. Several epistles. London 1669. sm. 4to. (Huth)

1670

Denton, Daniel. A brief description of New-York. [London, for J. Hancock and W. Bradley 1670]. (Imprint cut away). sm. 4to.

Penn, William. The peoples ancient and just liberties asserted. n.p. 1670. sm. 4to. First Edition

1671

Cotton, John. A treatise of the covenant of grace. London, for P. Parker 1671. 12mo. (Hudnut)

Eliot, John. A brief narrative of the progress of the Gospel. London, for J. Allen 1671. sm. 4to. (Eliot's Indian tracts No. 11). (White Kennett)

Mather, Eleazer. A serious exhortation. Cambridge, S. G. and M. J. 1671. sm. 4to. (Elizabeth Saltonstall–Warham Williams)

Penn, William. Truth exalted. London, Re-printed 1671. sm. 4to.

1672

Denys, Nicolas. Description geographique ... des costes de l'Amerique Septentrionale. Paris, L. Billaine 1672. 12mo.

Downing, *Sir* George. A discourse. London, for J. Lutton 1672. 12mo.

Josselyn, John. New-Englands rarities discovered. London, for G. Widdowes 1672. sm. 8vo. First Edition. (W. L. Andrews)

Lederer, John. The discoveries. London, J. C. for S. Heyrick 1672. sm. 4to. (White Kennett)

Americana

1673

[Montanus, Arnoldus].   Die unbekante neue welt . . . Durch Dr. O. D[apper].   Amsterdam, J. von Meurs 1673.   fol.

1674

Josselyn, John.   An account of two voyages to New-England.   London, for G. Widdows 1674.   12mo.   First Edition

Penn, William, *and* George Whitehead.   The Christian-Quaker.   n.p. 1674.   sm. fol.   First Edition.   (Thomas Penn)

1675

Penn, William.   England's present interest discover'd.   n.p. 1675.   sm. 4to.

1676

A continuation of the state of New-England.   London, T. M. for D. Newman 1676.   fol.   First Edition.   (King Philip's War narratives. Folios. No. 2)

Dassié, C. R.   Description generale des costes de L Ameriqve.   Rouen 1676.   12mo.   First Edition

Hubbard, William.   The happiness of a people in the wisdome of their rulers.   Boston, J. Foster 1676.   sm. 4to.

Mather, Increase.   A brief history of the vvarr with the Indians in Nevv-England.   Boston, J. Foster 1676.   sm. 4to.   (King Philip's War narratives. Quartos. No. 3).   (Huth)

———— A brief history of the vvar with the Indians in Nevv-England. London, for R. Chiswell 1676.   sm. 4to.   (Newdigate)

———— An earnest exhortation to the inhabitants of New-England. Boston, J. Foster 1676.   sm. 4to.

A new and further narrative of the state of New-England.   London, J. B. for D. Newman 1676.   fol.   First Edition.   (King Philip's War narratives. Folios. No. 3)

News from New-England.   London, for J. Coniers 1676.   sm. 4to. First Edition.   (King Philip's War narratives. Quartos. No. 4). (White Kennett)

The present state of New-England.   London, D. Newman 1676.   fol. Second Edition.   (King Philip's War narratives. Folios. No. 1)

Americana

A true account of the most considerable occurrences.   London, for B. Billingsley 1676.   fol.   First Edition.   (King Philip's War narratives. Folios. No. 4).   (Newdigate)

1677

Articles of peace between . . . Prince Charles II . . . and several Indian Kings and Queens.   London, J. Bill, C. Barker, T. Newcomb and H. Hills 1677.   sm. 4to.   (White Kennett)

Hubbard, William.   A narrative of the troubles with the Indians in New-England.   Boston, J. Foster 1677.   sm. 4to.   (King Philip's War narratives. Quartos. No. 8).   (White Hills map)

———— The present state of New-England.   London, for T. Parkhurst 1677.   sm. 4to.   (Wine Hills map)

Mather, Increase.   An historical discourse concerning the prevalency of prayer.   Boston, J. Foster 1677.   sm. 4to.

———— A relation of the troubles which have hapned in New-England.   Boston, J. Foster 1677.   sm. 4to.   (King Philip's War narratives. Quartos. No. 9)

1678

Blome, Richard.   A description of . . . Jamaica.   London, J. B. for D. Newman 1678.   8vo.   Second Edition.   (Thomas Hay, Earl of Kinnoull)

Fox, George, *and* John Burnyeat.   A New-England fire-brand quenched.   [London] 1678.   sm. 4to.   First Edition

1679

Fox, George.   Caesar's due rendred unto him.   [London] 1679.   sm. 4to.

1680

Godwin, Morgan.   The negro's & Indians advocate.   London, for the Author, by J. D. 1680.   12mo.

1681

Bos, Lambert van den.   Leben und tapffere thaten der aller-berühmtesten see-helden.   Nurnberg, C. Endters 1681.   sm. 4to.

Godwin, Morgan.   A supplement to the Negro's & Indian's advocate.   London, J. D. 1681.   sm. 4to.

Americana

[Penn, William]. Some account of the province of Pennsilvania. London, B. Clark 1681. fol.

Thévenot, Melchisedech. Recueil de voyages. Paris, E. Michallet 1681. sm. 8vo.

1682

The Articles, settlement and offices of the Free Society of Traders in Pennsilvania. London, for B. Clark 1682. fol.

Ash, Thomas. Carolina. London, for W. C. 1682. sm. 4to.

[Loddington, William]. Plantation work the work of this generation. London, for B. Clark 1682. sm. 4to.

Mather, Increase. Heaven's alarm to the world. Boston, for S. Sewall 1682. 16mo. Second Edition. (2 copies)

[Penn, William]. The frame of the government of the province of Pennsilvania. [London] 1682. fol. (Pembroke)

Rowlandson, Mary. A true history of the captivity & restoration of Mrs. Mary Rowlandson. Re-printed at London, and sold by J. Poole 1682. sm. 4to.

[Wilson, Samuel]. An account of the province of Carolina. London, G. Larkin for F. Smith 1682. sm. 4to. First Edition

1683

Hennepin, Louis. Description de la Louisiane. Paris, chez la veuve Sebastian Huré 1683. 12mo. First Edition

Mather, Increase. Kometographia. Boston, S. G[reen] for S. S[ewall] 1683. 8vo. First Edition. (Sir George Shuckburgh)

────── The latter sign. (Boston, S. G[reen] for S. S[ewall] 1683). 8vo. [With "Kometographia" 1683]

Penn, William. A letter . . . to the Committee of the Free Society of Traders. [London] A. Sowle 1683. fol. Third Edition

The present state of Jamaica. London, F. Clark for T. Malthus 1683. sm. 8vo. (Newdigate)

1684

Carolina described more fully then heretofore. Dublin 1684. sm. 4to. (Halsey)

Esquemeling, John. Bucaniers of America. London, for W. Crooke 1684. 4to. First Edition. (Hoe–C. L. F. Robinson)

Americana

Mather, Increase.   An essay for the recording of illustrious providences. Boston, S. Green for J. Browning 1684. sm. 8vo. First Edition

1685

[Citri de la Guette, Samuel].   Histoire de la conqueste de la Floride. Paris, D. Thierry 1685. 12mo.

P[enn], W[illiam].   The Quakers elegy on the death of Charles. London, J. P. for H. Playford 1685.   fol.

———— Tweede bericht ofte relaas.   Amsterdam, J. Claus [1685]. sm. 4to.

1686

Great Britain.   Several treaties of peace and commerce conducted between the late King [Charles II] . . . and other princes and states. London, His Majesties printers, and sold by E. Poole 1686.   sm. 4to.

———— Treaty of peace . . . in America, between . . . James II . . . and Lewis XIV . . . Novemb. 1686.   (London) T. Newcomb 1686. sm. 4to.

Hennepin, Louis.   Descrizione della Lvigiana.   Bologna, G. Monti 1686. 12mo.

Higginson, John.   Our dying Saviour's legacy of peace.   Boston, S. Green for J. Usher 1686. sm. 8vo.

1687

[Blome, Richard].   The present state of his Majesties isles . . . in America.   London, H. Clark for D. Newman 1687. 8vo. First Edition. (Newdigate)

Franck, Richard.   A philosophical treatise of the original and production of things. London, J. Gain 1687. sm. 8vo.

Great Britain.   Articles of peace and commerce between . . . James II . . . and the . . . Lords . . . of Algiers in Barbary: ratified . . . 1686. (London) T. Newcomb 1687. sm. 4to.

1688

Denys, Nicolas.   Geographische en historische beschrijving der kusten van Noord-America.   Amsterdam, J. Ten Hoorn 1688.   sm. 4to.

Americana

Hennepin, Louis. Beschryving van Louisiana. Amsterdam, J. Ten Hoorn 1688. sm. 4to.

——— Description de la Louisiane. Paris, A. Auroy 1688. 12mo.

Vega, Garcilaso de la, *El Inca.* The royal commentaries of Peru ... rendred into English, by Sir Paul Rycaut. London, M. Flesher for S. Heyrick 1688. fol. (Lord Somers)

1689

Byfield, Nathaniel. An account of the late revolution in New-England. London, for R. Chiswell 1689. sm. 4to.

——— ——— Edinburgh 1689. sm. 4to.

[Mather, Increase]. A brief relation of the state of New England. London, for R. Baldwine 1689. sm. 4to.

——— A narrative of the miseries of New-England. London, R. Janeway 1689. sm. 4to.

A sixth collection of papers relating to the present juncture of affairs in England. London, R. Janeway 1689. sm. 4to.

1690

Palmer, John. An impartial account of the state of New England. London, for E. Poole 1690. sm. 4to. (Britwell)

1691

Le Clercq, Chrestien. Nouvelle relation de la Gaspesie. Paris, A. Auroy 1691. sm. 8vo. First Edition

Mather, Cotton. Late memorable providences relating to witchcrafts. London, for T. Parkhurst 1691. sm. 8vo.

Palafox y Mendoza, Juan de. Vida interior. Sevilla, L. Martin 1691. sm. 4to.

[Stoughton, William, *and others*]. A narrative of the proceedings of Sir Edmond Androsse. [Boston] 1691. sm. 4to.

Willard, Samuel. The barren fig trees doom. Boston, B. Harris, and J. Allen 1691. 12mo.

1692

[Welde, Thomas, *and* John Winthrop]. A short story of the rise, reign and ruin of the Antinomians. London, for T. Parkhurst 1692. sm. 4to.

Americana

1693

Bayard, Nicholas, *and* Charles Lodowick.   A journal of the late actions of the French at Canada.   London, for R. Baldwin 1693.   sm. 4to. (White Kennett)

Keith, George.   The Christian Quaker.   London 1693.   sm. 4to. (White Kennett)

———— More divisions amongst the Quakers.   (London) 1693.   sm. 4to.   (White Kennett)

Mather, Cotton.   The wonders of the invisible world.   Printed first, at Bostun . . . and Reprinted at London, for J. Dunton 1693.   sm. 4to.

———— ———— Printed first, at Boston . . . and reprinted at London, for J. Dunton 1693.   sm. 4to.

1694

The judgment given forth by twenty eight Quakers against George Keith.   London, for R. Baldwin 1694.   sm. 4to.   (White Kennett)

[Keith, George].   The causeless ground of surmises . . . removed. London, for R. Levis 1694.   sm. 4to.   (White Kennett)

Mather, Cotton.   The life and death of the Reverend Mr. John Eliot. London, for J. Dunton 1694.   16mo.   Third Edition.   (Tho. Evelyn)

Narborough, *Sir* John, *and others.*   An account of several late voyages. London, for S. Smith and B. Walford 1694.   8vo.

[Scottow, Joshua].   A narrative of the planting of the Massachusets Colony.   Boston, B. Harris 1694.   12mo.

1695

Shepard, Thomas.   The parable of the Ten Virgins.   [London] 1695. fol.

1696

Luther, Martin.   Lutheri catechismus.   Stockholm, J. J. Genath 1696. 12mo.

Mather, Increase.   Angelographia.   Boston, B. Green & J. Allen for S. Phillips 1696.   12mo.

Americana

[Scottow, Joshua, *editor?*]. Massachusetts. Boston, B. Green and J. Allen 1696. 12mo. (Church)

Thévenot, Melchisedech. Relations de divers voyages curieux. Paris, T. Moette 1696. fol. (Amherst)

1697

Dampier, William. A new voyage round the world. London, for J. Knapton 1697. v. 1. 8vo. First Edition. (W. Prideaux). For v. 2 see 1699

Hennepin, Louis. Nouvelle decouverte d'un tres grand pays. Utrecht, G. Broedelet 1697. 12mo. First Edition

1698

Acarete de Biscay. An account of a voyage up the river de La Plata. London, for S. Buckley 1698. 8vo.

Acuña, Christoval de. Voyages and discoveries in South America. London, for S. Buckley 1698. 8vo.

Béchamel, François. A journal of the travels of John Grillet, and Francis Bechamel into Guiana. London, for S. Buckley 1698. 8vo.

Carolina. The two charters granted by King Charles IId. to the Proprietors of Carolina. London, Sold by R. Parker [1698?]. sm. 4to.

Hennepin, Louis. Aenmerckelycke historische reys-beschryvinge door verscheyde landen veel grooter als die van geheel Europa. Utrecht, A. Schouten 1698. sm. 4to.

———— A new discovery of a vast country in America. London, for M. Bentley, J. Tonson, H. Bonwick, T. Goodwin, and S. Manship 1698. 8vo. (George Freer)

———— Nouveau voyage d'un pais plus grand que l'Europe. Utrecht, A. Schouten 1698. sm. 8vo. First Edition

———— Nouvelle decouverte d'un tres grand pays. Amsterdam, A. van Someren 1698. 12mo.

Thomas, Gabriel. An historical and geographical account of . . . Pensilvania. London, for A. Baldwin 1698. sm. 8vo. (Lefferts)

Tonti, Henri de. An account of Monsieur de la Salle's last expedition. London, for J. Tonson, S. Buckly and R. Knaplock 1698. 12mo.

Americana

1699

Casas, Bartolomé de las.   An account of the first voyages and discoveries made by the Spaniards in America.   London, J. Darby for D. Brown, J. Harris and A. Bell 1699.   8vo.

Dampier, William.   A new voyage round the world.   London, for J. Knapton 1699.   v. 2.   8vo.   First Edition.   (W. Prideaux).   For v. 3 see 1703

A defence of the Scots Settlement at Darien.   n.p. 1699.   sm. 4to.

Hacke, William.   A collection of original voyages.   London, for J. Knapton 1699.   8vo.

Hennepin, Louis.   Neue entdeckung vieler sehr grossen landschafften in America.   Bremen, P. G. Saurman 1699.   12mo.

———— A new discovery of a vast country in America.   London, H. Bonwicke 1699.   8vo.   (J. B. Stanhope)

Hodges, James.   A just and modest vindication of the Scots design, for . . . a colony at Darien.   [London?] 1699.   8vo.

[Ward, Edward].   A trip to New-England.   London 1699.   sm. fol. First Edition.   (Church)

1700

Calef, Robert.   More wonders of the invisible world.   London, for N. Hillar and J. Collyer 1700.   sm. 4to.   First Edition.   (Lefferts)

Dickenson, Jonathan.   God's protecting Providence.   London, T. Sowle 1700.   8vo.

Doolittle, Thomas.   A treatise concerning the Lords Supper.   Boston, B. Green and J. Allen for S. Phillips 1700.   16mo.

An enquiry into the causes of the miscarriage of the Scots colony at Darien.   Glasgow 1700.   8vo.

Stoddard, Solomon.   The doctrine of instituted churches explained. London, for R. Smith 1700.   sm. 4to.

Willard, Samuel.   Love's pedigree.   Boston, B. Green and J. Allen 1700.   8vo.

1701

The arraignment, tryal, and condemnation of Captain William Kidd. London, for J. Nutt 1701.   fol.

[Mitchell, John]. A full account of the proceedings in relation to Capt.
Kidd. London, The Booksellers of London and Westminster 1701.
sm. 4to. First Edition

1702

Campanius, Thomas. Kort bestrifning om provincien Nya Swerige.
Stockholm, Truckt uti Kongl. Boktr. . . . of J. H. Werner 1702.
sm. 4to.

Hale, John. A modest enquiry into the nature of witchcraft. Boston,
B. Green and J. Allen for B. Eliot 1702. sm. 8vo. (H. LeRoy
Edgar)

Hennepin, Louis. Nieuwe ontdekkinge van een groot land. Amsterdam, A. van Damme 1702. sm. 4to.

Mather, Cotton. Magnalia Christi. London, for T. Parkhurst 1702.
fol. First Edition

Proposals for carrying on an effectual war in America, against the
French and Spaniards. London, for J. Nutt 1702. sm. 4to.

Whiting, John. Truth and innocency defended. London, T. Sowle
1702. 8vo.

1703

An account of the commitment, arraignment, tryal and condemnation
of Nicholas Bayard. London 1703. fol.

Bishop, George. New England judged. London, T. Sowle 1703.
8vo. (2 copies)

Dampier, William. A new voyage round the world. London, for J.
Knapton 1703. v. 3. 8vo. First Edition. (W. Prideaux). For
v. 4 see 1709

1701

Lahontan, *Baron de*. New voyages to North-America. London, for
H. Bonwicke, T. Goodwin, M. Wotton, B. Tooke and S. Manship
1703. 2 v. 8vo.

—— Nouveaux voyages. A La Haye, chez les Fréres l'Honoré
1703. 2 v. 12mo. First Edition

1704

Benzoni, Girolamo. Die gedenkwaardige West-Indise voyagien. Leyden, P. Vander Aa 1704. 4to. (John Jay Paul)

Americana

Hennepin, Louis. Aanmerkelyke voyagie. Rotterdam, B. Bos 1704. sm. 4to.

———— Voyage curieux. Leide, P. Vander Aa 1704. 12mo. (Marshall)

———— Voyage ou nouvelle decouverte d'un tres-grand pays. Amsterdam, A. Braakman 1704. 12mo.

Lahontan, *Baron de*. Dialogues. Amsterdam, chez la veuve de Boeteman 1704. 12mo. First Edition. (Sabin 38634)

Wafer, Lionel. A new voyage and description of the Isthmus of America. London, for J. Knapton 1704. 8vo. Second Edition

1705

[Beverley, Robert]. The history and present state of Virginia. London, for R. Parker 1705. 2 v. 8vo. First Edition

Carolina. The copy of an Act lately pass'd in Carolina . . . [1704]. n.p. n.d. [? 1705]. sm. 4to.

[Defoe, Daniel]. Party-tyranny. London 1705. sm. 4to.

1706

Keith, George. A journal of travels from New-Hampshire to Caratuck. London, J. Downing for B. Aylmer 1706. sm. 4to.

1707

[Beverley, Robert]. Histoire de la Virginie. Amsterdam, T. Lombrail 1707. 12mo.

Colman, Benjamin. A poem on Elijahs translation. Boston, B. Green for B. Eliot 1707. sm. 8vo. (McKee–Maier)

Funnell, William. A voyage round the world. London, W. Botham for J. Knapton 1707. 8vo. First Edition. (Copy 1, W. Prideaux; 2, Lord Willoughby de Broke)

Pemberton, Ebenezer. A funeral sermon on the death of . . . Mr. Samuel Willard. Boston, B. Green for B. Eliot 1707. sm. 8vo. (McKee–Maier)

Sloane, *Sir* Hans. A voyage to the islands Madera, Barbados . . . and Jamaica. London, M. B. for the Author 1707. v. 1. fol. First Edition. For v. 2 see 1725

Williams, William.   The danger of not reforming known evils.   Boston, B. Green 1707.   12mo.

1708

[Oldmixon, John].   The British Empire in America.   London, for J. Nicholson, B. Tooke, R. Parker and R. Smith 1708.   2 v.   8vo. First Edition

1709

Dampier, William.   A new voyage round the world.   London, W. Botham for J. Knapton 1709.   v.4.   8vo.   First Edition.   (W. Prideaux)

Lawson, John.   A new voyage to Carolina.   London 1709.   sm. 4to.

1710

Mather, Cotton.   Bonifacius.   Boston, B. Green for S. Gerrish 1710. 12mo.

1711

Moll, Herman.   Atlas geographus.   [London] J. Nutt 1711.   v. 1-2. 4to.   For v. 3 see 1712

A platform of church-discipline . . . agreed upon . . . at Cambridge . . . 1649.   New-York, W. and A. Bradford 1711.   sm. 8vo.

1712

Cooke, Edward.   A voyage to the South Sea.   London, H. M. for B. Lintot and R. Gosling, A. Bettesworth and W. Innys 1712.   8vo. (C. L. F. Robinson)

Kennett, White.   The lets and impediments in planting . . . the Gospel. London, J. Downing 1712.   8vo.

Mather, Cotton.   Thoughts for the day of rain.   Boston, B. Green 1712.   sm. 8vo.   First Edition

Moll, Herman.   Atlas geographus.   [London] J. Nutt 1712.   v. 3. 4to.   For v. 4 see 1714

Stoddard, Solomon.   Those taught by God.   Boston, B. Green for B. Eliot 1712.   12mo.

1713

The Assiento, or, Contract for . . . importing negroes into the Spanish America.   London, J. Baskett and the Assigns of T. Newcomb and H. Hills 1713.   sm. 4to.

Americana

Joutel, Henri. Journal historique du dernier voyage que feu M. de la Sale fit. Paris, E. Robinot 1713. 12mo. First Edition

1714

Flint, Henry. The doctrine of the Last Judgment. Boston, B. Green for B. Eliot 1714. sm. 4to. (Mark P. Robinson)

Joutel, Henri. A journal of the last voyage perform'd by Monsr. de la Sale. London, for A. Bell, B. Lintott and J. Baker 1714. 8vo.

Moll, Herman. Atlas geographus. [London] J. Nutt 1714. v. 4. 4to. For v. 5 see 1717

1715

Edmundson, William. A journal. Dublin, S. Fairbrother 1715. 4to. First Edition

[Mather, Cotton]. Just commemorations. Boston, B. Green [1715]. 12mo. First Edition, First Issue

1716

Mather, Increase. Two discourses. Boston, B. Green for D. Henchman 1716. 16mo. First Edition

1717

Moll, Herman. Atlas geographus. [London] E. Nutt for J. Nicholson 1717. v. 5. 4to.

Montgomery, *Sir* Robert. A discourse concerning ... a new colony to the south of Carolina. London 1717. 8vo. First Edition, First Issue

Williams, William. The great salvation revealed. Boston, T. Crump for S. Gerrish and D. Henchman 1717. 12mo. (2 copies)

———— A painful ministry. Boston, B. Green 1717. 12mo.

1720

Colman, Benjamin. Ossa Josephi. Boston, B. Green for B. Eliot 1720. 12mo. (Samuel Checkley)

A full and impartial account of the Company of the Mississippi. London, for R. Francklin, W. Lewis, J. Roberts, J. Graves and J. Stagg 1720. 8vo.

Americana

Het groote tafereel der dwaasheid. n.p. 1720. fol. (E. N. Crane–
C. L. F. Robinson)

[Hennepin, Louis]. A discovery of a large, rich, and plentiful country. London, for W. Boreham [1720]. 8vo.

—— La nouvelle France. Paris 1720. 12mo.

[——] Relations de la Louisiana. Amsterdam, J. F. Bernard 1720.
2 v. 8vo.

1721

Mather, Cotton. India christiana. Boston, B. Green 1721. 12mo.
(Britwell)

1722

Bacqueville de la Potherie, Claude Charles LeRoy. Histoire de l'Amerique Septentrionale. Paris, J. L. Nion et F. Didot 1722. 4 v.
12mo. First Edition

[Beverley, Robert]. The history of Virginia. London, for F. Fayram,
J. Clarke and T. Bickerton 1722. 8vo. Second Edition. (C. L. F.
Robinson)

Stoddard, Solomon. An answer to some cases of conscience. Boston,
B. Green 1722. sm. 4to.

1723

Gonzalez de Barcia Caballido y Zuñiga, Andres. Ensayo cronologico,
para la historia … de la Florida. Madrid, Oficina Real 1723. fol.

Stoddard, Solomon. Question whether God is not angry with the
country. [Boston, B. Green 1723]. sm. 4to.

Torquemada, Juan de. Primera [segunda, tercera] parte delos veinte
i vn libros rituales. Madrid, N. Rodriguez 1723. 3 v. fol.

1724

Charlevoix, Pierre François Xavier. La vie de la Mere Marie de l'In-
carnation. Paris, L. A. Thomelin 1724. 12mo. First Edition

[Checkley, John]. A defence of a book … entituled, A modest proof
of the order … settled by Christ. Boston, T. Fleet 1724. 8vo.

Jones, Hugh. The present state of Virginia. London, for J. Clarke
1724. 8vo. Second Edition. (William Byrd–Halsey)

Lafitau, Joseph François. Moeurs des sauvages Ameriquains. Paris,
Saugrain l'aîné, C. Estienne Hochereau 1724. 2 v. 4to.

[Mather, Cotton]. Parentator. Boston, B. Green for N. Belknap 1724. sm. 8vo. First Edition. (Mark P. Robinson)

1725

A confession of faith owned and consented unto by the . . . churches assembled at Boston . . . 1680. Boston, B. Eliot and D. Henchman 1725. 12mo.

Herrera, Antonio de. The general history of the vast continent . . . of America. Tr. by Capt. John Stevens. London, for J. Batley 1725. v. 1-2. 8vo. For v. 3-6 see 1726

Hessel, Andrea. Kort berettelse om then Swensta kyrtios narwarande tilstand i America. Norkioping 1725. sm. 4to.

Johnson, Charles. A general history of the pyrates. London, for T. Warner 1725. v. 1. 8vo. For v. 2 see 1726

The results of three synods. Boston, Re-printed for B. Eliot and D. Henchman 1725. 12mo. (2 copies)

Sloane, *Sir* Hans. A voyage to the islands Madera, Barbados . . . and Jamaica. London, M. B. for the Author 1725. v. 2. fol. First Edition

Symmes, Thomas. Lovewell lamented. Boston, B. Green junr. for S. Gerrish 1725. 8vo. First Edition

1726

Brown, John. Divine help implored. Boston, T. Fleet for S. Gerrish 1726. 8vo.

Herrera, Antonio de. The general history of the vast continent . . . of America. London, for J. Batley 1726. v. 3-6. 8vo.

Johnson, Charles. A general history of the pyrates. London, for T. Woodward [1726]. v. 2. 8vo.

[Mather, Cotton]. Manuductio ad ministerium. Boston, for T. Hancock 1726. sm. 8vo.

Penhallow, Samuel. The history of the wars of New-England with the eastern Indians. Boston, T. Fleet for S. Gerrish and D. Henchman 1726. 12mo. (Huth)

1727

Boone, Nicholas. The constables pocket-book. Boston, Printed . . . at the Bible in Cornhill 1727. 12mo. Second Edition

Americana

[Colden, Cadwallader]. The history of the five Indian nations. New-York, W. Bradford 1727. sm. 8vo. First Edition. (McKee–Halsey)

Hartwell, Henry, James Blair *and* Edward Chilton. The present state of Virginia. London, for J. Wyat 1727. 8vo. (Charles, Viscount Bruce of Ampthill)

Mather, Cotton. Hor-Hagidgad. Boston, for S. Gerrish, S. Kneeland, N. Belknap and B. Love 1727. 8vo.

Mayhew, Experience. Indian converts. London, for S. Gerrish 1727. 8vo. (C. L. F. Robinson)

1729

Foxcroft, Thomas. Eli the priest dying suddenly. Boston, for S. Gerrish 1729. 8vo.

1730

Boylston, Zabdiel. An historical account of the small-pox. Boston, for S. Gerrish and T. Hancock 1730. sm. 8vo.

Humphreys, David. An historical account of the incorporated Society for the propagation of the Gospel. London, J. Downing 1730. 8vo.

1731

Biörck, Tobias E. Dissertatio gradualis, de plantatione ecclesiae Svecanae in America. Upsaliae, Literis Wernerianis [1731]. sm. 4to. (Halsey)

Chauncy, Charles. Sermons. Boston 1731-69. 4v. 8vo.

1732

Pullen, *Sir* John. The original plan, progress and present state of the South-Sea-Company. London, for T. Warner 1732. 8vo.

The Vade mecum for America. Boston, S. Kneeland and T. Green, for D. Henchman 1732. 8vo.

1733

Martyn, Benjamin. Reasons for establishing the colony of Georgia. London, for W. Meadows 1733. sm. 4to. Second Edition

[Oglethorpe, James]. A new and accurate account of ... South-Carolina and Georgia. London, for J. Worrall 1733. 8vo.

Americana

1735

The complaint of James Alexander and William Smith to the Committee of the General Assembly of the Colony of New-York. (New York 1735). fol. (A. C. Bernheim)

Indian conference. Conference held at Deerfield . . . 1735. By & between . . . Jonathan Belcher, Esq; and Duntaussoogoe and others. [Boston 1735]. 4to.

Stoddard, Solomon. A guide to Christ. Boston, J. Draper for D. Henchman 1735. 12mo. (S. D. Reeves)

1736

Mason, John. A brief history of the Pequot war. Boston, S. Kneeland & T. Green 1736. sm. 4to.

Prince, Thomas. A chronological history of New-England. Boston, Kneeland & Green for S. Gerrish 1736. v. 1. 16mo. First Edition

1737

Edwards, Jonathan. A faithful narrative of the surprizing work of God. London, for J. Oswald 1737. 12mo. First Edition

[Hennepin, Louis]. Decouverte d'un pays plus grand que l'Europe. (Amsterdam, J. F. Bernard 1737). 12mo.

South Carolina. The report of the Committee of the Commons House of Assembly of . . . South Carolina. London, T. Wood 1737. 4to.

1738

[Douglass, William]. An essay concerning silver and paper currencies. Boston, S. Kneeland and T. Green [1738]. 8vo. First Edition

Edwards, Jonathan. A faithful narrative of the surprising work of God. Boston, S. Kneeland & T. Green 1738. 12mo. Third Edition

Keith, *Sir* William. The history of the British plantations in America. Pt. I. London, S. Richardson 1738. 4to.

Mather, Samuel. An apology for the liberties of the churches in New-England. Boston, T. Fleet for D. Henchman 1738. 8vo. First Edition. (Mark P. Robinson)

Remarks on the trial of John-Peter-Zenger.   London, for J. Roberts
1738. 4to.

The tryal of John Peter Zenger.   London, for J. Wilford 1738.   4to.

1739

Callender, John.   An historical discourse on the civil and religious affairs of ... Rhode-Island. Boston, S. Kneeland and T. Green 1739.
8vo. First Edition

1740

[Douglass, William].   A discourse concerning the currencies of the
British plantations in America.   Boston, S. Kneeland & T. Green
1740. 8vo.

A new history of Jamaica. London, J. Hodges 1740. 8vo. First Edition

——— ——— Second Edition. (H. LeRoy Edgar)

Pennsylvania.   In chancery ... John Penn, Thomas Penn, and Richard
Penn Esqr; Plaintiffs. Charles Calvert Esq; Lord Baltimore ...
Defendant ... upon a bill ... for setling the boundarys of ...
Pensilvania, the three lower countys, and ... Maryland.   (London
1740). fol.

1741

Charters.   A list of copies of charters ... Maryland ... Connecticut
... Rhode-Island ... Pensylvania ... Massachusetts Bay ... Georgia. London 1741. fol.

Coxe, Daniel.   A description of ... Carolana.   n.p., Olive Payne 1741.
8vo.

Tailfer, Patrick, *and others*.   A true ... account of ... Georgia.
Charles-Town, South-Carolina, for P. Timothy [1741]. 8vo.

1742

Bechtel, Johannes.   Kurzer catechismus.   Philadelphia, B. Franklin
1742. 16mo. (W. L. Andrews)

Blair, Samuel. The doctrine of predestination. Philadelphia, B. Franklin 1742. 16mo. First Edition

Pennsylvania. The charters of the province of Pensilvania and city of
Philadelphia. Philadelphia, B. Franklin 1742. fol.

Pennsylvania. A collection of all the laws of the province of Pennsylvania. Philadelphia, B. Franklin 1742. fol.

Williams, Solomon. The power and efficacy of the prayers of the people of God. Boston, S. Kneeland and T. Green 1742. sm. 8vo. First Edition

[Zinzendorf und Pottendorf, Nikolaus Ludwig, *Count von*]. Diejenigen anmerkungen, welche der Herr autor des Kurzen Extracts, &c. . . . begehret hat. Philadelphia, I. Warner 1742. sm. 4to.

1743

A confession of faith . . . adopted by the Baptist Association. Philadelphia, B. Franklin 1743. 12mo.

Griffith, Benjamin. A short treatise of church-discipline. Philadelphia, B. Franklin 1743. 12mo.

Lovell, John. A funeral oration . . . occasion'd by the death of . . . Peter Faneuil. Boston, Green, Bushell and Allen for S. Kneeland and T. Green 1743. sm. 4to.

1744

Charlevoix, Pierre François Xavier. Histoire . . . de la Nouvelle France. Paris, Nyon fils 1744. 3 v. 4to.

Cicero, Marcus Tullius. M. T. Cicero's Cato Major. Philadelphia, B. Franklin 1744. 8vo. First Edition.

Dobbs, Arthur. An account of the countries adjoining to Hudson's Bay. London, for J. Robinson 1744. 4to. First Edition

[Horsmanden, Daniel]. A journal of the proceedings in the detection of the conspiracy for burning the city of New-York. New-York, J. Parker 1744. 4to. First Edition. (Horsmanden–McKee)

Jennings, David. An abridgment of the life of . . . Cotton Mather. London, for J. Oswald and J. Brackstone 1744. 12mo. First Edition. (Mark P. Robinson)

The present state of the country and inhabitants . . . of Louisiana. London, for J. Millan 1744. 8vo.

[Prince, Thomas, *junior, editor*]. The christian history. Boston, S. Kneeland and T. Green 1744. v. 1. 8vo. For v. 2 see 1745

Tennent, Gilbert. Twenty three sermons. Philadelphia, W. Bradford 1744. sm. 4to.

1745

The confession of faith. Philadelphia, B. Franklin 1745. 12mo.

[Prince, Thomas, *junior, editor*]. The christian history. Boston, for S. Kneeland and T. Green 1745. v.2. 8vo.

The testimony of a number of New England-ministers. Boston, S. Kneeland and T. Green and J. Winter 1745. 8vo.

1746

Brainerd, David. Mirabilia Dei. Philadelphia, W. Bradford [1746]. 8vo.

[Franklin, Benjamin]. Reflections on courtship and marriage. Philadelphia, B. Franklin 1746. sm. 4to. (W. L. Andrews)

Pemberton, Ebenezer. A sermon delivered . . . July 31, 1746. New-York, J. Parker 1746. 8vo.

Prince, Thomas. A sermon delivered . . . August 14. 1746. Boston, for D. Henchman and S. Kneeland and T. Green 1746. 8vo.

1747

Colden, Cadwallader. The history of the five Indian nations. London, for T. Osborne 1747. 8vo.

Neal, Daniel. The history of New-England. London, for A. Ward [and others] 1747. 2 v. 8vo. Second Edition

Stith, William. The history of . . . Virginia. Williamsburg, W. Parks 1747. 8vo.

Stoddard, Solomon. The defects of preachers reproved. Boston, Kneeland and Green 1747. 12mo. Second Edition

Story, Thomas. A journal. Newcastle upon Tyne, I. Thompson and Company 1747. fol.

1748

Anson, George. A voyage round the world. London, for J. and P. Knapton 1748. 8vo. (Ashburton–Thomas Carlyle)

Ellis, Henry. A voyage to Hudson's-Bay. London, for H. Whitridge 1748. 8vo. First Edition

Norton, John. The redeemed captive. Boston, Printed . . . opposite the Prison 1748. 12mo. First Edition

Americana

1749

Edwards, Jonathan.   An account of the life of . . . David Brainerd. Boston, for D. Henchman 1749.   8vo.   First Edition

Ellis, Henry.   A voyage to Hudson's-Bay.   Dublin, for G. and A. Ewing 1749.   8vo.   (Menzies)

Thomas, *à Kempis*.   The christian pattern.   Germantown, C. Sowr 1749.   12mo.   (2 copies)

Turell, Ebenezer.   The life and character of . . . Benjamin Colman. Boston, Rogers and Fowle, and J. Edwards 1749.   sm. 4to.

1750

A short view of the encroachments of France in America.   London, for R. Spavan 1750.   8vo.

1751

Bartram, John.   Observations on the inhabitants, climate, soil, rivers . . . in . . . travels from Pensilvania to . . . Canada.   London, for J. Whiston and B. White 1751.   8vo.

[Franklin, Benjamin].   Idea of the English school.   (Philadelphia, B. Franklin and D. Hall 1751).   8vo.

The importance of settling and fortifying Nova Scotia.   London, for J. Scott 1751.   8vo.   First Edition

Peters, Richard.   Sermon on education.   Philadelphia, B. Franklin and D. Hall 1751.   8vo.   First Edition

1752

The Independent Reflector. From Nov. 30-Dec. 28, 1752.   New York, J. Parker 1752.   fol.   (William Vernon)

New York.   Laws of New-York, from . . . 1691, to 1751.   New York, J. Parker 1752.   2 v.   fol.

Rhode Island.   Acts and laws . . . 1745 to . . . 1752.   Newport, J. Franklin 1752.   fol.

Robson, Joseph.   An account of six years residence in Hudson's-Bay. London, for J. Payne and J. Bouquet . . . 1752.   8vo.   First Edition

1753

Ashley, Jonathan.   An humble attempt to give a clear account from Scripture. Boston, S. Kneeland 1753.   sm. 4to.

Americana

[Butel-]Dumont, [George Marie].   Mémoires historiques sur la
    Louisiane.   Paris, Cl. J. B. Bauche 1753.   2 v.   sm. 8vo.   First
    Edition

Hopkins, Samuel.   Historical memoirs, relating to the Housatunnuk
    Indians.   Boston, S. Kneeland 1753.   8vo.   (J. W. R. Crawford)

The Independent Reflector. From Jan. 4-Nov. 22, 1753.   New York,
    J. Parker 1753.   fol.   (William Vernon)

More, *Sir* Thomas.   The common-wealth of Utopia.   Philadelphia, J.
    Chattin for B. Lay 1753.   8vo.

1754

Clap, Thomas.   The religious constitution of colleges.   New-London,
    T. Green 1754.   8vo.

Edwards, Jonathan.   A careful and strict enquiry into the modern pre-
    vailing notions of that freedom of will.   Boston, S. Kneeland 1754.
    8vo.   First Edition.   (Learmont)

[Franklin, Benjamin].   Some account of the Pennsylvania hospital.
    Philadelphia, B. Franklin and D. Hall 1754.   4to.

[Jefferys, Thomas].   The conduct of the French with regard to Nova
    Scotia.   London, for T. Jefferys 1754.   8vo.   First Edition

Kennedy, Archibald.   Serious considerations on the present state of the
    affairs of the northern colonies.   London, for R. Griffiths [1754].
    8vo.

Nakskow, Peter.   The Articles of faith . . . and the Ausburg Confes-
    sion. Set forth in forty sermons.   New-York, J. Parker and W.
    Weyman 1754.   4to.

Washington, George.   The journal of Major George Washington.
    London, for T. Jefferys 1754.   8vo.

1755

Buell, Samuel.   Christ the grand subject of Gospel-preaching.   New-
    York, J. Parker and W. Weyman 1755.   8vo.

[Chauncy, Charles].   A letter to a friend.   Boston, Edes and Gill 1755.
    sm. 4to.   First Edition

——— A second letter to a friend.   Boston, Edes and Gill 1755.   sm.
    4to.   First Edition

[Cheever, Ezekiel]. A short introduction to the Latin tongue. Boston, B. Edes and J. Gill 1755. 16mo.

Clark, Peter. Religion to be minded. Boston, S. Kneeland 1755. 8vo.

Clarke, William. Observations on the late and present conduct of the French. London, for J. Clarke 1755. 8vo.

Davies, Samuel. Religion and patriotism. Philadelphia, J. Chattin 1755. 8vo. First Edition

Douglass, William. A summary ... of the first planting ... of the British settlements in North-America. London, for R. Baldwin 1755. 2 v. 8vo.

Evans, Lewis. Geographical ... essays. Philadelphia, B. Franklin and D. Hall 1755. 4to. First Edition

Finley, Samuel. The power of Gospel ministers. New-York, H. Gaine 1755. 8vo.

Franklin, Benjamin. Poor Richard improved ... an almanack for 1756. Philadelphia, B. Franklin and D. Hall [1755]. 12mo.

Gallica fides. London, for M. Cooper 1755. 8vo.

[Johnson, *Sir* William]. To the governours of the several colonies. [Boston 1755]. fol.

Knox, Hugh. The dignity and importance of the Gospel ministry. New-York, H. Gaine 1755. 8vo.

Lowell, John. The advantages of God's presence. Boston, J. Draper 1755. 8vo.

Mitchell, John. A map of the British and French dominions in North America. London, for Jefferys and Faden 1755. 8 sheets. atlas fol.

Morrill, Isaac. The soldier exhorted to courage. Boston, J. Draper 1755. 8vo.

The whole system of the XXVIII Articles of the Evangelical ... Confession. Presented at Ausbourgh. New-York, J. Parker and W. Weyman 1755. 4to.

1756

Burr, Aaron. A sermon preached ... September 30, 1756. New-York, H. Gaine 1756. 8vo.

Davies, Samuel. Religion and patriotism. London, for J. Buckland, J. Ward and T. Field 1756. 8vo.

Delaville, *Abbé*. État présent de la Pensilvanie. [Paris] 1756. 16mo.

Evans, Lewis. Geographical ... essays. Number II. Philadelphia, for the Author 1756. 4to.

Johnson, *Sir* William. An account of conferences held, and treaties made, between . . . Sir William Johnson, Bart. and . . . Indian nations. London, for A. Millar 1756. 8vo.

A letter to the King of * * * * * London, for A. and C. Corbett 1756. 8vo.

Macleane, Laughlin. An essay on the expediency of inoculation. Philadelphia, W. Bradford 1756. 8vo.

Mellen, John. The duty of all to be ready. Boston, S. Kneeland 1756. 8vo.

Mémoires des Commissaires du Roi. Paris, l'Imprimerie Royale 1756. 6 v. sm. 8vo.

[Moreau, Jacob N.]. Mémoire contenant le précis des faits. Paris, l'Imprimerie Royale 1756. 4to.

[Pemberton, Israel, *and others*]. Several conferences between some of the ... Quakers ... and ... the six Indian nations. Newcastle upon Tyne, I. Thompson and Company 1756. 8vo.

Le peuple instruit. [Paris] 1756. 16mo. (Translation by E. J. Genet of Shebbeare's "Fourth letter.")

Le peuple juge. [Paris] 1756. 16mo. (Translation by E. J. Genet of "Reasons humbly offered.")

Reasons humbly offered to prove that the letter printed at the end of the French memorial of justification is a French forgery. London, for M. Collyer 1756. 8vo.

1757

The American Magazine. Philadelphia, W. Bradford [1757-8]. v. 1. 8vo.

[Johnson, *Sir* William]. Relaçao de huma batalha, succedida no campo de Lake Giorge. Traduzida no idioma Portuguez. Lisboa 1757. sm. 4to.

[Livingston, William]. A review of the military operations in North-America ... 1753 to ... 1756. London, for R. and J. Dodsley 1757. 4to. First Edition

———— ———— Dublin, for P. Wilson and J. Exshaw 1757. 12mo.

The military history of Great Britain, for 1756, 1757. London, for J. Millan 1757. 8vo.

[Mitchell, John]. The contest in America between Great Britain and France. London, for A. Millar 1757. 8vo.

[Moreau, Jacob N.]. A memorial containing a summary view of facts translated from the French. Philadelphia, J. Chattin 1757. 8vo.

Smith, William, *junior*. The history of the province of New-York ... to the year 1752. London, for T. Wilcox 1757. 4to. First Edition

Venegas, Miguel. Noticia de la California. Madrid, la imprenta de la viuda de M. Fernandez 1757. 3 v. 8vo.

1758

An authentic account of the reduction of Louisbourg. London, for W. Owen 1758. 8vo.

[Byles, Mather]. The man of God thoroughly furnished to every good work. New-London, N. Green and T. Green, junr. 1758. 8vo.

The exercise for the militia of ... Massachusetts-Bay. Boston, J. Draper 1758. fol.

Leaming, Aaron, *and* Jacob Spicer. The grants, concessions, and original constitutions of ... New-Jersey. Philadelphia, W. Bradford [1758]. fol.

Le Page du Pratz. Histoire de la Louisiane. Paris, De Bure, la veuve Delaguette, Lambert 1758. 3 v. 8vo. (S. Wegg)

[Livingston, William]. A review of the military operations in North-America ... 1753 to ... 1756. New-England, Re-Printed 1758. sm. 4to.

Thompson, Thomas. An account of two missionary voyages. London, for B. Dod 1758. 8vo.

1759

An abstract of the Form of prayer and thanksgiving ... for ... the taking of Quebec. n.p. [1759]. 8vo. (Learmont)

Americana

Acrelius, Israel.   Beskrifning om de Swenska församlingars forna och närwarande tilstand.   Stockholm, Harberg & Hesselberg 1759. sm. 4to.   (Brinley)

Adams, Amos.   Songs of victory.   Boston, Edes and Gill 1759.   8vo.

Considerations on the importance of Canada.   London, for W. Owen 1759.   8vo.   First Edition

Cooper, Samuel.   A sermon preached . . . upon occasion of . . . reduction of Quebec.   Boston, Green & Russell, and Edes & Gill [1759]. 8vo.

Franklin, Benjamin.   Poor Richard improved . . . an almanack for 1760. Philadelphia, B. Franklin and D. Hall [1759].   12mo.

[Franklin, Benjamin?].   An historical review of the Constitution . . . of Pensylvania.   London, for R. Griffiths 1759.   8vo.   (Joseph Morris)

An impartial account of Lieut. Col. Bradstreet's expedition to Fort Frontenac.   London, for T. Wilcox . . . 1759.   8vo.

A letter to . . . William Pitt, Esq; from an officer at Fort Frontenac. London, for J. Fleming 1759.   8vo.

Post, Christian Frederic.   An enquiry into the causes of the alienation of the Delaware and Shawanese Indians.   London, for J. Wilkie 1759.   8vo.   (E. N. Crane)

———— The second journal.   London, for J. Wilkie 1759.   8vo. (E. N. Crane)

Stevens, Benjamin.   A sermon occasioned by the death of . . . Sir William Pepperrell, Bart.   Boston, Edes and Gill 1759.   4to.

Venegas, Miguel.   A natural and civil history of California.   London, for J. Rivington and J. Fletcher 1759.   2 v.   8vo.

1760

Bownas, Samuel.   An account of the captivity of Elizabeth Hanson. London, S. Clark 1760.   sm. 8vo.   First Edition

A confession of faith owned and consented to . . . at Say Brook.   New-London, T. Green 1760.   12mo.   Second Edition

A form of prayer . . . proper to be used . . . for a general thanksgiving, to Almighty God, for the continuance of his Divine Presence . . . with the forces of our . . . Sovereign, employ'd in North-America. New-York, W. Weyman 1760.   sm. 4to.   (Russell Benedict)

Americana

[Franklin, Benjamin]. The interest of Great Britain considered. London, for T. Becket 1760. 8vo. First Edition

Hart, William. Remarks on a late pamphlet, wrote by Mr. Hobart. New-Haven, J. Parker 1760. 8vo.

Jefferys, Thomas. The natural and civil history of the French dominions in North and South America. Pt. I. London, for T. Jefferys 1760. fol. (Sir John Ingilby)

Johnson, Samuel. A demonstration of the reasonableness... of prayer. New-York, W. Weyman 1760. sm. 4to.

P[enrose], J[ames]. The life of General James Wolfe. Boston, Fowle and Draper... 1760. 8vo.

[Pichon, Thomas]. Lettres et memoires pour servir à l'histoire naturelle... du Cap Breton. Leide, E. Luzac, et Londres, J. Nourse 1760. 12mo.

1761

A complete history of the present war, from... 1756, to 1760. London, for W. Owen... 1761. 8vo.

Franklin, Benjamin. Continuation of the Account of the Pennsylvania hospital. Philadelphia, B. Franklin and D. Hall 1761. 4to.

[———] The interest of Great Britain considered. London, for T. Becket 1761. 8vo. Second Edition

——— Poor Richard improved... an almanack for 1762. Philadelphia, B. Franklin and D. Hall [1761]. 12mo.

[Glen, James]. A description of South Carolina. London, for R. and J. Dodsley 1761. 8vo.

Harvard College. Pietas et gratulatio. Boston, J. Green & J. Russell 1761. 4to. First Edition, Second Issue

An historical memorial of the negotiation of France and England, from the 26th of March, 1761, to the 20th of September of the same year. London, for D. Wilson, and T. Becket and P. A. DeHondt 1761. 4to. Original wrappers uncut

Rutherfurd, John. The importance of the colonies to Great Britain. London, for J. Millan 1761. 8vo.

Stiles, Ezra. A discourse on the christian union. Boston, Edes and Gill 1761. 12mo. (Isaac Royall–Thomas Jolley)

Americana

1762

[Benezet, Anthony]. A short account of that part of Africa, inhabited by the negroes. Philadelphia 1762. 8vo.

[Bollan, William]. Coloniae Anglicanae illustratae. London 1762. 4to.

Chauncy, Charles. All nations of the earth blessed in Christ. Boston, J. Draper 1762. 8vo.

The comparative importance of our acquisitions from France in America. London, for J. Hinxman 1762. 8vo.

[Hume], John, *Bishop of Oxford*. A sermon preached before the incorporated Society for the propagation of the Gospel ... February 19, 1762. London 1762. 8vo. First Edition, original wrappers

Preliminary articles of peace, between his Britannick Majesty, the most Christian King, and the Catholick King. Signed at Fontainebleau, the 3d day of November, 1762. London, E. Owen and T. Harrison 1762. 4to. Original wrappers

Sewall, Joseph. A sermon ... September 16, 1762 ... on ... the reduction of the Havannah. Boston, J. Draper, and Edes and Gill 1762. 8vo.

Wilkes, John Caesar, *editor*. The political controversy. London, for S. Williams 1762-3. 5 v. 8vo. (Charles Grave Hudson)

1763

The definitive treaty of peace and friendship, between his Britannick Majesty, the most Christian King, and the King of Spain. Concluded at Paris, the 10th day of February, 1763. London, E. Owen and T. Harrison 1763. 4to. (2 copies)

Franklin, Benjamin. Poor Richard improved ... an almanack ... for ... 1764. Philadelphia, B. Franklin and D. Hall [1763]. 12mo.

Le Page du Pratz. The history of Louisiana. London, for T. Becket and P. A. de Hondt 1763. 2 v. 12mo.

Lockwood, James. Sermon ... July 6, 1763 ... on account of the peace, concluded with France and Spain. New-Haven, J. Parker [1763]. 8vo. (Thomas Williams)

Roberts, William. An account of the first discovery, and natural history of Florida. London, for T. Jefferys 1763. 4to. First Edition

Wheelock, Eleazar.   A plain and faithful narrative of the original design . . . of the Indian Charity-School at Lebanon, in Connecticut. Boston, R. and S. Draper 1763.   8vo.   (Wheelock tracts Ia)

1764

Bostwick, David.   A fair and rational vindication, of the right of infants, to the ordinance of baptism.   New-York, F. Holt 1764.   sm. 4to.   (W. L. Andrews)

The charter laws, and catalogue of books, of the Library Company of Philadelphia.   Philadelphia, B. Franklin and D. Hall 1764.   8vo.

A declaration and remonstrance of the distressed . . . inhabitants of . . . Pennsylvania.   [Philadelphia, W. Bradford] 1764.   8vo.

Dickinson, John.   A speech, delivered in the House of Assembly of . . . Pennsylvania, May 24th, 1764.   Philadelphia, W. Bradford 1764. 8vo.   (Thomas Hutchinson)

Draper, William.   Colonel Draper's answer, to the Spanish arguments. London, for J. Dodsley 1764.   8vo.

An essay on the trade of the northern colonies of Great Britain in North America.   Philadelphia, for T. Becket and P. A. de Hondt 1764. 8vo.   (J. Hammond Trumbull)

[Fitch, Thomas].   Reasons why the British colonies, in America, should not be charged with internal taxes.   New-Haven, B. Mecom 1764. 8vo.   (J. Hammond Trumbull)

Forsey, Thomas.   The report of an action of assault . . . tried in the Supreme Court . . . of New-York . . . between Thomas Forsey, plaintiff; and Waddel Cunningham, defendant.   New-York, J. Holt 1764.   4to.   (Ralph Izard)

[Hutchinson, Thomas].   The case of . . . Massachusetts-Bay and New-York, respecting the boundary line between the two provinces. Boston, Green and Russell 1764.   fol.   (DePuy)

New York. General Assembly.   Journal of the votes and proceedings . . . 1691-1743.   New-York, H. Gaine 1764.   v. I.   fol.   For v. II see 1766

Otis, James.   The rights of the British colonies asserted.   Boston, Edes and Gill 1764.   8vo.   First Edition

[Thacher, Oxenbridge].   The sentiments of a British American.   Boston, Edes & Gill 1764.   8vo.

1765

A brief state of the services and expences of . . . Massachusett's Bay. London, for J. Wilkie 1765. 8vo.

Clap, Thomas. An essay on the nature and foundation of moral virtue. New-Haven, B. Mecom 1765. 8vo. (Dyas Hinckley)

[Dickinson, John]. The late regulations, respecting the British colonies on the continent of America considered. London, for J. Almon 1765. 8vo.

[Dulaney, Daniel]. Considerations on the propriety of imposing taxes in the British colonies. North-America: Printed by a North-American 1765. 8vo.

Edwards, Jonathan. Two dissertations. Boston, S. Kneeland 1765. 8vo. First Edition

Galloway, Joseph. The speech of Joseph Galloway . . . in answer to the speech of John Dickinson. London 1765. 8vo.

Great Britain. *Parliament*. Anno Regni quinto Georgii III. Regis. 1765. Stamp-Act. [Boston, R. and S. Draper 1765]. fol.

Hutchinson, Thomas. The history of the colony of Massachusetts-Bay. London, for M. Richardson M.DCC.LX[*i.e.* M.DCC.LXV]. 8vo. Second Edition

A letter to a member of Parliament. London, for W. Flexney 1765. 8vo.

Morgan, John. A discourse upon the institution of medical schools in America. Philadelphia, W. Bradford 1765. 8vo. (2 copies)

Quincy, Edmund. A treatise of hemp-husbandry. Boston, Green & Russell 1765. 8vo.

Rogers, Robert. A concise account of North America. London 1765. 8vo. First Edition. (Cavendish Society–Andrews)

——— Journals. London 1765. 8vo. First Edition. (Cavendish Society–Andrews)

Smith, Samuel. The history of the colony of Nova-Caesaria, or New-Jersey. Burlington, in New-Jersey, J. Parker 1765. 8vo. (Pringle Taylor)

Timberlake, Henry. The memoirs. London 1765. 8vo.

Wheelock, Eleazar.   A continuation of the narrative of the state, &c. of the Indian Charity-School.   Boston, R. and S. Draper 1765. 8vo.   (Wheelock tracts 2)

1766

Ames, Nathaniel.   An astronomical diary . . . almanack for 1767. Boston, W. M'Alpine [1766].   12mo.   (W. L. Andrews)

Appleton, Nathaniel.   A thanksgiving sermon on the total repeal of the Stamp-Act. Boston, Edes and Gill 1766.   8vo.

The British antidote. London, for J. Pridden [1766].   12mo.

Chauncy, Charles.   A discourse on "the good news from a far country." . . . on . . . the repeal of the Stamp-Act.   Boston, Kneeland and Adams for T. Leverett 1766.   8vo.

Clap, Thomas.   The annals or history of Yale-College.   New-Haven, for J. Hotchkiss and B. Mecom 1766.   8vo.

Considerations upon the rights of the colonists to the privileges of British subjects. New-York, J. Holt 1766.   8vo.

Correct copies of the two protests against the bill to repeal the American Stamp Act. Paris, J. W. 1766.   8vo.

Emerson, Joseph.   A thanksgiving-sermon preach'd at Pepperrell, July 24th. 1766 . . . on . . . the repeal of the Stamp-Act.   Boston, Edes and Gill 1766.   8vo.

The general opposition of the colonies to the payment of the stamp duty. London, for T. Payne 1766.   8vo.

Great Britain. *Parliament*.   An Act . . . Passed in the Sixth Year of the Reign of . . . King George the Third, 1766. An Act for indemnifying persons who have incurred certain penalties . . . for granting certain stamp duties.   Boston, R. and S. Draper, and Green and Russell 1766.   fol.

Great Britain. *Parliament*.   Anno Regni Regis Georgii III. Sexto. 1766 . . . An Act for repealing certain duties in the British Colonies. Boston, R. and S. Draper, and Green and Russell . . . 1766.   fol.

Harrison, David.   The melancholy narrative of the distressful voyage . . . of Captain David Harrison.   London, for J. Harrison 1766. 8vo.

Hedendaagsche historie, of tegenwoordige staat van Amerika.   Amsterdam, I. Tirion 1766.   v. 1.   8vo.   For v. 2 see 1767

Americana

[Hopkins, Stephen]. The grievances of the American colonies candidly examined. London, for J. Almon 1766. 8vo.

A list of the minority in the House of Commons, who voted against the bill to repeal the American Stamp Act. Paris, J. W. 1766. 8vo.

Mayhew, Jonathan. The snare broken. Boston, R. & S. Draper . . . 1766. 8vo.

The necessity of repealing the American Stamp Act demonstrated. London, for J. Almon 1766. 8vo.

New York. *General Assembly*. Journal of the votes and proceedings . . . 1743-1765. New-York, H. Gaine 1766. II. fol.

A short history of the conduct of the present ministry, with regard to the American Stamp Act. London, for J. Almon 1766. 8vo.

[Smith, William]. An historical account of the expedition against the Ohio Indians . . . 1764. London, for T. Jefferies 1766. 4to.

Thoughts on the nature of war. Philadelphia, H. Miller 1766. sm. 8vo.

The true interest of Great Britain, with respect to her American colonies, stated. London, G. Kearsley 1766. 8vo.

Wheelock, Eleazar. A brief narrative of the Indian Charity-School. London, J. and W. Oliver 1766. 8vo. (Wheelock tracts 3a)

1767

Authentic account of the proceedings of the Congress held at New-York, in 1765, on the . . . Stamp Act. [London] 1767. 8vo.

Benezet, Anthony. A caution and warning to Great-Britain. Philadelphia, D. Hall and W. Sellers 1767. 12mo. (S. W. Pennypacker)

Chandler, Thomas Bradbury. An appeal to the public, in behalf of the Church of England in America. New-York, J. Parker 1767. v. 1. 8vo. For v. 2 see 1769

Chauncy, Charles. A letter to a friend containing remarks on certain passages. Boston, Kneeland and Adams for T. Leverett 1767. 8vo.

The commercial conduct of the province of New-York considered. New-York 1767. 4to. (DePuy)

Franklin, Benjamin. The examination of Doctor Benjamin Franklin, relative to the repeal of the . . . Stamp Act. [London] J. Almon 1767. 8vo.

Frothingham, Ebenezer.   A key, to unlock the door.   [Boston?] 1767.
12mo.

Hedendaagsche historie, of tegenwoordige staat van Amerika.   Amsterdam, I. Tirion 1767.   v. 2.   8vo.   For v. 3 see 1769

[Lloyd, Charles].   The conduct of the late administration examined.
London, for J. Almon 1767.   8vo.   First Edition

[Mitchell, John].   The present state of Great Britain and North
America.   London, for T. Becket and P. A. de Hondt 1767.   8vo.
(DePuy)

Two papers, on the subject of taxing the British colonies in America.
London, for J. Almon 1767.   8vo.

[Venegas, Miguel].   Histoire naturelle et civile de la Californie.   Paris,
Durand 1767.   3 v.   12mo.

Wheelock, Eleazar.   A brief narrative of the Indian Charity-School.
London, J. and W. Oliver 1767.   8vo.   Second Edition.   (Wheelock tracts 3b)

———— ———— London, J. and W. Oliver 1767.   8vo.   (Wheelock
tracts 3c)

———— ———— London, J. and W. Oliver 1767.   8vo.   (Wheelock
tracts 3d)

1768

Bossu, N.   Nouveaux voyages aux Indes Occidentales.   Paris, LeJay
1768.   sm. 8vo.   First Edition

[Dickinson, John].   Letters from a farmer in Pennsylvania.   Philadelphia, D. Hall and W. Sellers 1768.   8vo.

———— ———— London, for J. Almon 1768.   8vo.

Hutchinson, Thomas.   The history of the province of Massachusetts-
Bay.   London, J. Smith for G. Kearsley and W. Davenhill 1768.
8vo.   Second Edition.   (Lord Sheffield)

Kalm, Peter, *and* Gottlieb Mittelberger.   Histoire naturelle . . . de la
Pensylvanie.   Paris, Ganeau 1768.   12mo.

Livingston, William.   A letter to . . . John, Lord Bishop of Landaff.
New-York 1768.   8vo.   First Edition

Pownall, Thomas.   The administration of the colonies.   London, for
J. Walter 1768.   8vo.   (Brocket Hall)

Americana

An appeal to the world. Boston, Edes and Gill 1769. 8vo.

———— London, D. de Berdt 1769. 8vo.

Bernard, *Sir* Francis, *and others.* Letters to the ... Earl of Hillsborough. Boston, Edes and Gill 1769. fol. (E. B. Holden)

———— ———— London, for J. Almon, n.d. 8vo. (E. B. Holden)

[Bushe, Gervase Parker]. Case of Great Britain and America. Boston, Edes & Gill and T. & J. Fleet [1769]. sm. 4to.

Chandler, Thomas Bradbury. The appeal defended. New-York, H. Gaine 1769. 8vo.

Hedendaagsche historie, of tegenwoordige staat van Amerika. Amsterdam, I. Tirion 1769. v. 3. 8vo.

Hutchinson, Thomas. A collection of original papers. Boston, T. and J. Fleet 1769. 8vo. (John Watts–William Gordon)

Knox, John. An historical journal of the campaigns in North-America. London 1769. 3 v. 4to.

[Smith, William]. An historical account of the expedition against the Ohio Indians ... 1764. Dublin, for J. Milliken 1769. 12mo.

———— Relation historique de l'expédition contre les Indiens de l'Ohio ... 1764. Amsterdam, M. M. Rey 1769. 8vo.

Wheelock, Eleazar. A continuation of the narrative of the Indian Charity-School. London, J. and W. Oliver 1769. 8vo.

1770

Additional observations to A short narrative of the horrid massacre. Boston 1770. 8vo. First Edition. (W. L. Andrews)

Chauncy, Charles. Trust in God. Boston, D. Kneeland for T. Leverett 1770. 8vo.

[Cluny, Alexander]. The American traveller. [Philadelphia] 1770. 12mo. (William Dillwyn)

Dana, James. A century discourse. New-Haven, T. and S. Green [1770]. 8vo. (Presentation copy from the author to Ezra Stiles)

A fair account of the late unhappy disturbance at Boston. London, for B. White 1770. 8vo.

Kalm, Peter.   Travels into North America.   Warrington, W. Eyres 1770.   v. 1.   8vo.   For v. 2-3 see 1771

[Livingston, William].   A review of the military operations in North-America . . . 1753 to . . . 1756.   New-York, A. and J. Robertson 1770.   8vo.

Massachusetts Bay. *House of Representatives*.   A continuation of the proceedings.   Boston, Edes and Gill 1770.   8vo.   (Samuel Sprague)

[Milligan, Jacob].   A short description of the province of South-Carolina.   London, for J. Hinton 1770.   8vo.

Pittman, Philip.   The present state of the European settlements on the Mississippi.   London, for J. Nourse 1770.   4to.

Remarks upon a late paper of instructions calculated for the meridian of four counties, in the province of New-York.   New-York, J. Holt 1770.   8vo.

A short narrative of the horrid massacre in Boston.   [Boston] Edes and Gill 1770.   8vo.   First Edition, First Issue.   (W. L. Andrews)

———— [Boston] Edes and Gill and T. & J. Fleet 1770.   8vo.   First Edition, Second Issue

———— London, for W. Bingley 1770.   8vo.   (W. L. Andrews)

———— London, for E. and C. Dilly and J. Almon 1770.   8vo.

1771

Bancroft, Edward.   Remarks on the review of the controversy between Great Britain and her colonies.   New-London, T. Green 1771.   8vo.   (2 copies)

Blackford, Dominique de.   Précis de l'état actuel des colonies angloises.   Milan, les freres Reycends 1771.   12mo.

Chandler, Thomas Bradbury.   The appeal farther defended.   New-York, H. Gaine 1771.   8vo.

Kalm, Peter.   Travels into North America.   London 1771.   8vo.   v. 2-3

Lovell, James.   An oration delivered . . . to commemorate the bloody tragedy of the fifth of March, 1770.   Boston, Edes and Gill 1771.   sm. 4to.

The Massachusetts calendar ... for ... 1772. Boston, I. Thomas [1771].
8vo. (W. L. Andrews)

Wheelock, Eleazar. A continuation of the narrative of the Indian
Charity-School . . . to the incorporation of it with Dartmouth-
College ... 1771. n.p. 1771. 8vo. (Wheelock tracts 5a)

——— ——— (Wheelock tracts 5b)

1772

Ames, Nathaniel. An astronomical diary ... for ... 1773. Boston, R.
Draper, Edes & Gill and T. & J. Fleet [1772]. 12mo.

Boston. The votes and proceedings of the freeholders and other inhabitants. Boston, Edes and Gill and T. and J. Fleet [1772]. 8vo.

Gordon, William. The plan of a society for making provision for
widows, by annuities. Boston, J. Edwards and J. Fleeming 1772.
8vo.

Great Britain. *Lords of trade.* Report of the Lords Commissioners ...
for a grant of lands on the river Ohio. London, for J. Almon
1772. 8vo.

Mante, Thomas. The history of the late war in North America. London, for W. Strahan and T. Cadell 1772. 4to.

Occom, Samson. A sermon, preached at the execution of Moses Paul.
New-Haven, T. & S. Green [1772]. 8vo.

A platform of church-discipline. Boston, J. Boyles 1772. sm. 8vo.

Stanton, Daniel. A journal of the life ... of a faithful minister of Jesus
Christ. Philadelphia, J. Crukshank 1772. 8vo.

Ulloa, Antonio de. A voyage to South America. London, for L.
Davis 1772. 2 v. 8vo. Third Edition. (H. G. Otis–Freuden-
reich)

Wise, John. The churches quarrel espoused. Boston, J. Boyles 1772.
sm. 8vo.

——— A vindication of the government of New-England churches.
Boston, J. Boyles 1772. sm. 8vo.

[Zubly, John Joachim]. Calm and respectful thoughts on the negative
of the Crown. [Savannah, J. Johnston 1772]. 8vo. (Ezra Stiles)

Americana

[Benezet, Anthony]. Brief considerations on slavery. Burlington, I. Collins 1773. 8vo.

Church, Benjamin. An oration; delivered . . . to commemorate the bloody tragedy. Boston, Edes and Gill 1773. sm. 4to.

Hawkesworth, John. An account of the voyages . . . performed by . . . Commodore Byron, Captain Wallis, Captain Carteret, and Captain Cook. London, for W. Strahan and T. Cadell 1773. 3 v. 4to.

Henry, W. An historical account of all the voyages . . . by English navigators. London, for F. Newbery 1773. v. 3-4. 8vo. (Charles Pye). For v. 1-2 see 1774

Hutchinson, Thomas. The speeches of . . . Governor Hutchinson. Boston, Edes and Gill 1773. 8vo.

———— *and others*. Copy of letters sent to Great-Britain. Boston, Edes and Gill 1773. 8vo.

———— ———— Salem, S. & E. Hall 1773. 8vo.

[Nisbet, Richard]. Slavery not forbidden by Scripture. Philadelphia 1773. 8vo.

Personal slavery established. Philadelphia, J. Dunlap 1773. 8vo.

[Rawson, Edward, *and* Samuel Sewall]. The revolution in New-England justified. Boston, I. Thomas 1773. 12mo.

[Rush, Benjamin]. An address . . . on the slavery of the negroes. Philadelphia, J. Dunlap 1773. 8vo.

Sharp, Granville. An essay on slavery. Burlington, I. Collins 1773. 8vo.

Wheelock, Eleazar. A continuation of the narrative of the Indian Charity-School. [Portsmouth] New-Hampshire 1773. 8vo. (Wheelock tracts 6)

———— ———— Hartford 1773. 8vo. (Wheelock tracts 7)

[Young, Arthur]. Observations on the . . . waste lands of Great Britain. London, for W. Nicoll 1773. 8vo. (DePuy)

The Association, &c. of the delegates of the colonies . . . at Philadelphia, Sept. 1, 1774, versified. n.p. 1774. 8vo. (DePuy)

Americana

Bernard, *Sir* Francis.   Select letters on the trade and government of America. London, for T. Payne 1774. 8vo.

A brief review of the rise and progress . . . of New-England. London, for J. Buckland 1774. 8vo.

A brief review of the rise, progress, services and sufferings, of New-England. Norwich, Robertsons and Trumbull 1774. 8vo.

[Chauncy, Charles].   A letter to a friend. Giving a representation of the hardships.   Boston, Greenleaf's printing-office 1774.   8vo. First Edition

A complete history of the late war. Dublin, J. Exshaw 1774. 8vo.

Continental Congress. 1774. Extracts from the votes and proceedings. Philadelphia, W. and T. Bradford 1774. 8vo.

——— ——— Boston, Edes and Gill and T. and J. Fleet 1774. 8vo.

——— ——— London, for J. Almon 1774. 8vo.

——— Journal of the proceedings. Philadelphia, W. and T. Bradford 1774. 8vo. First Edition, First Issue. (G. L. Harrison-DePuy)

——— ——— First Edition, Second Issue

[Cooper, Myles].   A friendly address.   New-York [J. Rivington] 1774. 8vo. First Issue

——— The friendly address. New-York [J. Rivington] 1774. 8vo. (H. C. Bernheim)

[Dickinson, John].   An essay on the constitutional power of Great-Britain. Philadelphia, W. and T. Bradford 1774. 8vo. (H. Le-Roy Edgar)

——— A new essay . . . on the constitutional power of Great-Britain. London, for J. Almon 1774. 8vo. (Thomas Hutchinson)

[Duché, Jacob].   Observations on a variety of subjects. Philadelphia, J. Dunlap 1774. 12mo. First Edition

Great Britain. *Parliament*. The report of the Lords Committees, appointed . . . to enquire into the several proceedings in . . . Massachuset's Bay. London, C. Eyre and W. Strahan 1774. fol.

[Hamilton, Alexander].   A full vindication of the measures of the Congress. New-York, J. Rivington 1774. 8vo.

Americana

Hancock, John.   An oration; delivered . . . to commemorate the bloody tragedy.   Boston, Edes and Gill 1774.   sm. 4to.   First Edition

[Harvey, Edward].   The manual exercise as ordered . . . in 1764.   Boston, T. and J. Fleet [1774].   sm. 4to.

Hawkesworth, John.   A new voyage, round the world . . . by Captain James Cook.   New-York, J. Rivington 1774.   2 v.   8vo.

[Henry, W.].   An historical account of all the voyages . . . by English navigators.   London, for F. Newbery 1774.   v. 1-2.   8vo. (Charles Pye).   For v. 3-4 see 1773

[Jefferson, Thomas].   A summary view of the rights of British America. Philadelphia, J. Dunlap 1774.   sm. 12mo.

Judson, David.   Sermons on church government.   New-Haven, T. & S. Green [1774].   8vo.

[Lee, Charles].   Strictures on a pamphlet, entitled, "A friendly address."   Philadelphia, W. and T. Bradford 1774.   sm. 8vo.   First Edition.   (DePuy)

A letter to a member of Parliament on the present unhappy dispute between Great-Britain and her colonies.   London, for J. Walter 1774. 8vo.

[Livingston, Philip].   The other side of the question.   New York, J. Rivington 1774.   8vo.

[Seabury, Samuel, *and* Isaac Wilkins].   The congress canvassed.   n.p. 1774.   8vo.

———— Free thoughts.   n.p. 1774.   8vo.

———— A view of the controversy between Great-Britain and her colonies.   New-York, J. Rivington 1774.   8vo.

Shipley, Jonathan.   The whole of the celebrated speech of the Rev. Dr. Jonathan Shipley.   Newport, S. Southwick 1774.   8vo.

Solis y Ribadeneyra, Antonio de.   Histoire de la conquête du Mexique. Paris, Compagnie des libraires 1774.   2 v.   12mo.

[Wilkins, Isaac].   Short advice to the counties of New-York.   New-York, J. Rivington 1774.   8vo.

Williams, John.   The redeemed captive returning to Zion.   Boston, J. Boyle 1774.   8vo.

Americana

Adair, James.   The history of the American Indians.   London, for E. and C. Dilly 1775.   4to.

Almon, John.   The remembrancer.   London 1775-84.   17 v.   8vo.

[Burgoyne, John].   The speech of a general officer.   [London 1775]. 4to.   (J. Jeffreys)

Burke, Edmund.   The speech . . . for conciliation.   London, for J. Dodsley 1775.   4to.   First Edition.   (Groves)

[Chandler, Thomas Bradbury].   The strictures on the Friendly Address examined.   [New York] 1775.   8vo.   (DePuy)

———— What think ye of the congress now?   New-York, J. Rivington 1775.   8vo.

Clarke, John.   An impartial . . . narrative of the battle . . . on Bunker's Hill.   London 1775.   8vo.

A concise historical account of all the British colonies in North-America.   London, for J. Bew 1775.   8vo.

Continental Congress.   1774.   Journal of the proceedings.   London, for J. Almon 1775.   8vo.

The Crisis.   [London] T. W. Shaw 1775-6.   fol.   (No. 1, Jan. 21, 1775-No. 88, Sept. 21, 1776, including "The Crisis Extraordinary." Aug. 9, 1775.   Lacks Nos. 64, 65, 73, 89, 90, 91)

Cugnet, François Joseph.   Extraits des edits . . . de sa Majesté très chretienne.   Quebec, G. Brown 1775.   sm. 4to.

———— Traité abregé des ancienes loix.   Quebec, G. Brown 1775.   sm. 4to.

———— Traité de la loi des fiefs.   Quebec, G. Brown 1775.   sm. 4to.

———— Traité de la police.   Quebec, G. Brown 1775.   sm. 4to.

A declaration by the representatives of the United Colonies.   Philadelphia, W. and T. Bradford 1775.   8vo.   First Edition.   (H. LeRoy Edgar)

Duché, Jacob.   The duty of standing fast.   Philadelphia, J. Humphreys, junior 1775.   8vo.

[Galloway, Joseph].   A candid examination of the mutual claims of Great-Britain, and the colonies.   New-York, J. Rivington 1775. 8vo.

Americana

Government Scheme.   [?Philadelphia, c. 1775].   Leaflet.   8vo.

[Hamilton, Alexander].   The farmer refuted.   New-York, J. Rivington 1775.   8vo.

Hubbard, William.   A narrative of the Indian wars in New-England. Boston, J. Boyle 1775.   sm. 8vo.

[Johnson, Samuel].   Taxation no tyranny.   London, for T. Cadell 1775.   8vo.

Langdon, Samuel.   Government corrupted by vice.   Watertown, B. Edes 1775.   12mo.

[Lind, Jonathan].   Remarks on the principal Acts of the thirteenth Parliament of Great Britain.   London, for T. Payne 1775.   8vo. (Viscount Sydney)

Noble, Oliver.   Some strictures upon the sacred story.   Newbury-Port, E. Lunt and H. W. Tinges 1775.   8vo.

The patriots of North-America.   New-York 1775.   8vo.

The Pennsylvania Magazine.   Philadelphia, R. Aitken [1775].   2 v. 8vo.

Romans, Bernard.   A concise natural history of East and West Florida. New York 1775.   v. 1.   8vo.   (Halsey)

[Seabury, Samuel, *and* Isaac Wilkins].   An alarm to the Legislature of ... New-York.   New-York, for J. Rivington 1775.   8vo.

Stevenson, Roger.   Military instructions.   Philadelphia, R. Aitken 1775.   12mo.

Virginia. Convention. 1775.   The proceedings.   Williamsburg, A. Purdie [1775].   4to.   (T. A. Emmet)

Webster, Samuel.   Rabshakeh's proposals considered.   Boston, Edes and Gill 1775.   8vo.   First Edition

Wesley, John.   A calm address.   London, R. Hawes 1775.   8vo. First Edition.   (Groves)

Wheelock, Eleazar.   A continuation of the narrative of the Indian Charity-School.   Hartford, E. Watson 1775.   8vo.   (Wheelock tracts 8a)

———— ———— (Wheelock tracts 8b)

Americana

Adams, Samuel. An oration delivered . . . in Philadelphia. London, for E. Johnson 1776. 8vo.

Continental Congress. 1775. Journal. London, for J. Almon 1776. 8vo.

The genuine principles of the ancient Saxon, or English Constitution . . . By Demophilus. Philadelphia, R. Bell 1776. 8vo.

[Hendricks, William, *and* John Chambers]. A journal of the march of a party of provincials from Carlisle to Boston and from thence to Quebec. Glasgow, R. Chapman and A. Duncan 1776. 12mo.

[Hutchinson, Thomas]. Experience preferable to theory. London, for T. Payne 1776. 8vo. (Thomas Hutchinson)

—— Strictures upon the Declaration of the Congress at Philadelphia. London 1776. 8vo. (Thomas Hutchinson)

[Leacock, John]. The fall of British tyranny. Philadelphia, Styner and Cist 1776. 8vo. First Edition. (W. L. Andrews)

[Leonard, Daniel]. Massachusettensis. London, for J. Mathews 1776. 8vo.

Low, Nathaniel. An astronomical diary . . . for . . . 1777. Boston, J. Gill and T. and J. Fleet [1776]. 12mo.

[Mason, William]. A congratulatory poem on . . . the triumphant evacuation of Boston. Dublin, for W. Wilson 1776. 8vo.

Massachusetts. *House of Representatives.* An Act for providing a reinforcement to the American army. Boston, Edes & Gill [1776]. 4pp. fol.

New York Committee of Safety. To the inhabitants of the colony of New-York. New-York, J. Holt [1776]. 8vo.

[Paine, Thomas]. Common sense. Philadelphia, W. and T. Bradford [1776]. 8vo. First Edition. (James Madison)

—— —— London, for J. Almon 1776. 8vo.

Pennsylvania. The Constitution of . . . Pennsylvania. Philadelphia, J. Dunlap 1776. 8vo. First Edition

Pownall, Thomas. A topographical description of . . . North America. London, for J. Almon 1776. fol.

Americana

Price, Richard. Observations on the nature of civil liberty. London, for T. Cadell 1776. 8vo. (Thomas Hutchinson)

——— ——— Boston, T. and J. Fleet [1776]. 8vo.

Virginia. Convention. 1776. The proceedings. Williamsburg, A. Purdie [1776]. sm. 4to.

1777

Abingdon, Willoughby Bertie, *fourth Earl of*. Thoughts on the Letter of Edmund Burke. Oxford, W. Jackson [1777]. 8vo. First Edition

Almon, John. A collection of . . . papers. London, for J. Almon 1777. 8vo.

Articles of confederation . . . between . . . New-Hampshire, Massachusetts-Bay, Rhode-Island and Providence plantations, Connecticut, New-York, New-Jersey, Pennsylvania, Delaware, Maryland, Virginia, North-Carolina, South-Carolina and Georgia. Lancaster, Pennsylvania, F. Bailey 1777. fol.

——— ——— Exeter, New-Hampshire, Z. Fowle 1777. fol.

Backus, Isaac. A history of New-England. Boston, E. Draper 1777. v. 1. 8vo. First Edition. For v. 2 see 1784

Bickerstaff's Boston almanack, for . . . 1778. Danvers, E. Russell [1777]. 12mo. (W. L. Andrews)

Bossu, N. Nouveaux voyages dans l'Amérique Septentrionale. Amsterdam [*i.e.* Paris] Changuion 1777. 8vo. First Edition

Burke, Edmund. A letter . . . to John Faor and John Harris. London, for J. Dodsley 1777. 8vo.

Cook, James. A voyage towards the South Pole. London, for W. Strahan and T. Cadell 1777. 2 v. 4to.

New York. Convention. 1777. An ordinance. Fish-Kill, S. Loudon 1777. 8vo. First Edition. (Russell Benedict)

[Pemberton, Israel, *and others*]. An address to the inhabitants of Pennsylvania. Philadelphia, R. Bell 1777. 8vo.

[Purmann, J. G.]. Sitten und meinungen der wilden in America. Frankfurth am Mayn, J. G. Garbe 1777-81. 4 v. 12mo.

[Randolph, John]. Letters from General Washington to several of his friends. London, for J. Bew 1777. 8vo. First Edition

Scherer, Jean-Benoît.   Recherches historiques . . . sur le nouveau-monde. Paris, Brunet 1777. 8vo. First Edition. (S. L. M. Barlow)

1778

Articles, rules, and regulations, for preserving order . . . among the militia. Hartford, Watson and Goodwin 1778. 12mo. (Joseph Harris)

Carver, Jonathan.   Travels.   London 1778.   8vo.   First Edition. (George Washington)

Cassini, Jean Dominique, *Comte de*.   Voyage to Newfoundland and Sallee. London, for E. and C. Dilly 1778. 8vo.

Chappe d'Auteroche, Jean.   A voyage to California. London, for E. and C. Dilly 1778. 8vo. (Sir Walter Blount)

Continental Congress. 1775-6.   Journal of the proceedings . . . Sept. 5, 1775 to April 30, 1776. London, for J. Almon 1778. 8vo.

Howard, Frederick, *fifth Earl of Carlisle, and others*.   Collection of papers . . . relating to the proceedings of his Majesty's commissioners. New York, J. Rivington 1778. 8vo.

Murray, James.   An impartial history of the present war in America. Newcastle upon Tyne, for T. Robson [1778-81].   3 v.   8vo. (Dedication of v. 1 dated July 29, 1778)

The political duenna. Philadelphia, R. Bell 1778.   12mo.   First Edition.   (W. L. Andrews)

Proceedings of a general court martial . . . for the trial of Major General Schuyler. Philadelphia, Hall and Sellers 1778. fol.

Treaties of amity and commerce . . . between his most Christian Majesty and the thirteen United States of America. Philadelphia, J. Dunlap 1778. sm. 4to. First Edition

1779

Continental Congress. 1779.   A circular letter.   Philadelphia, D. C. Claypoole [1779].   8vo.

Galloway, Joseph.   The examination of Joseph Galloway.   London, for J. Wilkie 1779.   8vo.

[———]   A letter to . . . Viscount H– E, on his naval conduct in the American war. London, for J. Wilkie 1779. 8vo.

Galloway, Joseph. Letters to a nobleman. London, for J. Wilkie 1779. 8vo.

The history of the war in America. Dublin 1779. v. 1-2. 8vo. (S. L. M. Barlow). For v. 3 see 1785

Massachusetts. The report of a Constitution . . . for the Common-wealth. Boston, B. Edes & sons 1779. sm. 4to.

Muller, John. Treatise on artillery. Philadelphia, Styner and Cist 1779. 8vo. (C. L. F. Robinson)

Ramsay, David. Military memoirs of Great Britain. Edinburgh 1779. 8vo.

Treaties of amity and commerce . . . between his most Christian Maj-esty and the thirteen United States of America. Hartford, Hud-son and Goodwin 1779. sm. 4to.

A view of the evidence relative to the conduct of the American war under Sir William Howe. London 1779. 8vo. (H. Le Roy Edgar–F. H. Comstock)

Woodward, Samuel. The help of the Lord. Boston, J. Gill 1779. 8vo.

1780

An account of the rise and progress of the American war. London 1780. 12mo.

Burgoyne, John. A state of the expedition from Canada. London, for J. Almon 1780. 4to. First Edition

The candid retrospect. New York 1780. 12mo. [By William Smith, *junior*]

Chalmers, George. Political annals. London 1780. v. 1. 4to.

Cooper, Samuel. A sermon preached . . . October 25, 1780. [Boston] T. and J. Fleet and J. Gill [1780]. 8vo.

[Galloway, Joseph]. A reply to the Observations of . . . Sir William Howe, on a pamphlet, entitled Letters to a nobleman. London, for G. Wilkie 1780. 8vo.

[Hall, *Captain*]. The history of the Civil War in America. London, for T. Payne and Son, and J. Sewell 1780. 8vo.

The history of the origin, rise and progress of the war in America. Boston, T. & J. Fleet 1780. 3 v. 8vo.

Americana

An impartial history of the war in America.   London, for R. Faulder and H. Milliken 1780.   8vo.

Lee, Arthur.   Extracts from A letter . . . to the President of Congress. Philadelphia, F. Bailey 1780.   sm. 4to.

Massachusetts Bay. Convention.   An address of the Convention for framing a new Constitution . . . for . . . Massachusetts Bay.   Boston, White and Adams 1780.   8vo.

——— A Constitution . . . agreed upon.   Boston, B. Edes & Sons 1780. 8vo.

Proceedings of a Board of general officers . . . respecting Major John Andrè.   Philadelphia, F. Bailey 1780.   8vo.   (C. C. Jones–C. L. F. Robinson)

Proceedings of a general Court Martial . . . for the trial of Major General Arnold.   Philadelphia, F. Bailey 1780.   fol.

A short but comprehensive account of the rise and progress of the commotions in America.   Newcastle 1780.   8vo.

1781

Carver, Jonathan.   Travels through the interior parts of North America.   London, for C. Dilly, H. Payne and J. Phillips 1781.   8vo. Third Edition

The Constitutions of the several independent states.   Philadelphia, F. Bailey 1781.   12mo.

Hilliard d'Auberteuil, Michel René.   Essais historiques et politiques sur les Anglo-Américains.   Bruxelles 1781-2.   2 v.   8vo.

New Hampshire. Convention.   An address of the Convention for framing a new Constitution . . . for . . . New-Hampshire.   Portsmouth and Exeter 1781.   8vo.

North, Frederick, *second Earl of Guilford*.   The history of Lord North's administration.   London, for G. Wilkie 1781.   8vo.

Paul-Jones, ou Prophéties sur l'Amérique.   [Basle 1781].   12mo.

Le rêve d'un Suisse.   Basle 1781.   12mo.

Seward, Anna.   Monody on Major Andrè.   Lichfield, J. Jackson 1781. 4to.   First Edition

Warren, Joseph.   An eulogium on Major General Joseph Warren. Boston, J. Boyle 1781.   8vo.

Americana

[Wharton, Charles Henry].   A poetical epistle to . . . George Washington.   Providence, B. Wheeler 1781.   sm. 4to.

1782

[Crèvecoeur], J. Hector St. John [de].   Letters from an American farmer.   London, for T. Davies and L. Davis 1782.   8vo.   First Edition.   (I. Yates)

Deane, Silas.   Paris papers.   New-York, J. Rivington [1782].   12mo.

Estaing, Charles Henri, *Comte* d'.   Extrait du journal d'un officier de la marine.   [?Paris] 1782.   8vo.

Evans, Israel.   A discourse . . . on . . . the surrender of the British army.   Philadelphia, F. Bailey 1782.   8vo.

Fox, Charles James.   The speech . . . on American independence.   London, for M. Folingsby [1782].   8vo.   (C. L. F. Robinson)

[Jefferson, Thomas].   Notes on the state of Virginia.   [Paris] 1782.   8vo.   First Edition

Minot, George Richards.   An oration delivered . . . to commemorate the bloody tragedy.   Boston, B. Edes and Sons 1782.   sm. 4to.

Paine, Thomas.   A letter to the Abbe Raynal.   London, for C. Dilly 1782.   8vo.

The Pennsylvania pocket almanac, for . . . 1783.   Philadelphia, T. Bradford [1782].   16mo.

A pocket almanack for . . . 1783 . . . for Massachusetts.   Boston, T. & J. Fleet [1782].   18mo.   (W. L. Andrews)

Strong, Nehemiah.   An astronomical diary . . . for . . . 1783.   Springfield, Babcock & Haswell [1782].   12mo.

1783

Adams, Zabdiel.   The evil designs of men.   Boston, B. Edes & Sons 1783.   8vo.

[Chavannes de la Giraudière, H. de].   L'Amérique délivrée.   Amsterdam, J. A. Crajenschot 1783.   8vo.

Clinton, *Sir* Henry.   Narrative of . . . Sir Henry Clinton.   London, for J. Debrett 1783.   8vo.

———— Observations on . . . the Answer of Earl Cornwallis to Sir Henry Clinton.   London, for J. Debrett 1783.   8vo.

Americana

Congress. 1783. Address and recommendations to the states. Philadelphia, D. C. Claypoole 1783. 8vo.

——— ——— Hartford, Hudson & Goodwin 1783. sm. 4to. (William Williams)

——— ——— London, for J. Stockdale 1783. 8vo.

Constitutions des treize États-Unis de l'Amérique. Paris, Ph.-D. Pierres ... 1783. 8vo.

The Constitutions of the several independent states. London, for J. Stockdale 1783. 8vo.

——— London, for J. Walker and J. Debrett 1783. 8vo.

Cornwallis, Charles, *first Marquis and second Earl.* An answer to ... the Narrative of ... Sir Henry Clinton. London, for J. Debrett 1783. 8vo.

[Crèvecoeur], J. Hector St. John [de]. Letters from an American farmer. Belfast, J. Magee 1783. 12mo.

The definitive treaty between Great Britain, and the United States of America. London, T. Harrison and S. Brooke 1783. sm. 4to.

Edwards, Jonathan. The faithful manifestation of the truth. New-Haven, T. and S. Green [1783]. 8vo.

Frisbie, Levi. An oration ... on ... peace. Boston, E. Russell 1783. sm. 4to. (E. B. Holden)

Grasse, François Joseph Paul, *Comte de.* Mémoire. [Paris 1783]. 4to.

Paine, Thomas. A letter to the Earl of Shelburne. London, for J. Stockdale 1783. 8vo.

[Reed, Joseph]. Remarks on a late publication in the Independent Gazetteer. Philadelphia, F. Bailey 1783. 8vo.

Robin, Claude C. New travels through North-America. Philadelphia, R. Bell 1783. 8vo.

Washington, George. The last official address. Hartford, Hudson and Goodwin 1783. 8vo.

1784

Allen, Ethan. Reason the only oracle of man. Bennington, Vermont, Haswell & Russell 1784. 8vo.

[368]

Americana

Backus, Isaac.   A church history of New-England.   Providence, J. Carter 1784.   v. 2.   8vo.   First Edition.   For v. 3 see 1796

[Bordley, John Beale].   A summary view of the courses of crops. Philadelphia, C. Cist 1784.   4to.

Champion, Richard.   Considerations on the present situation of Great Britain and the United States.   London, for J. Stockdale 1784. 8vo.

Cincinnati Society.   The institution of the Society of the Cincinnati. New-York, S. Loudon 1784.   8vo.

Filson, John.   The discovery, settlement and present state of Kentucke.   Wilmington, J. Adams 1784.   8vo.   First Edition.   (Halsey)

Franklin, Benjamin.   Two tracts: Information to those who would remove to America.   Dublin, for L. White 1784.   8vo.

Gilbert, Benjamin.   A narrative of the captivity and sufferings of Benjamin Gilbert.   Philadelphia, J. Crukshank 1784.   8vo.   First Edition

Hilliard-d'Auberteuil, Michel René.   Mis MacRea.   Philadelphia 1784. 16mo.

Historisch-genealogischer calender.   Leipzig, Haude und Spener [1784].   24mo.

Hutchins, Thomas.   An historical narrative . . . of Louisiana, and West-Florida.   Philadelphia, R. Aitken 1784.   8vo.

Lathrop, Joseph.   A discourse, delivered at the funeral of . . . Robert Breck.   Springfield, Brooks and Russell 1784.   12mo.

A pocket almanack for . . . 1785 . . . for Massachusetts.   Boston, T. & J. Fleet [1784].   18mo.   (W. L. Andrews)

Remarks on a pamphlet, entituled "A dissertation on the political union . . . of the Thirteen United States."   [New Haven, T. and S. Green] 1784.   8vo.

Robin, Claude C.   New travels through North-America.   Boston, E. E. Powars and N. Willis 1784.   8vo.

Sheffield, *Lord* John.   Observations on the commerce of the American states.   London, for J. Debrett 1784.   8vo.

Smyth, J[ohn] F[erdinand] D[alziel]. A tour in the United States of America. London, for G. Robinson ... 1784. 2 v. 8vo.

The trial of John Peter Zenger. London, for Flexney, Davies, Merrill and Eddowes 1784. sm. 4to.

Trumbull, Benjamin. God is to be praised for the glory of His Majesty. New-Haven, T. and S. Green 1784. 8vo.

1785

Andrews, John. History of the war with America. London, for J. Fielding and J. Jarvis 1785. v. 1. 8vo. For v. 2-4 see 1786

Cook, James. A voyage to the Pacific Ocean. London, H. Hughs 1785. 3 v. 4to. (v. 3 written by James King). Atlas & plates. 2 v.

Filson, John. Histoire de Kentucke. Paris, Buisson 1785. 8vo. (S. W. Pennypacker)

Gaine, Hugh. Gaine's Universal Register ... for ... 1786. New-York, H. Gaine [1785]. 12mo.

The history of the war in America. Dublin 1785. v. 3. 8vo. (S. L. M. Barlow)

Ramsay, David. The history of the revolution of South-Carolina. Trenton, I. Collins 1785. 2 v. 8vo. First Edition

Stiles, Ezra. The United States elevated to glory and honour. Worcester, I. Thomas 1785. 12mo. Second Edition

Treaty. Wánskaps och handels tractat emellan hans Maj:t Konungen of Swerige. Stockholm, Kongl. Tryckeriet 1785. 8vo.

Virginia. A collection of all such public Acts of the General Assembly ... as are now in force. Richmond, T. Nicholson and W. Prentis 1785. fol.

1786

Andrews, John. History of the war with America. London, for J. Fielding and J. Jarvis 1786. v. 2-4. 8vo.

Articles of the Carpenters Company of Philadelphia. Philadelphia, Hall and Sellers 1786. 8vo.

Boston. The by-laws ... of the town of Boston. Boston, E. Freeman 1786. 8vo. (John Rogers)

Americana

The Columbian Magazine. [Philadelphia] December 1786. 8vo.

Congress. 1786. An address . . . to the legislatures of the several states. [New York, October 1786]. fol.

J[efferson, Thomas]. Observations sur la Virginie. Paris, Barrois 1786. 8vo.

1787

Bryan, Samuel. An die einwohner von Pennsylvanien. [Philadelphia, F. Bailey 1787]. 2 pp. fol.

The Columbian Magazine. Philadelphia, for T. Seddon . . . 1787. 8vo. (W. L. Andrews)

Constitution of the United States. (Philadelphia, J. Dunlap, September 1787). fol. (Second printed draft). (George Mason)

—— The Constitution, as recommended to Congress. Portsmouth, J. Melcher 1787. 8vo. (DePuy)

—— Articles agreed upon by the Federal Convention . . . September 17, 1787. New York, J. McLean (1787). fol.

—— The Constitution, or frame of government. Boston, Adams and Nourse 1787. 8vo.

—— —— [Boston, T. and J. Fleet 1787]. 8vo.

—— The Constitution, proposed . . . by the Federal Convention. Philadelphia, Hall & Sellers 1787. 8vo.

Crèvecoeur, J. Hector St. John de. Lettres d'un cultivateur Américain. Paris, Cuchet 1787. 3 v. 8vo.

Emmons, Nathaniel. The dignity of man. Providence, B. Wheeler [1787]. 8vo.

Franklin, Benjamin. Lettre . . . a Monsieur David LeRoy. Paris, Lagrange 1787. 8vo.

Lathrop, Joseph. A sermon, preached in the First Parish in West-Springfield. Springfield, J. Russell 1787. 8vo.

[Lee, Richard Henry]. Observations leading to a fair examination of the system of government. [New York, T. Greenleaf] 1787. 8vo.

M'Connell, Matthew. An essay on the domestic debts of the United States. Philadelphia, R. Aitken 1787. 8vo.

Americana

Mackenzie, Roderick.   Strictures on Lt. Col. Tarleton's history "Of the campaigns of 1780 and 1781 ..."   London 1787.   8vo.

Maryland.   Laws of Maryland.   Annapolis, F. Green 1787.   fol.

[Nicholson, John].   A view of the proposed Constitution.   Philadelphia, R. Aitken & Son 1787.   8vo.   (DePuy)

Northwest Ordinance of 1787.   An ordinance for the government of the territory . . . north-west of the river Ohio.   [New York 1787].   fol.

The Pennsylvania Packet, Extra, Sept. 19, 1787.   [Full text of Constitution as adopted Sept. 17, 1787].   Philadelphia, Dunlap and Claypool 1787.   4 pp.   fol.

Pennsylvania Society.   The Constitution of the Pennsylvania Society, for promoting the abolition of slavery.   Philadelphia, J. James 1787.   8vo.

Simcoe, John Graves.   A journal of the operations of the Queen's Rangers.   Exeter (1787).   4to.   First Edition

Soulés, François.   Histoire des troubles de l'Amérique anglaise.   Paris, Buisson 1787.   4 v.   8vo.

Tarleton, *Sir* Banastre, *Bart.*   A history of the campaigns of 1780 and 1781.   London, for T. Cadell 1787.   4to.

Varnum, James M.   The case, Trevett against Weeden.   Providence, J. Carter 1787.   sm. 4to.

1788

Account of the Grand Federal Procession, Philadelphia, July 4, 1788.   [Philadelphia] M. Carey [1788].   8vo.

Artykelen, die geaccordeerd zyn by de Foedderale Conventie.   Albany, J. Babcock [1788].   fol.   (DePuy)

The Columbian Magazine.   Philadelphia, for T. Seddon ... 1788.   8vo.   (W. L. Andrews)

[Dodsley, Robert].   The oeconomy of human life.   Bennington 1788.   12mo.

Edwards, Jonathan.   Observations on the language of the Muhhekaneew Indians.   New-Haven, J. Meigs 1788.   8vo.

The Federalist.   New-York, J. and A. M'Lean 1788.   2 v.   8vo.   (R. Izard)

Americana

[Galloway, Joseph]. The claim of the American loyalists. London, for G. and T. Wilkie 1788. 8vo.

[Hanson, Alexander Contee]. Remarks on the proposed plan of a Federal government. Annapolis, F. Green [1788]. 8vo.

[Jackson, E. Jonathan]. Thoughts upon the political situation of the United States. Worcester, I.Thomas 1788. 8vo. (Fisher Ames)

[Jay, John]. An address to the people of the state of New-York, on the subject of the Constitution. New-York, S. and J. Loudon [1788]. 4to. (A. C. and H. C. Bernheim)

Jefferson, Thomas. Notes on the state of Virginia. Philadelphia, Prichard and Hall 1788. 8vo.

[LeBoucher, Odet-Julian]. Histoire de la derniere guerre. Paris, Brocas 1788. 8vo.

Lee, Richard Henry. An additional number of letters from the Federal farmer to the Republican. [New York, T. Greenleaf] 1788. 8vo. (DePuy)

Massachusetts. Convention. 1788. Debates, resolutions and other proceedings. Boston, Adams and Nourse ... 1788. 8vo. First Edition

[Mazzei, Filippo]. Recherches historiques et politiques sur les États-Unis. Paris, Froullé 1788. 4 v. in 3. 8vo. (O. L. Merriam)

New Jersey. Convention. 1787. Minutes of the convention . . . at Trenton, the 11th day of December 1787. Trenton, I. Collins 1788. 4to.

New York. Convention. 1788. The debates and proceedings. New-York, F. Childs 1788. 8vo.

―――― Journal. Poughkeepsie, N. Power (1788). 4to.

North Carolina. To the people of the district of Edenton. [1788]. sm. 4to.

Occom, Samson. A sermon at the execution of Moses Paul. London 1789. 8vo.

[Smith, Melancthon]. An address to the people of the State of New-York. Printed in the State of New-York 1788. 8vo. (DePuy)

Townsend, Shippie. Peace and joy. Boston, E. Russell 1788. 8vo.

Americana

Virginia. Convention. 1788. Debates and other proceedings. Petersburg, Hunter and Prentis 1788. v. 1. 8vo. For v. 2-3 see 1789

——— In convention, Wednesday, the 25th of June, 1788. Richmond, A. Davis [1788]. 3 pp. fol.

1789

Adams, John. Twenty-six letters. New-York, J. Fenno 1789. 8vo.

Colles, Christopher. A survey of the roads of the United States. [New-
York] 1789. sm. 4to. First Edition

The Columbian Magazine. Philadelphia, for T. Seddon ... 1789. 8vo.
(W. L. Andrews)

Congress. 1789. An Act to establish the judicial courts of the United
States. [New York 1789]. fol.

——— Acts passed. New-York, F. Childs and J. Swaine [1789].
fol.

——— ——— Philadelphia, F. Childs and J. Swaine [1789]. fol.
(George Washington–W. S. Baker–W. F. Havemeyer)

——— A Bill to establish the judicial courts of the United States.
New-York, T. Greenleaf [1789]. fol.

——— Resolved ... that the following Articles be proposed ... as
amendments to the Constitution. New York, T. Greenleaf [1789].
3 pp. fol.

Congress. 1789-1810. The laws of the United States of America ...
1789-1810. 10 v. 8vo.

Extracts from the writings of divers eminent authors ... representing
the evils ... of stage plays. Philadelphia, J. James 1789. 8vo.

Ramsay, David. The history of the American Revolution. Philadelphia, R. Aitken & Son 1789. 2 v. 8vo. First Edition

Virginia. Convention. 1788. Debates and other proceedings. Petersburg, W. Prentis 1789. v. 2-3. 8vo.

1790

Almon, John. Memoirs. London 1790. 8vo.

Congress. 1790. Acts passed. New York, F. Childs and J. Swaine
[1790]. fol. (George Washington–W. S. Baker–W. F. Havemeyer)

Americana

Hamilton, Alexander. Report of the Secretary of the Treasury . . . relative to a provision for the support of the public credit. New-York, F. Childs and J. Swaine 1790. fol. (Caleb Strong)

Randolph, Edmund. Report of the Attorney-General . . . December 31, 1790. n.p. F. Childs and J. Swaine. fol.

Winthrop, John. A journal of the transactions . . . in the settlement of Massachusetts. Hartford, E. Babcock 1790. 8vo. (Ebenezer Clapp)

1791

[Anburey, Thomas]. Travels. London, for W. Lane 1791. 2 v. 8vo. (H. Holland Edwards)

Bartram, William. Travels. Philadelphia, James & Johnson 1791. 8vo. First Edition. (H. LeRoy Edgar)

Gumilla, Joseph. Historia natural, civil y geografica de las naciones situados en las riveras del Rio Orinoco. Barcelona, C. Gilbert 1791. 2 v. 4to. (Huth)

Hamilton, Alexander. [Letters from the] Treasury Department, January 6 [and 7], 1791. [Philadelphia 1791]. fol.

Long, John. Voyages and travels of an Indian interpreter and trader. London 1791. 4to.

Oldys, Francis. The life of Thomas Pain. London, for F. Stockdale 1791. 8vo. Second Edition

Sullivan, James. Observations upon the Government of the United States. Boston, S. Hall 1791. 8vo. (Groves)

United States. Census. Return of the whole number of persons within the . . . United States. Philadelphia, Childs and Swaine 1791. 12mo. (Caleb Strong)

1792

Articles in addition to and amendment of the Constitution of . . . New-Hampshire. Exeter, New-Hampshire, H. Ranlet 1792. 8vo.

Bartram, William. Travels. London, for J. Johnson 1792. 8vo.

Description topographique de six cents mille acres de terres dans l'Amérique Septentrionale. Paris 1792. 4to. (DePuy)

Dickenson, Jonathan. The remarkable deliverance of Robert Barrow. Dover [N. H.], E. Ladd 1792. 8vo.

Americana

Le Fédéraliste. Paris, Buisson 1792. 2 v. 8vo.

Gookin, Daniel. Historical collections of the Indians in New England. 1792. 8vo.

Paine, Thomas. A letter to Mr. Henry Dundas. London, for J. Ridgway 1792. 8vo.

―――― Rights of man. Part the second. London, for J. S. Jordan 1792. 8vo.

Thomas, Robert B. The farmer's almanack (1793-1831). Boston (1792-1830). 8vo.

1793

The address and petition of a number of the clergy ... in ... Philadelphia ... against vice. Philadelphia, W. Young 1793. 8vo.

Chipman, Nathaniel. Sketches of the principles of government. Rutland, Vermont, J. Lyons, June 1793. 12mo.

Filson, John. The discovery ... of Kentucky. New-York, S. Campbell 1793. 8vo.

Hardie, James. The Philadelphia directory. Philadelphia 1793. 8vo.

Imlay, Gilbert. A topographical description of the western territory of North America. New-York, S. Campbell 1793. 8vo.

[Smith, Daniel]. A short description of the Tennessee government. Philadelphia, M. Carey 1793. 8vo.

Whitney, Peter. The history of the county of Worcester ... Massachusetts. Worcester, I. Thomas 1793. 8vo. (Lefferts)

1794

Clinton, *Sir* Henry. Observations on Mr. Stedman's History of the American war. London, for J. Debrett 1794. 4to.

[Dwight, Timothy]. A discourse, on the genuineness ... of the New-Testament: delivered at New-Haven. New York, G. Bunce 1794. 8vo.

Lathrop, Joseph. The furtherance of the Gospel. Springfield, Massachusetts, J. R. Hutchins 1794. 8vo.

Long, John. Voyages chez différentes nations sauvages de l'Amérique Septentrionale. Paris, Prault [1794]. 8vo. (DePuy)

Paine, Thomas. The age of reason. Paris, Barrois 1794. 8vo.

Stedman, Charles.   The history of the origin . . . of the American war.
London 1794.   2 v.   4to.

Stiles, Ezra.   A history of three of the judges of Charles I.   Hartford,
E. Babcock 1794.   12mo.   First Edition

Wakefield, Gilbert.   An examination of the Age of reason . . . by
Thomas Paine.   New-York, G. Forman 1794.   8vo.

1795

Amerikanisches Magazin.   Hamburg, C. E. Bohn 1795.   I: 1.   8vo.   For
pts. 2-3 see 1796

The Assembly's catechism. In the Stockbridge Indian language. Stockbridge, L. Andrews 1795.   8vo.

Brackenridge, Hugh Henry.   Incidents of the insurrection in the
western parts of Pennsylvania.   Philadelphia, J. M'Culloch 1795.
8vo.   First Edition

[Callender, James Thomson].   The political progress of Britain.   Philadelphia, R. Folwell 1795.   8vo.

Coghlan, Margaret.   Memoirs.   New-York, T. & J. Swords 1795.
12mo.

Dutton, Thomas.   A vindication of the Age of reason, by Thomas
Paine.   London, Griffiths 1795.   8vo.

Lathrop, Joseph.   National happiness.   Springfield, J. W. Hooker and
F. Stebbins 1795.   8vo.

Mitchill, Samuel Latham.   The life, exploits, and precepts of Tam-
many.   New-York, J. Buel 1795.   8vo.

Paine, Thomas.   The age of reason.   London, D. I. Eaton 1795.   8vo.

———— ———— Part the second.   London, for H. D. Symonds 1795.
8vo.

———— Dissertation on first-principles of government.   Paris, English
press [1795].   8vo.   First Edition

Plan of Association of the North American Land Company.   Philadelphia, R. Aitken and Son 1795.   8vo.

Seabury, Samuel.   A discourse delivered . . . in New-London . . . before an assembly of . . . Masons.   New-London, S. Green 1795.
8vo.

Americana

Sullivan, James.   The history of the district of Maine.   Boston, I. Thomas and E. T. Andrews 1795.   8vo.

The Ten Pound Act.   Lansingburgh, S. Tiffany 1795.   sm. 8vo.

Treaty of amity, commerce, and navigation between his Britannic Majesty and the United States.   Philadelphia, Land & Ustick 1795. 8vo.   Second Edition

Washington, George.   Official letters.   London, for Cadell Junior and Davies 1795-6.   2 v.   8vo.

Williams, John.   The redeemed captive returning to Zion.   Boston, S. Hall 1795.   12mo.

1796

Abolition Societies.   Minutes of the proceedings of the third convention of delegates.   Philadelphia, Z. Poulson 1796.   8vo.

Amerikanisches Magazin.   Hamburg, C. E. Bohn 1796.   I: 2-3.   8vo. For pt. 4 see 1797

Backus, Isaac.   A church-history of New-England.   Boston, Manning & Loring 1796.   v. 3.   8vo.   First Edition

[Cobbett, William].   Porcupine's works.   Philadelphia, W. Cobbett [1796-7].   2 v.   8vo.

Findley, William.   History of the insurrection in the four western counties of Pennsylvania.   Philadelphia, S. H. Smith 1796.   8vo. First Edition

Martel, Michael.   Martel's Elements.   New York, C. C. Van Alen 1796.   sm. 8vo.   (E. B. Holden)

Paine, Thomas.   Letter to George Washington.   Philadelphia, B. F. Bache 1796.   8vo.   First Edition.   (Groves)

Wansey, Henry.   The journal of an excursion to the United States. Salisbury, J. Easton 1796.   8vo.

Washington, George.   Epistles domestic, confidential, and official. London, for F. and C. Rivington 1796.   8vo.

——— The President's address.   Philadelphia, September 20, 1796. 8vo.   First Edition.   (S. W. Pennypacker)

1797

Amerikanisches Magazin.   Hamburg, C. E. Bohn 1797.   I: 4.   8vo.

Americana

Boucher, Jonathan. A view of the causes and consequences of the American Revolution. London, for G. G. and J. Robinson 1797. 8vo.

Bülow, D. von. Der freistaat von Nordamerika. Berlin, J. F. Unger 1797. 2 v. 12mo.

[Callender, James Thomson]. The history of the United States for 1796. Philadelphia, Snowden & M'Corkle 1797. 8vo.

Connecticut. A continuation of the narrative of the missions to the new settlements. New-Haven, T. & S. Green 1797. 8vo.

Filson, John. The discovery ... of Kentucky. London, for J. Debrett 1797. 8vo.

[Fraser, Donald]. The recantation: being an anticipated valedictory address, of Thomas Paine. New-York 1797. 8vo.

Hamilton, Alexander. Observations on certain documents contained in ... "The history of the United States for the year 1796." Philadelphia, J. Bioren 1797. 8vo. First Edition

Morse, Jedidiah, *editor*. The American gazetteer. Boston, S. Hall ... 1797. 8vo.

1798

Allen, Ira. The natural and political history of the state of Vermont. London, J. W. Myers 1798. 8vo.

Burnaby, Andrew. Travels. London, for T. Payne 1798. 8vo.

Congress. 1798. Instructions to the envoys ... and ministers ... from the United States ... to the French Republic. Philadelphia, W. Ross [1798]. 8vo.

Franklin, Benjamin. The works. New-York, J. Tiebout 1798. sm. 8vo. First Edition. (W. L. Andrews)

———— ———— New-York, Tiebout & Obrian, n.d. 12mo.

Minot, George Richards. Continuation of the History of ... Massachusetts Bay. Boston, Manning & Loring 1798. v. 1. 8vo. For v. 2 see 1803

Vancouver, George. A voyage of discovery ... round the world. London, G. G. and J. Robinson, and J. Edwards 1798. 3 v. 4to.; atlas, fol.

Americana

1799

The Constitution of the United States of America. Philadelphia, J. H. Oswald 1799. 12mo.

The Federalist. New-York, J. Tiebout 1799. 2 v. 12mo. (2 copies)

La Rochefoucauld-Liancourt, François, *Duc de*. Travels. London, for R. Phillips 1799. 2 v. 4to. (F. M. R. Currer)

Williston, Seth. An address to parents. Suffield, E. Gray 1799. 16mo.

1800

A brief account of the late revivals of religion, in . . . the New England states. Windsor [Vermont], A. Spooner 1800. 8vo.

The Columbian almanac . . . for . . . 1801. Wilmington, P. Brynberg [1800]. 12mo. (W. L. Andrews)

[Holden, Oliver]. Sacred dirges, hymns, and anthems, commemorative of the death of General Washington. Boston, I. Thomas and E. T. Andrews [1800]. obl. 8vo.

Lee, Henry. A funeral oration on the death of George Washington. London 1800. 8vo. (E. B. Holden–C. L. F. Robinson)

Minot, George Richards. An eulogy on Gen. George Washington. London 1800. 8vo. (E. B. Holden–C. L. F. Robinson)

Minutes of debates in council on the banks of the Ottawa River . . . November 1791. Baltimore, Warner & Hanna 1800. 8vo.

Observations on the proposed state road, from Hudson's River, to Lake Erie. New-York, T. & J. Swords 1800. 8vo. (W. H. Samson)

Riedesel, Friedrich Adolph *and* Frederica Charlotte Louise. Auszüge aus den briefen und papieren des Generals Freyherrn von Riedesel und seiner gemalinn. Ihre beyderseitige reise nach America. [Berlin, 1800]. 8vo.

Webster, Daniel. An oration . . . the 4th day of July, 1800. Hanover, M. Davis 1800. 8vo. First Edition

Williams, John. The redeemed captive returning to Zion. Greenfield, Mass., T. Dickman 1800. 12mo.

1801

[Crèvecoeur, J. Hector St. John de]. Voyage dans la haute Pensylvanie. Paris, Crapelet 1801. 3 v. 8vo.

Americana

Mackenzie, Alexander. Voyages from Montreal. London, R. Noble 1801. 4to.

Report of the committee appointed to enquire into the official conduct of Winthrop Sargent. [Washington] 1801. 8vo.

United States. Census. Return of the whole number of persons within the ... United States, according to an act providing for the second census. [Washington 1801]. fol.

1802

Barry, Thomas. The singular adventures and captivity of Thos. Barry. [London] A. Neil 1802. 8vo.

[Cheetham, James]. An antidote to John Wood's poison. New-York, Southwick and Crooker 1802. 8vo.

———— A narrative of the suppression by Col. Burr, of the History of ... John Adams. New York, Denniston and Cheetham 1802. 8vo. (2 copies)

———— A view of the political conduct of Aaron Burr. New-York, Denniston & Cheetham 1802. 8vo.

Drayton, John. A view of South-Carolina. Charleston, W. P. Young 1802. 8vo. First Edition

Massachusetts Historical Society. Collections [Series I]. Boston, Munroe & Francis 1802. VIII. 8vo.

Moultrie, William. Memoirs of the American Revolution. New-York, D. Longworth 1802. 2 v. 8vo. (Henry Izard)

Williams, John. The redeemed captive returning to Zion. New-Haven, W. W. Morse 1802. 8vo.

Wood, John. A full exposition of the Clintonian faction. Newark 1802. 8vo.

———— The history of the administration of John Adams. New-York 1802. 8vo. First Edition

1803

Berquin-Duvallon. Vue de la colonie espagnole du Mississippi. Paris 1803. 8vo.

Burney, James. A chronological history of the discoveries in the South Sea. London, L. Hansard 1803. v. 1. 4to. For v. 2 see 1806

Cheetham, James.　Nine letters on . . . Aaron Burr's political defection. New-York, Denniston & Cheetham 1803.　8vo.

Hughes, James.　A report of the causes determined by the late Supreme Court for . . . Kentucky.　Lexington, J. Bradford 1803.　4to.

Minot, George Richards.　Continuation of the History of . . . Massachusetts Bay.　Boston, Manning & Loring 1803.　v. 2.　8vo.

1804

Backus, Isaac.　An abridgment of the church history of New-England. Boston, E. Lincoln 1804.　8vo.　First Edition

Burk, John.　The history of Virginia.　Petersburg, Virginia 1804. v. 1.　8vo.　For v. 2-3 see 1805

Heriot, George.　The history of Canada.　London 1804.　v. 1.　8vo. (all published).　First Edition

Mason, John M.　An oration. Commemorative of . . . Alexander Hamilton.　New-York, Hopkins and Seymour 1804.　8vo.

[Van Ness, William P.].　An examination of the various charges exhibited against Aaron Burr, Esq . . . by Aristides.　[New York] 1804.　8vo.

1805

Burk, John.　The history of Virginia.　Petersburg, Virginia 1805.　v. 2-3.　8vo.　For v. 4 see 1816

Hubley, Bernard.　The history of the American Revolution.　Northumberland, Pennsylvania, A. Kennedy 1805.　8vo.

1806

Beecher, Lyman.　A sermon, containing a general history of . . . East-Hampton.　Sag-Harbor, N.Y., A. Spooner 1806.　8vo.　(DePuy)

Burney, James.　A chronological history of the discoveries in the South Sea.　London, L. Hansard 1806.　v. 2.　4to.　For v. 3 see 1813

Jefferson, Thomas.　Message . . . communicating discoveries . . . by Captains Lewis and Clark.　City of Washington, A. & G. Way 1806.　8vo.　First Edition

Lowell, John.　The advantages of God's presence.　Newburyport, E. W. Allen 1806.　8vo.

Lowell, John.   A sermon, occasioned by the ... death of Col. Moses
   Titcomb.   Newburyport, E. W. Allen 1806.   8vo.

1807

Actes et mémoires concernant les négociations ... entre la France et
   l'États-Unis.   Londres, J. B. G. Vogel 1807.   3 v.   12mo.

Boston Massacre.   Orations, delivered at the request of the inhabitants
   of ... Boston.   Boston, W. T. Clap 1807.   12mo.

———— The trial of the British soldiers.   Boston, Belcher and Armstrong 1807.   8vo.

Gass, Patrick.   A journal of the voyages and travels ... under ... Capt.
   Lewis and Capt. Clarke.   Pittsburgh, Z. Cramer 1807.   12mo.
   First Edition

Heriot, George.   Travels through the Canadas.   London, for R. Phillips 1807.   4to.   First Edition

Leigh, Joseph.   Illustrations of the fulfilment of the prediction of
   Merlin.   Portsmouth 1807.   12mo.

Marshall, John.   Vie de George Washington.   Paris, Dentu 1807.   5 v.
   8vo.;   atlas, 4to.   (Max, Comte de Preysing)

1808

Clarkson, Thomas.   The history of the rise, progress, & accomplishment of the abolition of the African slave-trade.   Philadelphia
   1808.   II.   12mo.   (Thomas Jefferson)

M'Nemar, Richard.   The Kentucky revival.   Albany, E. and E. Hosford 1808.   12mo.

Smith, Joshua Hett.   An authentic narrative of the causes which led to
   the death of Major Andrè.   London, for Mathews and Leigh 1808.
   8vo.

The testimony of Christ's second appearing.   Lebanon, Ohio, J. M'Clean
   1808.   8vo.   First Edition

1809

Adams, John.   Correspondence.   Boston, Everett and Munroe 1809.
   8vo.   In 10 pts., as issued

Azara, Félix de.   Voyages.   Paris, Dentu 1809.   4 v.   8vo.;   atlas, 4to.

Americana

Clark, Daniel.   Proofs of the corruption of Gen. James Wilkinson. Philadelphia, W. Hall Jun. & G. W. Pierie 1809.   8vo.

Henry, Alexander.   Travels and adventures in Canada.   New-York, I. Riley 1809.   8vo.   First Edition

[Irving, Washington].   A history of New York.   New York, Inskeep & Bradford . . . 1809.   2 v.   12mo.   First Edition.   (Ives)

Lamb, R.   An original and authentic journal of occurrences during the late American war.   Dublin, Williamson & Courtney 1809.   8vo. (E. B. Holden–C. L. F. Robinson)

Ramsay, David.   The history of South-Carolina.   Charleston, D. Longworth 1809.   2 v.   8vo.   First Edition

1810

Cuming, F.   Sketches of a tour to the western country.   Pittsburgh, Cramer, Spear & Eichbaum 1810.   8vo.

[Davis, Matthew L.].   Letters of Marcus and Philo-Cato.   [New-York] 1810.   8vo.

The testimony of Christ's second appearing.   Albany, E. and E. Hosford 1810.   8vo.   Second Edition

1811

[Ashe, Thomas].   Travels in America performed in 1806.   New-York 1811.   8vo.

[Graydon, Alexander].   Memoirs.   Harrisburgh, J. Wyeth 1811. 12mo.   First Edition

1812

Brown, Thomas.   An account of the people called Shakers.   Troy, Parker and Bliss 1812.   8vo.

[Cutler, Jervis].   A topographical description of . . . Ohio.   Boston, J. Belcher 1812.   12mo.

The Essex Junto.   Salem 1812.   8vo.

Henry, John Joseph.   An accurate . . . account of the hardships and sufferings . . . in the campaign against Quebec.   Lancaster, W. Greer 1812.   12mo.   First Edition

[Irving, Washington].   A history of New-York.   New-York, Inskeep and Bradford 1812.   2 v.   12mo.   Second Edition

Americana

Lee, Henry.   Memoirs of the war.   Philadelphia, Bradford and Inskeep 1812.   2 v.   8vo.   First Edition

London Gazette.   Bulletins of the campaign 1812.   Westminster, R. G. Clarke 1812.   8vo.   (Baron Dimsdale–T. P. & Agnes Darby Parr–L. Darby Griffith)

[Sanders, Daniel Clarke].   A history of the Indian wars.   Montpelier, Vt., Wright and Sibley 1812.   16mo.   First Edition

1813

Burney, James.   A chronological history of the discoveries in the South Sea.   London, L. Hansard 1813.   v. 3.   4to.   For v. 4 see 1816

Clark, Thomas.   Sketches of the naval history of the United States.   Philadelphia, for M. Carey 1813.   12mo.

Dickinson, Rodolphus.   A geographical . . . view of Massachusetts proper.   Greenfield, Denio and Phelps 1813.   8vo.

Girdlestone, Thomas.   Facts tending to prove that General Lee, was never absent from this country.   London, for P. Martin 1813.   8vo.

London Gazette.   Bulletins of the campaign 1813.   Westminster, R. G. Clarke 1813.   8vo.   (Baron Dimsdale–T. P. & Agnes Darby Parr– L. Darby Griffith)

Westminster catechism.   The larger catechism.   New-York, J. Watts 1813.   12mo.

1814

Barbarities of the enemy, exposed in a report of the Committee of the House of Representatives.   Worcester, I. Sturtevant 1814.   8vo. (H. LeRoy Edgar)

Brown, Samuel R.   Views on Lake Erie.   Troy, F. Adancourt 1814. 8vo.

Flinders, Matthew.   A voyage to Terra Australis.   London, W. Bulmer 1814.   2 v.   4to.; atlas, fol.

Lewis, Merriwether, *and* William Clarke.   History of the expedition. Philadelphia, Bradford and Inskeep 1814.   2 v.   8vo.

London Gazette.   Bulletins of the campaign 1814.   Westminster, R. G. Clarke 1814.   8vo.   (Baron Dimsdale–T. P. & Agnes Darby Parr–L. Darby Griffith)

Americana

Madison Agonistes. London, D. Deans 1814. 8vo.

Schermerhorn, John F., *and* Samuel J. Mills. A correct view of that part of the United States . . . west of the Allegany Mountains. Hartford, P. B. Gleason 1814. 8vo. (Mark P. Robinson)

Webster, Daniel. Speech . . . on the 14th January, 1814. Alexandria, Snowden & Simms 1814. 8vo.

1815

Hartford Convention. The proceedings of a convention of delegates, from . . . Massachusetts, Connecticut, and Rhode-Island. Hartford, for Andrus and Starr 1815. 8vo.

London Gazette. Bulletins of the campaign 1815. Westminster, R. G. Clarke 1815. 8vo. (Baron Dimsdale–T. P. & Agnes Darby Parr–L. Darby Griffith)

Mills, Samuel J., *and* Daniel Smith. Report of a missionary tour. Andover, Flagg and Gould 1815. 8vo.

[Parish, Elijah]. A candid, analytical review of the "Sketches of the history of Dartmouth College." n.p. [?1815]. 8vo.

Sketches of the history of Dartmouth College. n.p. [?1815]. 8vo.

Waddell, I. H. The Dartmoor massacre. Boston 1815. 8vo.

1816

[Barbé-Marbois, François, *Comte*]. Complot d'Arnold et de Sir Henry Clinton. Paris, P. Didot 1816. 8vo.

Burk, John. The history of Virginia. Petersburg, Virginia, M. W. Dunnavant 1816. v. 4, continued by Skelton Jones and L. H. Girardin. 8vo.

Burney, James. A chronological history of the discoveries in the South Sea. London, L. Hansard 1816. 4to. v. 4. For v. 5 see 1817

[M'Afee, Robert B.]. History of the late war in the western country. Lexington, K., Worsley & Smith 1816. 8vo. First Edition

Wilkinson, James. Memoirs of my own times. Philadelphia, A. Small 1816. 3 v. 8vo.; atlas, 4to.

1817

Bradbury, John. Travels. Liverpool, Smith and Galway 1817. 8vo. First Edition

Americana

Burney, James.   A chronological history of the discoveries in the South Sea.   London, L. Hansard 1817.   v. 5.   4to.

1818

The Assembly's shorter catechism [in the Moheakunnuk, or Stockbridge Indian language].   n.p. [1818].   16mo.

James, William.   A full ... account of the military occurrences of the late war.   London 1818.   2 v.   8vo.

Lambrechtsen, N. C.   Korte beschrijving van de ontdekking en der verdere lotgevallen van Nieuw-Nederland.   Middelburg, S. Van Benthem 1818.   8vo.   (DePuy)

New Hampshire. *Superior Court.*   Opinion ... in the case of the Trustees of Dartmouth College, versus William H. Woodward.   Concord, I. Hill 1818.   8vo.

1819

Baines, Edward.   History of the wars of the French Revolution.   Philadelphia, M. Carey & Son 1819.   4 v.   8vo.   (Thomas Jefferson)

Claiborne, Nathaniel Herbert.   Notes on the war in the south [1812].   Richmond, W. Ramsay 1819.   12mo.

Darby, William.   A tour from the city of New York, to Detroit.   New York 1819.   8vo.

Miller, Andrew.   New states and territories.   [Keene, N. H.] 1819.   16mo.

1820

Franchère, G., *fils.*   Relation d'un voyage a la côte du nord-ouest de l'Amérique Septentrionale.   Montreal, C. B. Pasteur 1820.   8vo.

Shaw, Joshua.   Picturesque views of American scenery.   Philadelphia, M. Carey 1820-21.   3 v.   fol.

Spring, Gardiner.   Memoirs of the Rev. Samuel J. Mills.   New York 1820.   8vo.

1821

Drayton, John.   Memoirs of the American Revolution.   Charleston, A. E. Miller 1821.   2 v.   8vo.

James, William Dobein.   A sketch of the life of ... Francis Marion.   Charleston, S. C., Gould and Riley 1821.   8vo.   (2 copies)

Metcalf, Samuel L. A collection of some of the most interesting narratives of Indian warfare. Lexington, Ky., W. G. Hunt 1821. 8vo. First Edition. (J. K. Paulding)

Montule, Édouard. A voyage to North America. London, for Sir Richard Phillips 1821. 8vo. First Edition. (W. L. Andrews)

Onis, Luis de. Memoir upon the negotiations between Spain and the United States. Baltimore, F. Lucas, Junr. 1821. 8vo.

Schoolcraft, Henry R. Narrative journal of travels from Detroit. Albany, E. and E. Hosford 1821. 8vo.

Webster, Daniel. A discourse . . . at Plymouth . . . 1820. Boston, Wells & Lilly 1821. 8vo. Second Edition

1822

Dyer, Mary M. A portraiture of Shakerism. [Concord, N. H.] 1822. 12mo. First Edition

James, Edwin. Account of an expedition from Pittsburgh. Philadelphia, H. C. Carey and I. Lea 1822. 4to. (atlas). For text see 1823

Johnson, William. Sketches of the life . . . of Nathanael Greene. Charleston, A. E. Miller 1822. 2 v. 4to.

Mississippi. Constitution and form of government. Natchez, A. Marschalk 1822. 8vo.

Moore, Martin. Memoirs of . . . John Eliot. Boston 1822. 24mo. First Edition

Morse, Jedidiah. A report . . . on Indian affairs. New-Haven, S. Converse 1822. 8vo.

1823

Faux, W. Memorable days in America. London, for W. Simpkin and R. Marshall 1823. 8vo.

Haywood, John. The natural and aboriginal history of Tennessee. Nashville, G. Wilson 1823. 8vo. (Church)

James, Edwin. Account of an expedition from Pittsburgh. Philadelphia, H. C. Carey and I. Lea 1823. 2 v. 8vo. For atlas see 1822

The testimony of Christ's second appearing. Union Village (Ohio), B. Fisher and A. Burnett 1823. 8vo. Third Edition

Americana

1824

Beltrami, Giacomo Costantino.   La découverte des sources du Mississippi. Nouvelle-Orleans, B. Levy 1824. 8vo. (W. Eames)

Chapin, Stephen.   Triumphs of intellect.   Waterville, W. Hastings
1824. 8vo.

Dawson, Moses. A historical narrative of the civil and military services
of . . . William H. Harrison. Cincinnati, M. Dawson 1824. 8vo.

Hoyt, E. Antiquarian researches. Greenfield, Mass., A. Phelps 1824.
8vo.

Seaver, James E. A narrative of the life of Mrs. Mary Jemison. Canan-
daigua, J. D. Bemis 1824. 12mo. First Edition

1825

Weddell, James.   A voyage towards the South Pole.   London 1825.
8vo. First Edition

1826

[Royall, Anne]. Sketches of history, life, and manners in the United
States. New-Haven 1826. 12mo.

1827

Chastellux, François Jean, *Marquis de.*   Travels in North-America.
New-York 1827. 8vo.

DeRoos, F. Fitzgerald. Personal narrative of travels. London, W. H.
Ainsworth 1827. 8vo. Third Edition

McKenney, Thomas L.   Sketches of a tour to the lakes.   Baltimore
1827. 8vo.

1828

Bunn, Matthew. Narrative of the life and adventures. Batavia 1828.
8vo.

Greenbank, Thomas K.   Views of American scenery.   Philadelphia
1828. 8vo. (W. L. Andrews)

Haskett, William J. Shakerism unmasked. Pittsfield 1828. 12mo.

Hutchinson, Thomas.   The history of the province of Massachusetts-
Bay. London, J. Murray 1828. 8vo.

Royall, Anne. The black book. Washington City 1828. 2 v. 12mo.
First Edition

Americana

1829

[Field, David Dudley, *and others*]. A history of the county of Berkshire, Massachusetts. Pittsfield 1829. 12mo. First Edition

Hall, Basil. Forty etchings. Edinburgh 1829. 4to.

Royall, Anne. The black book. III. Washington 1829. 12mo. First Edition

White, Samuel. History of the American troops. Baltimore, B. Edes 1829. 12mo.

1830

Beltrami, Giacomo Costantino. Le Mexique. Paris 1830. 2 v. 8vo.

Cass, Lewis. A discourse, delivered at the first meeting of the Historical Society of Michigan. Detroit 1830. 8vo.

North Carolina. Debate on the Bill for establishing a bank of the state. Raleigh 1830. 8vo.

Smith, Joseph, *junior*. The Book of Mormon. Palmyra 1830. 8vo. (E. H. Gilbert–J. B. Thacher)

1831

Barber, John Warner. History and antiquities of New Haven. New Haven 1831. 8vo. First Edition. (W. L. Andrews)

Smith, James. An account of . . . the life and travels of Colonel James Smith. Philadelphia 1831. 16mo. (DePuy)

Thomas, Robert B. The old farmer's almanack (1832-1900). Boston (1831-99). 8vo.

Withers, Alexander S. Chronicles of border warfare. Clarksburg, Va., J. Israel 1831. 12mo.

1832

Davies, Samuel. Memoir. Boston 1832. 12mo.

1833

Black Hawk. Life of Ma-Ka-Tai-Me-She-Kia-Kiak or Black Hawk. Cincinnati 1833. 8vo.

Connecticut. The code of 1650 . . . commonly called Blue Laws. Hartford, Ct., Andrus & Judd 1833. 16mo.

Sewall, Lewis. The miscellaneous poems. Mobile 1833. 12mo.

Americana

1834

Cass, Lewis, *and others*. Historical ... sketches of Michigan. Detroit 1834. 12mo.

Hawkins, Alfred. Hawkins's picture of Quebec. Quebec 1834. 12mo. First Edition. (DePuy)

1835

Adams, John Quincy. Oration on ... Lafayette. Washington 1835. 8vo. First Edition

Doctrine and covenant of the Church of the Latter Day Saints. Kirtland, Ohio 1835. 12mo.

Lewis, J. O. The aboriginal portfolio. Philadelphia 1835-6. fol.

1836

Bancroft, George. An oration delivered ... July 4, 1836. Springfield 1836. 8vo. First Edition

Drake, Samuel Gardner. The old Indian chronicle. Boston 1836. 16mo. First Edition

1837

Edmonds, John W. Report ... the claims of creditors of the Potawatamie Indians. New York 1837. 8vo.

Rafn, Carl Christian. Antiquitates Americanae. Hafniae 1837. fol.

Williams, Stephen W. A biographical memoir of ... John Williams. Greenfield, Mass., 1837. 8vo.

1838

Kingsley, James L. A historical discourse ... before the citizens of New Haven. New Haven 1838. 8vo.

M'Kenney, Thomas L., *and* James Hall. History of the Indian tribes of North America. Philadelphia 1838. v. 1. fol. For v. 2 see 1842

1839

Forbes, Alexander. California. London 1839. 8vo.

1840

Finley, James B. History of the Wyandott Mission. Cincinnati 1840. 12mo.

Americana

1841

Kennedy, William. Texas. London 1841. 2 v. 8vo.

A narrative of the early days . . . of Oceola. London 1841. 8vo.

1842

M'Kenney, Thomas L., *and* James Hall. History of the Indian tribes of North America. Philadelphia 1842. v. 2. fol. For v. 3 see 1844

Richardson, John. War of 1812. [Brockville] 1842. 8vo.

A spelling-book in the Seneca language. Buffalo-Creek Reservation, Mission Press 1842. sm. 4to.

1843

Scott, James L. A journal of a missionary tour through Pennsylvania 1843. 12mo.

1844

M'Kenney, Thomas L., *and* James Hall. History of the Indian tribes of North America. Philadelphia 1844. v. 3. fol.

Neilson, Charles. An original . . . account of Burgoyne's campaign. Albany 1844. 12mo.

1846

Monette, John W. History of the discovery . . . of the valley of the Mississippi. New York 1846. 2 v. 8vo. First Edition

1847

Smith, John Jay, *and* John F. Watson. American historical and literary curiosities. Philadelphia 1847. fol. (Sir Edward W. Watkin)

1848

Hughes, John T. California. Cincinnati 1848. 12mo.

Smet, Pierre Jean de. Missions de l'Orégon. Gand [1848]. 12mo.

———— ———— Paris 1848. 12mo.

1849

Brahm, John Gerar William de. History of . . . Georgia. Wormsloe 1849. 4to.

Americana

[Nason, Daniel]. A journal of a tour from Boston to Savannah. Cambridge 1849. 12mo.

1851

Hale, Salma. Annals of the town of Keene. Keene 1851. 4to.

Hawes, Joel. A sermon, occasioned by the death of Calvin Chapin. Hartford 1851. 8vo.

1853

Choate, Rufus. A discourse . . . commemorative of Daniel Webster. Boston 1853. 8vo.

1854

New York State. *Assembly*. Report . . . in relation to the claims of the Mohawk and Stockbridge Indians. [Albany 1854]. 8vo. (DePuy)

1855

Addresses on the presentation of the sword of Gen. Andrew Jackson to the Congress of the United States. Washington 1855. 8vo.

Sargent, Winthrop. The history of an expedition against Fort DuQuesne, in 1755. Philadelphia 1855. 8vo.

1856

Kingsbury, C. P. Elementary treatise on artillery and infantry. New York 1856. 8vo. (U. S. Grant)

Olshausen, Theodor. Geschichte der Mormonen. Göttingen 1856. 8vo.

Stuart, Isaac William. Life of Nathan Hale. Hartford 1856. 12mo. Second Edition. (W. L. Andrews)

1857

Hawks, Francis L. History of North Carolina. Fayetteville, N. C. 1857-8. 2 v. 8vo.

1859

[Brown, John]. Provisional Constitution . . . for the . . . United States. n.p. 1859. 12mo.

1861

Arkansas. Journal of the convention. Little Rock 1861. 8vo.

Bartlett, John Russell. A history of the destruction of his Britannic Majesty's schooner Gaspee. Providence 1861. 8vo.

Americana

1863

Protestant Episcopal Church in the Confederate States of America. Constitution ... adopted ... 1862. Augusta 1863. 8vo. (W. L. Andrews)

—— Journal of the proceedings of the General Council ... 1862. Augusta 1863. 8vo. (W. L. Andrews)

1864

Confederate States of America. The statutes at large of the provisional government. Richmond 1864. 8vo.

Ketchum, William. An authentic ... history of Buffalo. Buffalo 1864. 2 v. 8vo.

Tocqueville, Alexis de. De la démocratie en Amérique. Paris 1864. 3 v. 8vo. (Smalley)

1866

Dimsdale, Thomas J. The vigilantes of Montana. Virginia City 1866. 8vo. First Edition. (J. A. Garfield)

Pouchot, M. Memoir upon the late war in North America. Roxbury 1866. 2 v. 8vo.

Protestant Episcopal Church in the Confederate States of America. Journal of the proceedings of the General Council ... 1865. Augusta 1866. 8vo. (W. L. Andrews)

1871

DeForest, John W. History of the Indians of Connecticut. Albany 1871. 8vo.

1874

Smet, Pierre Jean de. Voyages dans l'Amérique Septentrionale. Orégon. Bruxelles 1874. 8vo. Third Edition

1875

Gaffarel, Paul. Histoire de la Floride française. Paris 1875. 8vo.

Smet, Pierre Jean de. Lettres choisies. Bruxelles 1875. 8vo. Third Edition

1876

Muller, Frederik. Het tafereel der dwaasheid. Amsterdam 1876. 8vo. (E. N. Crane–C. L. F. Robinson)

Americana Broadsides and Maps 1660-1865

1660

Charles II, *King of England*. A Proclamation for apprehension of Edward Whalley and William Goffe. London, C. Barker and J. Bill 1660. fol.

?1740

A satyrical description of Commencement. Calculated to the meridian of Cambridge in New-England. Boston, Printed [by T. Fleet] and Sold at the Heart & Crown in Cornhill. fol.

1755

Blodget, Samuel. A Prospective plan of the Battle . . . near Lake George. [Boston 1755]. fol.

The Courant Extraordinary. [Account of the Battle of Lake George]. Kingston (Jamaica) for M. Daniell 1755. fol. (DePuy)

An Elogy on the death of Mr. Nathaniel Burt. [1755]. fol. (Jerusha M. Williams)

Shirley, William. A Proclamation [of a bounty for Indian scalps]. Boston, J. Draper 1755. fol.

Supplement to the Boston-Gazette. Account of the Battle at Lake George. [Boston, Edes and Gill 1755]. fol.

1765

Great Britain. *Stamp-Office*. A table of the prices of parchment and paper for the service of America. fol. (With seven original stamps attached)

1766

Bernard, *Sir* Francis. A Proclamation for a general Fast. Boston, R. Draper 1766. fol.

1768

Massachusetts. Convention. 1768. [Proceedings of a meeting Sept. 22, 1768, to consider protests made to Governor Bernard]. Boston, Edes & Gill 1768. fol.

1773

The Association of the Sons of Liberty, of New York. [Resolutions against the importation of tea while subject to a tax]. New-York 1773. fol.

Americana Broadsides and Maps

Boston Tea Party. [Proceedings of a meeting in Boston, Dec. 1, 1773, to determine upon the most effectual method of preventing the unloading of tea]. [Boston] Edes and Gill 1773. fol.

1774

Boston Port Covenant, 1774. [Boston 1774]. fol.

1775

A bloody butchery . . . Being the particulars of the victorious battle fought at and near Concord. Salem, E. Russell [1775]. fol.

A circumstantial account of an attack . . . on the 19th of April 1775. [Boston, J. Howe 1775]. fol.

George III, *King of England.* His Majesty's most gracious speech to both Houses of Parliament . . . October 27, 1775. Philadelphia, Hall & Sellers [1775]. fol.

Late last night an express arrived from Philadelphia . . . [Williamsburg, Va.] A. Purdie [1775]. fol. (Announces the Battle of Lexington)

A plan of the Battle, on Bunkers Hill. London, for R. Sayer & J. Bennett 1775. fol.

Rich, Elisha. A poem on the bloody engagement . . . on Bunker's Hill. Chelmsford, N. Coverly 1775. fol.

———— Poetical remarks upon the Fight at the Boston Light-House. Chelmsford, N. Coverly 1775. fol.

A song, composed by the British butchers, after the Fight at Bunker-Hill. 1775. fol.

Washington, George. [Advertisement for two runaway servants, in a broadside dated] Williamsburg, J. Pinkney [1775]. sm. 4to.

1776

Massachusetts. A Proclamation . . . January 23, 1776. (Advocates open hostilities against Great Britain). [1776]. fol.

Washington, George. [Letter dated "Head-Quarters, Newtown, 27th Dec. 1776." containing account of the Battle of Trenton]. Broadside begins: Baltimore, Dec. 31, 1776. This morning Congress received the following letter . . . Baltimore, M. K. Goddard [1776]. fol.

Americana Broadsides and Maps

1777

Massachusetts. [Broadside dated August 8 and 9, 1777, relating to Burgoyne's invasion and the loss of Ticonderoga]. [Boston, J. Gill 1777]. fol.

1778

Continental Congress. A Proclamation [appointing] Wednesday, the thirtieth day of December next ... as a day of public thanksgiving ... 1778. [Boston 1778]. fol. (Rev. Samuel Williams)

Manifesto and Proclamation ... by the Earl of Carlisle, Sir Henry Clinton, and William Eden, Esq ... this third day of October, 1778. [New York, J. Rivington 1778]. fol.

1779

Currency. [Broadside relating to the depreciation of the currency]. Boston, June 21, 1779. fol.

1780

A representation of the figures exhibited and paraded through the streets of Philadelphia, on Saturday, the 30th of September, 1780. [woodcut of Benedict Arnold at top]. [Philadelphia 1780]. fol.

1781

Cornwallis taken! Boston (Friday) October 26, 1781. [Boston] B. Edes and Sons [1781]. 4to. (H.V. Jones)

1783

Hancock, John. A Proclamation for a day of thanksgiving [for the Peace of 1783]. [Boston 1783]. fol. (Appoints Dec. 11, 1783)

1786

Congress. 1786. An ordinance for the establishment of the mint. n.p. [1786]. sm. fol.

1787

Bowdoin, James. A Proclamation [promising pardon and indemnity to all citizens of Massachusetts concerned in Shay's Rebellion]. Boston, Adams & Nourse [1787]. fol.

Hancock, John. A Proclamation, for a day of public thanksgiving. Boston, Adams and Nourse [1787]. fol. (Appoints Nov. 29, 1787)

Pennsylvania. House of Representatives. Eine addresse der endsunter-
schriebenen, glieder des letzteren Hauses der Representanten der
republik Pennsylvanien, an ihre Constituenten. [Philadelphia]
Samstag, den 29sten Sept. 1787. fol.

1788

Congress. 1788. [Official notification of the beginning of the Government under the Constitution of 17 Sept. 1787]. [New York 1788].
fol.

Order of procession, in honor of the establishment of the Constitution
. . . the 4th of July, 1788. Philadelphia, Hall and Sellers [1788].
fol.

Supplement Extraordinary to The Independent Journal. Monday, July
28, 1788. New-York, J. and A. M'Lean [1788]. fol. (Announces adoption of the Constitution, by the New York convention at Poughkeepsie, July 25)

1789

[Account of the Inauguration of George Washington]. Lansinburgh
[sic] May 6, 1789. fol.

1790

Congress. 1790. An Act for establishing the . . . seat of the Government . . . Approved, July the sixteenth, 1790. [New York] F.
Childs and J. Swaine [1790]. fol.

————— An Act to continue in force for a limited time, an Act, intituled
"An Act for the temporary establishment of the post-office." Ap-
proved, August the fourth, 1790. [New York, F. Childs and J.
Swaine 1790]. fol.

1798

Kentucky. House of Representatives. [Kentucky Resolutions], November 10th, 1798. fol.

1799

A farewell to General Washington. [Poem of twelve stanzas. ?Nor-
wich, Conn. 1799]. fol.

1813

Perry's Victory. [Woodcut of Battle of Lake Erie, followed by eleven
stanzas of eight lines each]. Boston [1813]. 4to.

Americana Broadsides and Maps

1821

Bowdoin College.   Catalogue of the officers and students . . . October, 1821.   Brunswick, Me., J. Griffin [1821].   (Wakeman)

1832

South Carolina.   [Nullification Act].   An ordinance, to nullify certain Acts of the Congress . . . [1832].   fol.

1860

The Union is Dissolved! . . . December 20th, 1860. An ordinance to dissolve the union between the state of South Carolina and other states . . . [Charleston 1860].   fol.

1862

Davis, Jefferson.   Inaugural address . . . February 22, 1862.   [Richmond 1862].   fol.   (Issued as the "Richmond Enquirer. Extra.")

1863

The Daily Citizen. Vicksburg, Miss. Thursday, July 2, 1863.   fol. on wallpaper.   (Vicksburg was taken by Grant July 4, 1863 and as this issue dated July 2 had evidently not appeared on time, it bears a note set up by a Federal compositor, dated July 4)

Lincoln, Abraham.   Emancipation Proclamation.   [Washington 1863]. fol.

1865

Lincoln, Abraham.   Inaugural address . . . March 4th, 1865.   fol.

Surrender of Gen. Lee.   War Department, April 9, 1865.   4to.

Woonsocket Patriot. Extra., Saturday Evening, April 15, 1865. Woonsocket, R. I., 1865.   fol.   Fourth Edition

American Manuscripts 1662-1926

Adams, John. A. L. S. Amsterdam, Sept. 1, 1780. To Mr. Luzac

Adams, John Quincy. A. L. S. Washington, Jan. 8, 1836. To James C. Doane

Arthur, Chester Alan. A. L. S. Albany, Oct. 11, 1862. To Lt. Col. H. P. Casey

Ashley, Azariah. A. D. S. Camp at Williamstown, July 9, 1787. A Return for the troops employed in the Service of . . . Massachusetts

Buchanan, James. A. L. S. Wheatland, March 25, 1850. To Rev. Henry Slicer

Cleveland, Grover. A. L. S. Albany, Dec. 18, 1883. To ——

—— A. L. S. New York, Oct. 22, 1889. To Hon. A. C. Chapin

—— A. MS. Address at the Centennial of the Louisiana Purchase. 1903

Cochrane, *Sir* Alexander. A. L. S. Iphigenia, Aug. 28 [1814]. To Sir George Cockburn

S. S. Constitution. Receipt for timber dockage. Boston, Sept. 28, 1798. To Henry Jackson. Signed by Thomas Mayhew

Coolidge, Calvin. A. L. S. Washington, Feb. 5, 1926. To Hon. Alfred C. Chapin

Davis, Jefferson. A. N. S. March 28, 1861. To C. G. Memminger

Endicott, John. A. L. S. Boston, July 2, 1662. To Philip Lowes

Fillmore, Millard. A. L. S. Albany, April 12, 1848. To H. C. Day

Franklin, Benjamin. A. L. S. Passy, Jan. 7, 1783. To Benjamin F. Bache

Garfield, James Abram. A. L. S. Washington, Dec. 22, 1862. To Jacob Garfield

—— A. L. S. Mentor, O., June 26, 1880. To Jacob Heaton

Grant, Ulysses Simpson. A. N. S. City Point, Va., Mar. 4, 1865. To Maj. Gen. Gibbon

—— A. L. S. Washington, May 17, 1865. To Maj. Gen. P. H. Sheridan

American Manuscripts

Grant, Ulysses Simpson. A.L.S. Washington, April 7, 1868. To his father

Greene, Nathaniel. A.D.S. [Ordering boats for the crossing of the Delaware]. Bougert's Tavern, Dec. 19, 1776

Hamilton, Alexander. A.MS. [Outline of points to be used in a suit on a land question]

Harrison, Benjamin. A.L.S. Washington, Nov. 26 & 29, 1890. To Hon. J. S. Clarkson

Harrison, William Henry. A.L.S. Seneca Towns, Aug. 1, 1813. To Brig'r. Gen. Clay

Hayes, Rutherford B. A.L.S. Spiegel Grove, Fremont, O., Jan. 27, 1892. To Gen. Marcus J. Wright

Hutchinson, Thomas. A.MS. History of the Province of Massachusetts Bay. v. 3. fol.

——— A.MS. [An account and defence of his conduct and actions in Massachusetts 1764-74]. 19 pp. fol.

Hutchinson, Thomas, Jr. Letter books 1805-19

Jackson, Andrew. A.L.S. Hermitage, Feb. 9, 1844. To Major E. G. D. Butler

Jefferson, Thomas. A.L.S. Monticello, Apr. 16, 07. To Wm. A. Burwell

——— A.L.S. Washington, May 26, 07. To M. de Lafayette

Johnson, Andrew. A.L.S. Senate Chamber, Feb. 3, 1889. To his son

Knox, Henry. A.N.S. West Point, March 8, 1783. To Martha Washington

Lafayette, Gilbert Motier, *Marquis de*. A.L.S. Headquarters, Jan. 9 [1778?]. To Robert Morris

Lincoln, Abraham. A.L.S. Executive Mansion, June 3, 1861. To Lieut. Genl. Scott

——— Extract from A.L.S. Oct. 17, 1861

——— A.L.S. Washington, Sept. 2, 1863. To Hon. Attorney General

McKinley, William. A.L.S. Fayetteville, Va., Dec. 15, 1861. To his sister and brother

American Manuscripts

Madison, James. A. L. S. Philadelphia, Mar. 19, 1797. To Thomas Jefferson

Monroe, James. A. L. S. Washington, Aug. 1823. To ——

Mott, Lucretia. A. L. S. Roadside, 4 Mo. 18th. 58. To Sarah Pugh

Pierce, Franklin. A. L. S. Washington, Feb. 9, 1842. To General ——

Polk, James K. A. L. S. Columbia, Sept. 18, 1835. To Col. Saml. H. Laughlin

Roosevelt, Theodore. A. L. S. Sagamore Hill, Jan. 30, 1917. To Hon. Alfred C. Chapin

—— A. MS. S. "What are the fourteen points?"

—— A. MS. S. Further consideration of the fourteen points

—— A. MS. S. Merit system versus the spoils system

Sill, Thomas H. A. L. S. Williams College, March 28, 1799. To Roger M. Sherman

Taft, William H. A. L. S. New Haven, Conn., Sept. 30, 1917. To Governor Hughes

—— A. L. S. Pointe a Pic, P. Q., Sept. 15, 1921. To Mrs. Alfred C. Chapin

Taylor, Zachary. A. L. S. Monterey, Mexico, Oct. 20, 1846. To Mr. Thomas W. Kinggold

Tyler, John. A. L. S. Sherwood Forest, Charles City County, Va., Nov. 28, 1850. To Mr. J. K. Martin

Van Buren, Martin. A. L. S. Lindenwald, April 24, 1845. To Mr. C. Rives

Washington, George. A. MS. Survey of a plot of 200 acres. Dec. 2, 1749

—— A. MS. S. Survey of a plot of 239 acres. Oct. 25, 1752

—— A. L. S. Mr. Lowe's, Oct. 20, 1776. To Robert R. Livingston

—— A. L. S. New Windsor, Dec. 8, 1780. To Governor Lee of Virginia

—— A. MS. S. A list of the U. S. Loan Office certificates in possession of and belonging to George Washington

American Manuscripts

Washington, George. A.L.S. Philadelphia, Feb. 3, 1794. To William Pearce

——— A.L.S. Philadelphia, Mar. 30, 1796. To Mrs. Betsey Law

——— A.L.S. Mount Vernon, July 15, 1798. To Gen. Marshall

——— A.L.S. Philadelphia, Dec. 6, 1798. To Alexander Addison

Washington, Martha. A.N.S. Newburgh, March 6, 1783. To General Knox

——— A.L.S. Philadelphia, Dec. 3, 1792. To Mrs. Frances Washington

Williams, Stephen. A.L.S. Camp at Half Moon, July 14, 1756. To his son. (Mark P. Robinson)

Williams, Warham. A.L.S. Watertown, Mass., Dec. 1, 1724. To Rev. Stephen Williams

Williams, William (signer from Connecticut). A.L.S. Lebanon, March 28, 1767. To Cap. Sturrling

——— A.L.S. Lebanon, Feb. 8, 1792. To Rev. Benjamin Trumbull

Williams, William (President of Free School at Williamstown). A.L.S. Dalton, Dec. 22, 1789. To Justin Ely

Wilson, Woodrow. A.L.S. Princeton, Jan. 6, 1901. To Mr. R.W. Gilder

Newspapers 1730-1865

1730

The Weekly News-Letter. Numb. 180. June 4-11, 1730. Boston, B. Green 1730. 2 pp. fol.

1755

Boston-Gazette. Supplement. [Boston, Edes and Gill] Sept. 29, 1755. 2 pp. fol.

The Courant Extraordinary. Kingston [Jamaica] for M. Daniell, Oct. 8, 1755. fol. (DePuy)

1756

Gazette. Nos. 1-52, Jan. 3-Dec. 25, 1756 (lacking No. 41, Oct. 9). Paris, Bureau d'Adresse 1756. 4to. (Paltsits–Samson–DePuy)

1757

Gazette. Nos. 1-53, Jan. 2-Dec. 31, 1757. Paris, Bureau d'Adresse 1757. 4to. (Paltsits–Samson–DePuy)

1787

The Pennsylvania Packet and Daily Advertiser [Extra Number]. Philadelphia, Dunlap and Claypool, Sept. 19, 1787. 4 pp. fol.

1788

Supplement Extraordinary to The Independent Journal. New-York, J. and A. M'Lean, July 28, 1788. fol.

1799

American Mercury. Hartford [Conn.] E. Babcock, Dec. 26, 1799. 4 pp. fol.

The Centinel of Freedom. Newark, N. J., J. Parkhurst & S. Pennington, Dec. 24, 1799. 4 pp. fol.

The Connecticut Courant. Hartford [Conn.] Hudson & Goodwin, Dec. 30, 1799. 4 pp. fol.

The Genius of Liberty. Morris-Town [N. J.] J. Mann, Dec. 26, 1799. 4 pp. fol.

Impartial Journal. Stonington, Conn., S. Trumbull, Dec. 31, 1799. 4 pp. fol.

Newspapers

New-Jersey Journal.   Elizabeth-Town [N. J.] S. Kollock, Dec. 24 & 31, 1799.   4 pp.   fol.

New-Jersey State Gazette.   Trenton [N. J.] Sherman, Mershon & Thomas, Dec. 31, 1799.   4 pp.   fol.

Springer's Weekly Oracle.   New-London [Conn.] J. Springer, Dec. 30, 1799.   4 pp.   fol.

The Vermont Gazette.   Bennington [Vt.] A. Haswell, Dec. 26, 1799. 4 pp.   fol.

Whitestown Gazette.   Utica [N. Y.] W. M'Lean, Dec. 30, 1799.   4 pp. fol.

1800

American Mercury.   Hartford [Conn.] E. Babcock, Jan. 2, 1800.   4 pp.   fol.

The Courier.   Norwich [Conn.] T. Hubbard, Jan. 1, 1800.   4 pp.   fol.

The Eastern Herald.   Portland [Me.] Baker & George, Jan. 13, 1800. 4 pp.   fol.

Federal Galaxy.   Brattleborough, Vt., B. Smead, Jan. 4, 1800.   4 pp. fol.

The Federal Spy.   Springfield, Mass., T. Ashley, Jan. 7, 1800.   4 pp. fol.

Jenks' Portland Gazette.   Portland [Me.] E. A. Jenks, Jan. 13, 1800. 4 pp.   fol.

The Salem Gazette.   Salem, Mass., T. C. Cushing, Jan. 3, 1800.   4 pp. fol.

1852

Deseret News. Extra.   Great Salt Lake City, U. T., W. Richards, Sept. 14, 1852.   48 pp.   4to.

1860

Charleston Mercury Extra.   Charleston, Dec. 20, 1860.   fol.

1862

Richmond Enquirer Extra.   Richmond, February 22, 1862.   fol.

1863

The Daily Citizen.   Vicksburg, Miss., July 2, 1863.   fol.

[405]

Newspapers

Boston Daily Advertiser.   Boston, April 19, 1865.   fol.

The Boston Herald.   Boston, April 18, 1865.   fol.

Boston Post.   Boston, April 19, 1865.   fol.

Hartford Daily Courant.   Hartford, Conn., April 17 & 19, 1865.   fol.

New London Democrat.   New London, Conn., April 22, 1865.   fol.

Norwich Weekly Courier.   Norwich, Conn., April 20, 1865.   fol.

The Richmond Whig.   Richmond, Va., April 17, 1865.   fol.

The True Citizen.   New Britain, Conn., April 21, 1865.   fol.

Woonsocket Patriot Extra.   Woonsocket, R. I., April 15, 1865.   fol.
Fourth Edition

American Literature

[Adams, Henry]. Democracy. New York, H. Holt 1880. 12mo. First Edition

————— A letter to American teachers of history. Washington 1910. 12mo. First Edition

Alcott, Louisa May. Little men. Boston, Roberts 1871. 12mo. First Edition

————— Little women. Boston, Roberts 1869. 2 v. 12mo. First Edition

Alden, Timothy. A collection of American epitaphs. New York 1814. 5 v. 12mo. 1, Second Edition; 2-5, First Edition. (H.V. Jones)

A[ldrich], T[homas] B[ailey]. The bells. New York, J. C. Derby 1855. 8vo. First Edition

Allen, James Lane. Flute and violin. New York, Harper 1892. 12mo. First Edition

Allen, Lucy. Hymns. Windsor, Vt., Reprinted by A. Spooner 1795. 12mo. stitched

American melodies. Philadelphia, H. F. Anners (1840). 12mo. First Edition

André, John. Cow-chace. New York, J. Rivington 1780. sm. 8vo. First Edition. (Stevens–McKee–Halsey)

————— ————— London, for J. Fielding 1781. 4to.

————— ————— New York, T. & J. Swords 1798. 8vo. stitched, uncut

Bancroft, George. Poems. Cambridge, University Press 1823. 8vo. First Edition

Barlow, Joel. The Columbiad. Philadelphia, C. and A. Conrad 1807. 4to. First Edition

[—————] The hasty-pudding. (New Haven 1796). 8vo. 12 pp. (W. L. Andrews)

Barnum, H. L. The spy unmasked. New York, J. & J. Harper 1828. 8vo.

[Belknap, Jeremy]. The foresters. Boston, I. Thomas and E. T. Andrews 1792. 12mo. First Edition

Beveridge, John. Epistolae familiares. Philadelphia, W. Bradford 1765. 8vo.

Bierce, Ambrose. Cobwebs from an empty skull. London and New York, G. Routledge 1874. 8vo. (Starrett 4)

———— The dance of death. San Francisco, H. Keller 1877. 8vo. (Starrett 6)

———— The dance of life. San Francisco News Company 1877. 8vo. (Starrett 7)

———— Fantastic fables. New York, G. P. Putnam's Sons 1899. 8vo. (Starrett 16)

———— In the midst of life. New York, G. P. Putnam's Sons 1898. 12mo. (Starrett 15)

———— [Letters, two to Charles Dexter Allen, two to Miss Ruth Robertson]. (Starrett 29)

———— Shapes of clay. San Francisco, W. E. Wood 1903. 8vo. (Starrett 17)

———— Tales of soldiers and civilians. San Francisco, E. L. G. Steele 1891. 12mo. (Starrett 8)

———— *and* G. A. Danziger. The monk and the hangman's daughter. Chicago, F. J. Schulte 1892. 12mo. (Starrett 9: 3)

Bigelow, Samuel. A poem. Worcester, for the Author 1776. 12mo. First Edition

Brackenridge, Hugh Henry. The battle of Bunkers-Hill. Philadelphia, R. Bell 1776. 8vo. First Edition. (W. L. Andrews)

———— The death of General Montgomery. Philadelphia, R. Bell 1777. 8vo. First Edition. (W. L. Andrews)

———— ———— Norwich, J. Trumbull 1777. 8vo. stitched

———— Modern chivalry. 4 v. I, II, IV, Philadelphia 1792, 1712 [sic], 1797; III, Pittsburgh 1712 [sic]. sm. 8vo. First Edition. (Halsey)

Bradstreet, Anne. The poems of Mrs. Anne Bradstreet (1612-1672). [New York] The Duodecimos 1897. 12mo.

———— Several poems. [Boston] 1758. 16mo. Third Edition

Brown, Charles Brockden.　Arthur Mervyn. Pt. I.　Philadelphia, H. Maxwell 1799.　8vo.　First Edition

―――― Jane Talbot.　Philadelphia, J. Conrad 1801.　12mo.　First Edition

[Brown, William Hill].　The power of sympathy.　Boston, I. Thomas 1789.　2 v.　16mo.　First Edition

Bryant, William Cullen.　A discourse on ... Washington Irving.　New York, G. P. Putnam 1860.　8vo.　First Edition.　(Bryant–Wallace)

[――――] The embargo.　Boston 1808.　12mo.　First Edition. (Hoffman–Hawkins–Hoe–Wallace)

―――― ―――― Boston, E. G. House 1809.　8vo.　Second Edition, stitched

―――― Hymns.　n.p. n.d. [New York 1864].　12mo.　(Line 2, last stanza, p. 9, reads: "Dwells on Thy works in deep delight,"). (Presentation copy from Bryant to Dr. West, September 1864)

―――― Poems.　Cambridge, Hilliard and Metcalf 1821.　12mo.　First Edition.　(Appleton–Ives)

―――― ―――― New-York, E. Bliss 1832.　12mo.

―――― Thirty poems.　New York, D. Appleton 1864.　12mo.　First Edition.　(Bryant–Wallace)

―――― Voices of nature.　New York, D. Appleton 1865.　12mo.　First Edition, pictorial wrappers.　(Bryant-Wallace)

―――― The white-footed deer.　New York, I. S. Platt 1844.　12mo.　First Edition, original printed wrappers, uncut.　(Wallace)

―――― *See also* Homerus

Buckingham, Joseph T.　Miscellanies [I-II].　Boston 1822.　12mo.　First Edition

Burroughs, John.　Indoor studies.　Boston, Houghton Mifflin 1889.　16mo.　First Edition

[Butler, William Allen].　Nothing to wear.　New York, Rudd & Carleton 1857.　12mo.　First Edition

Cabell, James Branch.　The eagle's shadow.　New York, Doubleday, Page 1904.　12mo.　First Edition

Cabell, James Branch.   Gallantry.   New York, Harper 1907.   12mo.
First Edition

────── The line of love.   New York, Harper 1905.   12mo.   First
Edition

Cable, George Washington.   Old Creole days.   New York, Charles
Scribner's Sons 1879.   12mo.   First Edition

────── Strange true stories of Louisiana.   New York, Charles Scribner's Sons 1889.   12mo.   First Edition

Campbell & Dunn.   The child's first book.   Richmond, Ayres & Wade
1864.   12mo.   First Edition, original wrappers

Carman, Bliss.   James Whitcomb Riley.   Metuchen, N. J., 1925-6.
8vo.

────── Sappho.   n.p. 1902.   8vo.   (Author's copy. One of sixty
copies, privately printed)

────── Sappho. One hundred lyrics.   Boston 1904.   fol.   (No. 32 of
an edition of 200 copies)

────── A vision of Sappho.   n.p. 1903.   8vo.   (One of sixty copies,
privately printed)

────── *and* Richard Hovey.   More songs from Vagabondia.   Boston
1896.   8vo.   First Edition.   (Presentation copy, inscribed, from
Hovey to Lightner)

Cather, Willa Sibert.   April twilights.   Boston 1903.   12mo.   First
Edition

Cavalcanti, Guido.   Sonnets and ballate . . . with translations of them
. . . by Ezra Pound.   London 1912.   12mo.   First Edition

A child's primer.   New York, n.d.   32mo.   Original wrappers

Clemens, Samuel Langhorne.   The celebrated jumping frog.   New
York, C. H. Webb 1867.   12mo.   First Edition

────── A Connecticut Yankee.   New York, C. L. Webster 1889.   4to.
First Edition.   (Will M. Clemens)

────── The mysterious stranger.   New York, Harper (1916).   4to.
First Edition

[──────] What is man?   New York, De Vinne Press 1906.   8vo.   First
Edition.   (No. 164 of an edition of 250 copies)

Columbia and Britannia. New-London, T. Green 1787. 12mo. stitched. (By Nathaniel Niles?)

The Confederate. Mobile, S. H. Gottzell 1863. (By a Carolinian). 12mo. First Edition, original wrappers. (W. L. Andrews)

Cooper, James Fenimore. Afloat and ashore. Philadelphia 1844. 2 v. 8vo. First Edition, original wrappers. (J. C. Chamberlain)

—————— The bravo. Philadelphia, Carey & Lea 1831. 2 v. 8vo. First Edition. (J. C. Chamberlain)

—————— The deerslayer. Philadelphia, Lea & Blanchard 1841. 2 v. 8vo. First Edition

—————— The Heidenmauer. Philadelphia, Carey & Lea 1832. 2 v. 8vo. First Edition. (J. C. Chamberlain)

—————— Home as found. Philadelphia, Lea & Blanchard 1838. 2 v. 8vo. First Edition

—————— Homeward bound. Philadelphia, Carey, Lea & Blanchard 1838. 2 v. 8vo. First Edition

—————— The last of the Mohicans. Philadelphia, H. C. Carey & I. Lea 1826. 2 v. 8vo. First Edition

—————— A letter to his countrymen. New York, J. Wiley 1834. 8vo. First Edition

—————— Mercedes of Castile. Philadelphia, Lea and Blanchard 1840. 2 v. 8vo. First Edition. (George C. F. Williams)

—————— The Monikins. Philadelphia, Carey, Lea & Blanchard 1835. 2 v. 8vo. First Edition

—————— The pathfinder. Philadelphia, Lea and Blanchard 1840. 2 v. 8vo. First Edition

—————— The two admirals. Philadelphia, Lea and Blanchard 1842. 2 v. 8vo. First Edition. (J. C. Chamberlain)

—————— The wept of Wish Ton-Wish. Philadelphia, Carey, Lea & Carey 1829. 2 v. 8vo. First Edition. (George C. F. Williams)

Crane, Stephen. Active service. New York, Stokes (1899). 8vo. First Edition

—————— The black riders. Boston, Copeland and Day 1895. 16mo. First Edition. (One of 50 copies on Japan vellum)

Crane, Stephen. George's mother. New York, E. Arnold 1896. 8vo. First Edition

———— Great battles of the world. Philadelphia 1901. 8vo. First Edition

———— The little regiment. New York, D. Appleton 1896. 8vo. First Edition

———— Maggie. [New York 1893]. 12mo. First Edition, original wrappers

———— ———— New York, D. Appleton 1896. 8vo. Second Edition

———— The monster. New York, Harper 1899. 8vo. First Edition

———— The open boat. New York, Doubleday & McClure 1898. 8vo. First Edition. (Henry Goldsmith)

———— Pictures of war. London, W. Heinemann 1898. 12mo.

———— The red badge of courage. New York, D. Appleton 1895. 8vo. First Edition

———— A souvenir and a medley. East Aurora, N. Y. 1896. 12mo. First Edition, original wrappers. (Roycroft Quarterly No. 1)

———— The third violet. New York, D. Appleton 1897. 8vo. First Edition

———— War is kind. New York, F. A. Stokes 1899. 8vo. First Edition

———— Whilomville stories. New York, Harper 1900. 8vo. First Edition

———— Wounds in the rain. New York, F. A. Stokes (1900). 8vo. First Edition

———— *and* Robert Barr. The O'Ruddy. New York (1903). 12mo. First Edition

Curtis, George William. The Potiphar papers. New York, G. P. Putnam 1854. 12mo.

[Dana, Richard Henry]. Two years before the mast. New York, Harper 1840. 16mo. First Edition

[Davis, Mrs. Mary Elizabeth]. The British partizan. Macon, Ga., Burke, Boykin 1864. 12mo. First Edition, original wrappers. (W. L. Andrews)

De Mille, James.   Behind the veil.   Halifax, N. S., T. C. Allen 1893. 4to.   First Edition

Derby, George Horatio.   Phoenixiana. Edited by J. V. Cheney.   Chicago, The Caxton Club 1897.   2 v.   8vo.

The Dial.   Boston 1841-4.   4 v. (all published).   8vo.

Drake, Joseph Rodman.   The culprit fay.   New York, G. Dearborn 1835.   8vo.   First Edition

Dreiser, Theodore.   Jennie Gerhardt.   New York, Harper 1911. 12mo.   First Edition

Dunlap, William.   Andre.   New York, T. & J. Swords 1798.   8vo. First Edition

[———]   The father.   New York, Hodge, Allen & Campbell 1789. 8vo.   First Edition, stitched, uncut

Dwight, Timothy.   Greenfield Hill.   New York, Childs and Swaine 1794.   8vo.   First Edition

Eddy, Mrs. Mary Baker.   Science and health.   Boston 1875.   8vo. First Edition

An elegiac poem; sacred to the memory of the Rev. George Whitefield. Boston, I. Thomas 1770.   4to.

Emerson, Ralph Waldo.   An address delivered . . . 15 July, 1838.   Boston, J. Munroe 1838.   8vo.   First Edition

———   ——— . . . 1st August, 1844.   Boston, J. Munroe 1844.   8vo. First Edition

———   The conduct of life.   Boston, Ticknor and Fields 1860.   12mo. First Edition, First Issue

———   ———   ———   Second Issue

———   Essays.   Boston, J. Munroe 1841.   12mo.   First Edition

———   ——— Second series.   Boston, J. Munroe 1844.   12mo.   First Edition

———   Letter . . . to the Second Church.   Boston, I. R. Butts (1832). 12mo.   First Edition.   (W. T. Newton–Wakeman)

———   Letters and social aims.   Boston, J. R. Osgood 1876.   12mo. First Edition

Emerson, Ralph Waldo. May-Day and other pieces. Boston, Ticknor and Fields 1867. 12mo. First Edition, First Issue

—— Poems. Boston, J. Munroe 1847. 12mo. First Edition

—— The preacher. Boston, G. H. Ellis 1880. 8vo. First Edition, original wrappers

—— Representative men. Boston, Phillips, Sampson 1850. 12mo. First Edition

—— Society and solitude. Boston, Fields, Osgood 1870. 12mo. First Edition

Fenollosa, Ernest, *and* Ezra Pound. 'Noh' or accomplishment. London 1916. 8vo. First Edition

Field, Eugene. Autobiography. [Chicago 1894]. 12mo. (Presentation copy inscribed by Field to Edward Freiberger)

—— My book. 4to. (One of ?250 copies privately printed on vellum [?1905] for W. K. Bixby)

—— Tribune primer. (Denver 1881). Tribune series No. 11. 16mo. First Edition, original blue printed wrappers. (Inscribed by Field)

Fields, James T. Poems. Boston, W. D. Ticknor 1849. sm. 4to. First Edition. (Presentation copy, inscribed by Fields to the Hon. R. C. Winthrop)

Fitch, Ebenezer. Useful knowledge and religion. Pittsfield, C. Smith (1799). 8vo. First Edition, stitched

Fitch, Elijah. The beauties of religion. Providence, J. Carter 1789. 8vo. First Edition

Foster, Stephen Collins. Ellen Bayne. New York, Firth, Pond & Co. (1854). fol. stitched. (American songs)

—— Eulalie. New York, Firth, Pond & Co. (1851). fol. stitched. (American songs)

—— Little Ella. New York, Firth, Pond & Co. (1853). fol. stitched. (American songs)

—— Lula is gone. New York, Firth, Pond & Co. (1858). fol. stitched. (American songs)

—— Nelly was a lady. New York, Firth, Pond & Co. (1849). fol. stitched. (American songs)

Foster, Stephen Collins. Old dog Tray. New York, Firth, Pond & Co.
(1853). fol. stitched. (American songs)

——— The voice of by gone days. New York, Firth, Pond & Co.
(1850). fol. stitched. (American songs)

——— Willie we have missed you. New York, Firth, Pond & Co.
(1854). fol. stitched. (American songs)

Freneau, Philip. A collection of poems. New York, D. Longworth
1815. 2 v. sm. 12mo.

——— Poems written between the years 1768 and 1794. Monmouth,
N. J. 1795. 8vo.

[———] The village merchant. Philadelphia, Hoff and Derrick 1794.
12mo. First Edition, wrappers

Frost, Robert. A boy's will. London 1913. 12mo. First Edition,
original wrappers

——— New Hampshire. New York 1923. 8vo. First Edition

——— North of Boston. London (1914). 4to. First Edition

[Furman, Garrit]. Napoleon's grave. New York, Gray and Bunce
1826. 8vo. First Edition. (Presentation copy, inscribed, from
the author to J. J. Monell)

——— Rural hours. (Maspeth 1824). 8vo. First Edition

Godfrey, Thomas. Juvenile poems. Philadelphia, H. Miller 1765.
4to. First Edition

——— The Prince of Parthia. Philadelphia, H. Miller 1765. 4to.
First Edition

The good child's little primer. New York, M. Day, n.d. nar. 16mo.
Original wrappers

[Hale, Edward Everett]. The man without a country. Boston, Ticknor and Fields 1865. 12mo. First Edition, original wrappers

Hanna, John Smith. A history of the life . . . of Captain Samuel
Dewees. Baltimore, R. Neilson 1844. 12mo. First Edition.
(W. L. Andrews)

The Harbinger. Boston, Carter, Hendee 1833. 12mo. First Edition.
(C. R. Child–Halsey)

Harris, Joel Chandler. Balaam and his master. Boston, Houghton Mifflin 1891. 12mo. First Edition

———— The chronicles of Aunt Minervy Ann. New York, Charles Scribner's Sons 1899. 12mo. First Edition

———— Free Joe. New York, Charles Scribner's Sons 1887. 12mo. First Edition

———— Nights with Uncle Remus. Boston, J. R. Osgood 1883. 12mo. First Edition

———— Stories from American history. New York, D. Appleton 1896. 4to. First Edition

———— Tales of the home folks. Boston, Houghton Mifflin 1898. 12mo. First Edition

———— Uncle Remus his songs and his sayings. New York, D. Appleton 1881. 12mo. First Edition

———— Uncle Remus returns. Boston, Houghton Mifflin 1918. 12mo. First Edition

Harte, Francis Bret. Condensed novels. New York, G. W. Carleton 1867. 12mo. First Edition. (M. L. Parrish)

———— Gabriel Conroy. Hartford 1876. 8vo. First American Edition

———— The heathen Chinee. Chicago, The Western News Co. (1870). 4to. (9 lithographic illustrations on cards in original envelope). First Edition, First Issue

———— The lost galleon. San Francisco, Towne & Bacon 1867. 12mo. First Edition

———— A millionaire of Rough-and-Ready and Devil's Ford. Boston, Houghton Mifflin 1887. 16mo. First Edition. (Whitall)

———— The pliocene skull. n.p. (1871). 4to. First Edition, Second Issue, original pictorial wrappers

The Harvard Register, No. 1-12, March 1827-February 1828. Cambridge, Hilliard and Brown 1827-8. 8vo. Original wrappers, uncut

Hawthorne, Nathaniel. Biographical stories for children. Boston, Tappan and Dennett 1842. 16mo. First Edition. (Maier–Wallace)

American Literature

[Hawthorne, Nathaniel]. Fanshawe. Boston, Marsh & Capen 1828. 12mo. First Edition

——— The gentle boy. Boston, Weeks, Jordan 1839. obl. 4to. First Edition

——— Grandfather's chair. Boston, E. P. Peabody 1841. 24mo. First Edition

——— Letters of Hawthorne to William D. Ticknor 1851-1864. Newark, N. J., The Carteret Book Club 1910. 2 v. 12mo.

——— Life of Franklin Pierce. Boston, Ticknor, Reed and Fields 1852. 12mo. First Edition. (Presentation copy, inscribed, from the author to Miss Maria Eastman)

——— Love letters 1839-1863. Chicago, The Society of the Dofobs 1907. 2 v. 8vo.

——— The marble faun. Boston, Ticknor and Fields 1860. 2 v. 12mo. First American Edition, First Issue

[———] Peter Parley's universal history. Boston, American Stationers' Company 1837. 2 v. sq. 12mo. First Edition. (H.V. Jones)

——— The scarlet letter. Boston, Ticknor, Reed and Fields 1850. 12mo. First Edition

——— Tanglewood tales. Boston, Ticknor, Reed and Fields 1853. 12mo. First Edition

——— True stories. Boston, Ticknor, Reed and Fields 1851. 12mo. First Edition, First Issue

[Hay, John]. The bread-winners. New York, Harper 1884. 12mo. First Edition

——— Jim Bludso. Boston, J. R. Osgood 1871. 12mo. First Edition, original wrappers

——— Little-Breeches. New York, J. S. Redfield 1871. 8vo. First Edition, original wrappers

Hearn, Lafcadio. Stray leaves from stray literature. Boston, J. R. Osgood 1844. 16mo. First Edition

Holmes, Oliver Wendell. An address delivered at the annual meeting of the Boston Microscopical Society. Cambridge, Riverside Press 1877. 8vo.

Holmes, Oliver Wendell. The autocrat of the breakfast-table. Boston, Phillips, Sampson 1858. 12mo. First Edition. (Copy 1, brown cloth, 5 rings on spine; copies 2-3, brown cloth and blue cloth respectively, 4 rings on spine)

———— Before the curfew. Boston, Houghton Mifflin 1888. 12mo. First Edition

———— Currents and counter-currents in medical science. Boston, Ticknor and Fields 1861. 12mo. First Edition

———— Dorothy Q. Boston, Houghton Mifflin 1893. 12mo.

———— Elsie Venner. Boston, Ticknor and Fields 1861. 2 v. 12mo. First Edition, First Issue

———— The guardian angel. Boston, Ticknor and Fields 1867. 12mo. First Edition

———— Homoeópathy. Boston, W. D. Ticknor 1842. 8vo. First Edition, original boards and label

———— The iron gate. Boston, Houghton Mifflin 1880. 12mo. First Edition

———— John Lothrop Motley. Boston, Houghton, Osgood 1879. 4to. First Edition. Large paper

———— Mechanism in thought and morals. Boston, J. R. Osgood 1871. 12mo.

———— Oration . . . on the fourth of July, 1863. Boston, J. E. Farwell 1863. 8vo. First Edition, original wrappers

———— Poems. Boston, Otis, Broaders 1836. 8vo. First Edition

———— The poet at the breakfast-table. Boston, J. R. Osgood 1872. 12mo. First Edition. (Presentation copy, inscribed, from the author to C. S. Calverley)

———— Songs in many keys. Boston, Ticknor and Fields 1862. 12mo. First Edition

———— Songs of many seasons. Boston, J. R. Osgood 1875. 12mo. First Edition

———— Soundings from the Atlantic. Boston, Ticknor and Fields 1864. 12mo. First Edition. (With autograph signature of F. B. Sanborn, Nov. 21, 1863)

American Literature

Homerus. The Iliad. Tr. by W. C. Bryant. Boston, Fields, Osgood 1870. 2 v. 8vo. First Edition. (F.W. Stearns)

Hovey, Richard. *See* Carman, Bliss, *and* Richard Hovey

Howe, Julia Ward. Later lyrics. Boston, J. E. Tilton 1866. 12mo. First Edition. (Presentation copy, inscribed, from the author to F. H. Hedge)

Howells, William Dean. The rise of Silas Lapham. Boston, Ticknor 1885. 12mo. First Edition

[———— *and* John James Piatt]. Poems of two friends. Columbus, Follett, Foster 1860. 12mo. First Edition

Humphreys, David. A poem, on the happiness of America. Hartford, Hudson and Goodwin [?1786]. 4to. Original wrappers

Irving, Washington. The Alhambra. Philadelphia, Carey & Lea 1832. 2 v. 8vo. First Edition

———— Astoria. Philadelphia, Carey, Lea & Blanchard 1836. 2 v. 8vo. First Edition

———— A chronicle of the conquest of Granada. Philadelphia, Carey, Lea & Carey 1829. 2 v. 8vo. First Edition

———— The Crayon miscellany. Philadelphia, Carey, Lea & Blanchard 1835. 3 v. 8vo.

———— The history of the life and voyages of Christopher Columbus. New York, G. & C. Carvill 1828. 3 v. 8vo. First Edition

James, Henry. The American scene. New York, Harper 1907. 8vo. First Edition. (Mark Twain's copy, with his autograph signature)

———— Essays in London. London, J. R. Osgood, McIlvaine 1893. 8vo. First Edition

———— French poets and novelists. London, Macmillan 1884. 12mo.

———— The ivory tower. London, W. Collins (1917). 12mo. First Edition

———— The Princess Casamassima. London, Macmillan 1886. 3 v. 12mo. First Edition. (A. L. Wyant)

———— The question of our speech. Boston, Houghton Mifflin 1905. 12mo. First Edition

James, Henry.   The sense of the past.   London, W. Collins (1917). 12mo.   First Edition

———— Transatlantic sketches.   Boston, J. R. Osgood 1875.   12mo. First Edition

Lanier, Sidney.   Poems.   Philadelphia, J. B. Lippincott 1877.   12mo. First Edition

Law, Andrew.   Select harmony.   [?Cheshire, Conn., c. 1782].   obl. 8vo.

[Livingston, William].   America.   New-Haven, T. and S. Green [1770].   sm. 4to.

Longfellow, Henry Wadsworth.   The belfry of Bruges.   Cambridge, J. Owen 1846.   12mo.   First Edition, First Issue, original wrappers, front wrapper dated 1845.   (Wallace)

———— Christus.   Boston, J. R. Osgood 1872.   3 v.   8vo.   First Edition

———— Excelsior.   New York 1872.   16mo.   First Separate Edition, stitched

———— From my arm-chair.   (Cambridge 1879).   sm. 8vo.   First Edition.   (Wakeman)

———— The golden legend.   Boston, Ticknor, Reed and Fields 1851. 12mo.   First Edition

———— Hyperion.   New York, S. Colman 1839.   2 v.   8vo.   First Edition

———— In the harbor. Ultima Thule. Pt. II.   Boston, Houghton Mifflin 1882.   12mo.   First Edition

———— The masque of Pandora.   Boston, J. R. Osgood 1875.   12mo. First Edition.   (Wakeman)

———— Michael Angelo.   Boston, Houghton Mifflin 1883.   8vo.   First Edition

———— The New-England tragedies.   Boston, Ticknor and Fields 1868.   12mo.   First Edition.   (M. L. Parrish)

[————] Outre-mer.   New York, Harper 1835.   2 v.   12mo.   First Complete Edition

———— Poems on slavery.   Cambridge, J. Owen 1842.   12mo.   First Edition. (Presentation copy, inscribed, from the author to Thomas Campbell)

Longfellow, Henry Wadsworth. Saggi de' novellieri italiani. Boston 1832. 12mo. First Edition. (Bierstadt–Wallace)

——— The song of Hiawatha. Boston, Ticknor and Fields 1855. 12mo. First Edition, First Issue. (Presentation copy, inscribed, from the author to George W. Greene)

——— The Spanish student. Cambridge, J. Owen 1843. 12mo. First Edition, uncut. (Maier–Wallace)

——— Syllabus de la grammaire italienne. Boston 1832. 12mo. First Edition, uncut. (Wallace)

——— Ultima Thule. Boston, Houghton Mifflin 1880. 8vo. First Edition, limp white cloth

——— Voices of the night. Cambridge, J. Owen 1839. 8vo. First Edition

——— The waif. Cambridge, J. Owen 1845. sm. 8vo. First Edition, original wrappers. (Wakeman)

——— *See also* Miscellaneous poems selected from the United States Literary Gazette

[——— *editor*]. Novelas españolas. Brunswick 1830. 12mo. First Edition, First Issue. (Halsey)

——— *tr.* Coplas de Don Jorge Manrique. Boston, Allen and Ticknor 1833. 12mo. First Edition. (Copy 1, Halsey; 2, Presentation copy, inscribed, to Dr. Nichols)

——— Elements of French grammar. Portland, S. Colman 1830. 12mo. (Chamberlain–Wallace)

——— French exercises. Portland, S. Colman 1830. 12mo. (Chamberlain–Wallace)

Lowell, James Russell. Address delivered . . . at Birmingham . . . 1884. (London, Harrison 1884). sm. 4to. Proof copy. (Wakeman)

——— Among my books. Boston, Fields, Osgood 1870. 12mo. First Edition

——— ——— Second series. Boston, J. R. Osgood 1876. 12mo. First Edition

——— The Biglow papers. Cambridge, G. P. Putnam 1848. 12mo. First Edition. (Presentation copy, inscribed, from "Homer Wilbur")

Lowell, James Russell.   The Biglow papers.   Second series.   Boston, Ticknor and Fields 1867.   12mo.   First Edition

——— ——— London, J. C. Hotten 1859.   16mo.   Unauthorized Edition

[———] Class poem. (Cambridge) 1838.   8vo.   First Edition, original wrappers.   (Maier)

——— Conversations on some of the old poets.   Cambridge, J. Owen 1845.   12mo.   First Edition, original wrappers, uncut

[———] A fable for critics. (New York) G. P. Putnam 1848.   12mo. First Edition, First Issue

——— Fireside travels.   Boston, Ticknor and Fields 1864.   12mo. First Edition. (Presentation copy, inscribed, from Lowell to Mrs. Gaskell)

——— Mason and Slidell. (Boston 1862).   8vo. (Wakeman)

——— Ode recited at the commemoration of the living and dead soldiers of Harvard University.   Cambridge, Privately printed 1865. roy. 8vo. (R. G. White–Chamberlain–Wallace)

——— On democracy.   Birmingham (1884).   8vo.   First Published Edition, First Issue, original wrappers

[———] Il pesceballo. [Cambridge 1862].   16mo.   First Edition, stitched. (Wallace)

——— ——— Chicago, The Caxton Club 1899.   8vo.

——— A year's life.   Boston, C. C. Little and J. Brown 1841.   12mo. First Edition

Lowell, Maria.   The poems of Maria Lowell.   Cambridge, Privately printed 1855.   4to.   First Edition. (Presentation copy, inscribed, from J. R. Lowell to Mrs. Wells)

McKinley, William.   Address . . . April 27, 1897.   Washington 1897. 4to. (With author's autograph signature on front wrapper)

Markham, Edwin.   The man with the hoe.   4to.   San Francisco, A. M. Robertson (1899).   First Edition, original wrappers, uncut

Masters, Edgar Lee.   A book of verses.   Chicago, Way & Williams 1898. 12mo.   First Edition

——— The new Spoon River.   New York, Boni and Liveright 1924. 8vo.   First Edition

American Literature

Masters, Edgar Lee. Spoon River anthology. New York, Macmillan 1915. 12mo. First Edition

Melville, Herman. Battle-pieces. New York, Harper 1866. 12mo. First Edition

———— The confidence-man. New York, Dix, Edwards 1857. 12mo. First Edition

———— Israel Potter. New York, G. P. Putnam 1855. 12mo. First Edition

———— Mardi. New York, Harper 1849. 2 v. 12mo. First Edition

———— Moby-Dick. New York, Harper 1851. 12mo. First Edition

———— Omoo. New York, Harper 1847. 12mo. First Edition

———— The piazza tales. New York, Dix & Edwards 1856. 12mo. First Edition

———— Pierre. New York, Harper 1852. 12mo. First Edition

———— Redburn. New York, Harper 1849. 12mo. First Edition

———— Typee. New York, Wiley and Putnam 1846. 12mo. First Edition

———— ———— ———— 1847. 12mo. Revised Edition

———— White-jacket. New York, Harper 1850. 12mo. First Edition

Mencken, Henry Louis. The American language. 8vo. New York, A. A. Knopf 1919. First Edition

Millay, Edna St. Vincent. Aria da capo. [London] 1920. 4to. First Edition, original pictorial wrappers, uncut. (The Chapbook, No. 14)

———— The ballad of the harp-weaver. New York, for F. Shay 1922. 4to. First Edition, original wrappers

———— A few figs from thistles. New York, F. Shay 1921. 4to. First Edition, original wrappers. (Salvo, No. I)

———— The harp-weaver. New York, Harper 1923. 12mo. First Edition

———— The lamp and the bell. New York, F. Shay 1921. 8vo. First Edition, original wrappers

Millay, Edna St. Vincent. Renascence. New York, M. Kennerley 1912. 12mo. (*In* The lyric year)

———— Renascence and other poems. New York, M. Kennerley 1917. 12mo. First Edition

———— Two slatterns and a king. Cincinnati, S. Kidd (1921). 12mo. First Edition, original wrappers

Miller, Joaquin. Chants for the Boer. San Francisco, Whitaker & Ray 1900. 4to. First Edition, original wrappers

———— '49 the gold-seeker of the Sierras. New York, Funk & Wagnalls 1884. 12mo. First Edition, inscribed by the author

———— Forty-nine. San Francisco, Whitaker & Ray-Wiggin Co. 1910. 12mo. First Edition, original wrappers

———— Joaquin, et al. Portland, Oregon, S. J. McCormick 1869. 12mo. First Edition

———— Pacific poems. London, Whittingham and Wilkins 1871. 16mo. First Edition. (Presentation copy, inscribed, from George F. Armstrong to Edward Dowden, March 1871)

———— Shadows of Shasta. Chicago, Jansen, McClurg 1881. 12mo. First Edition. (R. W. Emerton)

———— Songs of Italy. Boston, Roberts 1878. 12mo. First Edition, inscribed by the author

———— Songs of the Sierras. London, Longmans, Green, Reader and Dyer 1871. 12mo. First Edition. (Presentation copy, inscribed, from the author to Edward Dowden, May 17, 1871)

———— Songs of the soul. San Francisco, Whitaker & Ray 1896. 4to. First Edition

Miscellaneous poems selected from the United States Literary Gazette. Boston, Cummings, Hilliard . . . and Harrison Gray 1826. 16mo.

Mitchell, Donald Grant. Dream life. New York, Scribner 1851. 12mo. First Edition

———— Reveries of a bachelor. New York, Baker & Scribner 1850. 12mo. First Edition

Moore, Clement Clarke. Poems. New York, Bartlett & Welford 1844. 12mo. First Edition

Moore, Mrs. M. B. The Dixie speller. Raleigh, N. C., Branson & Farrar 1864. 16mo. (W. L. Andrews)

Moore, Mrs. M. B.   The geographical reader.   Raleigh, N. C., Branson, Farrar 1863.   4to.   Original pictorial boards.   (W. L. Andrews)

[Motley, John Lothrop].   Merry-Mount.   Boston, J. Munroe 1849. 2 v.   12mo.   First Edition

[———]   Morton's Hope.   New York, Harper 1839.   2 v.   12mo. First Edition

National songster.   Hagers-town, J. Gruber and D. May 1814.   8vo. Original wrappers

The New-England primer.   Boston, J. White, n.d.   sm. 4to.

———   New-England, for the Book sellers [1804-10].   24mo.   (Heartman 335)

———   Boston, Mass. Sabbath School Society 1839.   32mo.   Original wrappers

The New-England primer, enlarged and improved.   Boston, S. Hall [1789-92].   32mo.   (W. E. Spalding).   (Heartman 317)

The New-England primer improved.   Boston, W. M'Alpine 1767. sm. 4to.   (Heartman 26)

———   New York, for the Book sellers 1829.   32mo.   Original blue wrappers.   (Heartman 292)

Olmsted, T.   The musical olio.   Northampton, A. Wright 1805.   obl. 24mo.

O'Neill, Eugene.   All God's chillun got wings and Welded.   New York, Boni and Liveright (1924).   12mo.   First Edition

———   Before breakfast.   New York, F. Shay 1916.   First Edition, original wrappers

———   Bound east for Cardiff.   New York, F. Shay 1916.   8vo. Original wrappers.   (The Provincetown plays. First series)

———   Desire under the elms.   New York, Boni & Liveright 1925. 12mo.   First Edition

———   The Emperor Jones.   Cincinnati, S. Kidd (1921).   12mo. First Edition, original wrappers

———   Gold.   New York, Boni and Liveright (1920).   12mo.   First Edition

———   The great God Brown. The fountain. The moon of the Caribbees.   New York, Boni & Liveright 1926.   12mo.   First Edition

American Literature

O'Neill, Eugene.   The hairy ape. Anna Christie. The first man.   New York, Boni and Liveright (1922).   12mo.   First Edition

———— The moon of the Caribbees.   New York, Boni and Liveright 1919.   12mo.   First Edition

———— Thirst.   Boston, Gorham Press (1914).   12mo.   First Edition

Page, Thomas Nelson.   The burial of the guns.   New York, Charles Scribner's Sons 1894.   12mo.   First Edition

———— In ole Virginia.   New York, Charles Scribner's Sons 1887.   12mo.   First Edition

———— Social life in old Virginia.   New York, Charles Scribner's Sons 1897.   8vo.   First Edition

Parkman, Francis.   Vassall Morton.   Boston, Phillips, Sampson 1856.   12mo.   First Edition

Payne, John Howard.   Accusation.   London, for C. Chapple 1817.   12mo.   First Edition, stitched

———— Clari.   London, J. Miller 1823.   8vo.   First Edition, stitched

[————] Julia.   New York, D. Longworth 1806.   24mo.   First Edition.   (McKee)

———— Memoirs.   London, for J. Miller 1815.   8vo.   First Edition, uncut.   (Dick)

Pike, Albert.   Prose sketches and poems.   Boston, Light & Horton 1834.   12mo.   First Edition

Poe, Edgar Allan.   Al Aaraaf, Tamerlane, and minor poems.   Baltimore, Hatch & Dunning 1829.   8vo.   (C. B. Foote)

———— The conchologist's first book.   Philadelphia, Haswell, Barrington and Haswell 1839.   12mo.   First Edition

———— Eureka.   New York, G. P. Putnam 1848.   12mo.   First Edition

———— Mesmerism.   London, Short 1846.   8vo.   First Edition.   (Hailstone–Buxton Forman)

[————] The narrative of Arthur Gordon Pym.   New York, Harper 1838.   12mo.   First Edition

———— The raven and other poems.   New York, Wiley and Putnam 1845.   12mo.   First Edition, original wrappers

Poe, Edgar Allan. Tales. New York, Wiley and Putnam 1845. 12mo. First Edition

———— Tales of the grotesque and arabesque. Philadelphia, Lea and Blanchard 1840. 2 v. 8vo. First Edition

———— The works. New York, J. S. Redfield 1850. 2 v. 12mo. First Edition

Pound, Ezra. Cathay. London, E. Mathews 1915. 12mo. First Edition, original wrappers, uncut. (Presentation copy, inscribed, from the author to John Quinn)

———— Exultations. London, E. Mathews 1909. 12mo. First Edition

———— The fourth canto. (London) J. Rodker 1919. 8vo. First Edition. (No. 4 of 40 copies privately printed on Japanese vellum)

———— Gaudier-Brzeska. London, J. Lane 1916. 4to. First Edition. (Quinn)

———— Hugh Selwyn Mauberley. (London) J. Rodker 1920. 8vo. First Edition. (No. 20 of 20 signed copies numbered 16-35)

———— Indiscretions. Paris, Three Mountains Press 1923. 8vo. First Edition. (No. 19 of an edition of 300 copies)

———— Lustra. [London 1916]. 8vo. First Edition. (No. 144 of an edition of 200 copies)

———— Personae. London, E. Mathews 1909. 12mo. First Edition

———— Quia pauper amavi. London, The Egoist Ltd., n.d. 8vo. First Edition. (Quinn. No. 15 of an edition of 100 signed copies)

———— Umbra. London, E. Mathews 1920. sm. 4to. First Collected Edition. (Quinn)

———— *See also* Cavalcanti, Guido; Fenollosa, Ernest

The Provincetown plays. New York, F. Shay 1916. 8vo. First Edition, original wrappers

Pumphrey, Stanley. Indian civilization. With introduction by J. G. Whittier. Philadelphia 1877. 8vo. First Edition, original wrappers

Read, Daniel. The Columbian harmonist, No. 2. New Haven [1793]. obl. 8vo.

Reid, Whitelaw. Byron. London, Harrison 1910. 8vo. First Edition, original wrappers

────── One Welshman. London, Harrison 1912. 8vo. First Edition, original wrappers

────── The Scot in America. London, Harrison 1911. 8vo. First Edition, original wrappers

Riley, James Whitcomb. "The old swimmin'-hole." Indianapolis, G. C. Hitt 1883. 16mo. Original wrappers, uncut

Robinson, Edwin Arlington. The children of the night. Boston, Badger 1897. 12mo. First Edition

────── Dionysus in doubt. New York, Macmillan 1925. 8vo. First Edition. (No. 136 of an edition of 350 signed copies. Large paper)

────── The glory of the nightingales. New York, Macmillan 1930. 8vo. First Edition

────── The man against the sky. New York, Macmillan 1916. 16mo. First Edition

────── The man who died twice. New York, Macmillan 1924. 8vo. First Edition. (No. 85, signed by the author. Large paper)

────── The three taverns. New York, Macmillan 1920. 16mo. First Edition

────── The torrent and The night before. (Cambridge, Riverside Press) 1896. 16mo. First Edition, original wrappers, uncut. (Presentation copy, inscribed, from the author to G. W. Latham)

────── The town down the river. New York, Charles Scribner's Sons 1910. 16mo. First Edition

[Rogers, Robert]. Ponteach. London, J. Millan 1766. 8vo. First Edition

Sappho. The poems of Sappho. An interpretative rendition into English by J. M. O'Hara. Portland (Smith & Sale) 1910. 8vo. First Edition. (No. 111 of an edition of 500 copies)

Sargent, Epes. Songs of the sea. Boston, J. Munroe 1847. 8vo. First Edition. (Presentation copy to F. A. Durivage)

Saxe, John Godfrey. Leisure-day rhymes. Boston, J. R. Osgood 1875. 8vo. First Edition. (Presentation copy to Locker)

American Literature

Saxe, John Godfrey. The masquerade. Boston, Ticknor and Fields 1866. 8vo. First Edition. (Presentation copy to Locker)

[———] Pensées. [Albany, Privately printed 1872]. 8vo. (Presentation copy, Locker's jester bookplate)

Searson, John. Mount Vernon. Philadelphia, Folwell [1799]. 8vo. First Edition

Serious reflections on the times. Philadelphia, J. Chattin 1757. 12mo. First Edition. (W. L. Andrews)

Simms, Jeptha Root. The American spy. Albany, J. Munsell 1857. 8vo. Original wrappers

Simms, William Gilmore. Areytos. Charleston, J. Russell 1846. 12mo. First Edition, original wrappers, uncut. (Presentation copy, inscribed, to Alfred B. Street)

——— Donna Florida. Charleston, Burges and James 1843. 16mo. First Edition, original wrappers, uncut. (Presentation copy, inscribed, to Alfred B. Street)

——— Guy Rivers. New York, Harper 1834. 2 v. 12mo. First Edition. (W. T. Emmet)

[———] Mellichampe. New York, Harper 1836. 2 v. 12mo. First Edition

——— The vision of Cortes, Cain, and other poems. Charleston, J. S. Burges 1829. 16mo. First Edition

[Smith, Elihu Hubbard, *compiler*]. American poems. Litchfield, Collier and Buel [1793]. I (all published). 8vo. (Stevens–McKee–Sturges)

Stearns, Charles. The ladies' philosophy of love. Leominster, Mass., J. Prentiss 1797. sm. 4to. First Edition

Stein, Gertrude. Portrait of Mabel Dodge at the Villa Curonia. [Florence] n.d. 12mo. First Edition

Sterling, Richard, *and* J. D. Campbell. Our own Third reader. Greensboro, N. C., Sterling, Campbell, and Albright, n.d. 16mo. Stereotype Edition

Stoddard, Richard Henry. Foot-prints. New York, Spalding & Shepard 1849. 8vo. First Edition, original wrappers. (McKee)

Stowe, Harriet Beecher. A key to Uncle Tom's cabin. Boston, J. P. Jewett 1853. 8vo. First Edition, original wrappers

Stowe, Harriet Beecher.　Uncle Tom's cabin.　Boston, J. P. Jewett
　1852.　2 v.　12mo.　First Edition

───── ───── London, J. Cassell 1852.　8vo.　13 pts., original wrappers, plates by George Cruikshank

Taft, William Howard.　Our chief magistrate.　New York 1916.
　12mo.　First Edition.　(Presentation copy, inscribed, from the
　author to Alfred C. Chapin)

Taylor, James Bayard.　Rhymes of travel.　New York, G. P. Putnam
　1849.　12mo.　First Edition

───── Ximena.　Philadelphia, H. Hooker 1844.　16mo.　First Edition.　(Presentation copy, inscribed)

Thomas, Robert B.　The farmer's almanack (1793-1831).　Nos. 1-39.
　Boston (1792-1830).　8vo.

───── The old farmer's almanack (1832-1900).　Nos. 40-108.　Boston (1831-99).　8vo.

Thoreau, Henry David.　Letters to various persons.　Boston, Ticknor
　and Fields 1865.　12mo.　First Edition

───── Walden.　Boston, Ticknor and Fields 1854.　12mo.　First
Edition.　(Purdy)

───── A week on the Concord and Merrimack Rivers.　Boston, J.
　Munroe 1849.　12mo.　First Edition

Todd, John.　Long Lake.　Pittsfield, Mass., E. P. Little 1845.　16mo.
　First Edition

Trowbridge, John Townsend.　Cudjo's cave.　Boston, J. E. Tilton
　1864.　12mo.　First Edition.　(Eugene Field's copy, with his autograph)

[Trumbull, John].　M'Fingal.　Hartford, Hudson and Goodwin 1782.
　16mo.　(George Washington–Huth)

Tucker, Nathaniel.　The Bermudian.　Williamsburg, A. Purdie & J.
　Dixon 1774.　4to.　First Edition

───── ───── London, T. Cadell 1774.　4to.　(Presentation copy,
inscribed, from the author)

Twain, Mark.　*See* Clemens, Samuel Langhorne

The Uncle Tom's cabin almanack . . . for 1853.　London, J. Cassell.
　8vo.　Original wrappers

Ware, Eugene F. Rhymes of Ironquill. Topeka, Kansas 1889. 8vo. First Edition. (Presentation copy, inscribed, from the author to J. K. O. Sherwood)

—— Some rhymes of Ironquill of Kansas. Chicago, A. C. McClurg 1892. 12mo. First Edition. (Presentation copy, inscribed, from the author to Major J. B. Pond)

Washington, Booker. The story of the negro. New York 1909. 2 v. 8vo. First Edition. (Presentation copy, inscribed, from the author to James Carlton Young)

The Weal-reaf. Sept. 4, 5, 6, 7, 8, 10, 11, 1860. Salem, Mass., 1860. 7 nos. 4to. First Edition

Webster, Noah. A compendious dictionary. [Hartford] Hudson & Goodwin 1806. 12mo. First Edition

—— Dissertations on the English language. Boston, I. Thomas 1789. 8vo. First Edition

—— A grammatical institute of the English language. Pt. II. Hartford, Barlow & Babcock 1785. 16mo. First Edition

Wharton, Edith. Ethan Frome. New York 1911. 12mo. First Edition

Wheatley, Phillis. Poems on comic, serious, and moral subjects. London, for J. French, n.d. 12mo. Second Edition, corrected. (Heartman XIV)

Whitman, Walt. Complete poems & prose. (Philadelphia, Ferguson 1888). 8vo. (Presentation copy, inscribed, from the author to Miss Lucy H. Wilson). (No. 503 of an edition of 600 numbered copies)

—— The complete writings. New York, G. P. Putnam 1902. 10 v. 8vo. Paumanok Edition. (No. 120 of an edition of 300 sets)

—— Leaves of grass. Brooklyn 1855. sm. fol. First Edition, First Issue. Printed slip "London: Wm. Horsell, 492, Oxford-street." pasted on title

—— When lilacs last in the door-yard bloomed. (London) Essex House Press 1900. 12mo. (No. 127 of 135 copies on vellum)

Whittier, John Greenleaf. The bay of seven islands. Boston, Houghton Mifflin 1883. 12mo. First Edition

—— The chapel of the hermits. Boston, Ticknor, Reed and Fields 1853. 8vo. First Edition

Whittier, John Greenleaf.   Justice and expediency.   Haverhill, C. P. Thayer 1833.   8vo.   First Edition.   (Wakeman)

——— The King's missive.   Boston, Houghton Mifflin 1881.   12mo. First Edition.   (William Harris Arnold)

——— Mogg Megone.   Boston, Light & Stearns 1836.   32mo.   First Edition.   (Autographed by the author with his initials)

[———] Moll Pitcher.   Boston, Carter and Hendee 1832.   8vo.   First Edition, stabbed.   (Chamberlain–Wallace)

——— National lyrics.   Boston, Ticknor and Fields 1865.   16mo. First Edition

——— The panorama.   Boston, Ticknor and Fields 1856.   12mo. First Edition

——— Poems.   Philadelphia, J. Healy 1838.   12mo.   First Edition

——— Poems written during the progress of the abolition question. Boston, I. Knapp 1837.   12mo.   First Edition, First Issue.   (Maier– Wallace)

——— Songs of labor.   Boston, Ticknor, Reed and Fields 1850. 12mo.   First Edition

[———] The stranger in Lowell.   Boston, Waite, Peirce 1845.   8vo. First Edition, original wrappers, uncut

——— The supernaturalism of New England.   New York, Wiley & Putnam 1847.   12mo.   First Edition

——— The sycamores.   Nantucket 1857 [Hartford, Conn.].   32mo. First Edition.   (Presentation copy, inscribed, from the author to Hugh Tallant)

——— The tent on the beach.   Boston, Ticknor and Fields 1867. 12mo.   First Edition, First Issue

——— ——— ——— Second Issue

——— ——— ——— Third Issue

——— ——— ——— Fourth Issue

——— The vision of Echard.   Boston, Houghton, Osgood 1878. 12mo.   First Edition.   (ANS from Whittier inserted)

——— *See also* Pumphrey, Stanley

Wilson, Woodrow.   Inaugural address . . . March 4, 1913.   Washington 1913.   8vo.   (With Wilson's autograph signature)

American Literature

Wilson, Woodrow.   Mere literature.   Boston, Houghton Mifflin 1896. 12mo.   First Edition

———— The State.   Boston, D. C. Heath 1889.   12mo.   First Edition

Wister, Owen.   Lady Baltimore.   New York 1906.   8vo.   (No. 35, signed by the author)

Wolcott, Roger.   Poetical meditations.   New London, T. Green 1725. sm. 8vo.   First Edition.   (Brinley–Hoe–C. L. F. Robinson)

Woodberry, George Edward.   The Players' elegy on the death of Edwin Booth . . . Nov. 13, 1893.   New York, Privately printed 1893.   12mo.   First Edition, original blue wrappers.   (Presentation copy, inscribed, from the author to Frank Dexter Sherman)

York, Brantley.   York's English grammar.   Raleigh, N. C., Branson, Farrar 1864.   8vo.   Third Edition.   (W. L. Andrews)

Broadsides

Carpenter, William.   A poem, on the execution of William Shaw.   n.p. (1770).   4to.

Emerson, Ralph Waldo.   The Concord hymn.   n.p. [1836].   (First appearance in print of the hymn sung at the completion of the Concord Monument, 19 April 1836).   12mo.

Holmes, Oliver Wendell.   James Russell Lowell. 1819-1891.   [Boston 1891].   8vo.

Ingersoll, Robert Green.   Life.   n.p. Dec. 15, 1886.   sm. fol.

Niles, Nathaniel.   The American hero.   Norwich (Conn.) 1775.   sm. fol.

Smith, Samuel Francis.   [America].   [Boston] 1831.   fol.   (First appearance in print of the hymn "America," sung July 4, 1831 at the Celebration of American Independence by the Boston Sabbath School Union, at Park Street Church. This broadside gives the order of exercises of the Celebration)

Whittier, John Greenleaf.   Our countrymen in chains.   [New York] Sold at the Anti Slavery Office . . . [1835].   fol.

Manuscripts

Bancroft, George.   A. L. S.   New York, 9 Nov. 1852.   To John D. G. Shea concerning his book on the Mississippi Valley

American Literature

Bryant, William Cullen. A. Poem S. Williamstown, August 25, 1848

—— A. L. S. New York, December 21, 1854. To —— concerning the publication of "Thanatopsis"

Emerson, Ralph Waldo. A. L. S. Boston, 8 August 1832. To Rev. Charles Brooks. (Wakeman)

—— A. L. S. Boston, 14 August 1832. To Rev. Charles Brooks. (Wakeman)

Field, Eugene. A. Poem S. n.p. n.d.

Freneau, Philip. A. D. S. Philadelphia, July 1, 1793. (Receipt)

Halleck, Fitz-Greene. A. Poem S. Burns. New York, June 13, 1866

—— A. Poem S. Marco Bozzaris. n.p. May 27, 1866

Higginson, Thomas Wentworth. A. L. S. Cambridge, May 3, 1902. To J. C. Chamberlain

Longfellow, Henry Wadsworth. A. L. S. Bowdoin College, June 27, 1830. To George W. Greene, East Greenwich, R. I.

Lowell, James Russell. A. L. S. Elmwood, March 28, 1867. To Thos. W. Higginson

—— A. L. S. Elmwood, n.d. To Thos. W. Higginson

McCutcheon, George Barr. A. MS. S. The man from Brodney's. n.p. December 9, 1904

—— A. MS. S. The rose and the ring. n.p. Sept. 26, 1907

Payne, John Howard. A. MS. S. Home, sweet home. Washington, August 10, 1850

Poe, Edgar Allan. A. Poem S. n.p. n.d.

Smith, Samuel Francis. A. L. S. Newton Centre, May 7, 1874. To Mrs. Little

—— A. Poem S. America. [Newton Centre, May 7, 1874]

White, Richard Grant. A. N. S. n.p. December 16, 1867. To M. Henri Blot

Whittier, John Greenleaf. A. L. S. Amesbury, 6th. 5mo. 1871. To his publisher

Books by Greek Authors, Printed after 1500

This list includes also, translations of these works into languages other than English. It does *not* include Greek Bibles and liturgical books, or Greek works in Science. These, with Aldines, books by Greek authors printed before 1501, and *English* versions of Greek works, are listed in their several places under *Bibles*; *Science*; *Aldines*; *Incunabula*; and *English Literature*

SIXTEENTH AND SEVENTEENTH CENTURIES

Ælianus, *Tacticus*. De militaribus [Greek]. Venetiis, apud A. & I. Spinellos 1552. 4to. (Porson–Heber–Doble)

Anacreon. Teij odae [Greek]. Lutetiae, apud H. Stephanum 1554. 4to. First Edition. (Thomas Sydenham)

Aristophanes. Facetissimi comoedie novem [Greek]. Paris, G. de Gourmont 1528. 4to. (W. J. Canham–Huth)

——— Facetissimi comoediae undecim [Greek]. Basileae, apud A. Cratandrum & I. Bebelium 1532. 8vo. First Edition of the XI comedies together. (Cornelius Paine–Andrews)

Aristoteles. Dialectica resolutio. Edita per Alphonsum A vera Cruce. Mexici, I. paulus 1554. fol.

Chrysostom. *See* John, Chrysostom, *Saint*

Diodorus Siculus. [Bibliotheca, e graeco in latinum a Poggio traducta]. (Paris) Denis Roce [a. 1500?]. 4to. (Syston Park)

——— Historiarum libri [Greek]. Basileae, J. Oporinus 1539. 8vo. First Edition. (Baker–Harwood–Wodhull)

Eusebius *Pamphili, Bp.* Chronicon. Parisiorum . . . H. Stephanum 1518. 4to.

——— Ecclesiasticae historiae libri X [Greek]. Lutetiae Parisiorum, ex officina R. Stephani 1544. 4to. in eights. First Edition

Eustathius. Commentarii in Homeri Iliadem et Odysseam [Greek]. Romae, apud A. Bladum 1542-50. 4 v. fol. First Edition. (Syston Park)

Homerus. Ilias [Greek]. Typis regiis. Parisiis, apud A. Turnebum 1554. 8vo. (Sunderland)

——— Ilias [Greek]. Londini, G. Bishop 1591. 8vo. (Lord Sommers, Baron of Evesham)

Greek after 1500

Homerus. Ilias et Ulyssea [Greek]. Basileae, apud I. Hervagium 1541. 2 v. fol. (Jean Brinon, sieur de Villaines)

———— Odyssea . . . zu teütsch transferiert. Augspurg, A. Weissenhorn 1537. fol.

———— *See also* Eustathius

John, Chrysostom, *Saint*. Τοῦ 'εν ἁγιοις Πατρὸς ἡμων 'Ιωαννοῦ τοῦ χρυσοστόμου τὰ εὑρισκόμενα. Etonae, I. Norton 1610-12. 8 v. fol. (STC 14629a)

Josephus, Flavius. Opera [Greek]. Basileae, I. Froben 1544. fol. First Edition

Longus. Pastoralium, de Daphnide & Chloë [Greek]. Florentiae, apud P. Iunctam 1598. 4to. First Edition. (Hoe–C. L. F. Robinson)

Musaeus. Museipoete Greci . . . de insano, & ob id deuitando Leādri, ac Herus amore Poemation. Parisiis, in aedibus Ascensianis 1514. 4to.

Naugerius, Andrea. Orationes duae. Lutetiae Parisiorum, praelo A. Augurelli 1531. 4to.

Philo Judaeus. In libros Mosis [Greek]. Regiis typis. Parisiis, ex officina A. Turnebi 1552. fol. First Edition

Pindarus. Olympia. Pythia. Nemea. Isthmia [Greek]. Romae, Z. Calergi (1515). 4to. (Sunderland)

Plato. Opera [Greek & Latin]. (Paris) H. Stephanus 1578. 3 v. in 2. fol. (Syston Park)

Plutarchus. Vitae Romanorum & Graecorum [Greek]. Florentiae, in aedibus P. iuntae 1517. fol. First Edition. (Bibliotheca Colbertina)

Polybius. Römische historien . . . in die teutsche . . . durch G. Xylandrum. Basel, S. Henricpetri 1574. fol.

Sabellicus, Marcus Antonius Coccius. Duodecim oratōes. Impressum parrasijs 1513. 4to.

Theocritus. Opera [Greek]. Rome, Z. Callierges 1516. 8vo. (Andrew Lang)

Xenophon. Opera [Greek]. Florentiae, in aedibus P. iuntae 1516. fol. First Edition

Xenophon. Oeconomicus Xenophontis. Rome, per Ioannem Besicken 1506. fol.

EIGHTEENTH CENTURY

Æsopus. Fabularum ... collectio [Greek and Latin]. Oxoniae, e typographeo Clarendoniano 1718. 8vo. (Huth)

Anacreon. Teii odaria [Greek and Latin]. Parmae, ex regio typographeio (I. B. Bodoni) 1784. 8vo. (Dunn)

———— ———— ———— 1785. 4to. (Syston Park)

Aristophanes. Comoediae undecim [Greek and Latin]. Amstelodami, Sumptibus T. Fritsch 1710. 2 v. fol. (Charles Butler)

Aristoteles. Ethicorum Nicomacheorum libri decem [Greek and Latin]. Oxonii, e Theatro Sheldoniano 1716. 8vo. (Charles Butler)

Herodotus. Historia [Greek and Latin]. Glasguae: R. et A. Foulis 1761. 9 v. 8vo. (Thomas Brooke)

Josephus, Flavius. Opera omnia [Greek and Latin]. Amstelaedami, apud R. & G. Wetstenios 1726. 2 v. fol. (Robert Barclay)

Longus. ΤΩΝ ΚΑΤᾺ ΔΑΦΝΙΝ ΚΑῚ ΧΛΟΉΝ. Parmae, ex regio typographeio (I. B. Bodoni) 1786. 4to. (With 20 plates by Audran inserted)

Pindarus. Olympia, Nemea, Pythia, Isthmia [Greek]. Ex editione Oxoniensi. Glasguae: R. & A. Foulis 1754-7. 4 v. in 2. 32mo. (Thomas Brooke)

Xenophon. De Cyri expeditione libri septem [Greek and Latin]. Oxonii, e Theatro Sheldoniano 1735. 2 v. 4to. (Sykes–Gosford–Vernon)

———— De Cyri institutione libri octo [Greek and Latin]. Oxonii, e Theatro Sheldoniano 1727. (Sykes–Gosford–Vernon)

AFTER 1800

Homerus. Carmina [Greek and Latin]. Lipsiae, Weidmann; Londini, I. Payne & Mackinlay 1802. 8 v. 8vo. (Lord Rancliffe)

Orpheus. The book of the Orphic Hymns [Greek]. Kentish Town, J. Hibbert 1827. 8vo. (W. Eames)

Greek after 1500

Plutarchus.   Plutarchus and Theophrastus, On superstition [Greek].
Kentish Town, J. Hibbert 1828.   8vo.   (W. Eames)

Strabo.   Rerum geographicarum libri XVII [Greek and Latin].
Oxonii: e typographeo Clarendoniano 1807.   2 v.   fol.

Xenophon.   L'Anabase. Avec un commentaire . . . par Colonel Arthur
Boucher.   Paris, Berger-Levrault 1913.   4to.

Books by Latin Authors, Printed after 1500

This list includes also, translations of these works into languages other than English. It does *not* include Latin Bibles and liturgical books, or Latin works in Science. These, with Aldines, books by Latin authors printed before 1501, and *English* versions of Latin works, are listed in their several places under *Bibles; Science; Aldines; Incunabula;* and *English Literature*

SIXTEENTH CENTURY

Albertus Magnus. Das buch der haymligkaytenn . . . von artzney vñ tugendē der kreütter. Augspurg, H. Steiner, n.d. sm. 4to.

———— De animalibus. Venetijs, impensa heredū . . . O. Scoti . . . ac sociorum 1519. fol. (D. H. Madden)

Apuleius Madaurensis, Lucius. Metamorphoseos. Venetiis, in aedibus I. Tacuini de Tridino 1516. fol.

Ars moriendi. Questa operetta tracta dellarte del ben morire. Venetiis, J. B. Sessa [c. 1503]. sm. 4to. (H. de Stailleur–Britwell)

Augustine, *Saint*. De doctrina christiana. Cologne, E. Cervicornus 1529. 8vo.

———— De fide & operibus. [Cologne] E. Cervicornus 1528. 8vo.

———— De natura & gratia. [Cologne] E. Cervicornus 1528. 8vo.

———— De spiritu & litera. n.p., I. Soter 1530. 8vo.

Boniface VIII, *Pope*. Sexti libri decretaliū. Paris, T. Kerver 1508. 4to. (Sussex–Hanrott)

Brusonius, Lucius Domitius. Lucani facetiarum exemplorum. Romae, I. Mazochius 1518. fol. First Edition

Caesar, Caius Julius. Commentarii Caesaris recogniti per Philippum Beroaldum. n.p. 1512. 8vo. (Huth)

———— Historien vom Gallier. Meyntz, J. Schöffer 1530. fol.

———— ———— Menntz, J. Schöffer 1532. fol. (Bement)

Calendar. Kalendarium Gregorianum. Romae, ex typographia D. Basae 1582. [Colophon] Romae, excudebat F. Zanettus 1582. 8vo.

Cicero, Marcus Tullius. Des . . . M. T. Ciceronis buchlein vō dem alter. Augspurg, in kosten vñ verlegung S. Grym 1522. fol. (Didot). (Probably the first German translation of *De senectute*)

Latin after 1500

Cicero, Marcus Tullius.   Officia Ciceronis, teutsch.   Franckfurt am Meyn, C. Egenolffs erben 1565.   fol.

——— Officiorum lib. III, Cato Maior, Laelius, Paradoxa stoicorum VI, Somnium Scipionis, ex lib. VI De republica.   Parisiis, ex officina R. Stephani 1543.   sm. 8vo.   (Huth)

——— Der teutsch Cicero.   Augspurg, H. Steiner 1535.   fol.

Clemens V, *Pope*.   Constitutiones.   Paris (T. Kerver) 1508.   4to. (Sussex–Hanrott)

Dionysius, Periegetes.   De situ orbis.   Parisij 1501.   4to.   (Huth)

Elucidarius...vel Vocabularius poeticus.   Hagenaw, H. Gran impensis ...J. Rynman finit 1512.   4to.   (Huth)

Epigrammata et poematia vetera.   Paris, D. Duval 1590.   [Colophon] ...1589.   12mo.   (White Knights–Heber–Mexborough)

Gregory XIII, *Pope*.   *See* Calendar

Hermas.   *See* Liber trium virorum

Horatius Flaccus, Quintus.   Le morali epistole di Horatio ... insieme con la poetica. Ridotte da L. Dolce.   Vinegia, G. Giolito 1559. 8vo.

Isinderus, Melchior.   Disputatio theologica de poenitentia.   Witebergae, ex officina I. Lufft 1548.   8vo.   (Huth)

John XXII, *Pope*.   Extravagantes communes.   Paris (T. Kerver) 1507. 4to.   (Sussex–Hanrott)

Justinianus, Flavius Anicius.   Textus infortiati.   Parisiis, in edibus F. regnault, n.d.   8vo.

Lateran Council.   Sa. Lateranen. concilium novissimum sub Iulio. II et Leone. X. celebratum.   Romae, I. Mazochium 1520.   fol.

Liber trium virorum & trium spiritualium virginum.   Parisijs, ex officina H. Stephani 1513.   fol.

Livius, Titus.   Deche di Tito Livio vulgare hystoriate.   Venetia, B. de Zani 1511.   fol.

——— Römische historien.   Meyntz, J. Schöffer 1533.   fol.   (Didot)

——— Römsche history.   Strassburg, J. Grüninger 1507.   fol.

Livius, Titus.   T. Livius Patavinus Historicus.   Moguntiae, in aedibus
    I. Scheffer 1518.   fol.   (Sunderland–Michael Tomkinson)

———— Titus Livius und: Lucius Florus. Von ankunfft desz Römischen
    reichs.   Franckfurt am Mayn, G. Rab, S. Feyrabend und W. Han-
    erben 1568.   fol.   (Kress)

Maximus, Pacificus.   Elegie.   Camerino, J. I. de Benedictis 1523.   4to.

Ovidius Naso, Publius.   Metamorphosin.   Venetiis, G. de Rusconi
    1509.   fol.

Plautus, Titus Maccius.   Comoediae vigīti.   Venetiis, M. Sessa & P.
    de rauānis socios 1518.   fol.

Plinius Secundus, Caius (*Pliny the elder*).   Historia mundi naturalis.
    Francoforti ad Moenum, ex officina M. Lechleri 1582.   fol.

Scheurel, Christopher.   Commentarius de vita & obitu.   n.p. 1515.   fol.

Septem Sapientes.   Pontianus dicta aut facta Septem Sapientum.   Strass-
    burg 1512.   4to.

Statius, Publius Papinius.   Thebais.   (Paris, J. Marchant for J. Petit,
    c. 1505).   4to.   (Heber–Knight Bruce)

Suetonius Tranquillus, Caius, *and others*.   Omnia quam antehac emen-
    datiora annotationes Des. Erasmi & Egnatij cognitu dignae. C.
    Suetonius Tranquillus . . . quatuor libris.   Basileae, in officina Fro-
    beniana 1533.   fol.   (Chained book)

Tacitus, Cornelius.   Libri quinque.   Rome, E. Guillereti 1515.   fol.
    (Huth)

Terentius Afer, Publius.   Il Terentio Latino, comentato in lingua tos-
    cana.   Venice 1548.   4to.

Valerius Flaccus, Caius.   Argonauticon.   (Paris) in chalcographia I.
    Badii Ascensii 1519.   fol.   (Dunn)

Vigerius, Marcus.   Decachordum.   Fani, H. Soncinus 1507.   fol.

Virgilius Maro, Publius.   Los doze libros dela Eneida.   Anvers, en casa
    de I. Bellero 1557.   12mo.   (Sutherland)

———— Dryzehē Aeneadischē bücher.   Strassburg, I. Grüninger 1515.
    fol.   (Murray)

Vitruvius Pollio, Marcus.   De architectura.   Venetiis, I. de Tridino
    alias Tacuino 1511.   fol.

Latin after 1500

SEVENTEENTH CENTURY

Cicero, Marcus Tullius. Opera. Lugd. Batavorum, ex officina Elzeviriana 1642. 8 v. 12mo. (Thomas Western)

Gallaeus, Servatius. Dissertationes de sibyllis. Amstelodami, apud Henricum & viduam Theodori Boom 1688-9. 2 v. 4to. (Syston Park–Thomas Brooke)

Horatius Flaccus, Quintus. Q. Horatius Flaccus, cum erudito Laevini Torrentii commentario. Antverpiae, ex officina Plantiniana, apud I. Moretum 1608. 4to. (Pierre Grassin–Vernon)

Ovidius Naso, Publius. Les metamorphoses. Traduites en françois par P. du-Ryer. Paris, chez A. de Sommaville 1655. 4to. First Edition. (Bridgewater)

Sallustius Crispus, Caius. C. Sallustius Crispus, cum veterum historicorum fragmentis. Venetiis, apud Iuntas et Baba 1649. 12mo. (Huth)

Tacitus, Cornelius. Opera. Amstelodami, apud D. Elsevirium 1672-3. 2 v. 8vo. (Huth)

Virgilius Maro, Publius. Opera. Lugd. Batavor., ex officina Elzeviriana 1636. 12mo.

Vitruvius Pollio, Marcus. De architectura. Amstelodami, apud L. Elzevirium 1649. fol. (Thomas Brooke)

EIGHTEENTH CENTURY

Alfieri, Vittorio, *tr.* See Plinius Secundus, Caius

Galland, André, *editor.* Bibliotheca veterum patrum. Venetiis, ex typographia J. B. Albritii 1765-6. 14 v. fol. (H. N. Evans)

Horatius Flaccus, Quintus. Opera. Londini, I. Pine 1733-7. 2 v. 8vo.

———— ———— Birminghamiae: Typis J. Baskerville 1770. 4to. (I. M. Horsburgh)

Livius, Titus. Historiarum libri. Londini, M. Ritchie & J. Sammells 1794. 8 v. 8vo.

———— ———— Parisiis, Typis Barbou 1775. 7 v. 12mo.

Lucretius Carus, Titus. De rerum natura. Birminghamae: Typis J. Baskerville 1772. 4to. (Horace Walpole–R. G. Fitzgerald–Uniacke)

Ovidius Naso, Publius.   De gedaant-wisselingen . . . in het Latyn en nederduitsch . . . Met een groot getal keurlyke prentverbeeldingen, door B. Picart.   Amsterdam, R. en J. Wetstein, en W. Smith 1732. 2 v. in 1.   fol.

────── Metamorphoses . . . Adorned with sculptures, by B. Picart. Amsterdam, for the Wetsteins and Smith 1732.   2 v. in 1.   fol. (Charles Butler)

Petronius Arbiter, Titus.   Satyricon.   Trajecti ad Rhenum, apud G. van de Water 1709.   2 v. in 1.   4to.

Plinius Secundus, Caius (*Pliny the younger*).   Panegirico di Plinio a Trajano. Tradotto da Vittorio Alfieri.   Parigi, da torchj di Didot Maggiore 1789.   8vo.   Second Edition

Propertius.   *See* Tibullus

Prudentius, Aurelius Clemens.   Opera.   Parmae, ex regio typographeo (J. B. Bodoni) 1788.   2 v.   4to.   (Syston Park)

Sallustius Crispus, Caius.   La conjuracion de Catilina y la guerra de Jugurtha.   En Madrid, J. Ibarra 1772.   fol.

────── Opera.   Parisiis, Typis J. Barbou 1761.   12mo.   (Huth)

Tibullus, Albius.   Tibulli et Propertii opera.   Glasguae, R. & A. Foulis 1753.   8vo.

Virgilius Maro, Publius.   Bucolica, Georgica, et Aeneis.   Birminghamiae: Typis J. Baskerville 1757.   4to.

────── ────── Parisiis, P. Didot 1798.   fol.   (No. 107 of an edition of 250 copies. Signed by P. Didot l'aîné)

────── Codex antiquissimus . . . in Bibliotheca Mediceo-Laurentiana adservatur.   Florentiae, Typis Mannianis 1741.   4to.   (Syston Park)

AFTER 1800

Horatius Flaccus, Quintus.   Opera omnia cura E. C. Wickham.   London 1910.   8vo.

────── The works.   London, J. Murray 1849.   8vo.   (F. Bedford)

Juvenalis, Decius Junius.   Saturae. Edidit A. E. Housman.   London 1905.   8vo.

Lucanus, Marcus Annaeus.   Belli civilis libri decem. Edidit A. E. Housman.   Oxonii 1926.   8vo.

Latin after 1500

Petronius Arbiter, Titus. Satyricon. London 1910. Privately printed by Ralph Straus. 4to. (No. 225 of an edition of 265 copies, of which 250 were numbered and signed by the artist (Norman Lindsay) and the printer)

Tacitus, Cornelius. De vita et moribus Iulii Agricolae liber. Hammersmith, Doves Press 1900. 8vo. First Edition

Virgilius Maro, Publius. Opera omnia ex recensione H. Nettleship a P. Postgate relecta. London, Riccardi Press 1912. 2 v. 8vo.

———— P. Virgilius Maro varietate lectionis et perpetua adnotatione ... C. G. Heyne. Lipsiae 1800. 6 v. 8vo.

———— ———— Editio quarta curavit P. E. Wagner. Lipsiae 1830-41. 5 v. 8vo.

Books by French Authors, Printed after 1500

This list includes also, translations of these works into languages other than English. It does *not* include French Bibles and liturgical books, and French works in Science. These, with books by French authors printed *before* 1501, and *English* versions of French works, are listed in their several places under *Bibles*; *Science*; *Incunabula*; and *English Literature*

SIXTEENTH CENTURY

Advertissement a la royne . . . touchant les miseres du royaume. Orleans 1562. 8vo. (Huth–Murray)

Advertissement a tous bons et loyaux subiectz . . . pour n'estre surprins . . . par les propositions . . . des conspirateurs. Paris, pour Iean Dallier 1567. 8vo. (Huth–Murray)

Advertissement au Roy de Navarre de se reûnir avec le Roy & la foy catholique. n.p. 1585. 8vo. (Huth–Murray)

Advertissement de . . . Comte de Lyon . . . au clergé. Lyon, Ian Pillehotte 1585. 8vo. (Huth–Murray)

Advertissement sur la faulsete de plusieurs mensonges semez par les rebelles. Paris, chez Guillaume Morel 1562. 8vo. (Huth–Murray)

Advis aux princes, seigneurs, gentilshommes, et autres catholicques de France. Paris, chez Guillaume Bichon 1589. 8vo. (Huth–Murray)

Advis de Messieurs du Conseil General de l'union des catholiques estably a Paris, sur la nominatiō . . . de Monsieur le Duc de Mayenne. Lyon, Iean Pillehotte 1589. 8vo. (Huth–Murray)

Arrests de la court souveraine . . . côtre les meurtriers & assassinateurs de Messieurs les Cardinal & Duc de Guyse. Paris, chez Nicolas Nyvelle 1589. 8vo. (Huth–Murray)

Les articles concernans la . . . foy catholicque . . . 1562. Paris, par Guillaume Nyverd (1562). 8vo. (Huth–Murray)

Bernard, Jean. Discours des . . . faicts des roys . . . d'Angleterre. Paris, chez Gervais Mallot 1579. 8vo.

Bèze, Théodore de. Les vrais portraits des hommes. Tr. into French by Simon Goulart. [Geneva] Iean de Laon 1581. 4to. (Thomas Powell–Bement)

Billon, François de. Le fort inexpugnable de l'honneur du sexe feme-
nin. Paris, chez Ian d'Allyer 1555. sm. fol. First Edition

Blarru, Pierre de. Opus de bello Nanceiano. [Colophon] . . . in
Lothoringie pago divi Nicolai de portu per petrū iacobi 1518. sm.
fol. (Britwell)

Borluyt, Guillaume. Historiarum memorabilium ex Exodo . . . descriptio. Lugduni, apud Ioan. Tornaesium 1558. 8vo. (Hoe)

Bouchard, Alain. Les croniques annalles des pays dangleterre. [Colo-
phon] . . . Paris par Anthoine cousteau . . . Mil cinq cens. xxxi. Pour
. . . Jehan petit et Galliot du pre. fol. (Bateman)

Bouchet, Jean. Les annales dacquitaine. Poictiers . . . Jacques Bouchet
. . . Mil cinq cens trente cinq. sm. fol. Third Edition. (Auchin-
cruive)

Bouchier, Thomas. Historia ecclesiastica. Paris, Vaenundantur apud
Ioannem Poupy 1582. 8vo.

Bourdigné, Jean de. Hystoire agregative des annalles et cronicques
daniou. [Colophon] . . . Paris par Anthoyne cousteau . . . Pour
Charles de boigne et Clement alexandre . . . Mil cinq cens. xxix. sm.
fol. First Edition. (Maurice Hewlett)

Un catholique Lorrain au catholique Françoy. Paris, pour Iean Hurché
1589. 8vo. (Huth–Murray)

Les causes qui ont contrainct les catholiques à prendre les armes. n.p.,
pour Iacques Varengles, et Denis Binet (1589). 8vo. (Huth–
Murray)

Charles IX, *King of France*. Declaration du roy contre ceux qui ayants
amassé grand nombre de gens en armes, se sont saisis d'aucunes
villes. Paris, Rob. Estienne 1567. 8vo. (Huth–Murray)

———— Declaration du roy sur le faict . . . de la religion. Paris, pour
Vincent Sertenas et pour Iean Bonfons 1562. 8vo. (Huth–Murray)

———— Edict . . . concernant la residence des baillifs. n.p., Iean Dallier
1567. 8vo. (Huth–Murray)

———— Edict . . . contenant declaration qu'il ne se veut . . . servir de ses
officiers . . . qui sont de la nouvelle pretendue religion. Lyon,
Michel Iove 1568. 8vo. (Huth–Murray)

Charles IX, *King of France*.   Edict . . . contenant interdiction . . . de toute presche, assemblee, & exercice d'autre religion, que de la catholique.   Lyon, Michel Iove 1568.   8vo.   (Huth–Murray)

——— Edict . . . sur la pacification des troubles de ce royaume.   Lyon, Michel Iove 1570.   8vo.   (Huth–Murray)

——— Edict . . . sur le faict de la religion . . . 1561.   Paris, Iean Dallier (1561).   8vo.   (Huth–Murray)

——— Edict . . . sur les moyēs . . . d'appaiser les troubles . . . survenus pour le faict de la religion.   Paris, Robert Estienne 1562.   8vo. (Huth–Murray)

——— Lettres patentes de declaration . . . contre ceux qui ont prins les armes sans sa permission.   Paris, pour Iean Dallier et pour Iean Bonfons 1562.   8vo.   (Huth–Murray)

——— Lettres patentes, par laquelle est enioinct prendre . . . les biens apartenans aux seditieux & rebelles.   Paris, Guillaume de Nyverd (1567).   8vo.   (Huth–Murray)

——— Lettres patentes . . . par les-queles tous gentilshommes . . . qui sont de l'intelligence des perturbateurs du public, sont admonestés de ce departir d'iceux.   Paris, Robert Estienne 1567.   8vo.   (Huth– Murray)

——— Mandement . . . pour faire dilligence . . . de tous les gentilz-hommes, qui se sont retirez de puis le iour de la bataille.   Paris, Guillaume de Nyverd (1567).   8vo.   (Huth–Murray)

——— Second declaration . . . sur la grace & pardon à ceux qui ont esté de l'intelligence des perturbateurs du public.   Paris, Guil-laume de Nyverd (1567).   8vo.   (Huth–Murray)

Chastre, M. de la.   Discours de la deffaicte du Viconte de Thuraine. Paris, de l'imprimerie de Denis Binet 1589.   8vo.   (Huth–Mur-ray)

Colonna, Egidio, *Romano*.   Le mirouer exēplaire . . . selon la cōpilla-tion de Gilles de Rōme.   [Colophon] . . . Paris pour Guillaume eustace . . . lan mil cinq cens et dixsept.   sm. fol.   (Olin Lane Mer-riam)

Confession catholique du sainct sacrement de l'autel.   Paris, chez Nico-las Chesneau 1562.   8vo.   (Huth–Murray)

Cousteau, Pierre.   Pegma.   Lugduni, apud Matthiam Bonhomme 1555. 8vo.   First Edition.   (G. S. Cauntley)

French after 1500

Declaration de tres-illustres princes & seigneurs, les Duc d'Alençon & Roy de Navarre, portant tesmoignage de leur droicte intention . . . envers la Majesté du Roy. Paris, F. Morel 1574. 8vo. (Huth–Murray)

Declaration faite par la ville de Tolose . . . sur le despart de Monseigneur le Mareschal de Ioyeuse de ladite ville. Tolose, de l'imprimerie de Colomiés 1589. 8vo. (Huth–Murray)

La deffaite des trouppes Huguenottes . . . par le sieur de Sainct-Paul. Paris, chez Didier Millot 1589. 8vo. (Huth–Murray)

Discours sur le bruit qui court que nous aurons la guerre, à cause de la religion. n.p. 1562. 8vo. (Huth–Murray)

Discours veritable de ce qui est advenu aux estats generaux de France . . . 1588. Paris, chez Guillaume Bichon 1589. 8vo. (Huth–Murray)

Dolet, Etienne. Aurelii carminum libri quatuor. Lugduni 1538. 4to. (Sidney Graves Hamilton)

Estienne, Henri. Proiect du livre intitulé De la precellence du langage françois. Paris, Mamert Patisson 1579. 8vo. (Hoe)

Fauchet, Claude. Recueil de l'origine de la langue et poesie françoise. Paris, Mamert Patisson . . . au logis de Robert Etienne 1581. 8vo. in fours. First Edition. (Britwell)

Fillastre, Guillaume. La thoison dor. [Colophon] . . . Troyes par Nicolas le rouge . . . Mil cinq centz et trente. 4to. (Roxburghe–Frederick Perkins–Charles Butler–William Morris)

Froissart, Jean. Le premier volume . . . des croniques de france. [Colophon] . . . paris pour francois regnauld; Le second volume . . . pour Anthoyne Verard; Le quart volume . . . Lan de grace mil cinq cens et dixhuyt . . . pour Anthoine Verard. 4 v. in 1. 4to.

———— Le premier [second] volume de . . . cronique . . . reveu . . . par Denis Sauvage de Fontenailles. Lyon, Ian de Tournes 1559; Le tiers volume . . . 1560; Le quart volume . . . 1561. 4 v. in 2. fol.

Gaguin, Robert. Le sommaire historial de france. [Colophon] . . . paris, Phelippe le Noir (c. 1523). sm. fol.

Gilles, Nicole. Les treselegantes . . . annalles des . . . excellens moderateurs des belliqueuses Gaulles. Paris, Gilles de Gourmont, mil cinq cens. xxxiii. 2 v. in 1. sm. fol. (A. C. Swinburne)

French after 1500

Girard, Bernard de.   L'histoire de France.   Paris . . . Pierre l'Huillier 1576.   4 v.   fol.   First Edition.   (Hoe–C. L. F. Robinson)

Goulet, Robert.   Compendium de multiplici parisiesis universitatis magnificentia dignitate et excellētia eius fundatione.   Parisiis, Toussanum denis 1517.   4to.   First Edition

Grévin, Jacques.   Le theatre.   Paris, pour Vincent Sertenas et Guillaume Barbé 1562.   12mo.   First Edition

Henry IV, *King of France*.   Declaration de tres-illustre prince le Roy de Navarre, portant tesmoignage de sa droitte intention . . . envers la Majesté du Roy.   Paris, par Federic Morel 1574.   8vo.   (Huth–Murray)

———— Declaration . . . sur l'attentat, felonnie & rebellion des villes de Paris.   n.p. [1589].   8vo.   (Huth–Murray)

———— Declaration . . . sur les calomnies publiees contre luy.   Ortés 1585.   8vo.   (Huth–Murray)

———— Edict . . . sur la reunion de ses subjects à l'eglise catholique.   Paris, Federic Morel 1585.   8vo.   (Huth–Murray)

———— Edict . . . sur les plainctes et remonstrances du clergé de France 1579.   Paris, par Federic Morel 1580.   8vo.   (Huth–Murray)

Histoire comprenant en brief ce qui est advenu depuis le partement des Sieurs de Guise.   Orleans 1562.   8vo.   (Huth–Murray)

Hugo de Sancto Victore.   Opera utilissima a qualunche fidel christiano 1537.   [Colophon] . . . Vinegia, per Francesco Bindoni & Mapheo Pasini compagni.   8vo.

La Boétie, Etienne de.   La mesnagerie de Xenophon. Les regles de mariage, de Plutarque . . . Le tout traduict de grec en françois . . . Item, un discours sur la mort dudit Seigneur de la Boëtie, par M. de Montaigne.   Paris, Federic Morel 1571.   8vo.   First Edition

Lancelot de Lac.   Le premier volume . . . imprime a paris, Mil cinq cens. xxxiii.   On les vend a paris . . . par Phillippe le noir; Le second volume; Le tiers volume.   [Colophon] a paris pour Jehan Petit.   3 v. in 1.   fol.   (Hoe–C. L. F. Robinson)

Le Maire, Jean.   Les illustrations de Gaule.   [Colophon] . . . Paris, Francoys Regnault 1528.   4to.

La loi salicq.   Premiere loys des francoys.   [Colophon] . . . Guillaume nyverd . . . a paris, c. 1507.   4to.   (Firmin Didot–Murray)

[Lorris, Guillaume de, *et* Jean de Meung]. Le rommant de la rose. On les vent a Paris . . . a la boutique de Jehan longis. [Colophon] . . . Paris Lan mil cinq cens. xxxviii. 8vo. (Paul Girardot de Profond–Charles Dickinson–Charles Butler)

Louis I, de Bourbon, *Prince de Condé*. Les moyens de pacifier le trouble qui est en ce royaume, envoyez à la Royne, par Monsieur le Prince de Condé. n.p. 1562. 8vo. (Huth–Murray)

M., A. D. Lettre d'un catholique françois au Roy de Navarre, pour l'induire à se retourner à l'eglise apostolique. n.p. 1586. 8vo. (Huth–Murray)

Marguerite d'Angoulême. L'Heptameron. Paris, pour Vincent Sertenas 1559. 4to. (Earl of Chesterfield)

Molinet, Jean. Les faictz et dictz de . . . Jehan Molinet. Paris M.D. xxxvii. On les vend a Paris . . . chez Jehan yvernel. 8vo. (Huth)

Monstrelet, Enguerrand de. Le tiers volume de . . . monstrelet avecques les grandes cronicques des roys de france. [Colophon] . . . mil v. cens et douze . . . pour iehan petit et michel le noir. sm. fol.

Montaigne, Michel Eyquem de. Essais. Bourdeaus, par S. Millanges 1580. 2 v. in 1. 8vo. First Edition. (Édouard–Léon Roger, Comte du Nord)

—— Essais. Paris, chez Abel l'Angellier (1588). 4to. (Huth)

—— Les essais. Paris, chez Michel Sonnius 1595. fol. (Huth)

Nicolay, Nicolas de. Le navigationi et viaggi nella Turchia . . . Novamente tradotto di francese in volgare, da Francesco Flori da Lilla. In Anversa, M.D.LXXVI. Appresso Guiglielmo Silvio. 4to. (Sir Henry Hope Edwardes)

Paradin, Claude. Devises heroïques. Lion, Ian de Tournes, et Guil. Gazeau 1557. 8vo.

—— Figure del Nuovo Testamento. In Lione, per Gio. di Tournes 1559. 8vo. (W. L. Andrews)

—— Quadrins historiques de la Bible. Lyon, Iean de Tournes 1553. 8vo. First Edition

Paradin de Cuyseaulx, Guillaume. Historiarum memorabilium ex Genesi descriptio. Lugduni, apud Ioan. Tornaesium 1558. 8vo. (Hoe)

French after 1500

La probation de l'usaige d'avoir images de Iesus Christ . . . 1562. Paris, Guillaume Nyverd (1562). 8vo. (Huth–Murray)

Le proces verbal faict par ordonnance de la court de Parlemēt de l'execution de l'arrest donné le sixiesme iour de iuin dernier passé touchant les articles & la profession de foy d'icelle court. Paris 1562, chez Guillaume Morel. 8vo. (Huth–Murray)

Rabelais, François. Les oeuvres. n.p. 1556. 8vo. (Huth)

———— La vie treshorrificque du grand Gargantua. 1542. [Colophon] . . . Lyon, Frācoys Juste. sm. 8vo.

Raisons des politiques qui veullent faire Henry de Bourbon Roy de France. Lyon 1590. 8vo. (Huth–Murray)

Le remerciment des catholiques unis, faict à la declaration & protestation de Henry de Bourbon, dict Roy de Navarre. Paris, Rolin Thierry 1589. 8vo. (Huth–Murray)

Responce a certain pretendu manifeste, publie . . . par ce gouvernement, de la part des heretiques de Vienne . . . sous le nom du Sieur de Botheon. Lyon 1590. 8vo. (Huth–Murray). (Accompanied by the *Manifeste* of Béthune)

Robert le Diable. La terrible et merveilleuse vie de Robert le Diable. n.p. [c. 1530]. 4to.

Ronsard, Pierre de. Hymne de Bacus. Paris, chés André Wechel 1555. 4to.

Saldaigne, Charles. Coppie de quatre lettres . . . contre & au preiudice des bons & fidelles catholiques. n.p. [1589]. 8vo. (Huth–Murray)

Sentence contre Henry de Valoys . . . selon les saincts canons de l'eglise. n.p. 1589. 8vo. (Huth–Murray)

Tory, Geoffroy. L'art & science de la vraye proportion des lettres attiques. On les vend à Paris, par Vivant Gaultherot 1549. 12mo. Second Edition of *Champfleury*. (Pembroke)

[————] Champ fleury. [Colophon] . . . acheve dimprimer . . . mil cinq cens. XXIX. Pour maistre Geofroy Tory . . . et pour Giles Gourmont. sm. fol. First Edition. (Huth)

Tristan. Tristan . . . de la table ronde. (Redigé par Luce . . .). [Colophon] . . . paris pour anthoine verard [c. 1506]. sm. fol. (Chateau de la Roche Guyon)

French after 1500

SEVENTEENTH CENTURY

Advis de messieurs les curez de Paris . . . sur les mauvaises maximes de quelques nouveaux casuistes. Paris 1656. 4to. (Didot–Britwell)

Arliquiniana. Paris, chez F. & P. de Laulne et M. Brunet 1694. 12mo. (Mexborough–Utterson–Stanley)

Arnauld, Antoine. Lettre . . . a une personne de condition. Paris 1657. 4to. (Didot–Britwell)

Arrest de la cour de Parlement, contre . . . François Ravaillac. Paris, chez Antoine Vitray 1610. 12mo. First Edition. (Morar)

Balzac, Jean-Louis Guez de. Lettres familieres. Leiden, chez J. Else-vier 1656. 12mo. (Andrew Lang)

[Boisrobert, François le Metel de]. La belle invisible. Paris, chez Guillaume de Luyne 1656. 12mo. First Edition. (Bridgewater)

[———] La belle plaideuse. Paris, chez Guillaume de Luyne 1655. 12mo. First Edition. (Bridgewater)

[———] Les genereux ennemis. Paris, chez Guillaume Deluyne 1655. 12mo. First Edition. (Bridgewater)

Boissard, Jean Jacques. Bibliotheca chalcographica. Francofurti, Impensis Iohannis Ammonij 1650-2. 2 v. 4to. (Osterley Park–Andrews)

——— Romanae urbis topographiae. [Colophon] Franckfordii, Typis Ioannis Saurij, Impensis Theodori de Bry 1597-[1602]. 6 pts. in 2 v. fol.

Bontier, Pierre, et Jean Le Verrier. Histoire de la premiere des-couverte . . . des Canaries. Paris, chez Iean de Heuqueville 1630. 8vo. (Beaufoy)

——— Traicte de la navigation. Paris, chez Iean de Heuqueville et Michel Soly 1629. 8vo. (Beaufoy)

Boyer, [Claude]. Federic. Paris, chez Augustin Courbé 1660. 12mo. First Edition. (Bridgewater)

Brantôme, Pierre de Bourdeille, *Seigneur de*. Memoires . . . Les vies des dames galantes. Leyden, chez Iean Sambix le jeune 1666. (Amsterdam, Wolfgang). 2 v. 12mo. (C. L. F. Robinson)

Brantôme, Pierre de Bourdeille, *Seigneur de*. Memoires . . . Les vies des dames illustres. Leyden, chez Jean Sambix le jeune 1665. (Brussels, Foppens). 12mo. (C. L. F. Robinson)

—— Memoires . . . Les vies des hommes illustres & grands capitaines estrangers. Leyden, chez Jean Sambix le jeune 1665. (Hackius) 12mo. (C. L. F. Robinson)

—— Memoires . . . Les vies des hommes illustres & grands capitaines françois. Leyden, chez Jean Sambix le jeune 1666. (Amsterdam, Daniel Elzevier). 4 v. 12mo. (C. L. F. Robinson)

Broquart, Guillaume du. La Bellaure triomphante. Paris, chez Pierre Billaine 1630. 8vo. First Edition. (Bridgewater)

Cailly, Jacques de. Diverses petites poesies. Paris, chez André Cramoisy 1667. 12mo. 1 (no more published). First Edition. (Pichon–Hoe)

[Chappuzeau, Samuel]. Le Colin-Maillard. Paris, chez Iean Baptiste Loyson (1662). 12mo. First Edition. (Bridgewater)

[——] Le riche mecontent. Paris, chez Iean Baptiste Loyson 1662. 12mo. First Edition. (Bridgewater)

[Chevalier, Jean]. Les amours de Calotin. Paris, chez Thomas Iolly 1664. 12mo. First Edition. (Bridgewater)

[——] La desolation des filoux. Paris, chez Pierre Bienfait 1662. 12mo. First Edition. (Bridgewater)

[——] La disgrace des domestiques. Paris, chez Pierre Bienfait 1662. 12mo. First Edition. (Bridgewater)

[——] Les galans ridicules. Paris, chez Pierre Bienfait 1662. 12mo. First Edition. (Bridgewater)

Claveret, Jean. L'écuyer. Paris 1665. 12mo. First Edition. (Bridgewater)

La comedie de chansons. Paris, chez Toussainct Quinet 1640. 12mo. First Edition. (Bridgewater)

[Corneille, Pierre]. Andromede. Rouen, chez L. Maurry 1651. 12mo. First Edition

—— Cinna. Imprimé à Rouen . . . & se vendent. A Paris, chez Toussaint Quinet 1643. 4to. First Edition. (P. Guy Pellion)

Corneille, Pierre. Heraclius. Imprimé à Rouen, & se vend a Paris, chez Antoine de Sommaville 1647. 4to. First Edition

―――― L'illusion comique. Paris, chez Francois Targa 1639. 4to. First Edition

―――― L'imitation de Iesus-Christ. Rouen, L. Maurry 1653. 12mo. First Edition. (Buxton Forman)

―――― Medee. Paris, chez Francois Targa 1639. 4to. First Edition

―――― Le menteur. Imprimé à Rouen, & se vend a Paris, chez Antoine de Sommaville et Augustin Courbé 1664. 4to. First Edition

[――――] Pulcherie. Paris, chez Guillaume de Luyne 1673. 8vo. First Edition

―――― Rodogune. Imprimé à Rouen, & se vend a Paris, chez Antoine de Sommaville 1647. 4to. First Edition, First Issue

―――― La suite du menteur. Imprimé à Rouen, & se vend a Paris, chez Antoine de Sommaville . . . et Augustin Courbé 1645. 4to. First Edition

―――― Theodore. Imprimé à Rouen, & se vend a Paris, chez Antoine de Sommaville 1646. 4to. First Edition, First Issue

[――――] La toison d'or. Imprimée à Rouen, et se vend a Paris, chez Augustin Courbé et Guillaume de Luyne 1661. 12mo. First Edition

―――― Le theatre. Imprimé à Rouen et se vend a Paris, chez Louis Billaine 1664. 2 v. fol. First Folio Edition

[Corneille, Thomas]. Berenice. Imprimée à Rouen, & se vend a Paris, chez Augustin Courbé et Guillaume de Luyne 1659. 12mo. First Edition. (Bridgewater)

[――――] Camma. Imprimée à Rouen, et se vend a Paris, chez Guillaume de Luyne 1661. 12mo. First Edition

[――――] Le charme de la voix. Imprimé à Rouen, et se vend a Paris, chez Augustin Courbé et Guillaume de Luyne 1658. 12mo. First Edition. (Bridgewater)

[――――] Darius. Imprimée à Rouen, & se vend a Paris, chez Augustin Courbé et Guillaume de Luyne 1659. 12mo. First Edition. (Bridgewater)

―――― L'inconnu. Paris, chez Jean Ribou 1676. 12mo. First Edition

[Corneille, Thomas]. La mort de l'Empereur Commode. Imprimé à Rouen, et se vend a Paris, chez Augustin Courbé et Guillaume de Luyne 1659. 12mo. First Edition. (Bridgewater)

Desjardins, Marie Catherine Hortense. La favory. Paris, Thomas Iolly 1665. 12mo. First Edition. (Bridgewater)

Desmarets de Saint-Sorlin, Jean. Les delices de l'esprit. Paris, chez Florentin Lambert 1661. fol.

[Dorimond, Louis]. L'escole des cocus. Paris, chez Iean Ribou 1661. 12mo. First Edition. (Bridgewater)

Fénelon, François de Salignac de la Mothe-. Explication des maximes. Paris, chez Pierre Aubouin, Pierre Emery, Charles Clousier 1697. 12mo. First Edition

Gilbert, Gabriel. Les amours d'Angelique et de Medor. Paris, chez Guillaume de Luyne 1664. 12mo. First Edition. (Bridgewater)

———— Arie et Petus. Paris, chez Guillaume de Luyne 1660. 12mo. First Edition. (Bridgewater)

———— Chresphonte. Paris, Guillaume de Luyne 1659. 12mo. First Edition. (Bridgewater)

Gillet de la Tessonerie. Le campagnard. Rouen, pour Guillaume de Luyne à Paris 1657. 12mo. First Edition. (Bridgewater)

Guénébauld, Jean. Le réveil de Chyndonax. Diion, Claude Guyot 1621. 8vo. in fours. First Edition. (Rive–Firmin Didot–Hoe–Groves)

Jeanne d'Arc. Jeanne Darc natifve de Vaucouleur en Lorraine. Orleans, chez Olivier Boynard et Iean Nyon 1606. 8vo. First Edition. (Bridgewater)

La Fontaine, Jean de. Les amours de Psiche et Cupidon. Paris, chez Denys Thierry 1669. 8vo. First Edition

———— Fables choisies. Paris, chez Claude Barbin 1668. 4to. First Edition. (John Maude–Furner–Locker-Lampson)

[La Rochefoucauld, François]. Reflexions ou sentences et maximes morales. Paris, chez Claude Barbin 1665. 12mo. First Edition

[Lasne, Guillaume]. La dispute . . . contre Frere Anselme Turmeda. Pampelune, Guillaume Buisson 1606. 12mo. First Edition. (Bridgewater)

Leger, Jean.   Histoire generale des eglises evangeliques des vallees de Piemont.   A Leyde, chez Jean le Carpentier 1669.   fol.   First Edition

Le Gouz, François de La Boullaye.   Les voyages.   Troyes, Nicolas Oudot ... Paris, chez Gervais Clousier 1657.   4to.   Second Edition

Lettre d'un curé de Rouen a un curé de la campagne.   Paris 1656.   4to. (Didot–Britwell)

Le Verrier, Jean.   *See* Bontier, Pierre, *et* Jean Le Verrier

Lorraine, Henri II de, *Duc de Guise*.   Les memoires.   Paris, chez Edme Martin et Sebastien Mabre-Cramoisy 1668.   12mo.   Second Edition.   (Huth)

Malherbe, François de.   Les oeuvres.   Paris, chez Charles Chappellain 1630.   4to.

[Mareschal, A.].   Le dictateur romain.   Paris, chez Toussaint Quinet 1646.   12mo.   First Edition.   (Bridgewater)

Mersenne, Marin.   Harmonicorum libri.   Lutetiae Parisiorum, Sumptibus Guillielmi Baudry 1636.   fol.   (Earl of Kent–Wrest Park)

Molière, Jean Baptiste Poquelin de.   L'avare.   Paris, chez Iean Ribou 1669.   12mo.   First Edition

———— L'estourdy.   Paris, chez Gabriel Quinet 1663.   12mo.   First Edition

———— Les fourberies de Scapin.   Paris, chez Pierre le Monnier 1671. 8vo.   First Edition

———— George Dandin.   Paris, chez Iean Ribou 1669.   16mo.   First Edition

———— Le malade imaginaire.   Suivant la copie imprimée a Paris 1673. (Amsterdam, Daniel Elzevier).   12mo.   (Morin)

———— Le mariage forcé.   Paris, chez Iean Ribou 1668.   16mo.   First Edition

———— Le medecin malgré-luy.   Paris, chez Iean Ribou 1667.   12mo. First Edition

———— Le misantrope.   Paris, chez Iean Ribou 1667.   12mo.   First Edition

———— Les precieuses ridicules.   Suivant la copie imprimée a Paris 1674.   (Amsterdam, Daniel Elzevier).   12mo.   (Morin)

Molière, Jean Baptiste Poquelin de. Sganarelle. Paris, Guillaume de
Luyne 1662. 12mo.

———— Les oeuvres. Paris, chez Denys Thierry . . . Claude Barbin . . .
et chez Pierre Trabouillet 1682. 8 v. 12mo. First Complete Edition. (W. L. Andrews)

Montaigne, Michel Eyquem de. Les essais. Rouen, chez Iean Berthe-
lin. [Colophon] . . . mil six cens dix-neuf, à l'imprimerie de Iean
Durand. 8vo.

———— ———— Paris, chez Pierre Rocolet 1635. fol.

———— ———— Paris, chez Pierre le Petit 1657. fol.

———— ———— Amsterdam, chez Anthoine Michieis 1659. 3 v. 12mo.
(Smalley)

Naudé, Gabriel. Advis pour dresser une bibliotheque. Paris, chez
François Targa 1627. 8vo. in fours. First Edition

———— Apologie pour tous les grands personnages qui ont esté fausse-
ment soupçonnez de magie. Paris, chez François Targa 1625. 8vo.
(S. Hibbert Ware)

[————] Iugement de tout ce qui a esté imprimé contre le Cardinal
Mazarin. [Paris 1649]. 4to. Second Edition

Pascal, Blaise. Pensées. Paris, chez Guillaume Desprez 1670. 12mo.
First Edition

———— ———— Paris, chez Guillaume Desprez 1670. 12mo. Second Edition

[————] Les provinciales. Cologne, chez Pierre de la Vallée 1657.
4to. First Edition. (Didot–Britwell)

Pascal, Françoise. Sesostris. Lyon, chez Antoine Offray 1661. 12mo.
in eights. First Edition. (Bridgewater)

Perrault, Charles. Les hommes illustres. Paris, chez Antoine Dezallier
1696-1700. 2 v. in 1. fol. First Edition, Second Issue, with portraits and text of lives of Arnauld and Pascal cancelled and those of
Thomassin and Du Cange substituted. The present copy has the
cancelled portraits and text bound in. (Hoe)

Poisson, Raymond. Le fou raisonnable. Paris, chez Guillaume de
Luyne 1664. 12mo. First Edition. (Bridgewater)

Quinault, Philippe. L'amant indiscret. Paris, chez Toussainct Quinet
1656. 12mo. First Edition. (Bridgewater)

French after 1500

Quinault, Philippe.   Les coups de l'amour.   Imprimée à Rouen & se vend a Paris, chez Guillaume de Luyne 1660.   12mo.   First Edition.   (Bridgewater)

———— Le mariage de Cambise.   Paris, chez Augustin Courbé et Guillaume de Luyne 1659.   12mo.   First Edition.   (Bridgewater)

[————] La mere coquette.   Paris, chez Theodore Girard 1666.   12mo.   First Edition.   (Bridgewater)

———— La mort de Cyrus.   Paris, chez Augustin Courbé et Guillaume de Luyne 1659.   12mo.   First Edition.   (Bridgewater)

Racine, Jean Baptiste.   Bajazet.   Paris, chez Pierre le Monnier 1672.   12mo.   First Edition.   (P. Guy Pellion)

———— Berenice.   Paris, chez Claude Barbin 1671.   8vo.   First Edition

———— Mithridate.   Paris, chez Claude Barbin 1673.   8vo.   First Edition

———— Phedre & Hippolyte.   Paris, chez Claude Barbin 1677.   12mo.   First Edition

———— Les plaideurs.   Paris, chez Gabriel Quinet 1669.   12mo.   First Edition

———— La Thebayde.   Paris, chez Gabriel Quinet 1664.   12mo.   First Edition

———— Oeuvres.   Paris, chez Denys Thierrry 1679.   2 v.   8vo.   First Collected Edition.   (Bancel–Andrews)

———— ———— [Amsterdam, Wolfgang] 1682-91.   2 v.   12mo.

Responces aux Lettres provinciales.   Liege, chez Jean Mathias Hovius 1657.   12mo.   First Edition.   (Beaufoy–Robert Southey)

Richelieu, Jean-Armand du Plessis, *Duc de*.   Instruction du Chrestien. Paris, de l'Imprimerie Royale du Louvre 1642.   fol.   (Louis XIV– John Towneley)

Sonan, Arthur Biard, *Sieur de*.   Chriserionte de Gaule.   Lyon, pour Barthelemy Vincent 1620.   8vo.   First Edition.   (Baron Seillière– Lord Amherst)

Suite de l'extract de plusieurs mauvaises propositions des nouveaux casuistes.   Paris 1656.   4to.   (Didot–Britwell)

Sully, Maximilien de Béthune, *Duc de*.   Memoires.   1-2 (Château de Sully) 1638; 3-4, Paris, chez Augustin Courbé 1662.   4 v. in 2. fol.   First Edition.   (Griswold–Ives–Bement)

Le tableau de la croix.   Paris, chez F. Mazot 1651. (Achevé d'imprimer ce 20e. septembre 1653.   4to.   (Huth)

Tristan l'hermite.   Osman.   Paris, chez Guillaume de Luyne 1656. 8vo.   First Edition.   (Bridgewater)

[Villiers, M. de].   Les costeaux.   Paris, chez Thomas Iolly 1665.   12mo. First Edition.   (Bridgewater)

EIGHTEENTH CENTURY

Bayle, Pierre.   Dictionaire.   Amsterdam, P. Brunel 1730.   4 v.   fol. Fourth Edition.   (Villiers)

Beaumarchais, Pierre Augustin Caron *dit*.   La folle journée, ou Le mariage de Figaro.   Au Palais-Royal, chez Ruault 1785.   8vo.   First Édition, First Issue

———— ———— De l'Imprimerie de la Société Littéraire-Typographique . . . Et se trouve à Paris, chez Ruault 1785.   8vo.   First Édition, Second Issue

Boileau Despréaux, Nicolas.   Oeuvres.   Amsterdam, David Mortier 1718.   2 v.   fol.   (White Knights–Heber)

Brantôme, Pierre de Bourdeille, *Seigneur de*.   Memoires . . . Les anecdotes de la Cour de France.   Leyden, chez Jean Sambix le jeune 1722.   12mo.   (C. L. F. Robinson)

Les cent nouvelles nouvelles.   Cologne (Amsterdam) chez Pierre Gaillard 1701.   2 v.   8vo.   (Morar–Bement)

Chappe d'Auteroche, Jean.   Voyage en Sibérie.   Paris, chez De Bure 1768.   4 v.   4to.   First Edition.   (Philip Hammond)

Chenier, C.   Office des décades.   Paris, chez Dufart . . . IIeme année de l'ere républicaine (1793).   8vo.   (W. L. Andrews)

Couet-Gironville.   Charlotte Corday.   Paris (1795).   8vo.   First Edition

Courtois, Edmé Bonaventure.   Rapport fait au nom de la Commission chargée de l'examen des papiers trouvés chez Robespierre.   Paris, de l'Imprimerie Nationale des Lois, Nivôse, an IIIe. de la République.   8vo.

French after 1500

Fénelon, François de Salignac de la Mothe-.   Les aventures de Télémaque.   (Paris) de l'Imprimerie de Monsieur 1785.   2 v.   fol. (Lady Hester Stanhope)

Fontenelle, Bernard le Bovier de.   Oeuvres diverses.   Amsterdam, chez F. Changuion 1743.   3 v.   4to.   (Newdigate)

[Fortin, François].   Amusemens de la chasse.   Amsterdam et Leipzig, chez Arkstèe et Merkus 1743.   2 v.   12mo.   Fifth Edition

France.   La constitution française.   Paris, Didot jeune 1791.   12mo.

———— Constitution de la république française.   Paris, de l'imprimerie de la république (1799).   8vo.

Grécourt, Jean Baptiste Joseph Villart de.   Oeuvres complètes.   Paris, Imprimerie de Chaignieau ainé, l'an Ve (1796).   4 v.   8vo.

La Fayette, Marie Jean Paul Roch Yves Gilbert Motier, *Marquis de*. Vie privée.   Paris, M. de Bastide 1790.   8vo. in fours.   (Edward W. Dodd)

La Fontaine, Jean de.   Contes et nouvelles.   Amsterdam (Paris, Barbou) 1762.   2 v.   8vo.   Fermiers–Généraux Édition.   (George Keate)

———— Fables choisies.   Paris, chez Desaint & Saillant 1755-9.   4 v. fol.

Le Sage, Alain René.   Les avantures de Monsieur Robert Chevalier. Paris, chez Etienne Ganeau 1732.   2 v.   12mo.   First Edition

———— Aventuras de Gil Blas.   Valencia, D. Benito Monfort 1788-9. 4 v.   4to.   First Edition.   (Lord Glenbervie)

———— Le bachelier de Salamanque.   Paris, chez Valleyre fils et Gissey 1736.   8vo.   First Edition

———— Le diable boiteux.   Paris, chez la veuve Barbin 1707.   8vo. First Edition

———— Histoire de Gil Blas.   Paris, par les Libraires Associés 1747. 4 v.   8vo.

[Linguet, Simon Nicolas Henri].   Théorie des loix civiles.   Londres 1767.   2 v.   12mo.   First Edition

Marguerite d'Angoulême.   Les nouvelles.   Berne, chez Beat Louis Walthard 1780.   3 v.   8vo.

Millot, Claude François Xavier.   Histoire littéraire des troubadours. Paris, chez Durand neveu 1774.   3 v.   12mo.

Montesquieu, Charles le Secondat, *Baron de*.   Oeuvres.   Paris, chez Bernard . . . l'an IV.-1796.   5 v.   4to.

Montfaucon, Bernard de.   Les monumens de la monarchie françoise. Paris, chez Julien-Michel Gandouin 1729-33.   5 v.   fol.

[Moreau, Jacques-Nicolas].   Bibliotheque de Madame la dauphine. No. I. Histoire.   Paris, chez Saillant & Nyon 1770.   [Colophon] . . . 1771.   8vo.

Picart, Bernard.   Ceremonies et coutumes religieuses.   Amsterdam, chez J. F. Bernard 1723-43.   8 v. in 9.   fol.   (Collin–Huth)

———— Superstitions anciennes et modernes.   Amsterdam, chez J. F. Bernard 1733-6.   2 v.   fol.   (Collin–Huth)

Rabelais, François.   Oeuvres.   Amsterdam, chez J. F. Bernard 1741. 3 v.   4to.

Rousseau, Jean-Baptiste.   Oeuvres.   Bruxelles (Paris, Didot) 1743. 3 v.   4to.   (Britwell)

Rousseau, Jean Jacques.   Émile.   La Haye, chez Jean Néaulme 1762. 4 v.   8vo.   First Edition.   (Carl Edelheim)

Sacre et couronnement de Louis XVI.   Paris, Mailles 1775.   4to.   First Edition

Saint-Évremond, Charles de Marquetal de Saint Denis, *Seigneur de*. Oeuvres meslees.   Londres, chez Jacob Tonson 1709.   3 v.   4to. Second Edition.   (Ashburton)

Saint-Pierre, Jacques-Bernardin-Henri de.   Paul et Virginie.   Paris, de l'Imprimerie de Monsieur 1789.   12mo.   First Edition

Scarron, Paul.   Oeuvres.   Amsterdam, chez J. Wetstein 1752.   7 v. 12mo.

Sévigné, Marie de Rabutin-Chantal, *Marquise de*.   Lettres.   [Rouen] 1726.   2 v.   12mo.   Second Edition

Voltaire, François-Marie Arouet de.   Alzire.   Paris, Jean-Baptiste-Claude Bauche 1736.   8vo.   First Edition

[————] Candide.   n.p. 1759.   8vo.   First Edition

———— Herode et Mariamne.   Paris, chez la veuve de Pierre Ribou 1730.   8vo.   First Edition.   (Léon Rattier)

Voltaire, François-Marie Arouet de. Histoire de Charles XII roi de Suede. Basle, chez Christophe Revis 1731. 2 v. 12mo. First Edition

——— Lettres philosophiques. Londres 1781. 8vo. (Léon Rattier)

——— La pucelle d'Orleans. Paris 1755. 12mo. (Ely)

——— ——— Louvain 1755. 12mo. (Bengesco)

——— Le temple du goust. n.p., chez Hierosme Print-All 1733. 4to. First Edition

AFTER 1800

Balzac, Honoré de. César Birotteau. Paris 1838. 2 v. 8vo. First Edition

——— Honorine. Paris, Gratiot [1840]. 2 v. 8vo. First Edition. (Edmond de Goncourt)

——— Notes remises a . . . la Commission de la loi sur la propriété lit-téraire. Paris, J. Hetzel et Paulin 1841. 4to. First Edition. (Edmond de Goncourt)

Baudelaire, Charles. Lettres 1841-1866. Paris, Société du Mercure de France 1906. 8vo. First Edition. (McBurney)

——— Oeuvres posthumes. Paris, Société du Mercure de France 1908. 4to. First Edition. (McBurney)

——— Souvenirs. Paris, René Pincebourde 1872. 8vo. First Edition. (McBurney)

Beaumarchais, Pierre Augustin Caron *dit*. Théatre complet. Paris, D. Jouast 1869. 4 v. 8vo. (Jules Janin–Halsey)

Bourget, Paul. Les aveux. Paris, A. Lemerre 1882. 12mo. First Edition. (Presentation copy from Bourget to Zola)

——— Études et portraits. Paris, A. Lemerre 1889. 2 v. 8vo. First Edition. (Presentation copy from Bourget to Zola)

Brandan, *Saint*. Les voyages merveilleux. Paris, A. Claudin 1878. 8vo.

Claretie, Jules. Le dernier baiser. Paris, F. Sartorius 1864. 8vo. First Edition

——— La vie à Paris 1906. Paris, Charpentier 1907. 4to. First Edition. (McBurney)

Cousin, Victor. Des Pensées de Pascal. Paris, Ladrange 1843. 8vo. (Smalley)

Daudet, Alphonse. Sapho. Paris, Charpentier 1884. 12mo. First Edition

Desgranges, J. Poisle. Rouget de Lisle et La Marseillaise. Paris, Mme. Bachelin-Deflorenne 1864. 8vo.

Dufresny, Charles Rivière. Oeuvres choisies. Paris, Didot 1810. 2 v. 12mo. (Hoe)

Dumas, Alexandre, *fils*. La question du divorce. Paris, Calmann Lévy 1880. 8vo. First Edition. (McBurney)

———— Théatre complet. Paris, Calmann Lévy 1890-4. 9 v. 8vo. (Smalley)

Flaubert, Gustave. La tentation de Saint Antoine. Paris, Charpentier 1874. 8vo. First Edition. (McBurney)

Foucquet, Jean. Oeuvre de Jehan Foucquet. Paris, L. Curmer 1866-7. 2 v. 4to.

France, Anatole. Le crime de Sylvestre Bonnard. Paris, Calmann Lévy 1881. 12mo. First Edition

———— Pierre Nozière. Paris, A. Lemerre 1899. 12mo. First Edition, original wrappers. (With autograph inscription by the author)

———— Le puits de Sainte Claire. Paris, Calmann Lévy 1895. 12mo. First Edition, original wrappers. (With autograph inscription by the author)

———— La rôtisserie de la reine Pédauque. Paris, Calmann Lévy 1893. 12mo. First Edition, original wrappers. (With autograph inscription by the author)

———— *See also* Palissy, Bernard; Sade, Donatien-Alphonse-François de

Gautier, Théophile. Poésies. Paris, Charles Mary 1830. 8vo. First Edition

Gresset, Jean Baptiste Louis. Le parrain magnifique. Paris, chez Ant. Aug. Renouard 1810. 8vo. First Edition

Halévy, Ludovic. Madame et Monsieur Cardinal. Paris, M. Lévy Frères 1872. 12mo. First Edition. (Presentation copy from Halévy to James Carleton Young, with autograph inscription)

Hugo, Victor. L'année terrible. Paris, M. Lévy Frères 1872. 8vo. First Edition. (Presentation copy, inscribed, from Hugo to Dr. Axenfeld). (William Harris Arnold–Kern)

———— Hernani. Paris, Mame et Delaunay-Vallée 1830. 8vo. First Edition

———— Les misérables. Bruxelles, A. Lecroix, Verboeckhoven & Cᵉ 1862. 10 v. 8vo. First Edition

———— Notre-Dame de Paris. Paris, Charles Gosselin 1831. 2 v. 8vo. First Edition

———— Oeuvres inédites . . . Toute la lyre: dernière série. Paris, J. Hetzel & Cie 1893. 8vo. First Edition. (McBurney)

Huysmans, Joris Karl. Croquis parisiens. A vau l'eau. Un dilemme. Paris, P. V. Stock 1905. 12mo. First Edition. (McBurney)

La Borde, Jean Benjamin de. Choix de chansons. Rouen, J. le Monnyer 1881. 4 v. in 2. 8vo.

La Bruyère, Jean de. Les caractères. Paris, Librairie des bibliophiles 1873. 2 v. 8vo. (No. 76 of an edition of 100 copies on hand-made paper). (Smalley)

La Fontaine, Jean de. Oeuvres. Paris, chez Lefèvre 1822. 6 v. 8vo.

Le Roux de Lincy, Adrien-Jean-Victor, *et* Francisque Michel. Recueil de farces, moralités et sermons joyeux. Paris, chez Techener 1837. 4 v. 8vo. (Huth)

Le Sage, Alain René. Histoire de Gil Blas. Paris, Garnier Frères 1864. 2 v. 8vo.

Linati, C. Costumes . . . du Mexico. Bruxelles, Gobard (1828). 4to.

Lorris, Guillaume de, *et* Jean de Meung. Le roman de la rose. Paris, P. Didot l'ainé 1814. 4 v. 8vo.

Louÿs, Pierre. La femme et le pantin. Paris, Société du Mercure de France 1898. 8vo. First Edition. (McBurney)

Malherbe, François de. Oeuvres complètes. Paris, L. Hachette 1862-9. 6 v. 8vo.

Maupassant, Guy de. La main gauche. Paris, Paul Ollendorff 1889. 12mo. First Edition

———— Miss Harriet. Paris, Victor-Havard 1884. 12mo. First Edition. (Inscribed presentation copy from the author to Édouard Noel)

French after 1500

Maupassant, Guy de.   Mont-Oriol.   Paris, Victor-Havard 1887.
12mo.   First Edition

———— Pierre et Jean.   Paris, Paul Ollendorff 1888.   12mo.   First
Edition

———— Le rosier de Madame Husson.   Paris, Librairie Moderne 1888.
12mo.   First Edition

———— Une vie.   Paris, Victor-Havard 1883.   12mo.   First Edition.
(Inscribed presentation copy from the author to Édouard Noel)

Montaigne, Michel Eyquem de.   Une lettre inédite.   Paris, chez Did-
ron 1850.   8vo.

Musset, Alfred de.   La confession d'un enfant du siècle.   Paris, Felix
Bonnaire 1836.   2 v.   8vo.   First Edition

———— Oeuvres complètes.   Paris, Charpentier 1866.   10 v.   8vo.
(Hoe)

Napoléon I.   [Proclamation] Au Golfe Juan, le 1er Mars 1815. A
l'armée.   De l'imprimerie de Moronval.   4to.

———— [Proclamation] Au golfe Juan, le 1er Mars 1815. Au peuple
français.   4to.

———— [Address] A l'armée.   Imprimerie de Poulet, n.d.   4to.

———— Garde nationale de Paris. Ordre du jour du 11 Mars 1815.   De
l'imprimerie de Lefebvre.   4to.

———— Extrait du Moniteur, du 15 mars 1815.   De l'imprimerie
d'Aubry.   4to.

———— Extrait du Moniteur, du 15 Mars 1815.   De l'imprimerie de
Poulet.   4to.

———— Extrait du Moniteur, du 16 Mars 1815.   De l'imprimerie de
Poulet.   4to.

———— Entrée de l'Empereur Napoléon dans la capitale. Paris, le 20
mars 1815.   De l'imprimerie de J. M. Eberhart.   4to.

———— Extrait du Moniteur du 21 Mars, 1815.   Imprimerie d'Herhan.
4to.

———— Extrait du Moniteur du 22 Mars 1815.   De l'imprimerie de
Poulet.   4to.

———— Décrets imperiaux. Au palais des Tuileries, le 21, 22, 23, 24
mars 1815.   De l'imprimerie d'Herhan.   4to.

Napoléon I. Extrait du Moniteur, du 28 mars 1815. Details officiels de tout ce qui s'est passé pendant le voyage de sa Majesté l'Empereur, depuis son depart de l'Isle d'Elbe, jusqu'à son arrivée à Paris. De l'imprimerie d'Herhan. 4to.

———— Extrait du Moniteur du 2 Avril 1815. De l'imprimerie de Poulet. 4to.

———— Extrait du Moniteur du 13 avril. De l'imprimerie d'Herhan. 4to.

———— Extrait du Moniteur du Jeudi 13 Avril 1815. De l'imprimerie de Chaignieau aîné. 4to.

———— Extrait du Moniteur du 23 avril 1815. Acte additionel aux constitutions de l'Empire. De l'imprimerie d'Herhan. 4to.

———— Extrait du Moniteur du 3 Mai 1815. De l'imprimerie de J. M. Eberhart. 4to.

———— Extrait du Moniteur du 10 Mai 1815. De l'imprimerie de L. E. Herhan. 4to.

———— Extrait du Moniteur, du 12 Juin 1815. Imprimerie de Poulet. 4to.

———— Extrait du Moniteur du 18 Juin 1815. Ordre du jour. Imprimerie de J. Moronval. 4to.

———— Extrait du Moniteur, du 18 juin 1815. Nouvelles de l'armée. Depeche telegraphique. Ordre du jour. De l'imprimerie d'Aubry. 4to.

———— Extrait du Moniteur, du 18 Juin 1815. Baudouin, imprimeur. 4to.

———— Extrait du Moniteur du 19 Juin 1815. Imprimerie de J. Moronval. 4to.

———— Déclaration au peuple français. Au palais de l'Elysée, le 22 juin 1815. De l'imprimerie de C.-F. Patris. 4to.

———— Document written and signed by Napoleon. Mantova, le 15 Ventose An 5 de la République. fol.

———— A true and full account of the death of Bonaparte. Wednesday, July 4, 1821. Ipswich [1821]. sm. fol. (Broadside)

Orléans, Charles, *Duc* d'. Les poésies. Paris, J. Belin-Leprieur et Colomb de Batines 1842. 8vo. (P. Guy Pellion–Moura)

Palissy, Bernard.   Les oeuvres . . . publiées . . . par Anatole France.
Paris, Charavay Frères 1880.   12mo.   First Edition, original wrappers.   (Inscribed presentation copy from France to Zola)

Paris et Vienne.   Histoire du . . . Paris, et la belle Vienne.   Lyon, Louis
Perrin 1835.   8vo.   (Huth)

Pascal, Blaise.   Pensées.   Paris, Dezobry et E. Magdaleine 1852.   8vo.
(Smalley)

———— ———— Paris, Andrieux 1844.   2 v.   8vo.   (Smalley)

———— Texte primitif des Lettres provinciales.   Paris, L. Hachette
1867.   8vo.   (Smalley)

Pasquier, Etienne Denis, *Duc de*.   Histoire de mon temps.   Paris, Plon
1894.   6 v.   8vo.

Pauquet Frères.   Modes et costumes historiques.   Paris (1876).   fol.
First Edition

Pingret.   [Swiss costumes].   [Lucerne] 1824-5.   4to.   First Edition

Poésies nationales de la revolution française.   Paris, chez Michel fils ainé
1836.   8vo.

Quatremère de Quincy, Antoine Chrysostome.   Le Jupiter Olympien.
Paris, chez Firmin Didot 1814.   fol.

Rabelais, François.   Oeuvres.   Paris, chez Dalibon 1823.   9 v.   8vo.
Edition Variorum

Racine, Jean Baptiste.   Oeuvres.   Paris, Hachette 1865-73.   10 v.   8vo.

Reynard the Fox.   Le roman de Renart.   Paris, chez Treuttel et Würtz
1826.   4 v.   8vo.

Rimbaud, Arthur.   Poèmes. Les illuminations. Une saison en enfer.
Paris, Léon Vanier 1892.   12mo.   First Edition.   (McBurney)

Rochefort, Henri.   La lanterne.   Bruxelles (E. Wittman) 1869.   8 v.
8vo.   (Morar–W. T. Rabbitts)

Rutebeuf.   Oeuvres complètes.   Paris, chez Édouard Pannier 1839.
2 v.   8vo.   (Pichon–Moura)

Sade, Donatien-Alphonse-François, *Marquis de*.   Dorci . . . publié . . .
[par Anatole France].   Paris, Charavay Frères 1881.   4to.   First
Edition, original wrappers.   (McBurney)

Sévigné, Marie de Rabutin-Chantal, *Marquise de*.   Lettres.   Paris, chez
Bossange, Masson et Besson 1806.   8 v.   8vo.

French after 1500

Souvenirs des Pays Bas.   Amsterdam, F. Buffa (c. 1820).   4to.

Süe, Eugène.   Le juif errant.   Paris, Paulin 1845.   4 v. in 2.   4to.

Tabarin, Jean Salomon, *dit*.   Oeuvres complètes.   Paris, Guiraudet et
    Jouaust 1858.   2 v.   12mo.   First Complete Edition.   (Morin)

Urfé, Honoré d'.   L'Astrée.   Lyon, Masson 1925–8.   5 v.   4to.

Books by German Authors, Printed after 1500

This list includes also, translations of these works into languages other than English. It does *not* include German Bibles and liturgical books, or German works in Science. These, with books by German authors printed before 1501, and *English* versions of German works, are listed in their several places under *Bibles; Science; Incunabula* and *English Literature*

SIXTEENTH CENTURY

Adelff, Johann. Barbarossa. Strassburg, B. Grüninger 1535. fol.

——— Das ist der Passion. Straszburg, J. Grüninger 1509. fol. (Bement)

——— Die Türkisch chronica. Stassburg [sic], M. Flach 1508. fol. (Huth)

Agrippa, Cornelius Heinrich. De occulta philosophia. [Cologne] 1533. fol. (Robert Barclay)

Amman, Jost. Cleri totius Romanae ecclesiae subiecti. Francofurti ad Moenum, ex officina M. Lechleri 1585. sm. 4to. (Huth)

——— Künstliche . . . figuren der . . . Evangelien. Francofurti ad Moenum, P. Fabricius 1579. sm. 4to. (W. L. Andrews)

——— Thierbuch . . . durch Jost Amman unnd Hans Bocksperger . . . in reimen gestellt. Franckfort am Mayn bey J. Feyeraband in verlegung S. Feyerabends erben 1592. sm. 4to. (Huth)

[Ars memorandi]. With verses by Petrus de Rosenheim. [Pforzheim] T. Anshelm 1502. sm. 4to. (White Knights)

Bade, Josse. Navis stultifera. [Basle] N. Lamparter 1406 [for 1506]. sm. 4to. (Ives–Bement)

——— Stultifere navicule. [Strassburg] I. Prusz 1502. sm. 4to. (J. E. Hodgkin)

Bamberg. Ausrufung des Heiligthums. [Bamberg, J. Pfeil] 1509. sm. 4to. (Huth–Murray)

Beham, Hans Sebald. [Series of twelve copperplate engravings of the Apostles]. 8vo.

Charles V, *Emperor*. Abschiedt auff dem Reichstag zu Worms . . . MVXXj. Meintz, J. Schöffer 1521. 4to.

——— Geordent Camergericht auff dem Reichstag zu Worms . . . M.V.XXI. Meintz, J. Schöffer 1521. 4to.

German after 1500

Charles V, *Emperor*.   Lantfryd . . . uff dem Reichstag zu Worms . . .
M.V.XXI. Meintz, J. Schöffer 1521. 4to.

———— Romischer Kayserlicher Maiestat Regiment Lamergericht
lantfride und abschied uff dem Reichstag zu Wormbs anno
MVXXj. Meintz, J. Schöffer 1521. 4to.

Clavius, Christoph. *See* Klau, Christoph C.

Cochleus, Johann. Tetrachordū musice. Nurnberge, F. Peypus 1520.
sm. 4to. (Royal Society–Huth)

[Cranach, Lucas, *the elder*]. Das symbolum . . . der zwelff Aposteln.
Wittemberg, G. Rhaw 1539. sm. fol. (Huth)

Dedekind, Friedrich. Grobiannus. Franc[ofurti] apud Chr. Egenolph 1550. sm. 8vo. First Edition. (Inglis)

Dürer, Albrecht. Apocalipsis cum figuris. Nürnberg [H. Hölzel]
1511. fol.

———— De symmetria partium. Nürnberg, Hier. Formschneyder,
Impensis viduae Durerianae 1534. fol. (William Niven)

———— Etliche underricht, zu befestigung der stett. Nürnberg 1527.
fol.

———— Passio Christi. Nürnberg [H. Hölzel] 1511. sm. 4to. First
Edition

———— Passio Domini nostri. Nürnberg [H. Hölzel] 1511. fol. First
Edition

———— Underweysung der messung. Nürnberg 1525. fol.

———— ———— Nurnberg, Hier. Formschneyder 1538. fol.

———— Underweysung der messung versus è Germanica lingua in
Latinam. Paris, ex officina C. Wecheli 1535. fol. (Didot)

———— Vier bücher von menschlicher proportion. Nürnberg, Hier.
Formschneyder 1528. fol.

Eck, Johann von.   Ad criminatricem Martini luders Wittebergen.
Offensionē . . . responsio. [after 19 Oct. 1519]. sm. 4to. (Huth)

———— Contra Martini Ludder obtusum propugnatorem Andream
Rodolphi Bodenstein. [after 3 Dec. 1519]. sm. 4to. (Huth)

———— Repulsio articulorum Zwinglii . . . 1530. n.p. n.d. sm. 4to.
(Huth)

Eck, Johann von.   Subdomini Ihesv et Mariae patrocinio.   Ingolstadt
1530.   sm.4to.   (Huth)

Erasmus, Desiderius.   Adagiorum epitome.   Antwerp, apud I. Steel-
sium 1537.   sm.8vo.   (Dunn)

———— Exomologesis sive modus confitendi.   Antwerp, M. Hillenius
1524.   sm.8vo.

Fortunatus.   Augspurg 1518.   sm.4to.   (Singer–Huth)

Franck, Sebastian.   Weltbuch.   Tübingen, U. Morhart 1534.   fol.
First & Second Issues

Fruck, Ludwig.   Rhetoric.   Strassburg, C. Egenolph 1530.   sm.4to.
(Huth)

Geiler von Kaysersberg, Johann.   Navicula penitentie.   Augsburg, J.
Otmar 1511.   fol.   First Edition.   (Heber)

———— Navicula sive speculum fatuorum.   Strassburg [J. Prüss] 16
Jan. 1511.   4to.   (Bement)

———— Der Passion.   n.p. n.d.   fol.

———— Postill:vber die fyer Evangelis.   Strassburg, J. Schott 1522.
fol.   (Didot–Andrews)

Goltz, Hubert.   C. Iulius Caesar sive historiae imperatorum . . . ex anti-
quis numismatibus restitutae.   Bruges 1563.   fol.   (Sunderland)

———— Caesar Augustus sive historiae imperatorum . . . Liber secundus.   Bruges 1574.   fol.   (Sunderland)

———— Fastos magistratuum et triumphorum Romanorum.   Bruges
1566.   fol.   (Sunderland)

———— Graecia.   Bruges 1576.   fol.   (Sunderland)

———— Lebendige bilder gar nach aller Kaysern.   [Antwerp] in
Aegidij Copenij Diesthemij truckerey 1557.   fol.

Grünpeck, Joseph.   Speculum naturalis.   Nuremberg, G. Stuchs 1508.
sm.fol.   (Huth)

Hasenberg, Johann.   Ludus ludentem.   Procusum Lypsiae 1530.   sm.
4to.   (J. E. Hodgkin)

Herberstein, Sigmund von.   Comentari della Moscovia.   Venetia, G. B.
Pedrezzano 1550.   sm.4to.

Herberstein, Sigmund von.   Rerum Moscoviticarum commentarii. [Vienna 1549].   fol.   First Edition

Hermann von Wied, *Archbishop of Cologne*.   Bestendige verantwortung.   Bonn, L. von der Mülen 1545.   fol.   (Huth)

—— Einfaltigs bedencken warauff ein christliche in dem wort Gottes gegrünte Reformation.   Bonn, L. von der Mülen 1564 [for 1544].   fol.   (Huth)

Hroswitha.   Opera.   Nuremberg, Printer for the Sodalitas Celtica 1501.   fol.   First Edition.   (Firmin Didot–Thomas Brooke)

Ein hübsche histori vō der . . . stat troy.   Straszburg, J. Knoblouch 1510. fol.   (C. R. Price–Huth)

Hugo de Sletstat, Johannes.   Quadruviū ecclesie quatuor prelatorū officium.   Strassburg, I. Grüninger 1504.   fol.   (C. R. Price–Huth)

Huss, John.   *See* Processus consistorialis

Junius, Adrian.   Batavia.   [Antwerp] ex officina Plantiniana, apud F. Raphelengium 1588.   sm. 4to.   (Bibliotheca Elseghemensis)

Klau, Cristoph C.   Novi calendarii Romani apologia.   Romae, apud Sanctium, & Soc. 1588.   sm. 4to.   (Bibliotheca S. Petri ad Vinculis–Pierre Duhem)

Lazius, Wolfgang.   De gentium aliquot migrationibus.   Basileae, I. Oporinus 1557.   fol.

Liège.   Statuta synodalia Leodiens.   Lovanii, apud P. Phalesium & M. Rotarium 1549.   sm. 8vo.

Lips, Joest.   De cruce.   Antverpiae, ex officina Plantiniana, apud viduam, & I. Moretum 1594.   sm. 4to.

Luther, Martin.   Condemnatio doctrinalis . . . Respōsio Lutheriana ad eandem condemnationem.   n.p. 1520.   sm. 4to.   (Rosenheim)

—— De captivitate Babylonica ecclesiae. Praeludium Martini Lutheri.   n.p. n.d.   sm. 4to.   (Murray)

—— De confessione.   n.p. 1524.   sm. 4to.

—— Disputatio . . . pro declaratione virtutis indulgentiarum.   [Basel, A. Petri] 1517.   sm. 4to.

—— Enarratio psalmi XC.   Wittembergae, V. Creuzer 1541.   8vo.

German after 1500

Luther, Martin. Eyn geystlich edles buchleyn. Wittenbergk, J. Grunenbergk 1516. sm. 4to.

———— Ain gütte trostliche predig von der wirdigen berayttung zu dem hochwurdigen sacrament. Augspurg, S. Otmar 1518. sm. 4to. First Edition. (Charles Butler)

———— In Cantica Canticorum. Witenbergae, Typis I. Luft 1539. 8vo.

———— In Esaiam prophetam scholia. Wittemberge, I. Lufft 1534. 8vo.

———— In septimum primae ad Corinthios caput, exegesis. Strassburg 1525. 8vo.

[————] Passional Christi und Antichristi. [Wittenberg, J. Grünenberg 1521]. sm. 4to.

———— *See also* Ob der Künig vsz engelland

Magnus, Olaus. Historia de gentibus septentrionalibus. Antverpiae, ex officina C. Plantini 1558. sm. 8vo. Second Issue

Murner, Thomas. Logica memorativa. Strassburg, I. Grüninger 1509. 4to. in sixes. (Ives)

Ob der Künig vsz engelland ein lügner sey oder der Luther. Strassburg, J. Grieninger 1522. sm. 4to.

Oderborn, Paul. Ioannis Basilidis magni Moscoviae ducis vita. Witebergae, Haeredes I. Cratonis 1585. sm. 8vo.

Dye passie ons heeren als ons die vier ewangeliste. Thantwerpen, W. Vorsterman [c. 1510]. sm. 8vo. (Huth–Pittar)

Processus consistorialis martyrij Io. Huss. [Strassburg, J. Schott, c. 1525]. sm. 4to. (Yemeniz–Paul Schmidt)

Ramus, Joannes. Elegiarum de rebus gestis Archiducum Austriae. Lovanii, Typis Reyneri Velpij 1553. sm. 8vo.

Reusner, Nicolas. Aureolorum emblematum. Strassburg, apud B. Iobinum 1591. 8vo. (Beckford)

Ringmann, Matthias. Passio domini. Strassburg, I. Knoblouch 1508. fol.

———— ———— Strassburg, M. Hupfuff 1513. fol. (Bement)

Rüff, Jacob. Ein nüw vñ lustig spyl von der erschaffung Adams vnd Heua. Zürych, C. Froschouer 1550. sm. 8vo. (Huth)

Theuerdank. Nurnberg, H. Schonsperger (1517). fol. First Edition. (S. P. Avery)

Von der erschrocklichen zurstörung vnnd niderlag desz gantzen bapstumbs gepropheceyet . . . durch . . . Christum. n.p. n.d. 4to. in sixes. (Huth–Leighton)

Warhafftige zeytung vñ beschreibung von der gewaltigen Armada. Köln, N. Schreiber 1588. sm. 4to.

SEVENTEENTH CENTURY

Aspruck, Franz. [Series of thirteen copperplate engravings of Christ and the Apostles]. 1601. 8vo. (Huth)

Ayrer, Jacob. Opus theatricum. Nürmberg, B. Scherff. I, 1618; II, 1610. fol.

Braght, Tieleman Jans van. Het bloedig tooneel. T'Amsterdam, H. Sweerts, J. ten Hoorn, J. Bouman, en D. van den Dalen . . . 1685. fol. (Beckford–H.V. Jones)

Caesar, Joachimus. Rationis et adpetitus pugna. Hoc est de amore Edoardi III. Regis Angliae & Elipsiae . . . historia, quam ad famae fanum adjecit Æschacius Major. Halis Saxoniae . . . C. Bismarcus (1612). 12mo. (Huth)

Cluver, Philipp. Germaniae antiquae. Lugduni Batavorum, ex officina Elzeviriana 1631. fol.

———— Italia antiqua. Lugduni Batavorum; ex officina Elseviriana 1624. fol.

———— Sicilia antiqua. Lugduni Batavorum; ex officina Elseviriana 1619. fol.

Flitner, Johann. Nebulo nebulonum. Francofurti, apud I. de Zetter 1620. 8vo. (Bridgewater)

Die Fruchtbringende Gesellschaft. Der Fruchtbringenden Gesellschaft nahmen. Franckfurt am Mayn, M. Merian 1646. 4to. (George C. Fogg–E. L. Page)

Hentzner, Paul. Itinerarium. Noribergae, A. Wagenmann 1612. sm. 4to.

German after 1500

Luther, Martin. Der grosse catechismus deutsch. Regenspurg, bey C. Fischern in verlegung J. Auckbendobler 1655. sm. 8vo. vellum. (Huth)

Merian, Matthias. *See* Die Fruchtbringende Gesellschaft

Passe, Crispin van de. Liber Genesis aereis formis. Arnhemii, apud I. Iansonium 1616. sm. 4to. (Learmont)

Petter, Nicolas. Klare onderrichtinge der voortreffelijcke worstel-konst. T'Amsterdam, J. Janssonius van Waesberge 1674. 4to.

[Spinoza, Baruch]. Tractatus theologico-politicus. Hamburgi, apud H. Künrath 1670. sm. 4to. First Edition

Varenius, Bernhard V. Geographia generalis. Amstelodami, ex officina Elzeviriana 1671. 12mo. (Corfield)

EIGHTEENTH CENTURY AND AFTER

Bissing, Fr. W. Denkmäler äegyptischer sculptur. München, F. Bruckmann 1911. 2 v. 4to.

Braght, Tieleman Jans van. Der blutige schau-platz. Ephrata in Pennsylvanien, Drucks und Verlags der Brüderschafft 1748. fol.

Brucker, Jacob. Pinacotheca scriptorum nostra aetate literis illustrium. Augsburg, apud J. J. Haidium 1741-7. 2 v. fol. (Huth)

Fabricius, Johann Albert. Bibliographia antiquaria. Hamburgi, apud I. C. Bohn 1760. 4to. Third Edition

Goethe, Johann Wolfgang von. Egmont. Leipzig, G. J. Göschen 1788. 8vo. First Edition. (Robert Browning)

—— Faust. Ein fragment. [Leipzig 1790]. 8vo. (11 gatherings, folded, but not stitched). First Edition

—— Die natürliche tochter. Tübingen, in der Cotta'schen buchhandlung. [Colophon] Jena, Fromman und Wesselhoeft. (Taschenbuch auf das jahr 1804). sm. 8vo. First Edition

Holbein, Hans. L'alphabet de la mort. Paris, pour E. Tross 1856. 8vo. vellum. (Sir Henry Hope Edwardes–Susan Minns)

—— Windsor Castle reprints. Series of 84 red chalk drawings in reproduction. fol.

Meurs, Jan de. Elegantiae Latini sermonis. Lugd. Batavorum, ex typis Elzevirianis 1774. 8vo. (Smalley)

Posselt, Ernst Ludwig, *editor*. Taschenbuch für die neuste geschichte. Nürnberg, in der Bauer- und Mannischen buchhandlung 1794-1802. 8 v. 16mo. First Edition. (Joseph Jefferson)

Schiller, Johann Christoph Friedrich von. Gedichte. Leipzig, S. L. Crusius, 1800-1803. 2 v. 8vo. First Edition

—— Die jungfrau von Orleans. Berlin, J. F. Unger 1802. 12mo. First Edition

—— Wallenstein. Tübingen, in der J. G. Cotta'schen buchhandlung 1800. 8vo. First Edition

Schreck, Emmy, *tr*. Finnische märchen. Weimar, H. Böhlau 1887. 8vo. (Andrew Lang)

Shakespeare, William. Dramatische werke. Uebersetzt von A. W. von Schlegel. Berlin, G. Reimer 1825-33. 9 v. 8vo. (R. Hirsch)

Treitzsaurwein, Marx. Der weiss künig. Wien, auf kosten J. Kurzböckens 1775. fol. (Huth)

Books by Italian Authors, Printed after 1500

This list includes also, translations of these works into languages other than English. It does *not* include Italian Bibles and liturgical books, or Italian works in Science. These, with Aldines, books by Italian authors printed *before* 1501, and *English* versions of Italian works, are listed in their several places under *Bibles*; *Science*; *Aldines*; *Incunabula*; and *English Literature*

SIXTEENTH CENTURY

Alciati, Andrea. Livret des emblemes . . . mis en rime francoyse par Jean Le Fevre. Paris, C. Wechel 1536. 8vo. (Duc de la Vrillière–Heber–Britwell)

——— Omnia emblemata. Lugduni, apud G. Rovillium 1566. 8vo. (Learmont)

——— ——— Paris, apud F. Guessier 1589. 8vo. (Hoe)

Antonio da Pistoia. Operetta nova de doi nobilissimi amāti. Venetia, Zorzi di Rusconi 1518. 8vo.

Ariosto, Ludovico. Orlando Furioso. Vinegia, G. Giolito 1550. 8vo. (Vernon)

——— ——— Venetia, F. de Franceschi 1584. 4to. (La Vallière–Dawson Turner)

Bandello, Matteo. Canti XI. Guienna nê la città di Agen, A. Reboglio 1545. 8vo. (R. S. Turner–Mexborough)

——— Novelle. I-III. Lucca, Il Busdrago 1554. 3 v. 4to.

——— ——— IV. Lione, A. Marsilij 1573. 8vo. First Edition. (Marsden Perry)

Beolco, Angelo. *See* Ruzzante, Angelo

Betussi, Giuseppe. Il raverta. Venetia, G. Giolito 1544. 8vo. First Edition. (Mexborough)

Bibbiena, Bernardo. *See* Dovizi da Bibbiena, Bernardo

Boccaccio, Giovanni. Il Decamerone. Vinegia, G. de Gregorii 1516. 4to. (Vernon)

——— ——— Firenze, li heredi di P. di Giunta 1527. 8vo. (Vernon)

——— ——— Fiorenza, i Giunta 1573. 8vo. (Hagen)

Boccaccio, Giovanni. Die gantz römisch histori. Augsburg, H. Stayner 1542. fol. (Hoe–H.V. Jones)

—— Il philocolo. Vinegia, Nicolo di Aristotile 1530. 8vo. (Beckford)

—— Il philocope. Paris, D. Janot 1542. fol. (Hoe–C. L. F. Robinson)

Boiardo, Matteo Maria. Orlando innamorato. Vinegia, Pietro di Nicolini da Sabbio 1539. 4to. (Heber–Britwell)

—— —— Venetia, Comin da Trino di Monferrato 1565. 4to. (Hoe)

Borghini, Raffaello. L'amante furioso. Vinegia, G. Battista & G. Bernardo Sessa 1597. 8vo. First Edition

Bruno, Giordano. Candelaio. Paris, G. Guiliano 1582. 8vo. First Edition

Calmo, Andrea. Le giocose. Vinegia, I. Bertacagno 1553. 8vo.

Castiglione, Baldassare. Il libro del cortegiano. Venetia 1544. 8vo.

Cecchi, Gian Maria. Il corredo. Venetia, B. Giunti 1585. 8vo. First Edition

Cellini, Benvenuto. Due trattati uno intorno alle otto principali arti dell' oreficeria. Fiorenza, V. Panizzij & M. Peri 1568. 4to. (Hoe–H.V. Jones)

Cesari, Cesare de'. Scilla. Venetia, G. Griffio 1552. 8vo. First Edition

Commedia di Beco, et Randello & l'hoste. Firenze, D. Fantucci, n.d. 8vo. (Murray)

Il consiglio villanesco. Siena 1583. 8vo.

Crescenzi, Pietro. De agricultura vulgare. Venetiis 1519. 4to.

—— Erdwucher vnd bawleütē. Strassburg, H. Knoblouch 1531. fol. (Bement)

Dante Alighieri. Lo amoroso convivio. Venetia, Z. Antonio & Fradelli da Sabio 1521. 8vo. Second Edition

—— Comedia. Venetia, I. del Burgofrāco 1529. fol. (H.V. Jones)

—— —— Venegia, F. Marcolini 1544. 4to. (Gaisford–Mexborough)

Dante Alighieri. Comedia. Venetia, G. B. & M. Sessa 1564. fol. (Vernon)

———— De la volgare eloquenzia. Vicenza, T. I. da Bressa 1529. fol. First Edition. (Bywater)

———— Lo'nferno e'l Purgatorio e'l Paradiso. [Toscolano] P. & A. Paganini [c. 1515]. 8vo. (Vernon)

———— Opere. Venetia, B. Stagnino da Trino de monferra 1512. 4to. (Oliver H. Perkins)

———— ———— ———— 1520. 4to. (Gloddaeth Library)

Dolce, Lodovico. Dialogo. Venetia, G. B. & M. Sessa 1562. First Edition. (Mexborough)

Dovizi da Bibbiena, Bernardo. Calandra. Vinegia, F. Bindoni & M. Pasini 1537. 8vo.

———— ———— Venetia, P. Pietrasanta 1554. 8vo.

Faerno, Gabriello. Fabulae centum. Romae, V. Luchinus 1564. 4to. First Edition. (McBurney)

———— ———— Venetiis, apud F. Zilettum 1572. 8vo. (W. L. Andrews)

Fanti, Sigismondo. Triompho di fortuna. Vinegia, A. da Portese 1527. fol. (Huth)

Farsa del Povero & del Riccho. [Florence, c. 1520]. 8vo.

Fior di virtù hystoriato. Florence, G. di Carlo da Pavia 1519. 4to. (Royal Society–Huth–Leighton)

Firenzuola, Angelo. I lucidi. Firenze, I. Giunti 1552. 8vo. Second Edition

Fortunio, Francesco. Regole grammaticali della volgar lingua. Ancona, B. Vercellese 1516. 4to. First Edition

Fregoso, Gianbattista. Baptistae Fulgosi De dictis. Milan, I. Ferrarius 1509. fol. First Edition

Gelli, Giovanni Battista. La sporta. Firenze, F. Giunti 1593. 8vo.

Giambullari, Pier Francesco. Il gello. Fiorenza, Il Doni 1546. 4to. First Edition

———— Lezzioni. Firenze 1551. 8vo. First Collected Edition

Giannotti, Donato.   De la republica de Vinitiani.   Roma, A. Blado 1540.   8vo.   (Syston Park)

Gianutio della Mantia, Horatio.   Libro nel quale si tratta del la maniera di giuocar' à scacchi.   Turino, A. de' Bianchi 1597.   4to.   First Edition

Giovanni Fiorentino.   Il pecorone.   Milano, G. Antoni 1554.   4to. (Shakespeare Library)

Giovio, Paolo.   Dialogo delas empresas.   En Leon . . . en casa G. Roville 1561.   4to.   First Edition.   (Hoe–C. L. F. Robinson)

Giraldi, Lilio Gregorio.   Syntagma de musis.   Argentorat., M. Schürer 1511.   4to.

Giraldi Cinthio, Giovanni Battista.   De gli hecatommithi.   Monte Regale, L. Torrentino 1565.   2 v.   8vo.   First Edition.   (Marsden Perry)

——— Didone.   Venetia, G. C. Cagnacini 1583.   8vo.

——— Orbecca.   Venetia, F. Rampazetto 1564.   12mo.

——— Le tragedie.   Venetia, G. C. Cagnacini 1583.   8vo.   (Marsden Perry)

Godfrey of Viterbo.   Pantheon.   Basileae, ex officina I. Parci 1559. fol.

Grasso, Nicolo.   Eutichia.   Vinegia, Nicolo d'Aristotile 1530.   8vo.

Gualla, Jacopo.   Sanctuarium.   Papie, J. de Burgofrācho 1505.   4to. (Firmin Didot–Thomas Brooke)

Gualterotti, Raffaello.   La verginia.   Firenze, B. Sermatelli 1584.   8vo. First Edition

Guazzo, Marco.   Discordia d'amore.   Vineggia, Nicolo d'Aristotile 1528.   8vo.

Intronati da Siena.   Gli ingannati.   [? Venice] 1537.   8vo.   (Marsden Perry)

——— ——— Vinegia 1543.   8vo.   (Marsden Perry)

——— ——— Venetia, P. Pietrasanta 1554.   8vo.

——— ——— Vinegia, G. Giolito 1559.   8vo.   (Marsden Perry)

——— Il sacrificio.   [? Venice] 1537.   8vo.   (Marsden Perry)

——— Vinegia 1543.   8vo.   (Marsden Perry)

Intronati da Siena.   Il sacrificio.   Venetia, P. Pietrasanta 1554.   8vo.

———— ———— Vinegia, G. Giolito 1559.   8vo.   (Marsden Perry)

Leoni, Giovanni Battista.   La conversione del peccatore a Dio.   Vinegia, F. de Franceschi 1592.   8vo.   First Edition

Leonico, Angelo.   L'amore di Trolio, et Griseida.   Venetia, P. Gerardo 1553.   4to.

Loredano, Giovanni Francesco.   La malandrina.   Venetia, all' insegna della speranza 1587.   8vo.   First Edition

Machiavelli, Niccolò.   La mandragola.   Venetia, P. Pietrasanta 1554. 8vo.

Maffei Volaterranus, Raphael.   Commentarium urbanorum.   Romae, per Ioannem Besicken 1506.   fol.   First Edition

Mariconda, Antonio.   Tre giornate della favole de l'Aganippe.   Napoli, G. P. Suganappo 1550.   4to.   (Mexborough)

Marozzo, Achille.   Opera nova.   Mutinae, in aedibus A. Bergolae 1536.   4to.   (Heber–Britwell)

Masuccio di Salerno.   Il novellino.   Venetia, nella officina Gregoriana 1522.   4to.   (Mexborough)

Merlin.   La vita di Merlino.   Venetia, V. di Roffinelli 1539.   8vo. (Royal Society–Huth)

Opera nova contemplativa (Biblia pauperum).   Vinegia, G. Vavassore [c. 1510].   8vo.   (Blockbook)

Parabosco, Girolamo.   Il viluppo.   Vinegia, G. Giolito 1560.   8vo. First Edition

Phalethus, Hieronymus.   Poematum libri septem.   Ferraria, F. Rubeus 1546.   8vo.   (Mexborough)

Piccolomini, Alessandro.   L'Alessandro.   Venetia, P. Pietrasanta 1554. 8vo.

[————] L'amor costante.   Venetia, P. Pietrasanta 1554.   8vo.

———— ———— Vinegia, G. Giolito 1559.   12mo.

Porta, Giovanni Battista della.   De furtivis literarum notis.   Neapoli, I. M. Scotus 1563.   4to.   First Edition

Razzi, Girolamo.   La cecca.   Fiorenza, appresso i figliuoli di L. Torrentino 1563.   8vo.

Ricchi da Lucca, Agostino.   I tre tiranni.   Vinegia, B. de Vitali 1533.
4to.   First Edition

Rondinelli, Dionisio.   Il pastor Vedovo.   Vicenza, G. Greco 1599.
8vo.   First Edition

Ruscelli, Girolamo.   Delle comedie elette.   Venetia (P. Pietrasanta)
1554.   8vo.

Rusconi, Giovanni Antonio.   Della architettura.   Venetia, I. Gioliti
1590.   fol.   First Edition.   (Pembroke)

Ruzzante, Angelo (*pseud. of A. Beolco*).   Anconitana.   Venetia, G.
Bonadio 1565.   8vo.   (Ashburton)

———— Dialogo facetissimo.   Venetia, G. Bonadio 1565.   8vo.   (Ashburton)

———— Due dialoghi.   Venetia, G. Bonadio 1565.   8vo.   (Ashburton)

———— Fiorina.   Venetia, G. Bonadio 1565.   8vo.   (Ashburton)

———— Moschetta.   Venetia, G. Bonadio 1565.   8vo.   (Ashburton)

———— Piovana.   Venetia, G. Bonadio 1565.   8vo.   (Ashburton)

———— Rhodiana.   Venetia, G. Bonadio 1565.   8vo.   (Ashburton)

———— Tre orationi.   Vinegia, D. de Farri 1561.   8vo.   (Ashburton)

———— Vaccaria.   Venetia, G. Bonadio 1565.   8vo.   (Ashburton)

Salviano, Hippolito.   La ruffiana.   Roma, V. & L. Dorici 1554.   8vo.
First Edition.   (Bridgewater)

Sarayna, Torello.   De origine . . . Veronae.   Veronae, ex officina A.
Puttelete 1540.   fol.

S[ecchi, N.].   La camariera.   Venetia, F. & A. Zoppini 1587.   12mo.
First Edition

Silvestre, Guido Posthumo.   Elegiarum libri II.   Bononiae, H. de Benedictis 1524.   4to.   First Edition

Spirito, Lorenzo.   Le livre de passe tẽps de la fortune . . . dytalien en
francoys par . . . A. Faure.   n.p. 1528.   4to.   (Yemeniz–Hoe–C. L.
F. Robinson)

Straparola, Giovanfrancesco.   Le piacevoli notti.   Venetia, Comin da
Trino di monferrato 1562.   2 v.   8vo.   (Hamilton Palace)

Symeoni, Gabriele. Devisas o emblemas. En Leon . . . en casa de G. Roville 1561. 4to.

—— Le sententiose imprese, et dialogo. Lyone, G. Roville 1560. 4to. (Osterley Park)

Tasso, Torquato. Gierusalemme liberata. Ferrara, appresso gli heredi di F. de' Rossi 1581. 4to. (Sutherland)

—— —— Genova, G. Bartoli 1590. 4to. (Pierre Mariette–Charles, Viscount Bruce of Ampthill–Ailesbury)

—— Il re Torrismondo. Verona, G. Discepolo 1587. 8vo. (Nicolo Francesco Haym–Charles, Viscount Bruce of Ampthill–Ailesbury)

Varchi, Benedetto. De sonetti. Fiorenza, L. Torrentino 1555-7. 2 v. 8vo.

Vasari, Giorgio. Le vite de' piu eccellenti pittori, scultori, e architettori. Fiorenza, Giunti 1568. 2 v. in 3. 4to. (Shakespeare Library)

Vecellio, Cesare. Corona delle nobili . . . donne. Venetia, gli heredi della Regina 1591. 2 v. in 1. 4to. First Edition

—— De gli habiti antichi, et moderni. Venetia, D. Zenaro 1590. 8vo. First Edition. (Shakespeare Library)

Vicentino, Ludovico. La operina . . . da imparare di scrivere littera cancellarescha. Roma, V. Dorico & Luigi fratelli 1540. 8vo. (Hoe–C. L. F. Robinson)

Virgil, Polydore. Von den erfyndern der dyngen . . . durch M. Tatium . . . iñs tëutsch transferiert. Augspurg, H. Steyner 1537. fol. (Huth)

SEVENTEENTH CENTURY

Boccaccio, Giovanni. Il Decameron. Amsterdamo [D. Elzevier] 1665. 12mo. First Issue

—— —— —— Second Issue

Bosio, Antonio. Roma sotteranea. Roma, appresso G. Facilotti 1635. fol.

Buonarroti, Michelangelo. Rime. Firenze, I. Giunti 1623. 4to. First Edition. (Britwell)

Buonarroti, Michelangelo, *il giovine*. La tancia. Firenze, nella stamperia de' Landini 1638. 8vo.

Giraldi Cinthio, Giovanni Battista. Hecatommithi. Venetia, E. Deu-
chino & G. B. Pulciani 1608. 2 v. 4to. (Patrick Hume)

Magini, Giovanni Antonio. Italia. Bononiae 1620. fol. (De Thou)

Negri, Cesare. Le gratie d'amore. Milano, per l'her. del quon. Pa-
cifico Pontio & G. B. Piccaglia 1602. fol. (Huth)

Porto, Antonio. Libro da imparare a giocare a scacchi. Venetia, P.
Farri 1618. 12mo. (Sir F. Madden–Huth)

Ripa, Cesare. Iconologia. Roma, appresso Lepido Faeij 1603. 4to.

Rusca, Antonio. De inferno. Mediolani, ex Collegij Ambrosiani typographia 1621. 4to. (Huth)

Zoppio, Melchiorre. La Medea. Bologna, gli heredi di G. Rossi 1602.
8vo. First Edition

EIGHTEENTH CENTURY

Alfieri, Vittorio. L'America libera. Dalla tipografia di Kehl, co'caratteri di Baskerville 1784. 8vo. First Edition

———— La virtu sconosciuta. Dalla tipografia di Kehl, co'caratteri di
Baskerville 1786. 8vo. First Edition

Ariosto, Ludovico. Orlando Furioso. Birmingham, da torchj di G.
Baskerville: per P. Molini e G. Molini 1773. 4 v. 8vo.

Bandello, Matteo. Novelle I-III. Londra, S. Harding 1740. 4 v. in 3.
4to. (Bibliotheca Lamoniana–Wodhull)

Carrara, Ubertino. Columbus. Augustae, Sumptibus M. Wolff 1730.
8vo.

Dante Alighieri. Opere. Venezia, G. Pasquali 1741. 5 v. 8vo.
(Montigny–Vernon)

———— ———— Venezia, A. Zatta 1757-8. 8 v. in 5. 4to. (Charles
Barclay)

Faerno, Gabriello. Fabulae centum. Londini, G. Darres & C. du Bosc
1743. 4to. (Hoe–Learmont)

Lolli, Giovanni Battista. Osservazioni . . . sopra il guoco degli scacchi.
Bologna, T. d'Aquino 1763. fol.

Italian after 1500

Petrarca, Francesco.   Rime.   Firenze, nella stamperia all'insegna d'Apollo 1748.   8vo.   (Sutherland)

Piranesi, Giambattista.   Le antichita romane.   Roma, nella stamperia Salomoni 1784.   4 v.   fol.

AFTER 1800

Ariosto, Ludovico.   L'Orlando Furioso.   Pisa, dalla tipografia della Società Letteraria 1809.   5 v.   fol.   (Boswell)

Boccaccio, Giovanni.   Il Decamerone.   Chelsea, nella stamperia Ashendeniana 1920.   fol.

Bonnard, Camillo.   Costumi dei secoli XIII, XIV e XV.   Milano, Ranieri Fanfani 1832-5.   2 v.   fol.   First Edition

Buonarroti, Michelangelo.   Poesie.   Montagnola di Lugano, Officina Bodoni 1923.   fol.

Canudo, Ricciotto.   Le livre de la Genèse.   Paris, Éditions de la Plume 1905.   4to.   First Edition.   (One of seven copies on Japan paper).   (McBurney)

Cesaresco, Eugenio Martinengo.   L'arte di cavalcare.   Salò, Giovanni Devoti 1894.   5 v.   8vo.   First Edition.   (Presentation copy from the author to James Carleton Young)

Dante Alighieri.   La Divina Commedia.   Pisa, dalla tipografia della Società Letteraria 1804-9.   4 v.   fol.   (Boswell)

——— ——— Londra: dai torchj di R. Zotti 1808-9.   4 v.   8vo. (Vernon)

——— ——— Parigi, dai torchi di Dondey-Dupré 1818-9.   3 v.   8vo. (Vernon)

——— ——— Firenze, Tipografia all'insegna di Dante 1830.   12mo. (Vernon)

——— ——— Firenze, F. le Monnier e compagni 1837.   2 v. in 1. 8vo.   (Vernon)

——— ——— Londra, P. Rolandi 1842-3.   3 v.   8vo.   (Vernon)

——— La Divina Commedia.   Facsimile del Codice Landiano (Mcccxxxvj).   Firenze, L. S. Olschki 1921.   fol.

——— La Divina Commedia.   Bologna, N. Zanichelli (1923).   8vo.

Dante Alighieri.   Le prime quattro edizioni della Divina Commedia letteralmente ristampate.   Londra, Tommaso e Guglielmo Boone 1858.   4to.   (Presentation copy, inscribed, from Lord Vernon to Prince Louis Lucien Bonaparte)

———— Commento di F. da Buti sopra la Divina Comedia.   Pisa, fratelli Nistri 1858-60.   3 v.   8vo.   (James Russell Lowell)

———— Benevenuti de Rambaldis de Imola Comentum super Dantis ... Comoediam.   Florentiæ, Typis G. Barbera 1887.   5 v.   8vo.   (Presentation copy from William Warren Vernon to Lord Amherst)

———— L'Inferno.   Londra, Tommaso e Guglielmo Boone 1858-60.   3 v.   fol.   (Amherst)

———— Tutte le opere.   Chelsea, nella stamperia Ashendeniana 1909.   fol.   (DeVinne)

———— Blake, William.   Illustrations for the Divine Comedy.   London, The National art-collections fund 1922.   102 folio plates

———— ———— Six designs for the Divine Comedy.   [Pt. I].   [London 1922].   6 folio plates in color

———— ———— ———— [Pt. II].   [London 1926].   6 folio plates in color

———— Botticelli, Alessandro.   Zeichnungen zu Dante's Goettlicher Komoedie nach den originalen in ... Berlin.   Berlin, G. Grote 1887.   2 v.   fol.   (Vernon)

Francesco di Assisi, *Saint*.   Un mazzetto scelto di certi fioretti.   Chelsea, stamperia di Ashendene 1904.   fol.

Machiavelli, Niccolò.   Opera complete.   Firenze, Passigli, Borghi e compagni 1831.   8vo.   (Napoléon III)

Medici, Lorenzo de'.   Poesie volgari.   Edinburgh, Ballantyne Press 1912.   2 v.   8vo.

Petrarca, Francesco.   Rime.   Pisa, dalla tipografia della Società Letteraria 1805.   2 v.   fol.   (Boswell)

Tasso, Torquato.   La Gerusalemme liberata.   Pisa, dalla tipografia della Società Letteraria 1807.   2 v.   fol.   (Boswell)

Books by Spanish Authors, Printed after 1500

This list includes also, translations of these works into languages other than English. It does *not* include Spanish Bibles and liturgical books, or Spanish works in Science. These, with Aldines, books by Spanish authors printed *before* 1501, and *English* versions of Spanish works, are listed in their several places under *Bibles*; *Science*; *Aldines*; *Incunabula*; and *English Literature*

SIXTEENTH CENTURY

Alcala, Pedro de. Arte para ligeramēte saber la lēgua arauiga. Granada, Juan Varela 1505. 4to. First Edition. (Huth)

Amadis, de Gaule. Lisuarte di Grecia. Venetia, Michele Tramezzino 1550. 8vo. First Edition. (Roxburghe–Heber)

———— Los quatro libros. Venecia, Juan Antonio 1533. fol. (Huth)

Boscan, Juan. Las obras de Boscan y algunas de Garcilasso dela Vega. Anvers, en casa de Martin Nucio, n.d. 12mo.

Cancionero de romances. Enveres, en casa de Martin Nucio, n.d. 12mo. (Gancia–Huth)

———— Anvers, en casa de Martin Nucio 1555. 12mo. (Huth)

Caterina da Siena, *Saint*. Obres fetes en labor dela seraphica senta catherina d'sena. [Valencia, c. 1511]. 4to. (Gancia–Huth)

Celestina. [Anvers] en la officina Plantiniana 1595. 8vo. (Morante–Seillière–Thomas Brooke)

Chronica del . . . Alfonso el onzeno. Valladolid, Pedro Espinosa y Antonio d'Zamora 1551. fol. (2 copies: 1, Hernando de Corral–Hanrott–Heber–Richard Ford–Huth)

———— Valladolid (Sebastian Martinez) 1554. fol. (Hernando de Corral–Hanrott–Heber–Richard Ford–Huth)

Chronica del . . . Fernando tercero. Valladolid, Sebastian Martinez 1554. fol. (Hernando de Corral–Hanrott–Heber–Richard Ford–Huth)

Chronica del . . . Fernando [cuarto]. Valladolid, Sebastian Martinez 1554. fol. (Hernando de Corral–Hanrott–Heber–Richard Ford–Huth)

Chronica del . . . Rodrigo. Toledo, Iuan Ferrer 1549. fol.

Spanish after 1500

Cid Ruy Diaz de Vivar. Cronica. Medina del Campo, Juan Maria da Terranova y Jacome de Liarcari 1552. (Al fine) ... Francisco del cāto 1553. fol. Second Edition

Garrido de Villena, Francisco. Romance del Rey Moro q perdio a Valencia. Valencia, al molina de Rouella, n.d. 4to. (J. J. de Bure–Montino–Biblioteca Arozarena–Huth)

Ita, Ginés de. ... dos romances. Il primero ... de los amores de Reynaldos de Montalvan dō la ... Princesa Calidonia. El segudo es de don Garcia. n.p. n.d. 4to. (J. J. de Bure–Montino–Biblioteca Arozarena–Huth)

James, *Saint and Apostle, Order of.* Reegra & statutos: da ordem de Santiago. Lisbon, Galharde Frances 1548. sm. 4to.

Ledesma, Bartolomé de. De septem ... sacramentis summarium. Mexici, Antonius de Espinosa 1566. 4to.

Lopez de Mendoza, Inigo. Prouerbios. Seuilla, en casa de Juan Cromberger 1530. fol. (Huth)

Lopez de Segura, Ruy. De la invencion liberal y arte del juego del axedrez. Alcala, Andres de Angulo 1561. 8vo.

Madrigal, Alfonso de. Las catorze questiones del Tostado. Burgos 1545. fol.

Mena, Juan de. Copilaciō de todas las obras. Valladolid, Juan de Villaquiran 1536. fol. (Huth)

———— ———— [Toledo, Fernando de sancta catalina] 1548. fol. (Huth)

———— La coranacion. Valladolid, Juan de Villaquiran 1536. fol. (Huth)

———— ———— Toledo, Fernando de sancta catalina 1547. fol. (Huth)

[Moraes, Francisco de]. Il primo libro del ... Palmerino d'Inghilterra ... in lingua toscana. Vinegia, Francesco Portonaris dā Trino 1553. 8vo. (Bindley–Heber)

Nadal, Gerónimo. Evangelicae historiae imagines. Antwerp, Martin Nutius 1595. fol. (G. Luenckens–Bement)

Nebrija, Antonio de. Aurea expositō. (Saragossa, Georgius Coci 1510). 4to. (Gancia–Huth)

Oliveros de Castilla. La historia. Seuilla, Juan Cromberger 1535. fol. (Huth)

Padilla, Pedro de. Iardin espiritual. Madrid, en casa de Querino Gerardo Flamenco 1585. 4to. First Edition. (Huth)

Palmerin de Inglaterra. *See* [Moraes, Francisco de]

Palmerin de Oliva. Libro de Palmerin de Oliva. Seuilla, Juan Cromberger 1536. fol. (Huth)

Palomero, Martin. Romance del moro Calaynos. Valencia, junto al molino de Rouella, n.d. 4to. (J. J. de Bure–Montino–Biblioteca Arozarena–Huth)

Perez de Guzman, Fernan. La cronica del . . . Juan el segundo. Logrono, Arnao Guillen de Brocar 1517. fol. (Huth)

Reynoso, Diego de. Romance del Conde Claros de Montalvan. n.p. n.d. 4to. (J. J. de Bure–Montino–Biblioteca Arozarena–Huth)

Roselao de Grecia. Don Roselao de Grecia. Toledo, Juan de Ayala 1547. fol. (Huth)

Santiago, *Order of*. *See* James, *Saint and Apostle, Order of*

Siete romances de diuersas hystorias sacados. Alcala, en casa de Sebastian Martinez 1546. 4to. (J. J. de Bure–Montino–Biblioteca Arozarena–Huth)

Tostado, Alfonso. *See* Madrigal, Alfonso de

Tratado de re militari. (Alcala) Miguel de Eguya 1536. fol. (Huth). (Authorship attributed to Diego de Salazar)

Vega, Garcilaso de la. *See* Boscan, Juan

Ximenes Ayllon, Diego. Los famosos . . . hechos del . . . Cid Ruydiaz de Biuar. Anveres, en casa de la biuda de Iuan Lacio 1568. 4to. First Edition. (Hibbert–Heber–Britwell)

SEVENTEENTH CENTURY

Avila, Gaspar de. Comedia famosa El familiar sin demonio. Madrid, Diego Diaz de la Carrera 1652. 4to. (Huth)

Calderon de la Barca, Pedro. Comedias verdaderas. Madrid 1698-1731. 9 v. 4to.

Castro, Guillem de. Comedia famosa Las maravillas de Babilonia. Madrid, Diego Diaz de la Carrera 1652. 4to. (Huth)

Cervantes de Saavedra, Miguel de. Don Quixote. Madrid, Iuan de la Cuesta 1605, 1615. 2 v. 4to. I, Second Edition; II, First Edition. (Salvá)

————— ————— Valencia, Pedro Patricio Mey 1605. 8vo. (Huth–Murray). (Catchword of recto sig. †2 is "La")

————— ————— ————— 8vo. (Catchword of recto sig. †2 is "AL")

————— ————— Brusselas [I] Roger Velpius 1607; II, Huberto Antonio 1616. 2 v. 8vo.

————— ————— Madrid, Iuan de la Cuesta 1608. 4to. (Vernon)

————— ————— Amberes, Henrico & Cornelio Verdussen 1697. 2 v. 8vo.

————— Los trabaios de Persiles y Sigismunda. Pamplona, Nicolas de Assiayn 1617. 8vo. (Mexborough)

Comedia famosa Del pleito que tuuo el diablo. See Velez de Guevara; Francisco de Rojas; Mira de Mezqua

Enriquez Gomez, Antonio. Comedia famosa Zelos no ofenden al sol. Madrid, Diego Diaz de la Carrera 1652. 4to. (Huth)

Espinosa, Pedro de. Primera parte de las flores de poetas ilustres de España. Valladolid, Luys Sanchez 1605. 4to. (Huth)

Flor de las meiores doce comedias. Madrid, Diego Diaz de la Carrera 1652. 4to. (Huth). (Edited by Pedro de Logroño)

Gouvea, Antonio de, *editor.* Iornada do ... Frey Aleixo de Menezes. Coimbra, Diogo Gomez Loureyro 1606. fol. (Huth)

Herrera, Rodrigo de. Comedia famosa Castigar por defender. Madrid, Diego Diaz de la Carrera 1652. 4to. (Huth)

Hurtado de Mendoça, Antonio. Comedia famosa de Los empeños del mentir. Madrid, Diego Diaz de la Carrera 1652. 4to. (Huth)

————— Comedia famosa El Señor de Noches Buenas. Madrid, Diego Diaz de la Carrera 1652. 4to. (Huth)

————— Comedia famosa No ay amor donde ay agravio. Madrid, Diego Diaz de la Carrera 1652. 4to. (Huth)

Lope de Vega, Felix de. See Vega Carpio, Lope Felix de

Menezes, Aleixo de. See Gouvea, Antonio de; Synodo diocesano

Mezqua, Mira de.   Comedia famosa Del pleito que tuuo el diablo. Iornada tercera.   Madrid, Diego Diaz de la Carrera 1652.   4to. (Huth)

Olmo, José de.   Relacion historica del Auto general de fe.   (Madrid, Roque Rico de Miranda 1680).   4to.   (Huth)

Rojas Zorrilla, Francisco de.   Comedia famosa Del pleito que tuuo el diablo. Iornada segunda.   Madrid, Diego Diaz de la Carrera 1652. 4to.   (Huth)

Romancero general . . . emendado Pedro Flores.   Madrid, Juan de la Cuesta 1614. 4to.   (John Wyndham Bruce–Vernon)

Sigler de Huerta, Antonio.   Comedia famosa Competidores y amigos. Madrid, Diego Diaz de la Carrera 1652.   4to.   (Huth)

——— Comedia famosa No ay bien sin ageno daño.   Madrid, Diego Diaz de la Carrera 1652.   4to.   (Huth)

Solis y Ribadeneyra, Antonio de.   Comedias.   Madrid, Melchior Alvarez 1681.   4to.   First Collected Edition

Synodo diocesano da Igreia e Bispada de Angamale dos antigos Christaõs de San Thome . . . celebrado pello . . . Frey Aleixo de Menezes . . . 1599.   Coimbra, Diogo Gomez Loureyro 1606.   fol.   (Huth)

Vega Carpio, Lope Felix de.   Laurel de Apolo.   Madrid, Iuan Gonçalez 1630.   4to.   First Edition

Velez de Guevara, Luis.   Comedia famosa De la luna de la Sierra.   Madrid, Diego Diaz de la Carrera 1652.   4to.   (Huth)

——— Comedia famosa Del pleito que tuuo el diablo.   Iornada primera.   Madrid, Diego Diaz de la Carrera 1652.   4to.   (Huth)

Villaizan, Geronimo de.   Comedia famosa A gran daño gran remedio. Madrid, Diego Diaz de la Carrera 1652.   4to.   (Huth)

EIGHTEENTH AND NINETEENTH CENTURIES

A el gran monarca D. Phelype Quinto.   Madrid, Diego Martinez Abad, n.d. 4to.   (Huth)

A la fina, heroyca lealtat. Barcelona, Rafael Figuerò, n.d. 4to. (Huth)

Afectos amorosos. Cadiz, Christoval de Requena 1705. 4to. (Huth)

La Africa. Madrid, Andrés de Sotos, n.d. 4to. (Vernon)

Al feliz preñado de la Reyna. n.p. n.d. 4to. (Huth)

Los alcaldes de Carabanchel.   Madrid, Antonio Bizarròn, n.d.   4to.
(Huth)

La America. Madrid, Andrés de Sotos, n.d. 4to. (Vernon)

Aplausos christianos de . . . Felipe V.   Madrid, Antonio Bizarròn 1701.
4to. (Huth)

El Asia. Madrid, Andrés de Sotos, n.d. 4to. (Vernon)

Aznar Belez S., Garcia.   *See* Gonzalez de Barcia Caballido y Zuñiga,
Andres

Bartolo, y Pasquala. n.p. n.d. 4to. (Huth)

Bernaldo de Quiròs, Francisco Antonio.   Vaticinio heroico.   n.p. n.d.
4to. (Huth)

Blas de Leon. Cordoba, n.d. 4to. (Vernon)

Camara angelical de nuestra señora de Montserrate. Cordoba, n.d. 4to.
(Vernon)

El cardador de Segovia.   Madrid, Juan Estevan Bravo 1707.   4to.
(Huth)

Carta astrologica. n.p. n.d. 4to. (Huth)

Carta christiana. n.p. n.d. 4to. (Huth)

Carta escrita por el Gran Turco. n.p. n.d. 4to. (Huth)

Cautiverio, lagrimas, y redempcion de . . . nuestro Monarca.   n.p. n.d.
4to. (Huth)

Celebre pompa . . . y festivas demonstraciones. n.p. n.d. 4to. (Huth)

Certamen velico. n.p. n.d. 4to. (Huth)

Cervantes de Saavedra, Miguel de.   Comedias y entremeses.   Madrid,
Antonio Marin 1749. 2 v. 4to.

———— Don Quixote.   Londres, J. y R. Tonson 1738.   4 v.   4to.
(William Congreve Russell)

———— ———— Madrid, Joaquin Ibarra 1780. 4 v. 4to. (Matthew
Wilson–Frances M. R. Currer)

———— ———— Madrid, Gabriel de Sancha 1797-8. 5 v. 8vo.

———— ———— Berlin, Enrique Frölich 1804-5. 6 v. 8vo.

Spanish after 1500

Cervantes de Saavedra, Miguel de.   Don Quixote.   Madrid, D. E. Aguado 1833-9.   6 v.   4to.   (Baron Foley)

Coplas de Marica la ciega.   n.p. n.d.   4to.   (Huth)

Coplas espirituelas.   n.p. n.d.   4to.   (Huth)

Coplas para coplas.   n.p. n.d.   4to.   (Huth)

Curiosa relacion . . . de Jacinto Estica.   Cordoba, n.d.   4to.   (Vernon)

Curiosa relacion de la prodigiosa vida del Serafin de la Inglesia.   Valencia, n.d.   4to.   (Vernon)

Curiosa relacion . . . la fatal desgracia . . . de tres formas consagradas. Cordoba, n.d.   4to.   (Vernon)

Curiosa relacion, que refiere el cautiverio de Don Luis de Borja.   Madrid, n.d.   4to.   (Vernon)

Curiosa satyra nueva.   n.p. n.d.   4to.   (Huth)

Curioso romance . . . Bernardo del Montijo.   Cordoba, Luis de Ramos y Coria, n.d.   4to.   (Vernon)

Curioso romance de la muger fuerte Santa Maria Egypciaca.   Cordoba, Luis de Ramos y Coria, n.d.   4to.   (Vernon)

Curioso . . . romance, de un marabilloso milagro.   Cordoba, Colegio de la Assumpcion, n.d.   4to.   (Vernon)

Curioso . . . romance . . . Don Joseph Vallejo.   Sevilla, n.d.   4to.   (Vernon)

Curioso romance . . . Don Pedro de Teneri y Rocaberti.   Sevilla, Tomàs Lopez de Haro, n.d.   4to.   (Vernon)

Curioso romance . . . Isabel de Azevedo.   Sevilla, Francisco de Leefdael, n.d.   4to.   (Vernon)

Curioso romance . . . las infelices muertes.   Sevilla, Diego Lopez de Haro, n.d.   4to.   (Vernon)

Curioso romance . . . maravilloso prodigio, que ha obrado el Patriarca San Joseph en la villa de la Cabezas . . . 1755-6.   Jaen, Thomàs Copado, n.d.   4to.   (Vernon)

El danzante de Alcorcon.   Pamplona: Por un leal vassalo de nuestra Rey, n.d.   4to.   (Huth)

De Don Cecilio del Villar.   Cordoba, n.d.   4to.   (Vernon)

De D. Juan Estevan de Argalia.   Valencia, Agustin Laborda, n.d.   4to.
(Vernon)

De Mosen Senen.   Sevilla, n.d.   4to.   (Vernon)

Dèlos, Bernardo.   De la mejor triaca para atajar el veneno.   Madrid,
Andrés de Sotos, n.d.   4to.   (Vernon)

El desengaño a cargas, conducido a los Sebastianistas, por requa de Juan
Harriero.   Granada 1707.   4to.   (Huth)

Desengaño de engaños.   n.p. n.d.   4to.   (Huth)

Despertador espiritual.   Cordoba, Luis de Ramos y Coria, n.d.   4to.
(Vernon)

Los desposorios de San Joseph y la Virgen. Pt. I.   Cordoba, n.d.   4to.
(Vernon)

Devota . . . relacion . . . los señales que presederán . . . el fin del mundo.
Cordoba, n.d.   4to.   (Vernon)

Diamante, Juan Bautista.   Comedias.   Madrid, Los herederos de Antonio Gonçalez de Reyes 1722.   4to.

Disputo que tuuieron en esta corte.   n.p. n.d.   4to.   (Huth)

Don Cerezo, y Doña Cereza.   n.p. n.d.   4to.   (Huth)

Don Juan de Aviles.   Valencia, Agustin Laborda, n.d.   4to.   (Vernon)

Don Miguel Escriba.   Cordoba, n.d.   4to.   (Vernon)

Don Pedro de Veraguas.   Madrid, n.d.   4to.   (Vernon)

Doña Clara, y Don Miguel de Silva.   Valencia, Agustin Laborde, n.d.
4to.   (Vernon)

Doña Florencia Benavides, y D. Pedro de Contreras.   Cordoba, n.d.
4to.   (Vernon)

Donayres de Perico, y Marica.   n.p. n.d.   4to.   (Huth)

Escobar, Juan de.   Historia . . . del Cid Ruy Diaz de Vibar.   Madrid,
Don Pedro Joseph Alonso y Padilla 1747.   12mo.   (Huth)

Esquadron.   n.p. n.d.   4to.   (Huth)

La Europa.   Madrid, n.d.   4to.   (Huth)

Famoso romance . . . Francisco de Torres.   Madrid, n.d.   4to.   (Vernon)

Spanish after 1500

Famosa satyra nueva. n.p. n.d. 4to. (Huth)

Famosa xacara nueva. n.p. n.d. 4to. (Huth)

Famosa xacara nueva ... Antonio Gonçalez. Madrid 1706. 4to. (Huth)

Famosa xacara nueva ... de tres famosos ladrones. Zaragoza, Herederos de Manuel Roman, n.d. 4to. (Vernon)

Famosa xacara nueva ... Juan Viñas. Madrid 1706. 4to. (Huth)

Fey, Antonio de la. Tres romances. Valencia, n.d. 4to. (Vernon)

Flores, Antonio Francisco de. Romance hendechasilabo. Cadiz, Christoval de Requena 1706. 4to. (Huth)

Glorioso, alto, y generoso triunfo. Cadiz, Christoval de Requena, n.d. 4to. (Huth)

Gonzalez de Barcia Caballido y Zuñiga, Andres. El triumpho al Rey N. Señor. Por mano de Don Joseph Grimaldo. Madrid, Diego Martinez Abad 1707. 4to. (Huth)

Jacara heroica. Zaragoça, Francisco Revilla, n.d. 4to. (Huth)

Jornada celebre. Madrid, Juan Bot, n.d. 4to. (Huth)

Juan de Naballas. Cordoba, Juan de Medina, n.d. 4to. (Vernon)

Las labanderas de Caravanchel. n.p. n.d. 4to. (Huth)

Lagrimas de la lealtad. n.p. n.d. 4to. (Huth)

Lagrimas, que derramò Marin. n.p. n.d. 4to. (Huth)

Lastimo romance. Sevilla, n.d. 4to. (Vernon)

Leales expressiones. n.p. n.d. 4to. (Huth)

Loa, representada ... en la fiesta ... a S. Diego. n.p. n.d. 4to. (Huth)

Llora Valencia. n.p. n.d. 4to. (Huth)

El mapa de la composiciones. n.p. n.d. 4to. (Huth)

Matraca. n.p. n.d. 4to. (Huth)

Monstruo de Jerusalén. Cordoba, Luis de Ramos y Coria, n.d. 4to. (Vernon)

Mora, Molina y Fuente, Andres Ignacio de. Loa en celebracion de la feliz noticia ... de ... D. Phelipe V. Cadiz, Christoval de Requena 1706. 4to. (Huth)

Nuea relacion . . . de . . . Rosimonda.   Cordoba, Colegio de nuestra de la Señora Assumpcioo, n.d.   4to.   (Vernon)

Nueva relacion . . . de la milagrosa Imágen del Christo de San Salvador. Valencia, n.d.   4to.   (Vernon)

Nueva relacion de los horrendos estragos.   Madrid, n.d.   4to.   (Vernon)

Nueva relacion de un portentoso milagro.   Cordova, Colegio de nuestra Señora de la Assumpcion, n.d.   4to.   (Vernon)

Nueva relacion de un prodigioso portento.   Sevilla, n.d.   4to.   (Vernon)

Nueva relacion . . . el triunfo de San Jorge.   Valencia, Agustin Laborda, n.d.   4to.   (Vernon)

Nueva relacion . . . la vida, y muerte de cinquenta y dos hombres.   Madrid, Vicente Llofriu, n.d.   4to.   (Vernon)

Nueva relacion . . . una muger llamada Francisca Rosalines.   Madrid, n.d.   4to.   (Vernon)

Nueva relacion, y curioso romance.   n.p. n.d.   4to.   (Huth)

Nueva relacion, y curioso romance . . . de Ramon Guardiola.   Madrid, n.d.   4to.   (Vernon)

Nueva relacion, y curioso romance . . . de una muger, que dió veneno á su Madre.   Madrid, n.d.   4to.   (Vernon)

Nueva relacion, y curioso romance . . . Don Pedro de Roxas.   Madrid, Cosme Granja, n.d.   4to.   (Vernon)

Nueva relacion, y curioso romance . . . el portentoso exemplo.   Sevilla, n.d.   4to.   (Vernon)

Nueva relacion, y curioso romance . . . en . . . Manila.   Cordoba, n.d. 4to.   (Vernon)

Nueva relacion, y curioso romance, en que se declara el grande sentimiento con que se ha despedido Vigotillos de Oràn.   Valencia, n.d. 4to.   (Vernon)

Nueva relacion, y curioso romance . . . un raro caso, que sucediò en . . . Zaragoza.   Sevilla, n.d.   4to.   (Vernon)

Nueva, y curiosa relacion.   n.p. n.d.   4to.   (Huth)

Nueva y curiosa relacion . . . de San Albano.   Madrid, n.d.   4to.   (Vernon)

Nuevo romance ... de D. Manuel Gonzalez, y Dona Teresa Enriquez. Valencia, en la imprenta de la viuda de Geronimo Conejos, n.d. 4to. (Vernon)

Nuevo romance ... del ... Francisco Alva. Valencia, Joseph Lucas, n.d. 4to. (Vernon)

Nuevo romance del singular milagro. Valencia, Agustin Laborda, n.d. 4to. (Vernon)

Nuevo romance ... Don Carlos. Barcelona, Juan Jolis, n.d. 4to. (Vernon)

Nuevo romance ... el mas injusto castigo. Madrid, n.d. 4to. (Vernon)

Nuevo romance ... la maravillosa justicia. Sevilla, n.d. 4to. (Vernon)

Nuevo romance ... un lastimoso caso. Sevilla, n.d. 4to. (Vernon)

Nuevo, y curioso romance, a la renovacion del ... Templo de los Sagrados San Juan Bautista, y San Juan Evangelista. Cordoba, n.d. 4to. (Vernon)

Nuevo, y curioso romance ... Christo Señor nuestro. Valencia, Cosme Granja, n.d. 4to. (Vernon)

Nuevo, y curioso romance ... del ... D. Francisco Correa. Valencia, Cosme Granja, n.d. 4to. (Vernon)

Nuevo, y curioso romance, del valiente Antonio Delgado. Sevilla, Joseph Antonio de Hermosilla, n.d. 4to. (Vernon)

Nuevo, y curioso romance ... Don Diego del Castillo. Sevilla, Joseph Antonio de Hermosilla, n.d. 4to. (Vernon)

Nuevo, y curioso romance ... el maravilloso milagro, que obrò la serenisima Reyna de Cielo. Sevilla, n.d. 4to. (Vernon)

Nuevo, y curioso romance ... la Princesa de Tinacria. Cordoba, n.d. 4to. (Vernon)

Nuevo, y curioso romance ... un cavallero. Sevilla, Joseph Antonio de Hermosilla, n.d. 4to. (Vernon)

Nuevo, y curioso romance ... una lastimosa carta. Valencia, Agustin Laborda 1765. 4to. (Vernon)

Nuevo, y devoto romance ... del rosario de Maria. Valencia 1740. 4to. (Vernon)

Nuevo, y verdadero romance . . . D. Joseph Antonio Traspena.   Madrid, n.d.   4to.   (Vernon)

Olmo Alfonso, Lucas del.   Historia sagrada.   Valencia, Agostin Laborda, n.d.   Cordoba, n.d.   4to.   (Vernon)

———— Neuva relacion . . . la explicacion de los diez mandamientos. Madrid, Cordoba, n.d.   4to.   (Vernon)

———— Primera [y segunda] parte de el contador espiritual.   Valencia, Agustin Laborda, n.d.   4to.   (Vernon)

El patan de Carabanchel.   Madrid, Antonio Bizarròn, n.d.   4to. (Huth)

El patan de la Aldeguela.   n.p. n.d.   4to.   (Huth)

Pedro Andres.   Cordoba, n.d.   4to.   (Vernon)

Perales, Vicente.   Nuevo . . . romance . . . Francisco Pomares.   Valencia, Cosme Grancha, n.d.   4to.   (Vernon)

Perico, y Aneta.   n.p. n.d.   4to.   (Huth)

Perico, y Marica.   n.p. n.d.   4to.   (Huth)

El poeta Juan Camacho.   n.p. n.d.   4to.   (Huth)

Primera [segunda y tercera] parte de la . . . vida . . . de la gloriosa Santa Rosalía.   Valencia, Agustin Laborda, n.d.   4to.   (Vernon)

Primera [y segunda] parte de las muchas indulgencias.   Madrid, n.d. 4to.   (Vernon)

Primera [y segunda] parte de los romances de Bernardo del Carpio. Valencia, Agustin Laborda, n.d.   4to.   (Vernon)

Primera [y segunda] parte de los romances . . . de . . . Don Juan de Yelves.   Sevilla, n.d.   4to.   (Vernon)

Primera [y segunda] parte del gigante Cananeo San Cristoval.   Sevilla, n.d.   4to.   (Vernon)

Primera [y segunda] parte del . . . romance . . . de . . . San Isidro Labrador, y Santa Maria de la Cabeza.   Madrid, n.d.   4to.   (Vernon)

Primera [y segunda] parte en la qual se declaran los misterios de la Misa. Madrid, n.d.   4to.   (Vernon)

Primera [y segunda] parte, en la qual se refiere la fundacion de la Inglesia de nuestra Senora del Pilar de Zaragoza.   Valencia, Madrid, n.d. 4to.   (Vernon)

Spanish after 1500

Primera [y segunda] parte . . . Lorenzo de Texado. Cordoba, n.d. 4to. (Vernon)

Quien bien tiene, y mal escoge. Madrid 1706. 4to. (Huth)

Relacion, en que el Jabonero de Xetafe. n.p. n.d. 4to. (Huth)

Relacion . . . las piedras reliquias, que estan engastadas en las Santissima Cruz. Granada, Nicolàs Prieto 1721. 4to. (Vernon)

Relacion muy, gustosa. n.p. n.d. 4to. (Huth)

Relacion nueva de la lamentable tragedia. Sevilla, n.d. 4to. (Vernon)

Relacion nueva . . . de la . . . victoria que han conseguido . . . Don Felipe Quinto. Sevilla, n.d. 4to. (Vernon)

Relacion nueva de . . . San Agustin. Valencia, Agustin Laborda, n.d. 4to. (Vernon)

Relacion nueva, en que se refieren dos felizes vitorias. Madrid 1706. 4to. (Vernon)

Relacion verdadera, de la gran victoria. n.p. n.d. 4to. (Huth)

Relacion verdadera . . . Don Raymundo Moga. Sevilla, n.d. 4to. (Vernon)

Relacion verdadera . . . la imagen del Santo Christo. Sevilla, n.d. 4to. (Vernon)

Relacion verdadera, y curioso romance. n.p. n.d. 4to. (Huth)

Respuesta del . . . Rey de Francia. n.p. n.d. 4to. (Huth)

El Rey Claudio, y Teodomior, y la Princesa de Inglaterra. Cordoba, Luis de Ramos, y Coria, n.d. 4to. (Vernon)

Ribas, Diego de. Nuevo . . . romance . . . Melchor Carrillo. Sevilla, Francisco de Leefdael, n.d. 4to. (Vernon)

Romance de D. Ivan Antonio. Cordova, en la calle Carreteras, n.d. 4to. (Vernon)

Romance de la Baraxa. Sevilla, n.d. 4to. (Vernon)

Romance de . . . Pedro Ponce de Leon. Cordoba, n.d. 4to. (Vernon)

Romance de . . . Santa Rita de Cassia. Valencia, Agustin Laborda, n.d. 4to. (Vernon)

Romance espiritual de la abeja. Sevilla, n.d. 4to. (Vernon)

Spanish after 1500

Romance mystico. Valencia, Agustin Laborda, n.d. 4to. (Vernon)

Romance nuevo. Madrid 1706. 4to. (Huth)

Romance nuevo del lastimoso caso ... 1664. Sevilla, Reimpresso ...
1775. 4to. (Vernon)

Romance nuevo ... Phelipe Onofre. Sevilla, Diego Lopez de Haro, n.d.
4to. (Vernon)

Romance nuevo ... un cavallero ... de Licata. Sevilla, Diego Lopez de
Haro, n.d. 4to. (Vernon)

Romance nuevo ... una dama ... de Cordova. Valencia, Cosme Grancha, n.d. 4to. (Vernon)

Salutacion angelica. n.p. n.d. 4to. (Huth)

S. Antonio Abad. Valencia, n.d. 4to. (Vernon)

Santa Librada. Cordoba, Luis de Ramos y Coria, n.d. 4to. (Vernon)

La sarta de los garduños. n.p. n.d. 4to. (Huth)

Satira nueva. n.p. n.d. 4to. (Huth)

La tarde del dia de festa. n.p. n.d. 4to. (Huth)

Toma de Sevilla. Cordoba, Luis de Ramos, y Coria, n.d. 4to. (Vernon)

Tragica relacion del lamentable terremoto. Valencia 1790. 4to.
(Vernon)

Verdadera relacion de ... San Alexo. Madrid, n.d. 4to. (Vernon)

Verdadera relacion ... de un principal caberallo. Sevilla, Diego Lopez
de Haro, n.d. 4to. (Vernon)

Verdadera relacion ... del horroroso, temido caso. Cordoba, n.d. 4to.
(Vernon)

Verdadera relacion ... Iuan Bueno. Madrid, n.d. 4to. (Vernon)

Verdadera relacion, y curioso romance ... San Ramon Nonato. Cordoba, n.d. 4to. (Vernon)

Verdadera relacion, y curioso romance ... San Vicente Ferrer. Valencia, Cosme Granja, n.d. 4to. (Vernon)

Verdadera relacion, y curioso romance ... un cavallero de Granada.
Cordoba, n.d. 4to. (Vernon)

Spanish after 1500

Verdadera relacion, y curioso romance . . . una señora.   Sevilla, n.d. 4to.   (Vernon)

Verdadera relacion, y lastimoso romance . . . Marquès de Moscoso.   Sevilla, n.d.   4to.   (Vernon)

Verdadera relacion, y noticia cierta.   Madrid, Lucas Antonio de Bedmar y Narvaez, n.d.   4to.   (Huth)

Verdadera relacion, y romance curioso . . . el caso mas horroroso.   Sevilla, Francisco de Leefdael, n.d.   4to.   (Vernon)

Verdadero, y curioso romance . . . el caso mas cruel.   Sevilla, Joseph Antonio de Hermosilla, n.d.   4to.   (Vernon)

Verdadero, y curioso romance . . . un cautivo christiano.   Valencia, Agustin Laborda 1765.   4to.   (Vernon)

El viage en Valde.   Madrid 1706.   4to.   (Huth)

Vida de San Antonio de Padua.   Cordoba, Luis de Ramos y Coria, n.d. 4to.   (Vernon)

Vida de S. Casiano obispo y martir.   Sevilla, n.d.   4to.   (Vernon)

La vida de San Onofre.   Valencia, n.d.   4to.   (Vernon)

Las virtudes de la noche a lo divino.   Madrid, n.d.   4to.   (Vernon)

Las virtudes del dia.   Madrid, n.d.   4to.   (Vernon)

Zamora, Antonio de.   Epinicio metrico.   Madrid, Agustin Fernandez, n.d.   4to.   (Huth)

Los zelos de San Joseph.   Cordoba, n.d.   4to.   (Vernon)

Bibles and Liturgical Books

The arrangement is as follows: Polyglots; Whole Bibles listed alphabetically by their several languages and placed chronologically under each language; Parts of Bibles; Miscellany including books with woodcuts or copperplates illustrating the Bible; Liturgies

POLYGLOTS

1514-17 (Biblia polyglotta).   (Alcalá de Henares) in Academia Complutensi 1514-17. 6 v. in 4. fol. (Sunderland–Amherst)

1516 Psalterium, Hebreum, Grecū, Arabicū, & Chaldeū. Genuae, P. P. Porrus 1516. fol. (M. L. R. de Samarleio)

1629-45 Biblia.   Lutetiae Parisiorum, A. Vitré 1629-45.   10 v. in 9. fol. (Bibl. Residentiae Insul. S. J.–Bibl. des R. P. Jésuites de Lille–Bibl. Cyroniensis–Inzaghi)

1655-7 Biblia sacra polyglotta.   Londini, T. Roycroft 1655-7.   6 v. fol. (Sir John Cope)

1669 Lexicon heptaglotton. Londini, T. Roycroft 1669. 2 v. fol. (Castell's supplement to London Polyglot 1655-7). (Sir John Cope)

1713 Hexaplorum Origenis. Parisiis, apud L. Guerin . . . viduam J. Boudot . . . et C. Robustel 1713. 2 v. fol.

CONCORDANCES

1550 A concordāce. (By J. Marbecke). [London] R. Grafton July 1550. fol. (STC 17300)

BIBLES

Algonquian

1663, 61 Mamusse wunneetupanatamwe up-Biblum God naneeswe Nukkone Testament kah wonk Wusku Testament Ne quoshkinnumuk nashpe Wuttinneumoh Christ noh asoowesit John Eliot. Cambridge, S. Green and M. Johnson 1663, 61. 4to.

Armenian

1733 (The Holy Bible). Venice, A. Portoli 1733. fol. (Bute–Sussex–Aldenham Abbey–Tempsford Hall)

Bibles and Liturgical Books

Basque

1859-65 Bible Saindua, edo Testament Zahar eta Berria.   Londresen
(Strangeways & Walden) 1859-65.   5 pts.   8vo.   Original wrappers

Dutch

1548   Den gheheelen Bybel.   Loeuen, B. van Graue 1548.   fol.

English

1539   The Byble in Englyshe.   [Paris, F. Regnault, and London]
R. Grafton & E. Whitchurch, Apryll 1539.   fol.   First
Edition.   (Lea Wilson–Dunn–John Dunn Gardner–
Huth).   (STC 2068)

1541   The Byble in Englyshe.   [London] R. Grafton, November
1541.   fol. in eights.   Sixth Edition.   (J. W. Knightley).
(STC 2075)

1549   The Byble.   London, J. Daye and W. Seres, 17 August 1549.
fol. in sixes.   (C. D. Ginsburg).   (STC 2077)

1560   The Bible.   Geneva, R. Hall 1560.   4to.   First Edition.
(STC 2093)

1560-1   The Byble in Englyshe.   London, J. Cawood 1560-1.   4to.
in eights.   (STC 2094)

1568   The . holie . Bible.   London, R. Jugge [1568].   fol. in eights.
First Edition.   (STC 2099)

1572   The . holie . Bible.   London, R. Jugge 1572.   fol. in eights.
(STC 2107)

1597   The Bible.   London, Deputies of C. Barker 1597.   fol. in sixes.
(STC 2168)

1611   The Holy Bible.   London, R. Barker 1611.   fol.   First Edition.   (C. D. Ginsburg).   (STC 2216)

1616   The Holy Bible.   London, R. Barker 1616.   sm. fol.   (Huth).
(STC 2245)

1653   The Holy Bible.   London, J. Field 1653.   24mo.   (Copy 1,
Rev. Thomas Wilson–Huth; 2, Earl of Ellenborough)

1659   The Holy Bible.   Cambridge, J. Field 1659 (O. T. undated;
N. T. dated 1659).   fol.   (James Cowan of Ross Hall–
Earl of Aylesford)

1669 The Holy Bible. London, J. Bill and C. Barker 1669. 12mo. in eights

1678 The Holy Bible. London, J. Bill, C. Barker, T. Newcomb and H. Hills 1678. 8vo. (W. H. Corfield)

1683, 66 The Holy Bible. O. T., Cambridge, J. Hayes 1683 (date altered with pen from 1682); N. T., Cambridge, J. Field 1666. 4to.

1698-9 The Holy Bible. London, C. Bill and the Executrix of T. Newcomb 1698-9. 2 v. 24mo.

1751 The Holy Bible. London, T. Baskett and Assigns of R. Baskett 1751. fol. (Presentation copy from Thomas Baskett to Alice Cornish, May 1754)

1782, 81 The Holy Bible. Philadelphia, R. Aitken 1782, 81. 12mo.

1791 The Holy Bible. Worcester, Massachusetts, I. Thomas 1791. 2 v. fol.

1800 The Holy Bible. London, T. Bensley 1800. 7 v. fol. (Rowland Hunt)

1850 The Holy Bible. Oxford, University Press 1850. 4 v. 4to. (Huth)

1903 The English Bible. Hammersmith, Doves Press 1903. 5 v. fol.

1903 The English Bible. London, D. Nutt 1903. 6 v. 8vo. (The Tudor Translation)

French

1534 La saincte Bible. Anuers, M. Lempereur 1534. fol. (Huth)

1535 La Bible. Neuchâtel, P. de Wingle 1535. fol.

1644 La sainte Bible. Geneve [P. Chouet] 1644. fol.

1669 La sainte Bible. Amsterdam, L. & D. Elzevier 1669. fol.

1866 La sainte Bible. Tours, A. Mame 1866. 2 v. fol.

German

[1475-6] Die Bibel. Augspurg [G. Zainer 1475-6]. fol. (H*3133; GW 4298)

1564-5 Biblia. Wittemberg, H. Lufft 1565. fol.

Bibles and Liturgical Books

1731-5   Kupfer Bibel.   Augspurg und Ulm, C. U. Wagner 1731-5.
          5 v. fol. (Bement)

1743   Biblia. Germantown, C. Saur 1743. 4to.

1926-8   Biblia. [Munich] Bremer Presse 1926-8. 5 v. fol.

Greek

1518   Πάντα τὰ κατ᾽ ἐξοχὴν καλούμενα βιβλία.   Venetiis, in
          aedibus Aldi et Andreae soceri 1518. fol. (Roxburghe-
          Sir James Lewis Knight–Bruce)

1526-24   Τῆς Θείας Γραφῆς Παλαιᾶς δηλαδὴ καὶ νέας ἅπαντα.
          Argentorati, apud V. Cephalaeum (W. Köpphel) 1526,
          24 (v.4, N.T., 1524). 4 v. 8vo. (C. D. Ginsburg)

Hebrew

1753   Biblia Hebraica.   Lutetiae-Parisiorum, A. C. Briasson & L.
          Durand 1753. 4 v. fol. (T. L. De Vinne)

1814   Biblia Hebraica. Philadelphia, T. Dobson 1814. 2 v. 8vo.
          (T. D. Cock–E.W. Crane)

Italian

1471   Biblia Italica.   [Venice, Adam de Ambergau] 1471.   2 v.
          fol. (H 3148; GW 4321)

1562   La Bibia. (Geneva) F. Durone 1562. 4to. (D & M 5592
          var. A)

1562   La Bibia. (Geneva) F. Durone 1562. 4to. (D & M 5592
          var. B). (Roxburghe)

Latin

[c. 1454/5] [Mainz, J. Gutenberg, c. 1454/5, n.a. Aug. 1456].   fol.
          (H 3031; GW 4201). (One leaf)

[n.a. 1470] Biblia. [Strassburg, A. Rusch, n.a. 1470]. fol. (Sussex).
          (H*3034; GW 4209)

[n.a. 1474] Biblia.   [Basel, B. Richel, n.a. 1474].   fol.   (William
          Morris). (H*3041; GW 4212)

[n.a. 1475] Biblia. [Basel, B. Ruppel, B. Richel, n.a. 1475]. 2 v. fol.
          (G. C. Thomas). (H*3038, *3044; GW 4213)

1475   Biblia.   Venice, F. Renner & N. von Frankfurt 1475.   fol.
          (H*3054; GW 4216)

1476 Biblia. Venice, N. Jenson 1476. fol. (H*3061; GW 4222)

1477 Biblia. Nuremberg, A. Koberger, 30 July 1477. fol. (H *3065; GW 4227)

1478 Biblia. Venice, R. von Nimwegen & T. von Reynsburg 1478. fol. (H*3070; GW 4231)

1480 Biblia. Venice, F. Renner 1480. 4to. (H. W. Poor). (H *3078; GW 4241)

1480 Biblia. Ulm, J. Zainer, 29 Jan. 1480. fol. (H*3079; GW 4242)

1480 Biblia. Nuremberg, A. Koberger, 14 April 1480. fol. (H 3076; GW 4243)

1481 Biblia. Venice, L. Wild 1481. fol. (H*3082; GW 4247)

1481 Biblia. Venice [J. Herbort for] J. de Colonia, N. Jenson & Company, 31 July 1481. 4v. fol. (H*3164; GW 4286)

[1481] Biblia. [Strassburg, A. Rusch, shortly after 23 Sept. 1481]. 4v. fol. (H*3173; GW 4282)

1483 Biblia. Venice, F. Renner 1483. 4to. (Sunderland). (H *3089; GW 4253)

1483 Additiones ad postillas N. de Lyra. Venice, F. Renner 1483. fol. (Part of GW 4287)

1498 Biblia. Venice, S. Bevilaqua, 8 May 1498. 4to. (H*3124; GW 4280)

1511 Biblie. Venice, L. de Giunta 1511. 4to. (Dunn)

1513 Biblie. [Lyons] J. Sacon 1513. fol.

1516 Biblia. Lyons, J. Sacon 1516. fol. (Sunderland)

1528, 27 Biblia. Lyons, A. du Ry 1528, 27. sm. fol. in eights. (E. Bodon–E. Leigh–Dunn)

1592 Biblia. Rome, ex Typographia … Vaticana 1592. fol.

1616 Biblia. Venice, apud Iuntas 1616. 8vo.

Spanish

1569 La Biblia. [Basel, T. Guarinus] 1569. 4to. (Robert Curzon, Baron Zouche)

Bibles and Liturgical Books

OLD TESTAMENT

Dutch

1516　Dē bibel int corte.　Antwerp, C. de Grave 1516.　fol.　(W. Henskes–Bement)

English

1609-10　The Holie Bible.ᵉ　Doway, L. Kellam 1609-10.　2 v.　4to. (Huth).　(STC 2207)

Greek

1587　ʽΗ παλαιὰ διαθήκη.　Rome, F. Zannetti 1587.　fol.

Irish

1685　The...old testament.　London 1685.　4to.

Spanish

1661　Biblia.　Amsterdam 1661.　8vo.

Genesis. English

1578　Calvin, John.　A commentarie ... vpon ... Genesis.　London, H. Middleton 1578.　sm. 4to.　(STC 4393)

Psalms. English

1604　The psalter.　London, R. Barker 1604.　sm. fol.　(Sir John Savill).　(STC 2404)

1636　——— Edinburgh [E. Tyler for] R. Young 1636.　fol. (Huth).　(STC 16606)

1636　——— ——— fol.　Second Edition.　(STC 16607)

1718　Psalterium.　Boston, S. Kneeland 1718.　8vo.

Psalms. Greek

1486　[Psalterium].　Venice, Laonicus & Alexander, 15 Nov. 1486. 4to.　(Huth).　(H*13453; BMC.V.409)

[?1497]　Ψαλτήριον.　Venetiis, Aldus Manutius [?1497].　4to. (Sunderland–Dunn).　(H 13452; BMC.V.563)

Psalms. Latin

1537　Psalterium.　Vitebergae, I. Luffr[sic] 1537.　8vo.

Bibles and Liturgical Books

1657   Psalterium.   Antverpiae, ex officina Plantiniana 1657.   8vo.

Psalms, Metrical. Dutch

1540   Souter liedekens ghemaect . . . op all dye psalmen.   Antwerp, S. Cock 1540.   8vo.

Psalms, Metrical. English

1604   The whole booke of psalms.   London 1604.   sm. fol.   (Sir John Savill).   (STC 2512a)

1614   The whole booke of psalmes.   London 1614.   sm. 4to.   (Julian Marshall).   (STC 2549)

1618   The whole booke of psalmes.   London 1618.   fol.   (Huth).   (STC 2560)

1621   The whole booke of psalms.   London 1621.   12mo.   First Edition, Second Issue.   (STC 2575)

1627   The whole booke of psalmes.   London 1627.   sm. fol.   (Ashburton–G. C. Thomas).   (STC 2599)

1631   The psalmes. Tr. by King James I.   Oxford, W. Turner 1631.   8vo.   First Edition.   (STC 2732)

1636   ——— London, T. Harper 1636.   fol.   (STC 2736)

1636   A paraphrase upon the psalmes. By G. S[andys].   London [A. Hebb] 1636.   8vo.   First Edition.   (STC 21724)

1638   A paraphrase upon the divine poems. By G. Sandys.   London 1638.   sm. fol.   First Edition.   (Sussex–Sutherland).   (STC 21725)

1638   The psalmes . . . paraphras'd . . . by R. B[rathwaite].   London, R. Young 1638.   8vo.   First Edition.   (John Pearson).   (STC 3581)

1651   The psalmes. [By H. King].   London, E. Griffin 1651.   8vo.

1669   The whole book of psalms.   London, T. R. 1669.   12mo. in eights

1696   A new version of the psalms. By N. Tate and N. Brady.   London, M. Clark 1696.   12mo.   (Corser)

1699   The psalms.   Edinburgh, Heirs . . . of A. Anderson 1699.   4to.

1719   The psalms. By I. Watts.   London 1719.   12mo.

1767   The psalms. For the use of the Reformed Protestant Dutch Church of the City of New York. New-York, J. Parker 1767. 8vo.

Psalms, Metrical. French

1656   Les pseavmes . . . mis en rime françoise, par C. Marot, et T. de Bèze. Charenton, P. Des-Hayes & A. Cellier 1656. sm. 8vo. (S. P. Avery)

Psalms, Metrical. German

1807   Das neue und verbesserte gesangbuch, worinnen die psalmen . . . enthalten sind. Germantaun, M. Billmeyer 1807. 12mo.

Psalms, Metrical. Latin

[c.1565] Psalmorum Dauidis paraphrasis poetica. Authore G. Buchanano. [Paris] apud H. & R. Stephanum [c. 1565]. 8vo.

'The Books of Solomon'

1551   The bokes of Salomon. London, W. Copland 1551. 24mo. (Ashburnham). (STC 2758)

1587   The song of songs. Tr. [by D. Fenner]. Middelburgh, R. Schilders 1587. 8vo. (Huth). (STC 2769)

1909   The song of songs. London, Medici Society 1909. 4to.

NEW TESTAMENT

English

1549   The newe testament. Tr. by M. Coverdale. London, R. Wolfe 1549. 8vo. (Ashburnham). (STC 2858)

1550   The new testament . . . after the greeke translation annexed wyth the translation of Erasmus in Latin. Londini, in officina T. Gaultier 1550. 8vo. (G. C. Thomas). (STC 2821)

1552   The newe testament. London, R. Jugge [1552]. 4to. (Mexborough). (STC 2867)

1582   The new testament. Rhemes, J. Fogny 1582. 4to. First Edition. (STC 2884)

Bibles and Liturgical Books

1603   The new testament. Tr. . . . by T. Beza.   Dort, I. Canin 1603.
        8vo. (Ashburnham). (STC 2903)

1617   The new testament. Tr. out of . . . Latine . . . at Rhemes . . .
        Whereunto is added the translation out of . . . Greeke . . .
        with a confutation of . . . arguments . . . against . . . the
        translations used in the Church of England.   By W.
        Fulke. London 1617. fol. (Huth). (STC 2918)

1618   A confutation of the Rhemists translation . . . and annotations
        on the nevv testament. By T. Cartwright. [Leyden, W.
        Brewster] 1618. fol. (J. Hammond Trumbull). (STC
        4709)

1633   The new testament . . . with a confutation . . . by W. Fulke.
        London, A. Mathewes 1633.   fol.   (P. Hamilton).
        (STC 2947)

1731   The new testament. Tr. . . . by J. Wiclif . . . about 1378.   Lon-
        don, J. March 1731. fol.

French

1656   Le novveav testament.   Charenton, P. Des-Hayes & A. Cellier
        1656. 8vo. (W. P. Avery)

1673   Le nouveau testament. Mons, G. Migeot 1673. 8vo. (Huth)

German

1527   Das naw testament. Dresden, W. Stoeckel 1527. fol. (Huth)

Greek

1516   Novvm instrumentū omne.   Basileae, in aedibus I. Frobenij
        1516. fol. (Huth)

1519   Novvm testamentvm omne.   Basileae, in aedibus I. Frobenii
        1519. fol. (Huth)

1521   Novvm testamentvm graece.   Hagenoae, in aedibus T. An-
        shelmi 1521. sm. 4to. (Huth)

1546   Τῆς Καινῆς Διαθήκης ἅπαντα.   Lvtetiae, ex officina R.
        Stephani 1546.   16mo.   ("O mirificam" edition).
        (Knottesford–Dunn)

1550   Τῆς Καινῆς Διαθήκης ἅπαντα.   Lvtetiae, ex officina R.
        Stephani 1550. fol.

Bibles and Liturgical Books

1642   Ἡ Καινὴ Διαθήκη. Paris, Imprimerie Royale 1642. fol. (Presentation copy from Archbishop Sancroft to Edmund Bohun 1676)

1800   Ἡ Καινὴ Διαθήκη. Wigorniae (Worcester) Massachusettensi, I. Thomas 1800. 12mo.

Irish

1602   Tiomna nuadhr ar d Tighearna agus ar slanaightheora Iosa Criosd. Dublin, J. Franke 1602. fol. First Edition, Second Issue. (Baron Foley). (STC 2958)

Latin

1462   [New testament]. Mainz, J. Fust & P. Schoeffer, 14 Aug. 1462. fol. (G. Livermore). (H*3050; GW 4204)

[1481]   [New testament]. [Strassburg, A. Rusch, shortly after 23 Sept. 1481]. fol. (H*3173; GW 4282)

Spanish

1596   El testamento nvevo. (London) en casa de R. del Campo (R. Field) 1596. 8vo. (STC 2959)

Syriac

1555   Liber sacrosancti evangelii de Iesu Christo. Vienna, M. Zimmermann 1555. 4to. (De Thou–Huth)

Gospels. Anglo Saxon & English

1571   The gospels of the fower euangelistes. London, I. Daye 1571. sm. 4to. (STC 2961)

Gospels. Gothic & Anglo Saxon

1665   Quatuor . . . Jesu Christi euangeliorum versiones perantiquae duae. Dordrecht, H. & J. Essaeus 1665. 4to. (Huth)

Epistles. Latin

1512   Christus. Paris, ex officina H. Stephani 1512. sm. fol.

Epistles and Gospels. Arabic

1583   Epistola Pauli ad Galatas. Heidelbergae, I. Mylius 1583. 4to.

1591   Evangelium sanctum . . . conscriptum a quatuor evangelistis. Rome, in Typographia Medicea, 1590, 1591. fol.

Bibles and Liturgical Books

Epistles and Gospels. Latin

1508   Expositio epistolarum et evangeliorum. Lugduni, J. de Place
       & T. de Cloches 1508. 8vo.

Apocalypse. Italian

[c. 1467/8]   Apocalypsis cum glosis N. de Lyra [Italian]. [?Rome, U.
       Han, c. 1467/8]. 4to. (?H 9383; BMC. IV. 143)

BIBLE. MISCELLANEOUS

[c.1477]   Lyra, Nicolaus de. Postilla super psalterium. (Mantua, P.
       de Butzbach, c.1477). fol. (H 10376; Reichling I: 164)

s.a.   Beham, Hans Sebald. [Series of twelve copperplate engrav-
       ings of the Apostles]. 8vo.

1518   Rampegollis, Antonius de. Figure biblie. Parisij, J. Petit
       1518. 8vo.

1538   Holbein, Hans. Les simulachres & historiees faces de la mort.
       Lyon, M. & G. Trechsel 1538. sm. 4to. (De la Roche
       Lacarelle–Adolph Meyer)

1539   [Cranach, Lucas, *the elder*]. Das symbolum . . . der zwelff
       Aposteln. Wittemberg, G. Rhaw 1539. sm. fol. (Huth)

1542   Theophylactus. ἙΡΜΗΝΕΊΑ ΕἸΣ ΤᾺ ΤΈΣΣΑΡΑ ΕὐΑΓ-
       ΓΈΛΙΑ. Romae [A. Bladus] 1542. fol. (Huth)

1543   Holbein, Hans. Retratos o tablas de las historias del testa-
       mento viejo. Lugduni, apud I. & F. Frellonios 1543. sm.
       4to.

1547   —— Icones historiarum veteris testamenti. Lugduni,
       apud I. Frellonium 1547. sm.4to. (W. L. Andrews)

1549   The images of the old testament. Lyons, I. Frellon 1549.
       sm. 4to. (STC 3045)

1553   Paradin, Claude. Qvadrins historiqves de la Bible. Lyon, I.
       de Tovrnes 1553. 8vo.

1553   —— The true . . . purtreatures of the woll Bible. Tr. by P.
       Derendel. Lyons, Iean of Tournes 1553. sm. 8vo.
       First Edition. (H. S. Richardson–J. Pearson). (STC
       3043)

1559   —— Figvre del nvovo testamento. Tr. by D. Maraffi. In
       Lione, G. di Tovrnes 1559. 8vo. (W. L. Andrews)

1558   Borluyt, Guillaume.   Historiarum memorabilium ex Exodo.
Lugduni, apud I. Tornaesivm 1558.   8vo.   (Hoe)

1558   Paradin [de Cuyseaulx], Guillaume.   Historiarvm memora-
bilivm ex Genesi descriptio. Lugduni, apud I. Tornaesivm
1558.   sm. 8vo.   (Hoe)

1579   Amman, Jost.   Kuenstliche . . . figuren der . . . euangelien.
Francofurti ad Moenum, P. Fabricius 1579.   fol.   (W.
L. Andrews)

1593-5   Nadal, Gerónimo.   Evangelicae historiae imagines; Adnota-
tiones et meditationes in evangelia.   Antuerpiae, M.
Nutius 1593-5.   fol.   (G. Luenckens–Bement)

1601   Aspruck, Franz.   [Series of thirteen copperplate engravings
of Christ and the Apostles].   1601.   8vo.   (Huth)

1616   Passe, Crispin van de.   Liber Genesis aereis formis.   Arnhemii, apud I. Iansonium 1616.   sm. 4to.

1700   Mortier, Pieter.   Historie des ouden en nieuwen testaments.
Verrykt met . . . printverbeeldingen in koper gesneeden.
Amsterdam, P. Mortier 1700.   fol.   (Bement)

1721   Sturt, John.   The orthodox communicant.   London, Engraven . . . by J. Sturt 1721.   8vo.

1728   Saurin, Jacques.   Discours . . . sur les evenemens . . . du vieux
et du nouveau testament . . . Avec des figures gravees sur
les desseins de . . . Hoet, Houbraken & Picart.   A La
Haye, P. de Hondt 1728.   6 v.   fol.   (Mexborough)

LITURGIES

BREVIARIES

Breviarium Romanum

1566   Breviarium Romanum.   Antverpiae, in aedibus vidue & haeredum I. Steelsij 1566.   8vo.

Passau

1515   Breviarium Pataviensis.   Venetijs, L. & L. Allantse, 25 May
1515.   8vo.   (Pars aestivalis)

Bibles and Liturgical Books

Salisbury

1535   Portiforiũ seu Breuiarium ad vsum ecclesie Sarisburiẽsis. Paris, F. Regnault 1535. 4to. in eights. (Dunn). (STC 15833 Pars aestivalis)

Camaldulenses

1484   Breviarium Camaldulense. Florence, A. Miscomini, 13 April 1484. 8vo. (GW 5191 Psalterium only). vellum

HOURS OF THE BLESSED VIRGIN AND PRIMERS

Auxerre

[1509]   Les p̄sentes heures a lusaige de Ausserre. Paris, pour S.Vostre [1509]. 8vo.

Paris

1500   Ces presentes heures a lusaige de Paris. (Paris, P. Pigouchet) pour S.Vostre, 25 April 1500. 8vo. (Pittar)

[1508]   —— [Paris, S.Vostre 1508]. 8vo. (C.L.F.Robinson)

Rome

1496   Ces p̄sentes heures a lusage de Rõme. Paris (P. Pigouchet) pour S. Vostre, 20 Aug. 1496. 4to. (Didot). (H 8851). vellum

1497   Horae...secũdum consuetudinem romanae curiae. [Venice] Aldus Manutius, 5 Dec. 1497. 16mo. (W. H. Crawford). (H 8830; BMC.V. 558)

[1502]   Ces presentes heures a lusaige de Romme. Paris (P.Pigouchet) pour S.Vostre [1502]. 4to.

1502   Les presentes heures a lusaige de Romme. Paris (P.Pigouchet) pour S.Vostre, 20 Dec. 1502. 8vo.

[1505]   Ces presentes heures a lusaige de Rome. Paris, G. Anabat pour G. Hardouyn [1505]. 8vo. (Dunn)

1509   Heures a lusaige de Romme. (Paris) G. Hardouyn, 8 March 1509. 8vo. (Huth)

1509   Bonaventura, *Saint*. Psalterium intemerate dei genitricis Virginis Marie. Parisiis, T. Kerver, 28 Nov. 1509. 8vo. (Marie de Gueteville–Count Caumartin–Dumoulin du Lys–H.V.Jones)

[514]

Bibles and Liturgical Books

[?1510] Hore ... secundum vsum Romanum.   Paris, E. Hardouyn
[?1510]. 8vo. (James Comerford–Pittar)

1514   —— Parisius, T. Kerver, 29 May 1514. 8vo.

[c.1517] Horae . . . secundum consuetudinem Romanae Curiae
[Greek]. Hagnoae, ex Charisio Thomae Anshelmi, Jan.
[c.1517]. sm. 8vo. (Huth–Pittar)

[?1526] Hore ... secundum vsum Romanum.   Parisius, G. Hardouyn
[?1526]. 8vo. (Groves)

1707   Officio della B. Vergine Maria.   Roma, l'Eredi del Corbelletti
1707. 8vo.

Salisbury and General

1527   Hore ... ad verū Sarisburiēsis ecclesie ritū. Parisiis, in officina
N. Prevost, 18 July 1527. 4to. (STC 15953)

1537   This prymer of Salysbury use.   Rouen, pro F. Regnault 1537.
16mo. (John Fuller Russell). (STC 15995)

1538   Thys prymer in Englyshe, and in Laten.   [Rouen] N. le
Roux 1538. 8vo. (John Fuller Russell). (STC 16007)

[1538]   This prymer . . . (The Pystles and Gospels).   London, R.
Redman [1538]. 4to. (D. F. Appleton–G. C. Thomas).
(STC 16008 pt. II only)

1545   The primer, in Englishe and Latyn. London, R. Grafton, 6
Sept. 1545. sm. 4to. (D. F. Appleton–G. C. Thomas).
(STC 16040)

1557   The prymer in Englishe and Latine. London, Assygnes of I.
Wayland [1557]. 8vo. (Dogmersfield). (STC 16080)

MANUALS
Salisbury

1555   Manuale ad vsum . . . ecclesie Sarisburiensis.   Londini [R.
Caly] 1555.   4to. in eights.   (Samuel Goodenough–
Ashburnham–Dunn). (STC 16156)

MISSALS
Hildesheim

1499   Missale Hildeshemense.   Nuremberg, G. Stuchs, 17 Sept.
1499. fol. (BMC. II. 472)

[515]

Bibles and Liturgical Books

Ratisbon

1518   Missale secūdū vsum ecclesie ratispoñ. Bamberg, J. Pfeyl, 30
April 1518. fol.

Rome

1501   Missale secūdū morem sancte romane ecclesie. Venetijs, B.
Locatellus 1501. 8vo.

1520   Missale ad sacrosancte Romane ecclesie vsum. Paris, J. Bien-
ayse & J. Adam, 22 Nov. 1520. fol.

Salisbury

1519   Missale ad vsum . . . ecclesie Sarum.   Parisius, N. Higman
1519. sm. fol. (STC 16200)

1555   Missale ad vsum ecclesie Sarisburiensis. Lōdini, J. Kyngstō
et H. Sutton 1555. 4to. in eights. (STC 16218)

Fratres Praedicatores

1482   Missale Dominicanum s. Ord. Praedicatorum. Venetijs, O.
Scotus, 24 Dec. 1482. 4to. (H*11289; BMC.V. 277)

PONTIFICALS

1511   Pontificale. Lugduni, J. Moilin al's de cābray, 8 May 1511.
fol. (William Morris–Dunn–Murray)

PROCESSIONALS
Fratres Praedicatores

1494   Processionarium Ord. Praedicatorum. Seville, M. Ungut &
S. Polonus, 3 April 1494. 8vo. (H 13380)

1519   ———— Seville, J. Cromberger, 1 Sept. 1519.   4to. in eights.
(Groves)

ROSARIES
Carthusian

[c.1485] Rosarium beate marie v̇gīs. n.p. [c.1485]. 16mo.

BOOK OF COMMON PRAYER
Church of England

1549   The booke of the common prayer. Londini, in officina E.
Whitchurche, 16 June 1549. fol. (John Gott). (STC
16272)

Bibles and Liturgical Books

1552   The boke of common prayer.   Londini, in officina E. Whitchurche 1552. fol. (John Gott). (STC 16279)

1604   The booke of common prayer. London, R. Barker 1604. fol. (Sir John Savill). (STC 16327)

1616   The booke of common prayer. London, R. Barker 1616. fol. (Huth). (STC 16347a)

1627   The booke of common prayer.   London, B. Norton and J. Bill 1627. fol. (Ashburton–G. C. Thomas). (STC 16368)

1662   The book of common-prayer.   London, His Ma.ties printers 1662. fol. (Huth)

1665   The book of common prayer. London, J. Bill and C. Barker 1665. 12mo. in eights

1678   Book of common prayer. London, J. Bill, C. Barker, T. Newcomb and H. Hills 1678. 8vo. (W. H. Corfield)

1717   The book of common prayer.   London, Engraven (by J. Sturt) and printed by the permission of Mr. John Baskett 1717. 8vo.

1750   The book of common prayer.   London, T. Baskett and the Assigns of R. Baskett 1750. fol.

French

1616   La liturgie angloise. Tr. by P. de Laune. Londres, J. Bill 1616. 4to. First Edition. (Bridgewater). (STC 16431)

German

1704   Die englische liturgie. Franckfurt an der Oder, zu finden bey J. und J. C. Hartmann 1704. 4to.

Irish

1608   Leabhar na nurnaightheadh. Tr. by W. Daniel.   Dublin, J. Franckton 1608. fol. First Edition. (Thomas Baker–Godfrey Daniel–James Nugent–William Butler–Fritz Ponsonby). (STC 16433)

Latin

1551   Ordinatio ecclesiae.   Lipsiae, in officina W. Gunteri 1551. 4to. First Edition. (Huth). (STC 16423)

1574   Liber precum publicarum.   Londini, T. Vautrollerius per assignationem F. Florae 1574. 8vo. (Huth). (STC 16427)

Mohawk

1715   The morning and evening prayer. Tr. into the Mahaque Indian language, by L. Claesse.   New-York, W. Bradford 1715. 4to.

1769   The order for morning and evening prayer. Tr. under the direction of . . . W. Andrews . . . H. Barclay, and . . . J. Oglivie. [New York, W. Weyman and H. Gaine] 1769. 8vo. (Brinley)

1780   —— Revised . . . by D. Claus. [Quebec] 1780. 8vo. (Presentation copy, inscribed "Gift of Col. Clause 3 May 84 Montreal Louis Vincent"). (DePuy)

1787   The book of common prayer. Tr. by J. Brant.   London, C. Buckton 1787. 8vo.

Montagnais

1767   Nehiro-Iriniui Aiamike Massinahigan.   Uabistiguiatsh [Quebec]. Massinahitsetuau, Broun gaie Girmor 1767. 8vo.

BOOK OF COMMON PRAYER

Protestant Episcopal Church. United States of America

1786   The book of common prayer.   Philadelphia, Hall and Sellers 1786. 8vo.

1789   —— London, J. Debrett 1789. 8vo.

1790   —— Philadelphia, Hall and Sellers 1790. 8vo.

1795   —— New-York, H. Gaine 1795.   fol.

German

1865   Gebetbüchlein für soldaten.   St. Louis, Mo., A. Wiebusch u. Sohn 1865. 32mo.

BOOK OF COMMON PRAYER

Protestant Episcopal Church. Confederate States of America

1863   The book of common prayer.   Richmond, Virginia, J. W. Randolph 1863. 24mo. (F. E. Marshall)

Bibles and Liturgical Books

BOOK OF COMMON PRAYER
Church of Scotland

1584   The forme of prayers. n.p. 1584. 16mo. (Britwell).
(STC 16581)

1637   The booke of common prayer. Edinburgh [E. Tyler for] R.
Young 1637. fol. First Edition, First Issue. (Huth).
(STC 16606)

DIRECTORY

1644   A directory for the publique worship of God. London, for
E. Tyler ... 1644. 4to.

LA CONFRÉRIE DE L'ADORATION PERPÉTUELLE

1776   Réglement de la Confrerie de l'Adoration perpétuelle du S.
Sacrement ... en ... Montréal. Montreal, F. Mesplet &
C. Berger 1776. 32mo.

THE LITANY

[?1553] Teütsche letaney.   (Nuremberg) J. Gutknecht [?1533].
8vo. (Huth)

PRAYERS

1578   Day, Richard. A booke of christian prayers. London, J.
Daye 1578. 4to. (STC 6429)

1608   ———— A booke of christian praiers. London [H. Lownes]
1608. 4to. Fifth Edition. (Towneley–Bement).
(STC 6432)

1715   Oratio dominica in diversa omnium fere gentium linguas versa.
Amstelaedami, Typis G. & D. Goerei 1715. sm. 4to.
(Milles)

1733   Neu-ausgefertigtes Christ-evangelisches busz-beicht und
communion-büchlein. Augspurg, C. P. Detleffsen 1733.
nar. 12mo.

1738   Schmolck, Benjamin. Andächtiger hertzen beth-altar zur
allerheiligsten dreyfaltigheit. Breslau, M. Hubert 1738.
nar. 12mo.

[519]

Bibles and Liturgical Books

SPECIAL FORMS OF PRAYER

1688   Prayers to be used . . . during this time of publick apprehensions from the danger of invasion.   [Edinburgh] Holy-Rood-House, P[eter] B[ruce] 1688.   4to.   (W. Moir Bryce)

MANUALS OF PLAIN SONG

1513   Cantorinus Romanus.   Compendiũ musices.   Venetijs, p Lucantoniũ de Giunta, 3 Dec. 1513.   8vo.   (Huth)

Books in Science, Printed after 1500

SIXTEENTH CENTURY

Agricola, Georg. De re metallica. Basileae, in officina Frobeniana 1561. fol. Second Edition. (Bement)

Aristarchus. De magnitudinibus, et distantiis solis, et lunae. Pisauri, apud C. Francischinum 1572. 4to. (Charles Butler)

Bacon, Roger. The mirror of alchimy. London [T. Creed] 1597. sm. 4to. First Edition. (STC 1182)

Baker, George, *tr.* *See* Gesner, Conrad

Belon, Pierre. Les observations de plusieurs singularitez. Paris, G. Corrozet 1553. sm. 4to. First Edition

———— Portraits d'oyseaux, animaux, serpens. Paris, G. Cavellat 1557. sm. 4to. First Edition. (Inscribed "The gift of John Mytton Esq. of Halston ... 1776")

Billingsley, Henry, *tr.* *See* Euclides

Blundeville, Thomas. M. Blundevile his exercises. London, J. Windet 1597. sm. 4to. Second Edition. (STC 3147)

Boethius. Arithmetica. Paris, Volphgangus hopilius et H. stephanus 1503. fol.

———— ———— Paris, ex officina H. stephani 1510. fol.

Bovelle, Charles de. De cubicatione sphere; De quadratura circuli; Introductio in geometriam; Perspectiva introductio. (Paris 1503). fol.

Brunschwig, Hieronymus. Liber de arte distillandi. Straszburg 1512. fol. (Dunn)

———— The noble experyence of the vertuous handywarke of surgeri. Southwarke, P. Treveris 1525. fol. First Edition. (STC 13434)

Campanus de Novare. Tetragonismus. Venetiis, I. B. Sessa 1503. sm. 4to.

Cheradame, Jean, *tr.* *See* Hutten, Ulrich von

Clichtove, Josse. De praxi numerandi compendium; In Epitomen arithmeticā I. Stapulensis commentarius. (Paris 1503, 1510). fol.

Clusius, Carolus. *See* L'Ecluse, Charles de

Copernicus, Nicolaus. De lateribus et angulis triangulorum. Vittembergae, I. Lufft 1542. 4to.

———— De revolutionibus orbium coelestium. Norimbergae, I. Petreium 1543. fol. First Edition

———— ———— Basileae, ex officina Henricpetrina 1566. 4to. (Earl of Kent–Wrest Park)

Cruce, Johannes Andrea a. Chirurgiae universalis. Venetiis, apud R. Meiettum 1596. fol.

Digges, Leonard. A geometrical practise, named Pantometria. London, H. Bynneman 1571. sm. 4to. First Edition. (STC 6858)

Dioscorides, Pedanius. De medica materia. Basileae, apud M. Ising 1542. 8vo.

Dodoens, Rembert. A niewe herball. Tr. by H. Lyte. London, H. Loë, and sold at London by G. Dewes 1578. fol. First Edition. (STC 6984)

Euclides. Elementorum lib. XV. Basileae, apud I. Hervagium 1533. fol. First Edition

———— The elements of geometrie. Tr. by Sir H. Billingsley. London, J. Daye 1570. fol. First Edition. (STC 10560)

———— Die sechs erste buches. Basel, Vollendet durch J. Kundig . . . in J. Oporini kosten 1562. fol.

Faber Stapulensis, Jacobus. *See* Le Fèvre d'Étaples, Jacques

Frampton, John, *tr.* *See* Monardes, Nicolas

Fuchs, Leonhard. Historia de yervas, y plantas . . . Traduzidos . . . en español [por J. Jarava]. Anvers, por los herederos de A. Byrcman 1557. 8vo. (Murray)

Gale, Thomas. Certaine workes of chirurgerie. London, R. Hall 1563. 8vo. First Edition, First Issue. (STC 11529)

Gerard, John. The herball. London, E. Bollifant 1597. fol. First Edition. (STC 11750)

Gesner, Conrad. Fisch buch. Zürych, G. Froschower 1575. fol. (Huth. Binding dated 1592, with arms and initials of Herr von Biberstein)

Gesner, Conrad. The newe iewell of health. Tr. by G. Baker. London, H. Denham 1576. 4to. in eights. First Edition. (STC 11798)

Granollachs, Bernard de. Lunarium. n.p. [1502?]. 8vo.

The greate herball. London, J. Kynge 1561. fol. Fourth Edition. (Thomas Brooke). (STC 13179)

[Guido, *de Cauliaco*]. The questyonary of cyrurgens. Tr. by R. Copland. London, R. Wyer [1542]. sm. 4to. First Edition. (Huth). (STC 12468)

Hester, John, *tr. See* Paracelsus

Hutten, Ulrich von. De guaiaci medicina et morbo gallico. Mogutiae, in aedibus I. Scheffer 1519. 4to. First Edition

—— Lexperiēce . . . touchāt la medecine du boys dict guaiacum . . . traduicte . . . par . . . J. Cheradame. Paris, n.d. sm. 4to. (C. L. F. Robinson)

[——] Of the wood called guaiacum. Tr. by T. Paynell. Londini, in aed. T. Bertheleti 1539. 8vo. Third Edition. (Fontaine–C. L. F. Robinson). (STC 14026)

Hyginus. Aureum opus. J. lambert venundantur parrhisiis 1514. 4to. (Dunn)

Koebel, Jacob. Astrolabi declaratio. Parisiis, apud H. de Marnef & viduam G. Cavellat 1585. 8vo.

L'Ecluse, Charles de. Rariorum . . . stirpium per Hispaniae observatarum historia. Antverpiae, ex officina C. Plantini 1576. 8vo.

Le Fèvre d'Étaples, Jacques. Astronomici theorici corporum celestium libri. (Paris 1503). fol.

—— Epitome in libros arithmeticos . . . Boetij. (Paris 1503). fol.

Lobel, Matthias de, *and* Petro Pena. Nova stirpium adversaria. Antwerpiae, apud C. Plantinum 1576. fol. (Corfield)

Lucas de Burgo S. Sepulchri. Divina proportione. Venetiis, Paganinum de paganinis 1509. fol. First Edition

—— Summa de arithmetica geometria. Tusculano, paganino 1523. fol.

[Lupton, Thomas]. A thousand notable things of sundry sortes. London, for E. White [before 1601]. 4to. (STC 16958a)

Lyte, Henry, *tr.* *See* Dodoens, Rembert

Medina, Pedro de. L'arte del navegar. In Vinetia, ad instantia di G. Pedrezano 1555. [Colophon] In Vinetia, A. Pincio 1554. sm. 4to. (C. L. F. Robinson)

[Monardes, Nicolas]. Ioyfvll newes out of the newfound world. Tr. by J. Frampton. London, T. Dawson for W. Norton 1580. 4to. (STC 18006)

Paracelsus, Theophrastus. A hundred and fourteene experiments and cures. Tr. by J. Hester. London, V. Simmes 1596. sm. 4to. (STC 19180)

Paynell, Thomas, *tr.* *See* Hutten, Ulrich von

Pena, Petro. *See* Lobel, Matthias de, *and* Petro Pena

The questyonary of cyrurgens. *See* [Guido, *de Cauliaco*]

Riese, Adam. Rechenung nach der lenge auff den linihen und feder. Leipzig, J. Berwalt 1550. 4to.

Rondelet, Guillaume. L'histoire entiere des poissons. À Lion, M. Bonhomme 1558. 4to. (C. L. F. Robinson)

Stöffler, Johann. Calendarium romanum magnum. Oppenheym, J. Köbel 1518. fol.

——— Elucidatio fabricae ususque astrolabii. Tubingen, per T. Anshelmum 1514. fol.

——— ——— Parisiis, apud H. de Marnef & viduam G. Cavellat 1585. 8vo. (White Kennett)

Taisnier, Jean. Opus mathematicum. Coloniae Agrippinae, apud I. Birckmannum & Wernerum Richwinum 1562. fol.

Tunstall, Cuthbert, *Bp.* De arte supputandi. Londini, in aed. R. Pynsoni, 14 Oct. 1522. 4to. First Edition. (STC 24319)

Turner, William. A booke of the natures ... of the bathes in England. Collen [heirs of] A. Birckman 1568. fol. (A. M. Broadley). (Copy 2 of STC 24367 pt. IV)

——— The first and seconde partes of the herbal. Collen [heirs of] A. Birckman 1568. fol. in sixes. (STC 24367)

Science after 1500

SEVENTEENTH CENTURY

Babington, John. Pyrotechnia. London, T. Harper 1635. sm. fol. First Edition. (Sir Jenison Gordon). (STC 1099)

———— A short treatise of geometrie. London, T. Harper 1635. sm. fol. First Edition. (Sir Jenison Gordon). (STC 1100)

[Barlow, William]. Magneticall advertisements. London, E. Griffin 1616. sm. 4to. First Edition, First Issue. (STC 1442)

Bate, John. The mysteries of nature and art. London, T. Harper 1635. sm. 4to. Second Edition. (Castle Craig–Thomas Stevenson). (STC 1578)

Blundeville, Thomas. M. Blundevile his exercises. London, W. Stansby 1622. sm. 4to. Fifth Edition. (F. H. C. Day). (STC 3150)

Brahe, Tycho. Astronomiae instauratae mechanica. Noribergae, apud L. Hulsium 1602. fol. (Earl of Kent–Wrest Park)

———— De mundi aetherei recentioribus phaenomenis. Pragae Bohemorum, Typis Schumanianis 1603. 4to. (White Kennett)

Briggs, Henry. Logarithmicall arithmetike. London, G. Miller 1631. fol. First Edition in English. (Henry, Duke of Kent–Thomas Philip, Earl de Grey). (STC 3740)

Cocker, Edward. Arithmetick. London, for T. Passinger and T. Lacy 1678. 12mo.

———— ———— London, J. R. for E. Tracey 1696. 12mo.

Descartes, René. De homine. Lugduni Batavorum, apud F. Moyardum & P. Leffen 1662. 4to.

Digby, *Sir* Kenelm. Two treatises. London, for J. Williams 1658, 1657. 2 v. in 1. 4to.

Dobrzenski de Nigro Ponte, Jacob. Nova, et amoenior de admirando fontium genio . . . philosophia. Ferrariae, apud A. & I. B. de Marestis 1657. fol.

[Dubreuil, Jean]. La perspective pratique. Paris, chez la veufue François l'Anglois, dit Chartres 1647-51. 3 v. 4to. I, Second Edition; II-III, First Edition. (Lord Widdrington)

Euclides. Elements. London, R. Daniel for W. Nealand 1660. 12mo.

Figueroa, Juan de. Opusculo de astrologia. Lima 1660. 4to. (Ex Museo del Montino–W. H. H. Newman)

Gesner, Conrad. *See* Topsell, Edward

Gilbert, William. Guilielmi Gilberti . . . de magnete. London, P. Short 1600. fol. in sixes. First Edition. (STC 11883)

Guericke, Otto von. Experimenta nova . . . Magdeburgica de vacuo spatio. Amstelodami, apud J. Janssonium 1672. fol. (Robert Southwell)

Gunter, Edmund. Canon triangulorum. London, W. Jones 1623. 4to. Second Edition. (STC 12519)

[———] De sectore & radio. London, W. Jones 1623. 4to. First Edition. (STC 12520)

——— The works . . . corrected by H. Bond. London, W. Leybourn for F. Eglesfield 1662. 4to. Fourth Edition. (Sir John Cope)

Hale, *Sir* Matthew. Magnetismus magnus. London, for W. Shrowsbury 1695. 8vo.

Harvey, William. Anatomical exercitations. London, J. Young for O. Pulleyn 1653. 8vo.

——— Exercitatio anatomica de motu cordis. Francofurti, Sumptibus G. Fitzeri 1628. 4to. First Edition. (John Pearson)

Hernandez, Francisco. Nova plantarum, animalium et mineralium Mexicanorum historia in Indijs. Romae 1651, Sumptibus B. Deuersini & Z. Masotti. fol. (Huth)

[———] Quatro libros. De la naturaleza, y virtudes de las plantas, y animales . . . en la Nueva España. Tr. por F. Ximenez. En Mexico, en casa de la viuda de D. Lopez Davalos 1615. 4to. First Edition. (S. L. M. Barlow). (Lacks title)

Heydon, *Sir* Christopher. A defence of iudiciall astrologie. [Cambridge] J. Legat 1603. 4to. First Edition. (STC 13266)

Hibner, Israel. Mysterium sigillorum. Tr. into English for B. Clayton. London, W. Downing 1698. 8vo.

Hooke, Robert. Micrographia. London, for J. Martin 1667. fol. First Edition

Horrocks, Jeremiah. Opera posthuma. Londini, Prostant venales apud M. Pitt 1678. 4to.

Hughes, William. The American physitian. London, J. C. for William Crook 1672. 12mo. (White Kennett)

Kepler, Johann. Ad Vitellionem Paralipomena. Francofurti, apud C. Marnium & Haeredes I. Aubrii 1604. 4to. First Edition

———— Astronomia nova. Pragae 1609. fol. First Edition. (De Thou)

Kircher, Athanasius. Magnes sive De arte magnetica. Coloniae Agrippinae, apud I. Kalcoven 1643. 4to. Second Edition

Leybourn, William. Arithmetick. London, T. James for G. Sawbridge 1678. 2 v. 8vo. Fourth Edition

———— The art of numbring by speaking-rods. London, Published by W. L., Printed for W. Hayes 1667. 12mo.

———— The line of proportion. London, J. S. for G. Sawbridge 1673. 12mo.

Malpighi, Marcellus. Opera omnia. Londini: apud R. Littlebury 1687. fol. (Clarence H. Clark)

Mandey, Venturus, *and* James Moxon. Mechanick powers. London, n.d. 4to. (Sir James Cope)

Moore, Jonas. Arithmetick. London, J. G. for Nath. Brook 1660. 12mo.

Moxon, James. *See* Mandey, Venturus

Napier, John. A description of the admirable table of logarithmes. Tr. by E. Wright. London, N. Okes 1616. 12mo. First Edition. (STC 18351)

———— Logarithmeticall arithmetike. *See* Briggs, Henry

———— Mirifici logarithmorum canonis descriptio. Edinburgi, ex officina A. Hart 1614. 4to. First Edition. (Lord Napier). (STC 18349a)

———— ———— Lugduni, apud B. Vincentium 1620. 4to.

Partridge, John. ΜΙΚΡΟΠΑΝΑΣΤΡΩΝ. London, for W. Bromwich 1679. 12mo.

Paulli, Simon. Commentarius de abusu tabaci. Argentorati, Sumptibus authoris filij S. Paulii 1665. 4to. (Huth)

Person, David. Varieties. London, R. Badger 1635. 4to. in eights. First Edition. (J. B. Barrett). (STC 19781)

Pettus, *Sir* John. Fleta minor. London, T. Dawks 1683. fol. First Edition

La science curieuse, ou Traité de la chyromance. A Paris, chez F. Clousier 1665. 4to.

Somerset, Edward, *Marquis of Worcester*. A century of the names ... of such inventions. London, J. Grismond 1663. 12mo. First Edition

Sturmy, Samuel. The mariners magazine. London, E. Cotes 1669. fol. First Edition. (Lord Arundell of Wardour)

Sydenham, Thomas. Opera universa. Londini, Typis R. N., Impensis W. Kettilby 1685. 8vo. (Lord John Townshend)

Topsell, Edward. The historie of fovre-footed beastes ... Collected out of all the volumes of Conradus Gesner. London, W. Iaggard 1607. First Edition. (STC 24123)

—— The historie of serpents. London, W. Jaggard 1608. fol. First Edition. (STC 24124)

Vlack, Adriaen V. Trigonometria artificialis. Goudae, P. Rammasenius 1633. fol.

Wallis, John. Opera mathematica. Oxoniae, e Theatro Sheldoniano 1695-9. 3 v. fol. (Thomas Jelf Powys)

—— A treatise of algebra. London, J. Playford for R. Davis 1685. fol. (Edward, Duke of Norfolk)

Webster, John. Metallographa. London, A. C. for W. Kettilby 1671. 4to. (Sir John Cope)

[Wilkins, John, *Bp.*]. A discourse concerning a new world. London [Bk. I] I. Norton; [Bk. II] R. H[odgkinson] 1640. 8vo. (STC 25641)

Wingate, Edmund. Λογαριθμοτεχνία. London, M. Flesher 1648. 12mo. Third Edition

Worcester, *Marquis of*. *See* Somerset, Edward

Science after 1500

Abbot, John, *and* James Smith.   The natural history of the rarer lepidopterous insects of Georgia.   London, T. Bensley 1797.   2 v. fol.

Anderson, John.   Institutes of physics.   Glasgow, R. Chapman and A. Duncan 1786.   8vo.   Fourth Edition.   (George Washington–M. Polack–W. F. Havemeyer)

Archimedes.   Archimedis quae supersunt omnia cum Eutocii Ascalonitae commentariis.   Oxonii, e Typographeo Clarendoniano 1792.   fol.

Bailey, William.   The advancement of arts.   London, W. Adlard 1772. 4to.

[Barrington, Daines].   The probability of reaching the north pole. London 1775.   4to.   First Edition

Bellinger, F.   A treatise concerning the small-pox.   London 1721. 8vo.

Blackmore, *Sir* Richard.   A treatise upon the small-pox.   London 1723. 8vo.

Borlase, William.   The natural history of Cornwall.   Oxford, W. Jackson 1758.   fol.

C., J.   A dissertation on the method of inoculating the small-pox. [London] 1721.   8vo.

Carver, Jonathan.   A treatise on the culture of the tobacco plant.   London 1779.   8vo.

Catesby, Mark.   The natural history of Carolina.   London 1731-43. 2 v.   fol.   (Gosford)

Chapman, William.   Observations on the various systems of canal navigation.   London, I. and J. Taylor 1797.   sm. 4to.

Clinch, William.   An historical essay on the rise and progress of the small-pox.   London 1724.   8vo.

[Colden, Cadwallader].   An explication of the causes of action in matter.   New York, J. Parker 1745.   12mo.   First Edition.   (DePuy)

———— ———— London 1746.   8vo.

Crawford, J.   The case of inoculating the small-pox consider'd.   London 1722.   8vo.

Desaguliers, J.T. A course of experimental philosophy. London 1744-5. 2 v. 4to. I, Second Edition; II, First Edition. (R. Massie)

A discourse concerning the small pox. London 1729. 8vo.

Dissertations upon the ingraftment of the small-pox. t.p.m. 8vo.

———— London 1722. 8vo.

Dod, Pierce. Several cases in physick. London 1746. 8vo.

Euclides. The . . . commentaries of Proclus, on the first book of Euclid's Elements. London 1792. 2 v. 4to.

Faujas de Saint-Fond, Barthélemy. Description des expériences de la aérostatique de MM. de Montgolfier. Paris, chez Cuchet 1784. 8vo. Second Edition

Fitch, John. The original steam-boat supported. Philadelphia, Z. Poulson, Junr. 1788. 8vo.

Flemyng, Malcolm. A proposal for improving the practice of medicine. Hull, J. Rawson 1742. 8vo.

[Franklin, Benjamin]. An account of the new invented Pennsylvanian fireplaces. Philadelphia, B. Franklin 1744. 8vo. First Edition

[————] Descrizione della stufa di Pensilvania. Venezia 1788, nella Stamperia Craziosi à S. Apollinare. sm.4to.

Fulton, Robert. A treatise on the improvement of canal navigation. London, I. and J. Taylor 1796. sm.4to.

Halley, Edmund. Tabulae astronomicae. Londini, apud G. Innys 1749. 4to.

Hauksbee, Francis. Physico-mechanical experiments. London, R. Brugis 1709. 4to.

Helvetius, J. C. A. An essay on the animal oeconomy. London 1723. 8vo.

Hulls, Jonathan. A description . . . of a new-invented machine for carrying vessels or ships out of, or into harbour. London 1737. nar. 12mo.

Jenner, Edward. An inquiry into the causes and effects of the variolae vaccinae. London, S. Low 1798. 4to. First Edition

Jurin, James. An account of the success of inoculating the small pox. London 1724, 1726-7. 8vo.

Jurin, James. A letter to the learned Caleb Cotesworth. London 1723. 8vo.

Knorr, George Wolfgang. Delices physiques choisies. Nuremberg 1766-7. 2 v. fol.

Laplace, Pierre Simon de. Traité de mécanique céleste. Paris, Crapelet 1798-1825. 5 v. 4to.

Lavoisier, Antoine Laurent, *and others*. Méthode de nomenclature chimique. Paris, chez Cuchet 1787. 8vo.

A letter to ... Pierce Dod. London 1746. 8vo.

Lynn, Walter. An essay towards a more easie and safe method of cure in the small pox. London 1714. 8vo.

Maitland, Charles. Mr. Maitlands account of inoculating the small pox. London, J. Downing 1722. 8vo.

Massey, Isaac. Remarks on Dr. Jurin's last yearly account of the success of inoculation. London 1727. 8vo.

———— A short ... account of inoculation. London 1722. 8vo.

Miscellanea curiosa. London, J. M. 1708. 3 v. 8vo.

Montucla, Jean Etienne. Histoire des mathématiques. Paris, chez H. Agasse 1799-1802. 4 v. 4to.

[Morris, Robert]. An historical account of the rise, progress and present state of the canal navigation in Pennsylvania. Philadelphia, Z. Poulson, Junior 1795. sm. 4to.

Newton, *Sir* Isaac. Opera. Londini, J. Nichols 1779-85. 5 v. 4to. (Frances M. R. Currer)

———— Opticks. London 1704. 4to. First Edition. (Samuel Kerrich)

Oliver, Andrew. An essay on comets. Salem, S. Hall 1772. 8vo.

Pike, Nicholas. A new ... system of arithmetic. Newbury-Port, J. Mycall 1788. 8vo. (Copy 1 (Ebenezer White) lacks errata slip; 2, with errata slip)

Plattes, Gabriel. A discovery of subterranean treasure. Philadelphia, R. Bell 1784. 8vo. (DePuy)

Proclus. *See* Euclides

Réaumur, René Antoine Ferchault de. L'art de convertir le fer forgé en acier. Paris, chez M. Brunet 1722. 4to. (Baron Foley)

Robinson, Bryan. The case of five children, who were inoculated in Dublin...1725. London 1725. 8vo.

Rowe, Jacob. All sorts of wheel-carriage, improved. London 1734. 4to.

Rumsey, James. A short treatise on the application of steam. Philadelphia, J. James 1788. 8vo.

Sloane, *Sir* Hans. A voyage to the islands Madera, Barbados . . . and Jamaica. London 1707-25. 2 v. fol. (Earl Gower)

Sparham, Legard. Reasons against the practice of inoculating the small-pox. London 1722. 8vo. Third Edition

Strother, Edward. Experienc'd measures how to manage the small pox. London, n.d. 8vo.

———— ———— London 1721. 8vo.

Sturm, Leonard Christofle. Le veritable Vauban. A La Haye, chez N. Wilt 1709. 8vo.

White, Gilbert. The natural history and antiquities of Selborne. London, T. Bensley 1789. 4to. First Edition

[Williams, Jonathan]. Thermometrical navigation. Philadelphia, R. Aitken 1799. 8vo.

Woodward, John. Naturalis historia telluris. Londini, Typis J. M. 1714. 8vo.

AFTER 1800

Agricola, Georg. De re metallica. Tr. by H. C. Hoover and L. H. Hoover. London 1912. fol. First Edition

Audubon, John James, *and* John Bachman. The viviparous quadrupeds of North America. New York, J. J. Audubon 1844-54. 5 v. 8vo. fol.

———— ———— New York, J. J. Audubon 1846-54. 3 v. roy. 8vo.

Barrow, Isaac. The mathematical works. Cambridge, University Press 1860. 8vo.

———— *See also* Euclides

Berthelot, Pierre Eugène Marcellin. Les carbures d'hydrogène. Paris, Gauthier-Villars 1901. 3 v. 8vo. (Inscribed presentation copy from the author to James Carleton Young)

———— Collection des anciens alchimistes grecs. Paris, G. Steinheil 1887-8. 4 v. 4to. (Inscribed presentation copy from the author to James Carleton Young)

———— Correspondance 1847-92. Paris, Calmann Lévy 1898. 8vo. (Inscribed presentation copy from the author to James Carleton Young)

———— 1851-1901. Cinquantenaire scientifique de M. Berthelot 24 novembre 1901. Paris, Gauthier–Villars 1902. 4to. (Inscribed presentation copy from the author to James Carleton Young)

———— Essai de mécanique chimique. Paris, Dunod 1879. 2 v. 8vo. (Inscribed presentation copy from the author to James Carleton Young)

———— Leçons sur les méthodes générales de synthèse. Paris, Gauthier-Villars 1864. 8vo. (Inscribed presentation copy from the author to James Carleton Young)

———— La révolution chimique Lavoisier. Paris, F. Alcan 1902. 8vo. Second Edition. (Inscribed presentation copy from the author to James Carleton Young)

———— Science et morale. Paris, Calmann Lévy 1897. 8vo. (Inscribed presentation copy from the author to James Carleton Young)

———— La synthèse chimique. Paris, F. Alcan 1903. 8vo. (Ninth Edition). (Inscribed presentation copy from the author to James Carleton Young)

———— Thermochimie. Paris, Gauthier-Villars 1897. 2 v. 8vo. (Inscribed presentation copy from the author to James Carleton Young)

Boole, George. A treatise on the calculus of finite differences. Cambridge, Macmillan 1860. 8vo.

Bowdich, *Mrs.* T. Edward. The fresh-water fishes of Great Britain. London, R. Ackermann 1828. 3 v. 4to.

Busby, C. A. An essay on the propulsion of navigable bodies. New-York, B. G. Jansen 1818. 8vo.

Chess. *See* Jaenisch, C. F. de

[Colden, Cadwallader].   A brief exposition of the views of John L. Sullivan. New-York, W. A. Mercein 1822. 8vo.

———— A vindication of the steam-boat right.   New-York, W. A. Mercein 1819. 8vo.

Congreve, *Sir* William.   The details of the rocket system.   London, J. Whiting 1814. obl. 4to. First Edition. (Library of the Royal Artillery Institution)

Curtis, John. British entomology. London 1823-40. 8 v. 8vo.

Daguerre, Louis Jacques Mandé.   Historique et description des procédés du daguerréotype.   Paris, Lerebours, Susse Frères 1839. 8vo.

Darwin, Charles. On the origin of species. London, J. Murray 1859. 8vo. First Edition

Davy, *Sir* Humphrey. On the fire-damp of coal mines. London, W. Bulmer 1816. 8vo.

DeMorgan, Augustus. The differential and integral calculus. London, Baldwin and Cradock 1842. 8vo.

Dircks, Henry. Perpetuum mobile. London, E. & F. N. Spon 1861. 8vo.

Earle, Thomas. Treatise on rail-roads. Philadelphia, Mifflin & Perry 1830. 8vo.

Elliot, Daniel Giraud. The life and habits of wild animals. London, A. Macmillan 1874. 4to.

Fulton, Robert. Torpedo war. New-York, W. Elliot 1810. obl. 4to. First Edition. (Autographed by Fulton)

Gardiner, J. Stanley. The fauna and geography of the Maldive and Laccadive archipelagoes. Cambridge, University Press 1903-6. 2 v. 4to.

Gould, John. The mammals of Australia. London, Taylor and Francis 1863. 3 v. fol.

Hamilton, *Sir* William Rowan. Elements of quaternions. London, Longmans, Green 1866. 8vo.

———— Lectures on quaternions. Dublin, Hodges and Smith 1853. 8vo.

Herbert, Henry William. Frank Forester's Horse and horsemanship of the United States. New York, Stringer & Townsend 1857. 2 v. 4to. First Edition. (McBurney)

Hewitson, William C. Illustrations of diurnal Lepidoptera. Lycaenidae. London, J. van Voorst 1862-78. 2 v. 4to.

———— Illustrations of exotic butterflies. London, J. van Voorst (1856-76). 5 v. 4to.

Holbrook, John Edwards. Ichthyology of South Carolina. Charleston, S. C., Russel and Jones 1860. 4to. I (all published)

———— North American herpetology. Philadelphia, J. Dobson 1842. 5 v. 4to.

Hunt, Robert. A popular treatise on the art of photography. Glasgow, R. Griffin 1841. 8vo.

Jaenisch, C. F. de. Traité des applications de l'analyse mathématique au jeu des échecs. Saint-Pétersbourg 1862. 8vo.

Jaume-Saint-Hilaire, Jean-Henri. Plantes de la France. Paris, P. Didot l'aîné 1808-9. 4 v. in 8. 8vo.

Le Gray, Gustave. A practical treatise on photography, upon paper and glass. London, T. & R. Willats 1850. 8vo.

M'Adam, John Loudon. Remarks on the present system of road making. Bristol, J. M. Gutch 1816. 8vo. First Edition

Moreau, P. *See* Stocker, J. P., *tr.*

Morgan, Lewis Henry. The American beaver. Philadelphia, J. B. Lippincott 1868. 8vo.

Murdock, William. An account of the application of the gas from coal to oeconomical purposes. n.t.p. London, Abraham, Printer (1808). 8vo.

Newman, Edward. An illustrated natural history of British butterflies and moths. London, W. Glaisher, n.d. 4to.

Perrin, *Mrs.* Henry. British flowering plants. London, B. Quaritch 1914. 4 v. 4to.

Sander, F. Reichenbachia. Orchids illustrated and described. St. Albans, F. Sander 1888-94. 4 v. 4to.

Sharp, David, *editor.* Fauna Hawaiiensis. Cambridge, University Press 1913. 3 v. 4to.

Sowerby, James.   British mineralogy.   London, R. Taylor 1804-17. 5 v.   8vo.   (Thomas Tylee)

———— Exotic mineralogy.   London, B. Meredith 1811-17.   8vo.

Stainton, Henry Tibbatts.   The natural history of the Tineina.   London, J. van Voorst 1855-73.   13 v.   8vo.

Stocker, J. C., *tr.*   Description of the rail road from Liverpool to Manchester by P. Moreau.   Boston, Hilliard, Gray 1833.   12mo.   First Edition

Sullivan, John L.   Remarks on the importance of inland navigation. Boston, J. Eliot 1813.   8vo.

———— *See also* Colden, Cadwallader

Swainson, William, *and* John Richardson.   Fauna Boreali-Americana. London, J. Murray 1831.   4to.   First Edition.   (Gallatin)

Tatham, William.   An historical and practical essay on the culture and commerce of tobacco.   London, T. Bensley 1800.   8vo.   (Lossing)

Todhunter, Isaac.   A history of the mathematical theories of attraction. London, Macmillan 1873.   2 v.   8vo.

———— A history of the progress of the calculus of variations.   Cambridge, Macmillan 1861.   8vo.

White, Gilbert.   Natural history and antiquities of Selborne.   London, Macmillan 1876.   2 v.   4to.

Willmott, Ellen.   The genus rosa.   London, J. Murray 1914.   2 v. fol.

Books About Birds

Audubon, John James.   The birds of America.   New York 1827-8. 4 v.   double elephant fol.

———— Ornithological biography.   Edinburgh, A. Black 1831-9.   5 v. 8vo.

Beebe, William.   A monograph of the pheasants.   London 1918-22. 4 v.   4to.

Bonaparte, Charles Lucian.   American ornithology.   Philadelphia, Carey, Lea & Carey 1825-30.   4 v.   fol.

Buller, *Sir* Walter Lawry.   A history of the birds of New Zealand. London 1888.   2 v.   4to.   Second Edition.   Supplement. 1905. 2 v. in 1.   4to.

Butler, Arthur G.   British birds.   Brumby & Clarke [1896-8].   6 v. 4to.

Capen, Elwin A.   Oölogy of New England.   Boston, A. Mudge 1886. fol.

Dresser, Henry Eeles.   Eggs of the birds of Europe.   London 1910. 2 v.   4to.

——— A history of the birds of Europe.   London 1871-96.   9 v.   4to.

——— A monograph of the Meropidae, or family of the bee-eaters. London 1884-6.   fol.   (Gallatin)

Elliot, Daniel Giraud.   The birds of North America.   New York 1869. 2 v.   fol.

——— A monograph of the Bucerotidae, or . . . hornbills.   n.p. 1882. fol.

——— A monograph of the Paradiseidae, or birds of paradise.   n.p. 1873.   fol.

——— A monograph of the Phasianidae or . . . pheasants.   New York 1872.   2 v.   fol.

——— A monograph of the Pittidae, or . . . ant thrushes.   New York, D. Appleton 1863.   fol.

——— A monograph of the Tetraoninae, or . . . grouse.   New York 1865.   fol.

Gould, John.   The birds of Asia.   London, Taylor and Francis 1850-83.   7 v.   fol.

——— The birds of Australia.   London, R. and J. E. Taylor 1848-69. 7 v. & suppl.   fol.   (E. L. Betts)

——— The birds of Europe.   London, R. and J. E. Taylor 1837.   5 v. fol.   First Edition.   (F. D. Godman)

——— The birds of Great Britain.   London, Taylor and Francis 1873. 5 v.   fol.

——— A century of birds from the Himalaya Mountains.   London 1832.   fol.

Gould, John.   Handbook to the birds of Australia.   London 1865.
2 v.   8vo.   First Edition

—————— A monograph of the Odontophorinae, or partridges of America.   London, R. and J. E. Taylor 1850.   fol.

—————— A monograph of the Ramphastidae, or . . . toucans.   London,
Taylor and Francis 1854.   fol.

—————— A monograph of the Trochilidae, or . . . humming-birds.   London, Taylor and Francis 1861-77.   5 v. & suppl.   fol.

—————— A monograph of the Trogonidae, or . . . trogons.   London,
Taylor and Francis 1875.   fol.

—————— & R. B. Sharpe.   The birds of New Guinea.   London, H. Sotheran 1875-88.   5 v.   fol.

Gray, George Robert.   The genera of birds.   London, Longman,
Brown, Green and Longmans 1849.   3 v.   fol.

Grieve, Symington.   The great auk.   London, T. C. Jack 1885.   4to.
(J. L. Childs)

Hudson, William Henry.   Birds of La Plata.   London, J. M. Dent 1920.
2 v.   4to.   First Edition

—————— Rare vanishing & lost British birds.   London, J. M. Dent 1923.
8vo.   First Edition

—————— *See also* Sclater, Philip Lutley

Legge, W. Vincent.   A history of the birds of Ceylon.   London 1880.
4to.

Lesson, René Primevère.   Histoire naturelle des colibris.   Paris, A. Bertrand 1831.   8vo.

—————— Histoire naturelle des oiseaux de paradis.   Paris, A. Bertrand
1835.   8vo.

—————— Histoire naturelle des oiseaux-mouches.   Paris, A. Bertrand
1829.   8vo.

—————— Les Trochilidées.   Paris, A. Bertrand 1832.   8vo.

Levaillant, François.   Histoire naturelle des oiseaux d'Afrique.   Paris,
J. J. Fuchs 1799.   6 v.   4to.   (Gallatin)

—————— Histoire naturelle des oiseaux de paradis et des rolliers.   Paris,
Denné le jeune 1806-7.   3 v.   fol.

Levaillant, François. Histoire naturelle des perroquets. Paris, Levrault 1801-5. 2 v. fol. (Gallatin)

Lilford, *Baron*. *See* Powys, Thomas Littleton

Malherbe, Alfred. Monographie des Picidées. Metz, J. Verronais 1861. 4 v. in 2. fol. (Gallatin)

Marshall, G. H. T. *&* G. F. L. Marshall. A monograph of the Capitonidae. London 1870-1. 4to. (Gallatin)

Mathews, Gregory M. The birds of Australia. London, Witherby 1910-27. 16 v. 4to.

———— The birds of Norfolk & Lord Howe Islands. London, Witherby 1928. 4to.

Millais, J. G. The natural history of the British surface-feeding ducks. London, Longmans, Green 1902. 4to.

Newton, Alfred. A dictionary of birds. London, A. and C. Black 1896. 8vo.

Nicoll, Michael. Birds of Egypt. n.p., H. Rees 1930. 2 v. 4to.

Powys, Thomas Littleton, *fourth Baron Lilford*. Coloured figures of the birds of the British Islands. London, R. H. Porter 1891-7. 7 v. 8vo. Second Edition

———— Notes on the birds of Northamptonshire. London, R. H. Porter 1895. 2 v. 8vo.

Poynting, Frank. Eggs of British birds. London, R. H. Porter 1895-6. 4to.

Pycraft, William Playne. Birds in flight. London, Gay & Hancock 1922. 8vo. First Edition

Rippon, Robert H. F. Icones ornithopterorum. n.p. 1898-1906. 2 v. fol.

Rothschild, Walter. Extinct birds. London, Hutchinson 1907. atlas 4to.

———— A monograph of the genus Casuarius. London 1900. 4to.

Salvin, Osbert, *&* F. D. Godman. Biologia Centrali-Americana. Aves. n.p. 1879-1904. 4 v. in 3. 4to.

———— *See also* Sclater, Philip Lutley

Sclater, Philip Lutley & W. H. Hudson. Argentine ornithology. London, R. H. Porter 1888-9. 2 v. 8vo. First Edition

———— & Osbert Salvin. Exotic ornithology. London, B. Quaritch 1866-9. 13 v. fol. Original issue in parts. (J. L. Childs)

Seebohm, Henry. A monograph of the Turdidae or ... thrushes. London, H. Sotheran 1902. 2 v. fol.

Sharpe, Richard Bowdler. An analytical index to the works of ... John Gould. London, H. Sotheran 1893. 8vo. (F. D. Godman)

———— A monograph of the Alcedinidae, or ... kingfishers. London 1868-71. 4to.

———— A monograph of the Hirundinidae or ... swallows. London, H. Sotheran 1885-94. 2 v. 4to.

———— Monograph of the Paradiseidae, or birds of paradise. London, H. Sotheran 1891-8. 2 v. fol.

Shelley, George Ernest. The birds of Africa. London 1896-1912. 5 v. in 7. fol.

———— A monograph of the Nectariniidae, or ... sun-birds. London 1876-80. 4to. (Gallatin)

Souancé, Charles de. Iconographie des perroquets. Paris, P. Bertrand 1857. fol. (Gallatin)

Whitaker, Joseph I. S. The birds of Tunisia. London, R. H. Porter 1905. 2 v. 8vo.

Whymper, Charles. Egyptian birds. London, A. and C. Black 1909. 4to.

Willughby, Francis. The ornithology of Francis Willughby. London 1678. fol.

Wilson, Alexander. American ornithology. Philadelphia, Bradford and Inskeep 1808-14. 9 v. 4to.

Wilson, Scott B. Aves Hawaiienses. London, R. H. Porter 1890-99. 4to.

Index

Index

A

Index

Index

Index

Index

Index

Index

Index

Index

Index

Index

Index

Index

Index

Index

Index

Index

Index

Index

Index

Index

[563]

Index

Index

Hamilton, *Sir* William Rowan, 534

Hammond, John, 319

Hammond, William, 176

Hancock, John, 359, 397

Hanna, John Smith, 415

Hanson, Alexander Contee, 373

Hanson, Elizabeth. *See* Bownas, Samuel

The Harbinger, 415

Hardie, James, 376

Harding, Samuel, 83

Hardy, Thomas, 250

Hardyng, John, 83

Harington, John, 176

Harington, *Sir* John, 83

—— *tr. See* Ariosto, Ludovico

Harrington, James, 176

Harris, Joel Chandler, 416

Harrison, Benjamin, 401

Harrison, David, 351

Harrison, Mary St. Leger, 251

Harrison, William Henry, 401

Hart, William, 347

Harte, Francis Bret, 416

Hartford. Convention, 386

Hartford Daily Courant, 406

Hartley, J., 176

Hartlib, Samuel, 318

Hartwell, Henry, James Blair *and* Edward Chilton, 336

Harvard College, 347, 395

Harvard Register, 416

Harvey, Christopher, 176

Harvey, Edward, 359

Harvey, William, 83, 526

Hasenberg, Johann, 471

Haskett, William J., 389

Haughton, William, 83

Hauksbee, Francis, 530

Hausted, Peter, 83

Havard, William, 176

Hawes, Joel, 393

Hawes, Stephen, 83

Hawkesworth, John, 357, 359

Hawkesworth, John, *tr. See* Fénelon: Telemachus [1796]

Hawkins, Alfred, 391

Hawkins, Henry, 83

Hawkins, *Sir* Richard, 83, 308

Hawkins, William, 176

Hawks, Francis L., 393

Hawthorne, Nathaniel, 416, 417

Hay, John, 417

Hayes, Rutherford B., 401

Hayne, Thomas, 176

Hayward, Abraham, 251

Hayward, *Sir* John, 84

Haywood, John, 388

Hazlitt, William, 251

Head, Richard, 176

Healey, John, *tr. See* Augustine, *Saint*

Hearn, Lafcadio, 417

Heath, James, 176

Heath, Robert, 177

Hedendaagsche historie, 351, 353, 354

Heliodorus, 84

Hellowes, Edward, *tr. See* Guevara, Antonio de

Helps, *Sir* Arthur, 251

Helvetius, J. C. A., 530

Helyas, 251

Henderson, Alexander, 314

Hendricks, William, 362

Henley, Samuel, *tr. See* Beckford, William

Henley, William Ernest, 251

—— *and* R. L. Stevenson, 251

Hennepin, Louis, 324, 325, 326, 328, 329, 330, 331, 334, 337

Henricus de Firmaria, 20

Henrietta Maria de Bourbon, 187

Henry VIII, *King of England*, 84, 177

Henry Frederick, *Prince of Wales*, 84

Henry IV, *King of France*, 449

Henry of Hesse, 20

Index

Henry, Alexander, 384

Henry, John Joseph, 384

Henry, W., 357, 359

Hentzner, Paul, 474

Herbals. *See* Dodoens; Gerard; The greate herball; Herbarius; Hortus sanitatis; Parkinson; Turner

Herbarius, 20

Herberstein, Sigmund von, 471, 472

Herbert, Edward, *Baron Herbert of Cherbury*, 177

Herbert, George, 84, 177

Herbert, Henry William, 535

Herbert, Mary, *Countess of Pembroke, tr. See* Garnier, Robert

Heriot, George, 382, 383

Herle, Charles, 177, 313

Hermann von Wied, *Archbishop of Cologne*, 472

Hermas. *See* Liber trium virorum

Hermes Trismegistus, 20, 177

Hernandez, Francisco, 526

Herodianus, 20

Herodianus, Aelius. *In* Gaza, Theodorus

Herodotus, 20, 45, 437

Herolt, Joannes, 84

Heron-Allen, Edward, *tr. See* Omar Khayyám

Herrera, Antonio de, 308, 335

Herrera, Rodrigo de, 490

Herrick, Robert, 177, 251

Hervet, Gentian, *tr. See* Xenophon

Hesiod, 20

Hessel, Andrea, 335

Hester, John, *tr. See* Paracelsus, Theophrastus

Hewitson, William C., 535

Hewlett, Maurice, 251

Hexham, Henry, 85

Heydon, *Sir* Christopher, 85, 526

Heydon, John, 177

Heylyn, Peter, 85

Heyrick, Thomas, 177

Heywood, Jasper, *tr. See* Seneca, Lucius Annaeus

Heywood, John, 85

Heywood, Thomas, 85, 86, 177

—— *and* Richard Brome, 86

Hibner, Israel, 526

Hickeringill, Edmund, 178

Hickes, William, 178

Hierocles, 20

Hieronymus, 4, 20, 21

Hieronymus, *von Braunschweig. See* Brunschwig, Hieronymus

Hiffernan, Paul, 178

Higden, Ranulphus, 86

Higgins, John. *See* Mirror for magistrates

—— *tr. See* Junius, Adrian

Higginson, Francis, 86, 310

Higginson, John, 325

Higginson, Thomas Wentworth, 434

Hill, Aaron, 178

Hill, John, 178

Hill, Thomas, 86

—— *tr. See* Cocles, Bartholomaeus

Hilliard d'Auberteuil, Michel René, 366, 369

Hilton, Walter. *See* Hylton, Walter

Hippisley, John, 178

Hippocrates, 21

Histoire . . . depuis le partement des Sieurs de Guise, 449

Historia septem sapientum Romae, 21

—— *See also* Septem Sapientes

An historical description of the glorious conquest of . . . Buda, 178

An historical memorial of the negotiations of France and England, 347

Historisch-genealogischer calender, 369

The history and adventures of little Henry, 251

The history of the origin . . . of the war in America, 365

The history of the war in America, 365, 370

Index

Index

Index

Jacobus de Theramo, 23

Jaenisch, C. F. de, 535

Jamaica, 324, 338

James, *Saint and Apostle, Order of,* 488

James I, *King of England,* 89, 181

James, Edwin, 388

James, Henry, 419, 420

James, Thomas, *Captain,* 89, 310

James, Thomas, *D.D.,* 89

James, William, 387

James, William Dobein, 387

Jaume-Saint-Hilaire, Jean-Henri, 535

Jay, John, 373

Jeanne d'Arc, 455

Jefferies, Richard, 253

Jefferson, Thomas, 359, 367, 371, 373, 382, 401

Jefferys, Thomas, 342, 347

Jenkins, Elijah, *pseud. See* Mottley, John

Jenks' Portland Gazette, 405

Jenner, Edward, 294, 530

Jennings, David, 339

Jephson, Robert, 182

Jesus Christ, 89, 293

Jewel, John, *Bp.,* 89

Jobson, Richard, 89

Johannes Damascenus, 23, 45

Johannes de Capua. *See* Bidpai

John, Chrysostom, *Saint,* 3, 23, 89, 436

John XXII, *Pope,* 440

John, of Trevisa, *tr. See* Bate, John; Higden, Ranulphus

Johnson, Andrew, 401

Johnson, Charles (1679-1748), 182

Johnson, Charles (*fl.* 1724-1736), 335

Johnson, Edward, 318

Johnson, James, 182

Johnson, Richard, 182

Johnson, Samuel (1691-1773), 182

Johnson, Samuel (1696-1772), 347

Johnson, Samuel (1709-1784), 182, 183, 253, 361

Johnson, William, 388

Johnson, *Sir* William, 343, 344

Johnstone, John, 183

Jones, Ebenezer, 253

Jones, Henry, 184

Jones, Hugh, 334

Jones, Inigo, 89, 184

Jones, John, 254

Jones, Owen, 254

Jones, Zachary, *tr. See* Le Loyer, Pierre

Jonson, Benjamin, 89, 90, 184

—— *tr. See* Horatius Flaccus, Quintus

Jordan, Thomas, 184

Jordanus *Nemorarius,* 23

Jordanus de Quedlinburg, 23

Joseph, *ben Gorion,* 90

Josephus, Flavius, 23, 90, 436, 437

Josselyn, John, 321, 322

Joutel, Henri, 333

Joyner, William, 184

The judgment given forth by twenty eight Quakers, 327

Judson, David, 359

Junius, Adrian, 90, 472

Jurin, James, 530, 531

Justice of Peace, 90

Justinianus, Bernardus, 23

Justinianus, Flavius Anicius, 23, 440

Justinus, 24, 45

Juvenalis, Decimus Junius, 24, 45, 184, 443

Juvencus, 45

K

Kalm, Peter, 353, 355

Keats, John, 254

Keble, John, 254

Keith, George, 327, 331

Index

Index

Late last night an express arrived from Philadelphia, 396
Lateran Council, 440
Latham, Simon, 92
Lathrop, Joseph, 369, 371, 376, 377
Latimer, Hugh, 92
Latter Day Saints, 390, 391
Laud, William, *Abp.*, 92
Laudonnière, René de, 304
Laune, Pierre de, *tr. See* Liturgies. Book of common prayer. *French*
Lavender, Theophilus, *editor. See* Biddulph, William
Lavoisier, Antoine Laurent, 531
Law, Andrew, 420
Law, John, 186
Law, William, 186
Lawrence, D. H., 256
Lawrence, Leonard, *tr. See* San Pedro, Diego
Lawson, John, 332
Lazius, Wolfgang, 472
Leacock, John, 362
Leaming, Aaron, 345
Leanerd, John, 186
Le Blanc, Vincent, 319
Le Boucher, Odet-Julian, 373
Lechford, Thomas, 312
Le Clercq, Chrestien, 326
L'Ecluse, Charles de, 523
Lectionary, 3
Leddra, William. *See* Robinson, William, *and* William Leddra
Lederer, John, 321
Ledesma, Bartolomé de, 302, 488
Lee, Arthur, 366
Lee, Charles, 359
Lee, Henry, 380, 385
Lee, Nathaniel, 186
—— *See also* Dryden, John, *and* Nathaniel Lee
Lee, Richard Henry, 371, 373
Lee, Robert E., 399
Lefèvre, Raoul, 256
Le Fèvre d'Étaples, Jacques, 24, 523

Le Forestier, Jourdain. *See* Jordanus Nemorarius
Leger, Jean, 456
Legge, W. Vincent, 538
Legh, Gerard, 92
Le Gouz, François de La Boullaye, 456
Le Grand, Jacques, 24
Le Gray, Gustave, 535
Leigh, Joseph, 383
Leigh, Percival, 256
Leighton, Alexander, 92
Leighton, *Sir* William, 92, 93
Le Jeune, Paul, 311
Leland, John, 93
Le Loyer, Pierre, *Sieur de la Brosse*, 93
Le Maire, Jacob, 308
Le Maire, Jean, 449
Le Mercier, François, 311, 318
Lennox, Charlotte, 186
Leolinus Siluriensis. *See* Machen, Arthur
Leonard, Daniel, 362
Leoni, Giovanni Battista, 481
Leonico, Angelo, 481
Le Page du Pratz, 345, 348
Le Roux de Lincy, Adrien-Jean-Victor, 464
Le Roy, Pierre, 93
Léry, Jean de, 303
Le Sage, Alain René, 186, 460, 464
Lescarbot, Marc, 306, 307, 308
Leslie, Charles, 186
Lesson, René Primevère, 538
A letter from a clergyman, 187
A letter to a member of Parliament, 350
A letter to a member of Parliament on the present unhappy dispute, 359
A letter to the King of *****, 344
A letter to William Pitt, 346
Lettre d'un curé de Rouen, 456
Levaillant, François, 538, 539

Index

Index

Index

Index

Index

Moleville, Bertrand de, 260
Molière, Jean Baptiste Poquelin de, 456, 457
Molina, Alonso de, 303
Molinet, Jean, 450
Molitoris, Ulricus, 27
Moll, Herman, 332, 333
Mombritius, Boninus, 27
Monardes, Nicolas, 101, 524
Monette, John W., 392
Monroe, James, 402
Monstrelet, Enguerrand de, 27, 450
Montagu, Charles. *See* Prior, Matthew, *and* Charles Montagu
Montagu, Elizabeth, 193
Montagu, Walter, 193
Montaigne, Michel Eyquem de, 101, 260, 450, 457, 465
Montalvan, Perez de. *See* Perez de Montalvan, Juan
Montanus, Arnoldus, 322
Montemagno, Bonaccursius de, 27
Montemayor, Jorge de, 102
Montesquieu, *M. de Secondat, Baron de,* 193, 461
Montfaucon, Bernard de, 461
Montgomery, *Sir* Robert, 333
Montreux, Nicolas de, 102
Montucla, Jean Etienne, 531
Montule, Édouard, 388
Moore, Clement Clarke, 424
Moore, Edward, 194
Moore, George, 260, 261
Moore, Jonas, 527
Moore, *Mrs.* M. B., 424, 425
Moore, Martin, 388
Moore, Thomas, 261, 262
Moore, *Sir* Thomas, 194
Mora, Molina y Fuente, Andres Ignacio de, 495
Moraes, Francisco de, 102, 488
More, Cresacre, 102
More, Henry, 194
More, *Sir* Thomas, 102, 194, 342
—— *tr. See* Pico della Mirandola

Moreau, Jacob N., 344, 345
Moreau, Jacques-Nicolas (1717-1804), 461
Morgan, John, 350
Morgan, Lewis Henry, 535
Morgan, Matthew, 194
Morgan, Sylvanus, 194
Morison, David, 194
Morison, *Sir* Richard, *tr. See* Vives, Juan Luis
Morland, Samuel, 194
Morley, Thomas, 102
Morrill, Isaac, 343
Morris, Robert, 194, 531
Morris, William, 262, 263
—— *tr. See* Homerus; The tale of Beowulf
Morrison, Arthur, 263, 264
Morse, Jedidiah, 388
—— *editor,* 379
Mortier, Pieter, 513
Morton, Nathaniel, 321
Morton, Thomas, 102, 194, 311
Morwyng, Peter, *tr. See* Joseph, *ben Gorion*
Moryson, Fynes, 102
Motley, John Lothrop, 425
Mott, Lucretia, 402
Motteux, Peter Anthony, 194, 195
—— *editor,* 195
—— *tr. See* Rabelais, François
Mottley, John, 195
Moulton, Louise Chandler, 264
Moultrie, William, 381
Mountfort, William, 195
Mourt, G., *editor,* 102, 309
Moxon, James. *See* Mandey, Venturus, *and* James Moxon
Mulcaster, Robert, *tr. See* Fortescue, *Sir* John
Muller, Frederik, 394
Müller, Johann, 27
Muller, John, 365
Mumford, Joseph, 195
Mun, Thomas, 195

[576]

Index

Index

Index

O'Shaughnessy, Arthur William Edward, 265
—— *See also* Moulton, Louise Chandler
—— *and* Eleanor O'Shaughnessy, 265
Osorio da Fonseca, Jeronimo, *Bp.*, 105
Ossian, 197
Otis, James, 349
Otway, Thomas, 197, 198, 265
—— *tr. See* Citri de la Guette
Ovidius Naso, Publius, 4, 28, 46, 106, 198, 265, 441, 442, 443
Oviedo. *See* Fernandez de Oviedo y Valdes, Gonzalo
Owen, John, 198
Owen, Lewis, 106
Oxberry, William, *editor*, 265
Oxford University, 106, 198, 265

P

P., H. *See* Peacham, Henry
P., R. *See* Paltock, Robert
P., W., 198
P., W. *See* Penn, William
Padilla, Pedro de, 489
Paetus, Luc, 46
Pagan, Blaise François de, *Comte*, 319
Page, Thomas Nelson, 426
Paine, Thomas, 362, 367, 368, 376, 377, 378
Painter, William, 106
Palaeopolitanus, Franciscus. *See* More, Henry
Palafox y Mendoza, Juan de, 312, 326
Palingenius, Marcellus, *tr. See* Manzolli, Pierre Angelo
Palissy, Bernard, 467
Palladine of England. *See* Florando de Inglaterra
Palladio, Andrea, 198

Palladius, Rutilius Taurus Aemilianus. *See* Scriptores rei rusticae
Palmer, John, 326
Palmerin de Inglaterra. *See* Moraes, Francisco de
Palmerin de Oliva, 489
Palomero, Martin, 489
Paltock, Robert, 198
Pamela's conduct in high life, 198
A panegyrick on the author of Absolom and Achitophel, 198
Panormitanus, Nicolaus, 28
Parabosco, Girolamo, 481
Paracelsus, Theophrastus, 106, 524
Paradin, Claude, 106, 450, 512
Paradin de Cuyseaulx, Guillaume, 450, 513
Paris et Vienne, 467
Paris Gazette, 404
Parish, Elijah, 386
Park, James, 198
Parke, Robert, *tr. See* Gonzalez de Mendoza, Juan
Parker, Henry, 28, 106
Parker, Martin, 198, 199
Parker, Matthew, *Archbishop*, 295
Parkes, William, 106
Parkinson, John, 106
Parkman, Francis, 426
Parliament. *See* England. *Parliament*
Parnell, Thomas. *See* Goldsmith, Oliver, *and* Thomas Parnell
Parsons, Robert, 107
A parte of a register, 107
Partridge, John, 527
Pascal, Blaise, 199, 457, 467
Pascal, Françoise, 457
Pasquier, *Duc de*, 467
Pasquill, *of England*, 107
Passe, Crispin van de, 475, 513
Dye passie ons heeren, 473
Pater, Walter Horatio, 266
—— *See also* Studies in European literature
—— *editor*, 266

[579]

Index

Index

Index

Index

R

Index

Index

S

Index

Index

Index

Spicer, Jacob. *See* Leaming, Aaron, *and* Jacob Spicer
Spiera, Ambrosius, 37
Spinoza, Baruch, 475
Spinoza, Benedict, 214
Spirito, Lorenzo, 37, 482
Spottiswood, John, 214
Sprat, Thomas, 214
Sprenger, Jacob, *and* Henricus Institoris, 37
Sprigg, Joshua, 214
Spring, Gardiner, 387
Springer's Weekly Oracle, 405
Stafford, Anthony, 120
Stainton, Henry Tibbatts, 536
Stamp Act, 351, 352, 353
Stanbridge, John, 120
Stanhope, Philip Dormer, *Earl of Chesterfield*, 214
Stanley, Thomas, 214
—— *tr.* *See* Perez de Montalvan, Juan; Preti, Girolamo
Stanton, Daniel, 356
Stapleton, *Sir* Robert, 214
—— *tr.* *See* Juvenalis; Musaeus
Stapleton, Thomas, *tr.* *See* Beda
Statham, Nicholas, 37, 120
Statius, Publius Papinius, 47, 215, 441
Statuta Angliae, 37
Statuta Mediolani, 37
Stearns, Charles, 429
Stedman, Charles, 377
Steele, *Sir* Richard, 215
—— *See also* The Tatler
Steendam, Jacob, 316, 317
Stein, Gertrude, 429
Stephanus Byzantius, 47
Stephens, James, 273, 274
Stephens, John, 120
Stephenson, Marmaduke, 319
Sterling, Richard, *and* J. D. Campbell, 429
Sterne, Laurence, 215, 216
Steuart, Adam, 313, 314
Stevens, Benjamin, 346

Stevenson, Robert Louis, 274
—— *See also* Henley, William Ernest, *and* R. L. Stevenson
Stevenson, Roger, 361
Stewart, James, 216
Stiles, Ezra, 347, 370, 377
Stith, William, 340
Stocker, J. C., 536
Stoddard, Richard Henry, 429
Stoddard, Solomon, 329, 332, 334, 337, 340
Stöffler, Johann, 524
Storer, Thomas, 120
Story, Thomas, 340
Stothard, Thomas, 216
Stoughton, William, 326
Stow, John, 120
Stowe, Harriet Beecher, 429, 430
Strabo, 438
Straparola, Giovanfrancesco, 482
Strode, William, 216
Strong, Nehemiah, 367
Strother, Edward, 532
Stuart, Isaac William, 393
Stubbe, Henry, 216
—— *tr.* *See* Gothofredus, Jacobus
Stubbs, John. *See* Fox, George, John Stubbs *and* Benjamin Furly
Studies in European literature, 274
Studley, John, *tr.* *See* Seneca, Lucius Annaeus
Stukeley, Thomas, 120
Stukeley, William, 216
Sturm, Leonard Christofle, 532
Sturmy, Samuel, 528
Sturt, John, 513
Suardus, Andreas, 37
Suckling, *Sir* John, 216
Sue, Eugène, 468
Suetonius Tranquillus, Caius, 37, 120, 441
Suidas, 37
Suite de l'extract de plusieurs mauvaises propositions, 458
Sullivan, James, 375, 378

[588]

Index

[589]

Index

Index

Tundalus, 39

Tunstall, Cuthbert, *Bp.*, 123, 524

Turberville, George, 123

Turco, Carlo, 48

Turell, Ebenezer, 341

Turner, William, 123, 524

Turrecremata, Johannes de, 39, 40

Twain, Mark. *See* Clemens, Samuel Langhorne

Twenty four country dances, 221

Two papers, on the subject of taxing the British colonies in America, 353

Twyne, Thomas, *tr. See* Petrarca, Francesco

Tyler, John, 402

Tymme, Thomas, *tr. See* Calvin, Jean: A commentarie

Tyndale, William, 123, 124

U

Udall, Nicholas, *tr. See* Erasmus, Desiderius

Ulloa, Antonio de, 356

Uncle Tom's cabin almanack, 430

Underdowne, Thomas, *tr. See* Heliodorus

Underhill, John, 124, 311

The Union is Dissolved!, 399

United States census, 375, 381

Urbanus Bellunensis, 40, 48

Urfé, Honoré d', 468

Urquhart, *Sir* Thomas, *tr. See* Rabelais, François

Ursula, *Saint*, 40

Utino, Leonardus de, 40

Utterson, Edward Vernon, *editor*, 278

V

The Vade mecum for America, 336

Vaenius, *or* Van Veen, Otto. *See* Rowlands, Richard: Amorvm emblemata

Valerius Flaccus, Caius, 40, 441

Valerius Maximus, Caius, 40

Valla, Laurentius, 40

Valturius, Robertus, 40

Vanbrugh, *Sir* John, 221, 278

—— *and* Colley Cibber, 221

Van Buren, Martin, 402

Vancouver, George, 379

Van Ness, William P., 382

Varchi, Benedetto, 483

Varenius, Bernhard V., 475

Varnum, James M., 372

Varro, Marcus Tullius, 40, 41

Vasari, Giorgio, 483

Vaughan, Henry, 221

Vaughan, Thomas, 222

Vaughan, William, 124, 309

Vecellio, Cesare, 483

Veer, Gerrit de, 124, 306

Vega, Garcilaso de la. *See* Boscan, Juan

Vega, Garcilaso de la, *El Inca*, 306, 307, 326

Vega Carpio, Lope Felix de, 491

Vegetius Renatus, Flavius, 41

Velez de Guevara, Luis, 491

Venables, Robert, 222

Venegas, Miguel, 345, 346, 353

Verardus, Carolus, 41, 298

Vere, *Sir* Francis, 222

Vergerius, Petrus Paulus, 41

Verklaringe van hare ho. mogende de heeren Staten Generael, 320

Vermigli, Pietro Martire, 124

The Vermont Gazette, 405

Verstegen, R., *pseud. See* Rowlands, Richard

Vespuccius, Americus, 301

Vespuccius-Waldseemüller, 298

Vibius Sequester, 48

Vicars, John, 315

Vicentino, Ludovico, 483

Vico, Aenea, 48

Victor, P., 48

[591]

Index

Index

Watson, John F. *See* Smith, John Jay, *and* John F. Watson

Watson, Thomas, 125

Watson, *Sir* William, 279

Watts, Isaac, 224

Weal-reaf, 431

Weaver, Thomas, 224

Webster, Daniel, 380, 386, 388

Webster, John (1580?-1625?), 125, 279

—— *See also* Dekker, Thomas, *and* John Webster

Webster, John (1610-1682), 225, 528

Webster, Noah, 431

Webster, Samuel, 361

Wecker, John, 225

Weddell, James, 389

The Weekly News-Letter, 404

Weever, John, 125

Welde, Thomas, *and* John Winthrop, 326

Wells, Herbert George, 279

—— *See also* Gregory, R. A., *and* H. G. Wells

Wesley, Charles, 225

Wesley, John, 225, 361

—— *and* Charles Wesley, 225

Wesley, Samuel, 225

West, Andrew Fleming, *tr. See* Bury, Richard de

West, Thomas, *Baron De La Warre*, 125, 307

Westmacott, Charles Molloy, 280

Westminster catechism, 385

Weston, Joseph, 225

Wharton, Charles Henry, 367

Wharton, Edith, 431

Wheatley, Phillis, 431

Wheelock, Eleazar, 349, 351, 352, 353, 354, 356, 357, 361

Whetstone, George, 126

Whibley, Charles, *editor*, 280

Whincop, Thomas, 225

Whistler, James Abbott McNeill, 280

Whitaker, Joseph I. S., 540

Whitbourne, Richard, 126, 308, 309

White, Gilbert, 532, 536

White, John, *Bp.*, 126

White, John, *of Dorchester*, 126, 310

White, John, (*fl.* 1790), 225

White, R., *tr. See* Digby, *Sir* Kenelm: A late discourse

White, Richard Grant, 434

White, Samuel, 390

White, William Hale, 280

Whitehead, George. *See* Penn, William, *and* George Whitehead

Whitehead, William, 225

Whitehorne, Peter, *tr. See* Machiavelli, Niccolò

Whitestown Gazette, 405

Whitfield, Henry, 317

Whitforde, Richard, 126

Whiting, John, 330

Whitman, Walt, 431

Whitney, Geoffrey, 126

Whitney, Peter, 376

Whittier, John Greenleaf, 431, 432, 433, 434

Whittingham, William, 126

Whittinton, Robert, 126, 127

—— *tr. See* Cicero, Marcus Tullius

Whymper, Charles, 540

Wiclif, John, 127

Wilcox, Thomas. *See* Field, John, *and* Thomas Wilcox

Wild, Robert, 225

Wilde, Oscar, 280, 281

Wilkes, John, 225

Wilkes, John Caesar, *editor*, 348

Wilkins, George, 127

—— *tr. See* Trogus, Pompeius

Wilkins, Isaac, 359

—— *See also* Seabury, Samuel, *and* Isaac Wilkins

Wilkins, John, *Bp.*, 127, 528

Wilkins, Richard, 225

Wilkinson, James, 386

Wilkinson, Richard, 226

[593]

Index

Willan, Leonard, 226
Willard, Samuel, 326, 329
Williams, John, 359, 378, 380, 381
Williams, Jonathan, 532
Williams, Roger, 313, 317
Williams, Solomon, 339
Williams, Stephen, 403
Williams, Stephen W., 391
Williams, Warham, 403
Williams, William (1665-1741), 332, 333
Williams, William (1731-1811), 403
Williams, William (*President of Free School at Williamstown*), 403
Willis, Francis, *tr. See* Anacreon
Williston, Seth, 380
Willmott, Ellen, 536
Willughby, Francis, 540
Wilmot, John, *second Earl of Rochester*, 226
Wilson, Alexander, 540
Wilson, John, 226
Wilson, Samuel, 324
Wilson, Scott B., 540
Wilson, Thomas, 127
—— *tr. See* Demosthenes
Wilson, Woodrow, 403, 432, 433
Wine, beer, ale, and tobacco, 226
Wingate, Edmund, 528
Winslow, Edward, 315, 317
Winstanley, William, 226
Winthrop, John, 375
—— *See also* Welde, Thomas, *and* John Winthrop
Wise, John, 356
Wise, Thomas James, *editor*, 281
Wiseman, Jane, 226
Wister, Owen, 433
Wither, George, 127, 128, 226
—— *tr. See* Nemesius, *Bp.*
Withers, Alexander S., 390
The witty rogue, 226
Wolcott, Roger, 433
Wolfe, Charles, 281
The woman turn'd bully, 227

Wood, John, 381
Wood, Thomas, *tr. See* Anacreon
Wood, William, 128, 311
Woodberry, George Edward, 433
Woodes, Nathaniel, 128
Woodhouse, James, 227
Woodward, John, 532
Woodward, Samuel, 365
Woonsocket Patriot, 399, 406
Worcester, *Marquis of. See* Somerset, Edward
Wordsworth, William, 227, 281, 282
—— *and* Samuel Taylor Coleridge, 227
The World, 227
Wortley, *Sir* Francis, 227
Wotton, *Sir* Henry, 227
Wright, Edward, *tr. See* Napier, John
Wright, James, 227
Wright, Thomas, 227
Wyche, *Sir* Peter, *tr. See* Lobo, Jerome
Wycherley, William, 227, 282
Wyclif, John. *See* Wiclif, John
Wyn, Elis, 282
Wythers, Stephen, *tr. See* Calvin, Jean: A very profitable treatise; Philippson, Joannes, *Sleidanus*

X

Xenophon, 42, 48, 128, 436, 437, 438
Xeres, Francisco de, 300
Ximenes Ayllon, Diego, 489

Y

Yarranton, Andrew, 228
Yeats, William Butler, 282
York, Brantley, 433
Young, Arthur, 228, 357
Young, Bartholomew, *tr. See* Montemayor, Jorge de
Young, Edward, 228

Index

Five hundred copies of A Short-Title List *have been Printed for the* Chapin Library *of* Williams College *by The Southworth-Anthoensen* Press, Portland, Maine, 1939.